Elements of Modern Mathematics

Relations

SECOND EDITION

J. J. DEL GRANDE, M.A.

J. C. EGSGARD, M.A.

 **gage** PUBLISHING LIMITED
TORONTO ONTARIO CANADA

ISBN: 0-7715-3638-0

7 8 9 10 11 12 BP 88 87 86 85 84 83

THE METRIC USAGE IN THIS TEXT HAS BEEN REVIEWED BY
THE METRIC SCREENING OFFICE OF THE CANADIAN
GOVERNMENT SPECIFICATIONS BOARD.

METRIC COMMISSION, CANADA, HAS GRANTED USE OF
THE NATIONAL SYMBOL FOR METRIC CONVERSION

CONTENTS

1 / Functions

2 / The Circular Functions

3 / The Circular Functions of Number Combinations

4 / Plane Transformations

5 / The Conics

6 / Properties of Conics

10/ Statistics

11/ Mathematics of Investment

12 / Introduction to Mathematical Logic

PREFACE TO THE SECOND EDITION

The need to update RELATIONS to meet the requirements of a metric Canada has given us an opportunity to revise the text. Seven teachers were asked for their suggestions on how to improve the book. The common message was to add some additional problems in strategic places. Two hundred problems have been added to give a greater variety, more options and some interesting applications in these places. Otherwise the text remains unchanged except for some corrections and minor clarifications.

Although we strongly recommend the use of calculators we must warn that using this modern technology might interfere with the learning process and can make some problems harder to do. In some cases premature evaluation might prevent simplifications that often result in numerical computations involving numbers like II. Also fractional forms have more meaning in some cases. One can readily solve $\cos\theta = \frac{1}{\sqrt{2}}$ but would need additional work using $\cos\theta = 0.707$. Calculators make some tables obsolete, but looking up tables is a skill students must have when obtaining information such as that given in mortality tables.

We would also like to thank Ms. Dianne Hamil of Kitchener and Mr. Chester Psica of William Lyon Mackenzie Secondary School for some very positive input.

1 / Functions

The concept of a function was introduced into mathematics at about the time of the beginnings of calculus in the seventeenth century. Rudimentary ideas of a function were used by Newton and Leibniz, the inventors of calculus. Slowly the concept of function evolved and developed, always in close relation to the applications of mathematical analysis. A function notation $f(x)$ was first used by John Bernoulli about 1718. After the researches of Euler (1707–1783) and especially of Fourier (1768–1830), mathematicians began to distinguish between a function and a formula. With the invention of set theory by Cantor about 1880, the language and the concepts for a clear definition of functions became available. In the ideas and concepts that you study, you will be taking advantage of the results of over two hundred years of careful thought by many famous mathematicians.

1.1/Relations and Functions

1.1 Relations and Functions

Binary relations, that is relations involving two numbers, are closely associated with ordered pairs and Cartesian products.

The Cartesian product of two sets A and B is defined as

$$A \times B = \{(x, y) \mid x \in A \text{ and } y \in B\}.$$

Thus, $A \times B$ is the set of *all* ordered pairs whose first components are selected from A and second components from B.

An open sentence in two variables may be used to define a relation. For example,

$$S = \{(x, y) \in I \times I \mid x + y = 5\}$$

yields a set of ordered pairs. S is called a relation. The open sentence $x + y = 5$ is used as a *set selector* or *defining sentence*, selecting those members of $I \times I$ that satisfy $x + y = 5$.

When a relation is described as a set of ordered pairs (x, y), the set of all first components, x, is called the *domain* of the relation and the set of all second components, y, is called the *range* of the relation.

A *binary relation* is a set of ordered pairs.

Example 1

If $A = \{1, 2, 3, 4, 5, 6, 7\}$ and $B = \{2, 3, 4, 5, 6\}$, graph $M = \{(x, y) \in A \times B \mid y > x + 1\}$. Find the domain and range of M.

Solution

$A \times B = \{(1, 2), (1, 3), \ldots, (7, 6)\}$
$M = \{(1, 3), (1, 4), (1, 5), (1, 6),$
$\qquad (2, 4), (2, 5), (2, 6),$
$\qquad (3, 5), (3, 6),$
$\qquad (4, 6)\}$

The points indicated by • belong to the graph of $A \times B$ and by ⊙ belong to the graph of M.

The domain of M, $D_M = \{1, 2, 3, 4\}$

and the range of M, $R_M = \{3, 4, 5, 6\}$.

There is a special class of relations, called *functional relations*, or simply, *functions*, that play an important role in mathematics.

If with each element of a set A, there is associated in some way exactly one element of a set B, this association forms a set of ordered pairs called a *function from A into B*. Thus, a function is a relation.

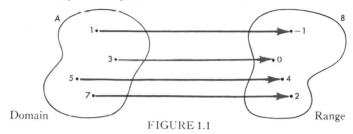

Domain   FIGURE 1.1   Range

Figure 1.1 illustrates such an association that represents the function

$$F = \{(1, -1), (3, 0), (5, 4), (7, 2)\}.$$

The arrow from 1 in A to -1 in B indicates that $(1, -1)$ belongs to F. For a functional relation, *two arrows never originate from the same point*. (But two arrows can terminate in the same point.)

Figure 1.1 implies that a function is a *mapping from A into B*. A function can be thought of as "carrying each member x of its domain onto a unique number y of its range." We shall say x is *mapped onto y* by the function. We may also say that y is the *image* of the corresponding element x. Thus, in Figure 1.1 we may say that 3 is mapped onto 0 and 0 is the image of 3.

A mapping f is a *function* if to each element of its domain there corresponds a single element of the range.

If f is a function, and if x is a number in the domain of f, then we shall designate the number onto which f maps x by $f(x)$.

$f(x)$ is frequently read "f at x"

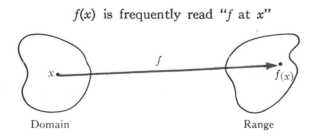

Domain   Range

This mapping is denoted symbolically as

$$f\colon x \to f(x), \ x \in R$$

and is read "the function f that maps x onto $f(x)$, where x belongs to R." For example, if $f\colon x \to x^2 + 1$, then each element x of the domain, R, is mapped by f onto the number $(x^2 + 1)$ of the range. In this case, $f(x) = x^2 + 1$. Notice the range is $\{y \in R | y \geq 1\}$. See Figure 1.2.

$$f(x) = x^2 + 1$$

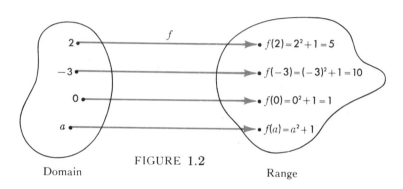

FIGURE 1.2

Domain   Range

Example 2

Determine if the relation expressed by

$$\{(x, y) \in R \times R | y = x^2 - 2\}$$

is a function, $x, y \in R$.

Solution

Construct a table that partially gives the relation and its graph.

x	-3	-2	-1	0	1	2	3
y	7	2	-1	-2	-1	2	7

∵ $y = x^2 - 2$, for a given $x \in R$ there corresponds exactly one number $y \in R$, namely $x^2 - 2$.

For each x in the domain there corresponds exactly one y in the range. Thus, our relation is a function.

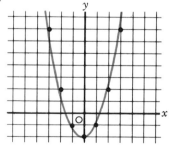

4

We can use a graph to determine whether a relation is a function. A function maps each element of its domain onto *only one* element of its range. Graphically this means that there is only one value of y that can correspond to any value of x. For example, $(3, 4)$ and $(3, 5)$ are not elements of the same function because 3 maps onto 4 and 5. Notice that the points $(3, 4)$ and $(3, 5)$ lie vertically one above the other. This illustrates the *vertical line test* for a function.

> Any *vertical line* intersects the graph of a function in at most one point.

Example 3

Determine whether $M = \{(x, y) \in R \times R \,|\, 3y^2 + x = 7\}$ is a function.

Solution

If
$$3y^2 + x = 7$$
$$y^2 - \frac{7 - x}{3}$$
$$y = \sqrt{\frac{7 - x}{3}} \quad \text{or} \quad y = -\sqrt{\frac{7 - x}{3}}$$

For each value of $x < 7$ there now correspond two real values of y. For example, if $x = 1$ then $y = \sqrt{2}$ or $y = -\sqrt{2}$ corresponding to the points $(1, \sqrt{2})$ and $(1, -\sqrt{2})$. Since the number 1 is associated with two numbers of the range, M is *not* a function.

Notice that if a graph had been employed the line $x = 1$ would intersect the graph at $(1, \sqrt{2})$ and $(1, -\sqrt{2})$. Thus, the vertical line test for a function shows that M is not a function.

In order to give a more concise description of a function or relation we sometimes omit the domain of the variables. *It should be understood in such cases that the domain of the variables is R and that the function or relation is a subset of $R \times R$.* Thus,

$$\{(x, y) \in R \times R \,|\, 3y^2 + x = 7\} \quad \text{becomes} \quad \{(x, y) \,|\, 3y^2 + x = 7\}.$$

When the domain of a function is the set R of real numbers or a subset of R, the function is called a *function of a real variable*. If the range of the function is a subset of R the function is called a *real-valued function*.

Exercise 1.1

A
1. Given $A = \{1, 2, 3, \ldots, 9, 10\}$.

   (*a*) How many members has $A \times A$?
   (*b*) How many members of $A \times A$ have the form (x, x)?
   (*c*) How many members have the form (x, y) where $x \neq y$?
   (*d*) How many members have the form $(4, x)$?

2. Consider the following graphs in $A \times A$ where

$$A = \{-3, -2, -1, 0, 1, 2, 3, 4\}.$$

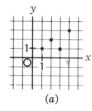 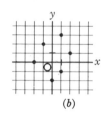 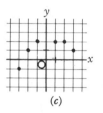 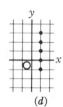

   (*a*) Which graphs define functions?
   (*b*) For each function give its domain and range.
   (*c*) For each non-functional relation, state why it is not a function.

3. Which of the following are graphs of functions in the real number plane?

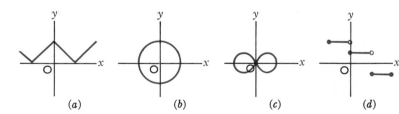

   (Recall that the small open circle indicates that an *end point* is *not* contained in the graph.)

4. For each of the following explain why the relation is not a function.

   (*a*) $M = \{(1, 2), (3, 7), (1, 4), (2, 5)\}$
   (*b*) $M = \{(1, 1), (1, 2), (2, 2), (2, 3)\}$

5. With each of the following mappings is associated a set of ordered pairs. In each case list the ordered pairs. Which mappings are functions?

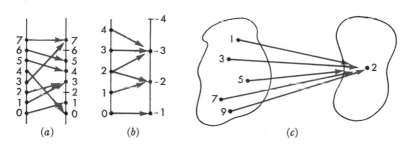

(a)   (b)   (c)

6. If $g(x) = 3x + 2$, find each of the following.

(a) $g(1)$ (d) $g(-3)$ (g) $g(5)$

(b) $g(0)$ (e) $g(3)$ (h) $g(10)$

(c) $g(-1)$ (f) $g(-2)$ (i) $g(-100)$

7. In $f: x \rightarrow x^3$, $x \in R$ what is the image of 2? of -2? of a?

8. Given $f: x \rightarrow x^3$, $x \in R$.

(a) Is f a function? Explain.

(b) Is f a real valued function? Explain.

(c) Is f a function of a real variable? Explain.

9. Given $f: x \rightarrow 3$, $x \in R$.

(a) Is f a function? Explain.

(b) Is f a real valued function? Explain.

(c) Is f a function of a real variable? Explain.

(d) Describe the graph of f.

B 10. List the set of ordered pairs that defines the function in each of the following. The domain of each is $\{-1, 0, 1, 2, 3\}$. Use two number lines to illustrate the function as a mapping.

(a) $f: x \rightarrow 2x$ (d) $f: x \rightarrow x^2 + x$

(b) $f: x \rightarrow 3x + 1$ (e) $f: x \rightarrow x^3$

(c) $f: x \rightarrow x^2$ (f) $f: x \rightarrow x^4$

1.1/Relations and Functions

7

11. Express each of the following in the form $f: x \rightarrow \dots .$

(a) $f = \{(x, y) \mid y = x^2\}$

(b) $f = \{(x, y) \mid y = x + 2\}$

(c) g defined by $g(x) = x^3$

(d) h defined by $h(x) = |x|$

(e) $f = \{(x, y) \mid 2x + y = 12\}$

(f) $h = \{(x, y) \mid x^2 + y + 2 = 0\}$

12. Graph the relation

$$M = \{(x, y) \in A \times A \mid y^2 = 5 - x\}$$

if A is given in each of the following.

(a) $A = \{0, 1, 2, 3, 4, 5\}$

(b) $A = N$, the set of natural numbers

(c) $A = I$, the set of integers

(d) $A = R$, the set of real numbers

(e) Determine the domain and range of the relation in each of the preceding parts.

13. If $f(x) = 5x, \ x \in R$, show that $f(a + b) = f(a) + f(b)$.

14. If $f(x) = 1 + x, \ x \in R$, find the following.

(a) $f(2x)$

(c) $f\left(\dfrac{1}{x}\right), \ x \neq 0$

(b) $f(x + h)$

(d) $f(x^2)$

15. If $f = \{(x, y) \in R \times R \mid y = 2\}$, find $f(1), f(3), f(0)$ and $f(-1)$.

16. Graph the following relations in $R \times R$ and determine which are functions.

(a) $\{(x, y) \mid 2x + y = 5\}$

(b) $\{(x, y) \mid y < x\}$

(c) $\{(x, y) \mid y = x^2\}$

(d) $\{(x, y) \mid y > x^2\}$

(e) $\{(x, y) \mid x^2 + y^2 = 25\}$

(f) $\{(x, y) \mid y = |x|\}$

C 17. If $f(a + b) = f(a) + f(b), \ a, b \in Q$, show that f has the following properties.

(a) $f(2x) = 2f(x), \qquad x \in Q$

(b) $f(nx) = nf(x), \qquad x \in Q, \ n \in N$

(c) $f(x) = \dfrac{1}{n} f(nx), \qquad x \in Q, \ n \in N$

(d) $f\left(\dfrac{m}{n}\right) = \dfrac{m}{n} f(1), \qquad m, n \in N$

1.2 The Inverse of a Function

The inverse of a relation M is obtained by interchanging the elements in each ordered pair of M. For example,

$$M = \{(0, 8), (1, 9), (2, 10), (3, 11), (4, 12), (5, 14)\}$$
$$P = \{(8, 0), (9, 1), (10, 2), (11, 3), (12, 4), (14, 5)\}$$

P is the inverse of M, and

M is the inverse of P.

We shall denote the *inverse of M* by M^{-1}. Thus,

$$P = M^{-1} \qquad \text{and} \qquad M = P^{-1}.$$

If $M = \{(a, b) \mid b = g(a)\}$, then
$M^{-1} = \{(b, a) \mid b = g(a)\}$.

In general, the inverse of a relation is also a relation. This suggests that we should ask the following related question: Is the inverse of a function also a function?

Consider the following arrow diagrams for functions f and g.

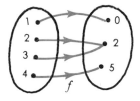 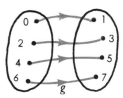

Each diagram represents a function because at most one arrow leaves each point of the domain. To obtain the inverses of f and g we reverse the arrows.

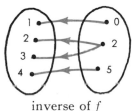 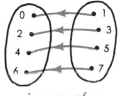

inverse of f   inverse of g

The inverse of f is not a function because two arrows are drawn from 2. That is, 2 is associated with both 2 and 3. Note that g and its inverse g^{-1} are both functions. Mappings for which each element of the domain has a unique image, and each element of the range is the image of a unique element of the domain, are called *one-to-one correspondences*.

Since each element of the domain has a unique image, a one-to-one mapping is a function.

Similarly since each element of the range is the image of a unique element of the domain, the inverse mapping is also a function.

> A relation and its inverse are both functions, if and only if the relation is a one-to-one correspondence.

Example 1

Given $f: x \rightarrow x^2$.
(a) Is f a one-to-one mapping?
(b) Is the inverse of f also a function?

Solution

(a) Since x and $-x$ are both mapped onto x^2 for each $x \in R$,
∴ f is not a one-to-one mapping.
(b) The inverse of a given function is also a function if and only if the given function is a one-to-one mapping.
∴ f^{-1} is not a function.

We may use a graph to illustrate the result of Example 1. Notice,

$$(2, 4), (-2, 4) \in f.$$

∴ $(4, 2), (4, -2) \in f^{-1}$

∴ f^{-1} is not a function

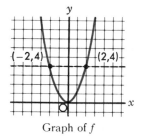

Graph of f

These results lead to the following observation.

> The graph of a one-to-one correspondence cannot intersect any line parallel to either axis in more than one point.

Suppose we are given the defining equation of a 1:1 function. How can we find the defining equation of its inverse?

If $f: x \rightarrow 3x + 2$, we may call $x \rightarrow 3x + 2$ a *rule of correspondence*. For each number, x, of the domain of f, the corresponding image is obtained by the following operations.

(1) multiply x by 3   (1) subtract 2
(2) add 2   (2) divide by 3

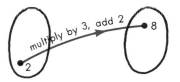   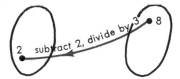

$f(x) = 3x + 2$ $f^{-1}(x) = \dfrac{x - 2}{3}$

$$f = \{(x, y) \mid y = 3x + 2\}$$

$$f^{-1} = \left\{(x, y) \mid y = \frac{x - 2}{3}\right\}$$
$$= \{(x, y) \mid 3y = x - 2\}$$
$$= \{(x, y) \mid x = 3y + 2\}$$

Compare the defining equations of f and f^{-1}.
$$y = 3x + 2$$
$$x = 3y + 2$$

In general, if $y = f(x)$ is the defining equation of a function f, where $x \rightarrow y$, then $x = f(y)$ is a defining equation of the inverse relation f^{-1}, where $x \rightarrow y$, which may or may not be a function. The following example proves this to be true.

Example 2

Prove: If $f = \{(x, y) \mid y = f(x)\}$,
then $f^{-1} = \{(x, y) \mid x = f(y)\}$.

Solution

$$f = \{(x, y) \mid y = f(x)\}$$
$$\therefore \quad f = \{(a, b) \mid b = f(a)\}$$
$$\therefore \quad f^{-1} = \{(b, a) \mid b = f(a)\}$$
$$\therefore \quad f^{-1} = \{(x, y) \mid x = f(y)\}$$

> A defining equation of f^{-1} is obtained by interchanging x and y in the defining equation of f.

Example 3

Graph $f = \{(-2, 0), (-1, 1), (0, 3), (2, 7)\}$ and its inverse f^{-1}. Find the midpoints of segments joining corresponding points in the graphs of f and f^{-1}.

Solution

$$f^{-1} = \{(0, -2), (1, -1), (3, 0), (7, 2)\}$$
$$f = \{(-2, 0), (-1, 1), (0, 3), (2, 7)\}$$

The coordinates of the required midpoints are

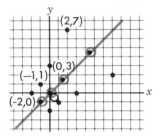

$(-1, -1), (0, 0), (1.5, 1.5), (4.5, 4.5)$

Notice that each midpoint lies on the line $y = x$.

Example 1 suggests that the corresponding points on the graphs of any function f and its inverse f^{-1} have a midpoint lying on the line $y = x$.

Example 4

Prove (a) the midpoint of $P(a, b)$ and $Q(b, a)$ lies on the line $y=x$.
(b) PQ is perpendicular to the line $y = x$.

Solution

(a) The midpoint of PQ is $T\left(\dfrac{a + b}{2}, \dfrac{a + b}{2}\right)$

∵ the x and y coordinates of T are equal.
∴ T lies in the line $y = x$.

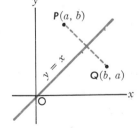

(b) Slope $PQ = \dfrac{a - b}{b - a}$

$= -1$

Slope of the line $y = x$ is 1
Since the product of the slopes is -1
∴ $PQ \perp$ line $y = x$

The point P is the "*mirror image*" of the point Q in the line $y = x$.

1.2/The Inverse of a Function

Since f^{-1} is obtained from f by interchanging the coordinates in its ordered pairs we may conclude the following.

> The graph of f^{-1} is the mirror image of the graph of f in the line $y = x$.

The graphs of f and f^{-1} are said to be *symmetric* about the line $y = x$.

Exercise 1.2

A

1. State the inverse relation in each of the following.
   (a) $\{(1, 2), (3, 5), (7, 11)\}$
   (b) $\{(-1, 3), (0, -1), (-3, -5)\}$

2. How is the function $\{(0, 0), (1, 1), (2, 2), (3, 3)\}$ related to its inverse?

3. State the inverse of each of the following relations.
   (a) $\{(x, y) \mid y = 4x - 1\}$ (c) $\{(x, y) \mid y = x^2 - 2\}$
   (b) $\{(x, y) \mid 2x + 3y = 7\}$ (d) $\{(x, y) \mid 2x^2 + 3y^2 = 1\}$

4. Each of the following mappings determines a function. Which have inverses that are also functions? Explain.

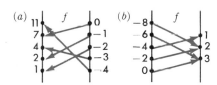 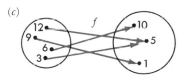

5. For each of the following name, in order, the operations that are performed on a number x to obtain its image.
   (a) $f : x \rightarrow 5x + 2$ (c) $f : x \rightarrow 3 - 2x$
   (b) $f : x \rightarrow 7x - 5$ (d) $f : x \rightarrow 5x^2 + 3$

B

6. For the function $f : x \rightarrow 2x - 1$ each of the following is an element of f^{-1}. Find the missing component in each.
   (a) $(9,\ )$ (c) $(0,\ )$ (e) $(\ , -1)$
   (b) $(-6,\ )$ (d) $(\ , 4)$ (f) $(\ , 0)$

7. Given $f = \{(0, 2), (1, 3), (2, 4), (3, 5)\}$. List f^{-1}. Is f^{-1} a function?

8. Find the inverse of each of the following. In each case state whether or not the inverse is a function.

(a) $f = \{(x, y)\,|\,y = 4x - 5\}$
(b) $g = \{(x, y)\,|\,y = x^2 + 1\}$
(c) $h : x \rightarrow -2x + 4$
(d) $m : x \rightarrow \sqrt{x + 1}$

9. Given $f = \{(x, y)\,|\,y = 3x + 1\}$.

(a) State a defining equation of f^{-1}.
(b) Graph f and f^{-1} using the same axes.
(c) Find $f \cap f^{-1}$.

10. Given $g: x \rightarrow 2x - 3$, express g^{-1} as $g^{-1}: x \rightarrow \ldots$.

11. Given $g = \{(x, y)\,|\,y = \tfrac{1}{4}x^2\}$.

(a) Graph g
(b) Express g^{-1} as a set.
(c) Graph g^{-1}.
(d) Is g a one-to-one correspondence? Explain.

12. Graph $g: x \rightarrow x^3$ and determine by considering lines parallel to the axes whether g is a function and g^{-1} is a function.

13. Show that f^{-1} is not a function where $f: x \rightarrow 5$.

14. Given $f: x \rightarrow \dfrac{1}{x}$. Show that $f^{-1} = f$.

15. Given $f = \{(x, y)\,|\,y = \sqrt{x}\}$.

(a) Graph f.
(b) Determine the defining equation of f^{-1}.
(c) Graph f^{-1}.
(d) Determine whether f is a one-to-one correspondence.

16. Suppose f and f^{-1} are inverse functions and $f(x) = 3x + 7$.

(a) Find $f^{-1}(x)$
(b) Find n given $f(-2) = f^{-1}(n)$.

17. How do the following functions compare with their inverses?

(a) $\{(x, y)\,|\,y = x\}$ (b) $\{(x, y)\,|\,y = |x|\}$ (c) $\{(x, y)\,|\,xy = 12\}$

18. (a) Graph the quadratic function $g : x \rightarrow -x^2 + 2x$.
(b) Use the fact that g and g^{-1} are mirror images in the line $y = x$ to graph g^{-1}.
(c) Is g a function? Is g^{-1}?
(d) Find $g \cap g^{-1}$

19. Given $g: x \rightarrow x^2 + 2x$.

    (a) Graph g.   (b) Graph $y = x$ and g^{-1}.   (c) Find $g \cap g^{-1}$.

20. Show that if $h: x \rightarrow \sqrt{x}$ and $k: x \rightarrow -\sqrt{x}$ that
$$h \cup k = g^{-1} \quad \text{where} \quad g: x \rightarrow x^2.$$

C 21. For any two relations M and N prove that
$$(M \cap N)^{-1} = M^{-1} \cap N^{-1}.$$

22. Prove that if f is a non-constant linear function then f^{-1} is a linear function.

1.3 The Algebra of Functions

Recall that, for real valued functions the operations of addition, subtraction, multiplication and division can be defined. For a constant c and a function f we define cf as follows:
$$f = \{(x, f(x))\} \text{ then } cf = \{(x, cf(x))\}$$

Example 1

Given $f : x \rightarrow x^2 - 4$, graph f, $2f$ and $-f$ in the interval $-4 \le x \le 4$.

x	$f(x)$	$2f(x)$	$-f(x)$
-4	12	24	-12
-3	5	10	-5
-2	0	0	0
-1	-3	-6	3
0	-4	-8	4
1	-3	-6	3
2	0	0	0
3	5	10	-5
4	12	24	-12

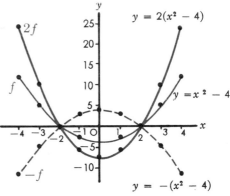

For two functions f and g we defined $f + g$ as follows:

> If $f: x \rightarrow f(x)$ and $g: x \rightarrow g(x)$,
> then $f + g. x \rightarrow f(x) + g(x)$.
> Similarly $f - g: x \rightarrow f(x) - g(x)$,
> and $|f|: x \rightarrow |f(x)|$.

Example 2

Given $f(x) = x^2 - 4$, $g(x) = 2x$, graph f, g and $f + g$ in the interval $-4 \le x \le 4$.

Solution

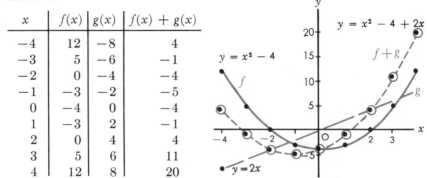

x	$f(x)$	$g(x)$	$f(x) + g(x)$
-4	12	-8	4
-3	5	-6	-1
-2	0	-4	-4
-1	-3	-2	-5
0	-4	0	-4
1	-3	2	-1
2	0	4	4
3	5	6	11
4	12	8	20

The product of two functions:

> If $f: x \to f(x)$ and $g: x \to g(x)$,
>   then $f \cdot g: x \to f(x) \cdot g(x)$.
>
> A similar definition holds for division:
> $$\frac{f}{g}: x \to \frac{f(x)}{g(x)}, \; g(x) \ne 0.$$

Example 3

Given $f: x \to x^2 - 4$ and $g: x \to x$, graph f, g and $f \cdot g$ in the interval $-4 \le x \le 4$.

Solution

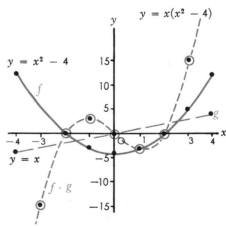

x	$x^2 - 4$	$x(x^2 - 4)$
-4	12	-48
-3	5	-15
-2	0	0
-1	-3	3
0	-4	0
1	-3	-3
2	0	0
3	5	15
4	12	48

It is convenient to define three special functions:

The constant function $f: x \rightarrow c, \, c \in R$
The zero function $f: x \rightarrow 0$
The identity function $f: x \rightarrow x$

Exercise 1.3

A 1. Given $f: x \rightarrow x^2 + 7$, state a defining equation of each of the following functions.

(a) $3f$ (c) $8f$ (e) $f \cdot f = f^2$
(b) $-f$ (d) $-3f$ (f) f^3

2. Given $f: x \rightarrow x^2 + 7$ and $g: x \rightarrow 3x$, state a defining equation for each of the following functions.

(a) $f + g$ (c) $2f + 3g$ (e) $f \cdot g$
(b) $f - g$ (d) $g - f$ (f) $\dfrac{f}{g}$

3. Given the identity function $f: x \rightarrow x$ and the constant function $g: x \rightarrow 1$, state the algebraic combinations of f and g that give the functions defined by the following equations.

(a) $y - 3x + 4$ (c) $y = -2x^2 + 4$
(b) $y = x^2 + 2x + 1$ (d) $y = -x^3 - 7$

B 4. Given the graph of f, find the graph of each of the following.

(a) $f + 4$ (c) $2f$ (e) $\dfrac{1}{f}$
(b) $-f$ (d) f^2 (f) $|f|$

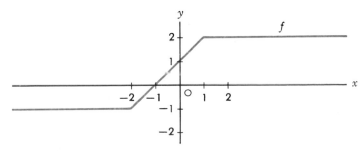

5. Given the graph of f and g, find the graph of each of the following functions.

(a) $f + g$

(b) $f - g$

(c) $g - f$

(d) $\frac{1}{2}f + g$

(e) $f \cdot g$

(f) $f \cdot |g|$

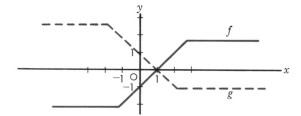

6. Given $f: x \to x^2 - 8$ and $g: x \to x$, graph each of the following functions in the interval $-5 \le x \le 5$.

(a) $f - 2g$

(b) $f + 2g$

(c) $f \cdot g$

(d) $|f|$

(e) $|f - 2g|$

(f) $|f + 2g|$

1.4 Rational Functions

Functions generated from the identity function $f: x \to x$ and the constant function $g: x \to 1$ and the three operations of multiplication, addition and subtraction are called *polynomial functions*. For example,

$$f: x \to x^2 + 7x - 2$$

$$g: x \to x^3 + \frac{3}{4}x - \sqrt{2}$$

are polynomial functions.

With the restrictions we have imposed on the polynomial functions and operations, we cannot generate functions such as

$$f: x \to \frac{1}{x}$$

$$g: x \to 2^x$$

$$h: x \to \sqrt{x + 1}$$

or $\quad k: x \to \dfrac{x}{x - 1}$

Functions such as f and k above are called *rational functions* because they are quotients of polynomial functions and can be generated using the operation of division.

Example 1

Graph $f: x \rightarrow x(x + 1)(x - 1)(x - 3)$ in the interval $-2 \leq x \leq 4$.

Solution

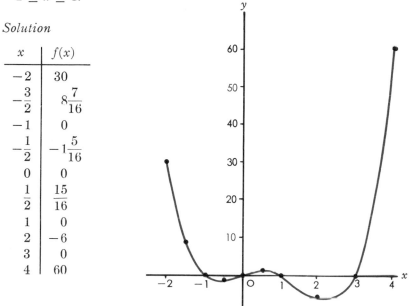

x	$f(x)$
-2	30
$-\dfrac{3}{2}$	$8\dfrac{7}{16}$
-1	0
$-\dfrac{1}{2}$	$-1\dfrac{5}{16}$
0	0
$\dfrac{1}{2}$	$\dfrac{15}{16}$
1	0
2	-6
3	0
4	60

Polynomial functions, such as f in Example 1, are defined by equations of the type

$$P(x) = a_n x^n + a_{n-1} x^{n-1} + \ldots + a_1 x + a_0.$$

The degree of the polynomial is n and the coefficients are

$$a_n, a_{n-1}, \ldots, a_1, a_0.$$

If the coefficients are restricted to rational numbers, we say "P is a polynomial function over the rational field." If the coefficients are real numbers, we call P a polynomial over the real field.

The *zeros* of a function f are those numbers x in the domain of f for which $f(x) = 0$. In Example 1, the zeros of f are -1, 0, 1, and 3.

Rational functions are defined as quotients of polynomial functions.

If f and g are polynomials with no common nonconstant factors, then

$\dfrac{f}{g}$ is defined by $\dfrac{f}{g}(x) = \dfrac{f(x)}{g(x)}$, for all x for which $g(x) \neq 0$.

Example 2

For the rational function f defined by

$$f(x) = \frac{x^2}{1 - x^2},$$

find the domain of f and graph f.

Solution

$1 - x^2 = 0$ for $x = 1$ and $x = -1$.
$\therefore$ 1 and -1 are not in the domain of f.

The domain of f is all real numbers except 1 and -1. To graph f we consider the cases:

    (I) $x < -1$ (II) $-1 < x < 1$ (III) $x > 1$

Case (I) $x < -1$
$$x^2 > 1,\ 1 - x^2 < 0 \text{ and } \frac{x^2}{1 - x^2} < 0$$

As x approaches -1 in value, x^2 approaches 1, $1 - x^2$ approaches 0 and $\left|\frac{x^2}{1 - x^2}\right|$ becomes large. As $|x|$ becomes large, x^2 becomes large, $1 - x^2$ becomes large negatively and $\frac{x^2}{1 - x^2}$ approaches -1.

Case (II) $-1 < x < 1$
$$x^2 > 0,\ 1 - x^2 > 0 \text{ and } \frac{x^2}{1 - x^2} > 0$$
$$\text{at } x = 0,\ \frac{x^2}{1 - x^2} = 0$$

As x approaches -1 in value,

x^2 approaches 1, $1 - x^2$ approaches 0 and $\frac{x^2}{1 - x^2}$ becomes large.

As x approaches 1,

x^2 approaches 1, $1 - x^2$ approaches 0 and $\frac{x^2}{1 - x^2}$ becomes large.

Case (III) $x > 1$

This analysis is the same as for Case (I).

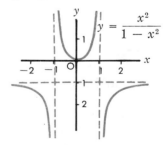

The curve in Example 1 "sweeps towards" the lines $x = 1$ and $x = -1$. These lines are called *vertical asymptotes*. The equations of the vertical asymptotes can be obtained by setting the denominator $1 - x^2$ equal to zero. The line $y = -1$ is called a horizontal asymptote.

We often use the expression "x approaches infinity" to mean x becomes very large. We write $x \to \infty$.

If $|x|$ becomes large and $x < 0$, we say "x approaches negative infinity" and write $x \to -\infty$.

Notice in this context the arrow ($\to$) means "approaches." The symbol "∞" is not a number and should only be used in the context described above.

Exercise 1.4

A

1. State the zeros of the function defined by each of the following equations.

   (a) $y = x(x - 2)(x - 3)$
   (c) $f(x) = 2x(x - 1)(x + 2)$

   (b) $y = (x^2 - 9)(x^2 - 4)$
   (d) $g(x) = \dfrac{3}{4}(x + 2)(x - 3)(x + 7)$

2. State equations of the vertical asymptotes of the graphs of the following functions.

   (a) $f: x \to \dfrac{x}{x^2 - 1}$
   (c) $h: x \to \dfrac{2x - 3}{x(x - 2)}$

   (b) $g: x \to \dfrac{x}{2x - 1}$
   (d) $k: x \to \dfrac{x}{x^2 - 7x + 12}$

3. Discuss whether or not the graph of $f: x \to \dfrac{x}{1 + x^2}$ has a vertical asymptote.

4. Explain why $x^4y + 3x^3y + 5x^2 + y - x + x^5 + 1 = 0$ may be a defining equation of a rational function?

B

5. Graph the polynomial functions defined in each of the following.

   (a) $f(x) = x(x - 1)(x + 1)$
   (e) $y = x^2 - 5x - 14$

   (b) $g(x) = x(x - 1)(x - 2)$
   (f) $y = 2x^2 + 7x - 15$

   (c) $h(x) = (x - 1)(x - 2)(x - 3)$
   (g) $y = x^3 - 6x^2 + 11x - 6$

   (d) $f(x) = x(x - 1)(x - 2)(x - 3)$
   (h) $y = 2x^3 - 5x^2 + x + 2$

6. (a) Graph $h: x \to x^2(x - 1)(x - 2)$

   (b) Graph $g: x \to (x - 1)^2(x + 2)^2$

7. For each of the following find equations of all horizontal and vertical asymptotes. State the numbers that must be excluded from the domain of each function. Draw the graph of each of the following rational functions.

(a) $f(x) = \dfrac{x}{x^2 + 1}$

(d) $p(x) = \dfrac{x^2 + 1}{x^2 - 1}$

(b) $g(x) = \dfrac{x^2}{x^2 + 1}$

(e) $g(x) = \dfrac{1}{(x^2 - 1)^2}$

(c) $h(x) = \dfrac{x^2 - 1}{x^2 + 1}$

(f) $r(x) = \dfrac{3x^2}{x^2 - 4}$

8. (a) Draw the graph of $f: x \to \dfrac{x^2 - 1}{x - 1}$.

(b) Are there any real numbers for which f is undefined?

9. Show that the graph of $f: x \to \dfrac{x^8}{x^{10} + 9}$ has a horizontal asymptote.

10. Draw the graph of the polynomial function defined by

$$y = \frac{1}{3}(x^2 + x + 1)(x + 1).$$

C 11. (a) Draw the graph of the polynomial function defined by $y = x^3 - x + 1$.

(b) From the graph find, approximately, the real zero of the function.

1.5 Algebraic Functions

We have defined the functions in the previous sections in terms of the operations of addition, subtraction, multiplication and division. To produce the *algebraic function* we introduce the operation of *solving algebraic equations*.

Suppose we have the equation

$$x^2 + y^2 = 25$$

and we attempt to solve for y.

$$y^2 = 25 - x^2$$
$$y = \sqrt{25 - x^2} \text{ or } y = -\sqrt{25 - x^2}$$

Notice that equation $x^2 + y^2 = 25$ defines two functions,

$f_1: x \rightarrow \sqrt{25 - x^2}$ and $f_2: x \rightarrow -\sqrt{25 - x^2}$

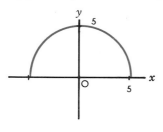

graph of f_1

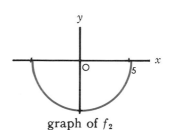

graph of f_2

Consider the function f defined by

$$y = -2 + \frac{1}{\sqrt{x}} \quad (1)$$

The domain of f is $\{x \in R \mid x > 0\}$

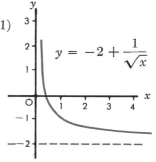

$$y = -2 + \frac{1}{\sqrt{x}}$$

Rewrite (1) as $y + 2 = \dfrac{1}{\sqrt{x}}$

or $\sqrt{x}(y + 2) = 1$

or $x(y + 2)^2 = 1$ (by squaring)

or $xy^2 + 4xy + 4x - 1 = 0$ (2)

The defining equation for f can be obtained by solving equation (2) for y. There is an equation for a different function that can be obtained by solving (2) for y. What is the other equation?

We now define an algebraic function.

If f is a function whose defining equation is $y = f(x)$ and x and y satisfy an algebraic equation,

$$P_n(x)y^n + P_{n-1}(x)y^{n-1} + \cdots + P_0(x) = 0$$

where $P_0(x)$, $P_1(x)$, $\cdots$, $P_n(x)$ are polynomials in x with real coefficients, then f is an *algebraic function*.

Our techniques for solving algebraic equations are limited to quadratic types and special types of higher degree.

Example 1

Solve $(2x^2 + 3)y^3 - (x + 5) = 0$ for y.

Solution

$$(2x^2 + 3)y^3 = x + 5$$

$$y^3 = \frac{x + 5}{2x^2 + 3}$$

$$y = \sqrt[3]{\frac{x + 5}{2x^2 + 3}}$$

There are two other functions that can be obtained but they involve non-real complex numbers.

Exercise 1.5

B   1. Graph the algebraic function defined in each of the following.

(a) $y = \sqrt{9 - x^2}$ (c) $y = \sqrt{x^2 - 9}$

(b) $y = \sqrt[3]{x^2}$ (d) $y = 1 + \sqrt[3]{x}$

2. Show that each function in Question 1 is algebraic by showing that $y = f(x)$ satisfies an equation of the form

$$P_n(x)y^n + \cdots + P_0 = 0.$$

3. Graph the function defined by $y = \sqrt{x(x^2 - 1)}$. State the interval in which the function is defined.

4. Given $f(x) = \sqrt{x} + \dfrac{1}{\sqrt{x}} + 2$, show that f is an algebraic function.

C   5. Find the defining equations of two functions $x \rightarrow y$ whose equations can be derived from $y^2 - 2xy + 5x = 0$.

6. Show that the algebraic equation
$2x^2 - xy - 6y^2 + 13x + 9y + 15 = 0$ yields two linear functions $x \rightarrow y$.

24   *1.5/Algebraic Functions*

1.6 Transcendental Functions

Functions that are not algebraic are called. *transcendental.* You have studied three types of transcendental functions, namely

(1) exponential functions,
(2) logarithmic functions,
and (3) circular functions.

Circular functions are studied in Chapter 2, so we will consider the exponential and logarithmic functions only in this section.

For each real number $a > 0$, the function f such that

$$f: x \rightarrow a^x$$

is called the *exponential function for base a.*

If $a = 1$, then $a^x = 1$, and f is a constant function.

Example 1

Graph (a) $f: x \rightarrow 2^x$
(b) $f: x \rightarrow (\frac{1}{2})^x$

Solution

(a) $y = 2^x$

x	y
-2	$\frac{1}{4}$
-1	$\frac{1}{2}$
0	1
1	2
2	4
3	8

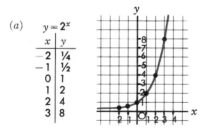

(b) $y = (\frac{1}{2})^x$

x	y
2	$\frac{1}{4}$
1	$\frac{1}{2}$
0	1
-1	2
-2	4
-3	8

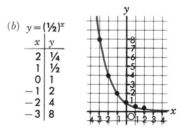

From the graphs of Example 1 we notice the following.

If $a > 1$, then f is an increasing function. That is, as x increases the value of f increases.

If $a < 1$, then f is a decreasing function.

The domain of f is R and the range is the set of positive real numbers.

The base a is taken as positive because a negative base would lead to some difficulty. For example, $(-3)^x$ would be undefined for $x = \frac{1}{2}$.

$$(-3)^{\frac{1}{2}} = \sqrt{-3}$$

which is not a real number. Thus, for some values of x the corresponding value of the exponential function would be undefined.

The inverse of the exponential function

$$f = \{(x, y) \mid y = 2^x\}$$
is
$$f^{-1} = \{(x, y) \mid x = 2^y\}.$$

Since the domain of f is R, the range of f^{-1} is also R. Since the range of f is the set of positive real numbers, the domain of f^{-1} is also the set of positive real numbers.

The inverse of an exponential function is called a *logarithmic function*. Thus, we may express

$$x = 2^y \quad \text{as} \quad y = \log_2 x.$$

Example 2

Graph $f: x \to 2^x$ and its inverse f^{-1}.

Solution

The inverse of f is $f^{-1}: x \to \log_2 x$.

$y = 2^x$	
x	y
-2	$\frac{1}{4}$
-1	$\frac{1}{2}$
0	1
1	2
2	4
3	8

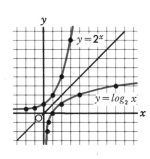

$y = \log_2 x$	
x	y
$\frac{1}{4}$	-2
$\frac{1}{2}$	-1
1	0
2	1
4	2
8	3

In general:

> The exponential function $f: x \to a^x$ has an inverse, which is the logarithmic function $f^{-1}: x \to \log_a x$.

26

Exercise 1.6

A 1. Evaluate.

(a) $8^{\frac{1}{3}}$ (c) 3^{-2} (e) $(4)^{-\frac{1}{2}}$

(b) 7^0 (d) $(\frac{1}{2})^{-2}$ (f) $16^{\frac{3}{2}}$

2. Restate each of the following in logarithmic form.

(a) $2^3 = 8$ (c) $10^0 = 1$ (e) $125^{\frac{1}{3}} = 5$

(b) $3^4 - 81$ (d) $a^x - b$ (f) $9^{1.5} = 27$

3. Evaluate.

(a) $\log_3 3^5$ (c) $\log_2 16$ (e) $\log_2 (\frac{1}{4})$

(b) $\log_2 2^6$ (d) $\log_5 25$ (f) $\log_9 3$

4. Evaluate.

(a) $\log_a a$ (b) $\log_a a^t$ (c) $a^{\log_a x}$

5. Given $\log_a (a \times b) = \log_a a + \log_a b$.

(a) Express each of the following as a sum.

$\log_2 (19 \times 73)$; $\log_5 (17.3 \times 26.7)$; $\log_e MN$

(b) Express each of the following as the logarithm of a product.

$\log_{10} 40 + \log_{10} 2.5$; $\log_7 14 + \log_7 3.5$;

$\log_4 (\frac{2}{3}) + \log_4 96$

6. Given $\log_a(\frac{p}{q}) = \log_a p - \log_a q$.

(a) Express each of the following as a difference.

$\log \dfrac{18}{123}$; $\log_3 (18.7 \div 1.5)$; $\log_7 \dfrac{193.5}{562.7}$

(b) Express each of the following as the logarithm of a quotient.

$\log_2 25 - \log_2 12$; $\log_a 24 - \log_a 6$; $\log_a xy - \log_a x$

7. Given $\log_a p^n = n \log_a p$.

(a) Express each of the following as the product of a number and a logarithm.

$\log_3 10^5$; $\log_2 7^5$; $\log_{10} y^4$; $\log_2 10^{-0.5}$

(b) Express each of the following as a logarithm of a power.

$2 \log_{10} 7$; $17 \log_3 25$; $3 \log_{10} x$; $\pi \log_{10} 5$

B 8. Graph using the same axes for each.

(a) $f : x \rightarrow 2^x$
  $g : x \rightarrow 3^x$
  $h : x \rightarrow 5^x$

(b) $p : x \rightarrow 2^{-x}$
  $q : x \rightarrow 3^{-x}$
  $r : x \rightarrow 5^{-x}$

(c) $m : x \rightarrow 2^{x^2}$
  $n : x \rightarrow 2^{-x^2}$

9. Using the same axes, graph the following logarithmic functions.

(a) $f : x \rightarrow \log_3 x$

(b) $g : x \rightarrow \log_5 x$

10. (a) If f is an exponential function show that

$$f(x + y) = f(x) \times f(y)$$

(b) What is the corresponding relationship if f is a logarithmic function?

11. Explain why $\log_a x$ cannot be defined for $a = 1$.

12. If the number of bacteria doubles each day and an initial culture has 150 bacteria, determine the number of bacteria in the culture after each of the following intervals.

(a) after 1 d

(b) after 3 d

(c) after 10 d

(d) after n d

13. Graph the function $f = \{ (x, y) \mid y = 2^x + 2^{-x} \}$ where $-3 < x < 3$. The graph of f illustrates the shape of the curve of a chain freely suspended between two points. The curve is called a *catenary*.

C 14. Graph the function $p = \{ (x, y) \mid y = 2^{-\frac{x^2}{2}} \}$ for $-4 \le x \le 4$. The graph of p is of great importance in the study of probability and statistics. It is sometimes called a *bell curve* or *normal curve*.

15. Two important functions in applied mathematics are

$$\cosh : x \rightarrow \frac{e^x + e^{-x}}{2} \text{ and } \sinh : x \rightarrow \frac{e^x - e^{-x}}{2}$$

where e is an irrational number: $e \doteq 2.718$.

(a) Prove that (i) $\sinh x = -\sinh (-x)$

(ii) $\cosh x = \cosh (-x)$

(iii) $(\cosh x)^2 - (\sinh x)^2 = 1$

(b) Prove that $\sinh (x + y) = \sinh x \cosh y + \cosh x \sinh y$.

1.6/Transcendental Functions

16. The population, $P(t)$, of a city at time t is given by

$$P(t) = 10\ 000\ e^{0.05t}$$

(a) Find the population at times $t = 0$ and $t = 10$. *Use a calculator with an e^x key!*

(b) Find t when $P(t) = 20\ 000$.

17. The number of items sold, $S(t)$, of a new product in a time t is given by

$$S(t) = 10\ 000 - 8\ 000\ e^{-t}$$

(a) Calculate $S(t)$ for $t = 0, 1, 2, 3, 4$ to the nearest integer.

(b) Graph $S(t) = 10\ 000 - 8\ 000\ e^{-t}$.

(c) Why does $t < 0$ have no meaning?

(d) Describe the nature of sales as t increases and suggest possible products whose sales may behave in this way.

18. A sociologist has shown that the percentage of a population, $P(t)$, that has heard a rumour after time t (in days) is approximated by the formula

$$P(t) = \frac{10\ e^{0.01t}}{1 - 10(1 - e^{0.01t})}$$

(a) Find $P(t)$ for $t = 0, 5, 10$ and 20 to two decimal places.

(b) Draw a graph of the rumour curve.

(c) Discuss the implications for a murder trial where the jury must consist of people who have not heard details of the alleged crime.

(d) Discuss possible reasons for the restrictions on crime reporting in newspapers.

19. The number of items produced, $P(t)$, in a time t by workers new to an operation of a machine on an assembly line is given by the exponential function

$$P(t) = 50 - 50\ e^{-0.3t}$$

(a) Find $P(0), P(1), P(5), P(10), P(20)$.

(b) Draw the curve $P(t) = 50 - 50\ e^{-0.3t}$.

(c) The graph in (b) is called a *learning curve*. Explain in terms of learning and production why the curve has the shape it has.

20. Knowledge learned is forgotten in a period of time. A *forgetting curve* is given by

$$K(t) = 100 \left(\frac{1 + e}{1 + e^{1+t}} \right) \qquad (t \text{ in days})$$

where $K(t)$ is the number of knowledge items remembered after time t (in days).

(a) Show that $K(0) = 100$. That is, 100 items are learned to start.

(b) Find $K(1)$ and show that a person forgets about 50% of what he learns within 24 h.

(c) Find $K(2)$, $K(3)$, $K(4)$ to the nearest integer.

(d) Plot the curve $K(t) = 100 \left(\frac{1 + e}{1 + e^{1+t}} \right)$.

(e) Discuss the implications for your academic learning.

1.7 Composition of Functions

In Section 1.3 we defined addition, subtraction, multiplication and division of functions. There is still another operation called *composition of functions*.

Consider two mappings f and g as illustrated in Figure 1.3. Notice

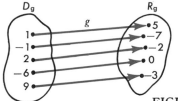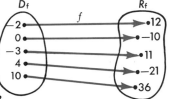

FIGURE 1.3

in this example that the numbers -2, 0, and -3 belong to the range of g and the domain of f. It is possible then with two successive mappings $2 \rightarrow -2 \rightarrow 12$, to map 2 into 12.

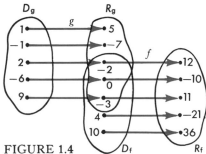

FIGURE 1.4

Consider the two mappings given by

$$g : x \to 2x + 3, \qquad f : x \to x^2$$
$$\therefore \quad g(x) = 2x + 3, \qquad f(x) = x^2$$

For certain elements in D_g, for example, the element 2, we may perform *two* successive mappings as follows.

More generally for any $x \in D_g$ for which $g(x) \in D_f$ we have the following diagram.

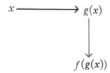

The diagram suggests that we could complete the triangle by means of a third mapping, h say, so that we have the following,

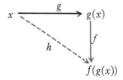

where $h(x) = f(g(x))$. Since f and g are functions, the given x and $g(x)$ are unique and therefore $f(g(x))$ is unique. Thus,

$$h : x \to f(g(x))$$

and h is a function. This new function, h, is called the *composite* of f and g. It is the function that completes the above mapping diagram and it is denoted by $f \circ g$ or by $f(g)$. Thus,

$$f(g)(x) = f \circ g(x) = f(g(x))$$

and can be read

"the composite of f and g at x equals f at g at x".

The domain of $f \circ g$ consists of those elements of D_g that map into D_f. In Figure 1.4

$$D_{f \circ g} = \{2, -6, 9\}.$$

Thus, $D_{f \circ g}$, D_f and the range R_f are related as in the following diagram.

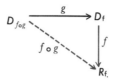

Example 1

If $f(x) = 2x + 3$, $g(x) = x^2$, find $g \circ f(x)$ and $f \circ g(x)$.

Solution

$$\begin{aligned}
g \circ f(x) &= g(f(x)) & \text{But} \quad f \circ g(x) &= f(g(x)) \\
&= g(2x + 3) & &= f(x^2) \\
&= (2x + 3)^2 & &= 2x^2 + 3 \\
&= 4x^2 + 12x + 9 & & \\
\therefore \quad g \circ f(x) &= 4x^2 + 12x + 9 & f \circ g(x) &= 2x^2 + 3
\end{aligned}$$

In general,

$$f \circ g \neq g \circ f.$$

Exercise 1.7

B

1. If $f = \{(-5, -4), (-2, -4), (-1, 0), (2, 1), (-3, 5), (5, 3)\}$ and $g = \{(-4, -3), (-2, 3), (2, 0), (3, 2), (0, 2)\}$, make a diagram similar to Figures 1.3 and 1.4 and determine the following.

   (a) $f \circ g$ (c) $D_{f \circ g}$
   (b) $g \circ f$ (d) $D_{g \circ f}$

2. If $f(x) = 3x - 2$, $g(x) = 5 - 2x$, determine the following.

   (a) $f \circ g\,(x)$ (e) $g \circ f\,(x)$
   (b) $f \circ g\,(3)$ (f) $g \circ f\,(-2)$
   (c) $f \circ g\,(-1)$ (g) $g \circ f\,(5)$
   (d) $f \circ g\,(0)$ (h) $g \circ f\,(0)$

   For what values of x is $g \circ f(x) = f \circ g(x)$?

3. For each of the following find $g \circ f(x)$ and $f \circ g(x)$.

   (a) $f: x \rightarrow x^2 + 2,\ g: x \rightarrow 3x - 1$
   (b) $f: x \rightarrow 2x^2 - 3,\ g: x \rightarrow 5 - 6x$

4. Prove that if $f(x) = 1 - x^2$ and $g(x) = \sqrt{x - 2}$ then $g \circ f = \phi$, where ϕ is the null set.

5. If $f: x \rightarrow 3x + 2$, prove $f \circ f^{-1} = f^{-1} \circ f = i$ where i is the *identity function* $i: x \rightarrow x$.

6. For any function f show that

$$f \circ i = i \circ f = f.$$

7. If $f = \{(x, y) \in R \times R \,|\, 2x + 3y = 7\}$

   and $g = \{(x, y) \in R \times R \,|\, 5x - 4y = 0\}$

   find $h(x)$ in each of the following.

   (a) $h = f \circ g$ (c) $h = g \circ g$
   (b) $h = g \circ f$ (d) $h = f \circ f$

8. Find $f \circ g$ for each of the following.

   (a) $f: x \rightarrow \sin x,\qquad g: x \rightarrow 3x$
   (b) $f: x \rightarrow 2x,\qquad g: x \rightarrow \cos x$

9. If $f: x \rightarrow 3^x$ and $g: x \rightarrow \log_3 x$ find $f \circ g$ and $g \circ f$.

10. If $f: x \rightarrow x^2,\ g: x \rightarrow x + 3$ and $h: x \rightarrow x + 2$ show that

$$f \circ (g \cdot h) = (f \circ g) \cdot (f \circ h).$$

11. If $f: x \rightarrow x + 3,\ g: x \rightarrow x + 2$ and $h: x \rightarrow x + 4$ show that

$$(f + g) \circ h = (f \circ h) + (g \circ h).$$

12. Given the functions

$$f: x \rightarrow \frac{2}{x},\ x \neq 0$$
$$g: x \rightarrow x - 1$$
$$h: x \rightarrow 9 - x^2$$

Prove that $(f \circ g) \circ h = f \circ (g \circ h)$.

C 13. If f and g are linear functions, show the following.

   (a) $f \circ g$ is a linear function.
   (b) $f \circ g \neq g \circ f$ in general.
   (c) Give an example of linear functions for which $f \circ g = g \circ f$.

14. If f and g are distinct linear functions, prove that $f \circ g = g \circ f$ only if both their graphs have slope 1 or if the graphs intersect on the line $y = x$.

15. Show that the composition of a linear and a quadratic function is a quadratic function.

Review Exercise 1.8

A 1. If $A = \{0, 1, 2\}$ and $B = \{7, 8\}$ find each of the following Cartesian products.

(a) $A \times A$ (c) $B \times A$

(b) $A \times B$ (d) $B \times B$

2. Which of the following is the graph of a function? Explain.

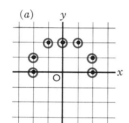 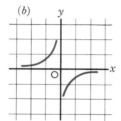 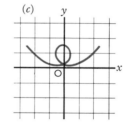

3. If $h(x) = x^2 - 3$, evaluate the following.

(a) $h(-1)$ (d) $h(0)$ (g) $h(20)$

(b) $h(-5)$ (e) $h(7)$ (h) $h(-20)$

(c) $h(-3)$ (f) $h(4)$ (i) $h(a + 2)$

4. Explain why $f: x \to -2$, $x \in R$ is a function. Describe the graph of f.

5. State the inverse relation for each of the following.

(a) $\{(0, 3), (1, 4), (2, 6), (3, 9)\}$

(b) $\{(-1, 1), (-2, 2), (-3, 3), (-4, 4)\}$

B   6. Use the given mapping to list $g \circ f$.

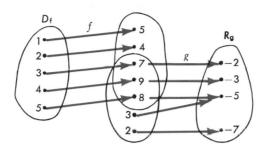

7. State the inverse relation in each of the following.

(a) $\{(x, y) \mid y = 2x\}$

(b) $\{(x, y) \mid y = x^2\}$

(c) $\{(x, y) \mid 3x + 4y = 12\}$

(d) $\{(x, y) \mid x^2 + xy = 1\}$

8. Given $f: x \rightarrow x^2 - 3$, $g: x \rightarrow 2x + 1$, state the defining equation for each of the following functions.

(a) $2f$

(b) $3g$

(c) $-f$

(d) $f + g$

(e) $f - g$

(f) $g - f$

(g) $f \cdot g$

(h) $2f + 3g$

(i) $\dfrac{f}{g}$

9. State the zeros of the following polynomial functions.

(a) $f: x \rightarrow (x - 1)(x + 3)(x - 5)$

(b) $g: x \rightarrow x(2x - 1)$

10. State the equations of the vertical asymptotes of the graphs of each of the following functions.

(a) $f: x \rightarrow \dfrac{x}{(x - 2)(x + 3)}$

(b) $g: x \rightarrow \dfrac{x + 2}{1 - x^2}$

(c) $h: x \rightarrow \dfrac{3x + 2}{2x - 5}$

(d) $k: x \rightarrow \dfrac{2}{x^2 - x - 12}$

11. If $f(x) = \dfrac{x^2}{x + 1}$ find the following. $x \neq -1$.

(a) $f(1)$

(b) $f(-3)$

(c) $f(0)$

(d) $f(a + 2)$

(e) $f(b - 1)$

(f) $f(a^2)$

(g) $f(x + 2)$

(h) $f(x - 1)$

(i) $f(x^2)$

1.8/Review Exercise

12. Which of the following are defining equations of functions?

(a) $y = 2x + 5$

(b) $y^2 = 2x$

(c) $y = x^2 - 5$

(d) $x^2 + 2y^2 = 1$

(e) $x^3 + xy + y = 2$

(f) $y = \sqrt{x}$

13. Given the graph of g, draw the graph of each of the following functions.

(a) $g - 3$

(b) $2g$

(c) $-g$

(d) $|g|$

(e) $2g - 1$

(f) $|2g - 1|$

(g) g^2

(h) $|g| + g$

(i) $\dfrac{1}{g}$

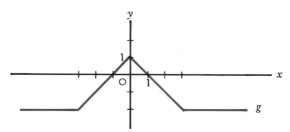

14. Given $f: x \to x$ and $g: x \to 1$.

(a) Graph f and g.

(b) Graph $f \cdot f$.

(c) Graph $f \cdot f - f$.

(d) Graph $f \cdot f - f - 6g$.

15. Graph the function defined in each of the following.

(a) $y = x(x - 2)(x + 1)$

(b) $y = x(x^2 - 9)$

(c) $y = (x^2 - 1)(x^2 - 9)$

(d) $y = x^2(x^2 - 4)$

(e) $y = \dfrac{x + 2}{1 - x^2}$

(f) $y = \dfrac{x}{2x - 1}$

16. Graph each of the following algebraic functions.

(a) $f: x \to \sqrt{16 - x^2}$

(b) $g: x \to \dfrac{3}{2}\sqrt{16 - x^2}$

(c) $h: x \to \sqrt{x^2 - 16}$

(d) $k: x \to \dfrac{3}{2}\sqrt{x^2 - 16}$

36

17. Show graphically that $A = \{(x, y) \,|\, 4x^2 - y^2 = 0\}$ is not a function.

18. Given $f: x \to 5x + 2$.

    (a) Express f^{-1} as $f^{-1}: x \to \ldots$.
    (b) Graph f and f^{-1}.
    (c) Find $f \cap f^{-1}$.
    (d) Find $(f^{-1})^{-1}$.

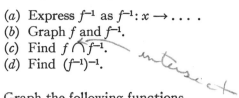 intersect

19. Graph the following functions.

    (a) $f: x \to \sqrt{x}$ and its inverse f^{-1}
    (b) $g: x \to x^2$ and its inverse g^{-1}

20. If g is a linear function and $(-1, 2) \in g$, $(3, 5) \in g$, find g.

21. Is the exponential function a one-to-one correspondence? Explain.

22. Graph the function $f: x \to x - 2^{-x}$.

23. If $f(x) = x^2 + 2$ and $g(x) = 3x + 1$ find each of the following.

    (a) $f \circ g(x)$ (b) $g \circ f(x)$

24. For each of the following express $f \circ g(x)$ and $g \circ f(x)$ as polynomials.

    (a) $f: x \to 3x - 5$ $g: x \to x^2 + x$
    (b) $f: x \to x^2 - 5$ $g: x \to x^2$
    (c) $f: x \to 1 - x^2$ $g: x \to 1 + x^2$

25. Given the defining equation of f find the defining equation of f^{-1}.

    (a) $f(x) = 3x - 5$ (d) $f(x) = \sqrt{x - 2}$

    (b) $f(x) = \dfrac{x - 3}{5}$ (e) $f(x) = 2\sqrt{x + 3}$

    (c) $f(x) = \sqrt{x^2 - 5}$ (f) $f(x) = \dfrac{1}{2 - x}$

26. Find the conditions on the constants a, b, c and d so that the function defined by

$$y = \frac{ax + b}{cx + d} \left(ad - bc \neq 0, \, x \in R, \, x \neq -\frac{d}{c} \right)$$

is its own inverse.

$\mathcal{2}/$ The Circular Functions

Of particular interest in mathematics and science are those functions that have the property of being "periodic", exhibiting a repetitive behaviour like the rising and setting of the sun, the tides, heart beats, or a pendulum in motion. The most important of all periodic functions are the circular or trigonometric functions.

2.1 The Sine and Cosine Functions

In this chapter and the next we shall consider in detail a family of functions that are of major importance, the *circular or trigonometric functions*. Since it is assumed that you have already studied these functions, the following development, though self-contained, will proceed at a fairly rapid pace, and a number of important details will be left for the exercise.

We shall make use of a Cartesian coordinate system, but because it is desirable to save the letters x and y for another use, we shall label the axes u and v. Consider the unit circle $u^2 + v^2 = 1$ in a plane. A number line is placed tangent to the circle as shown in Figure 2.1.

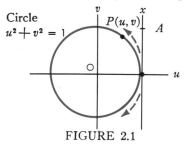

Circle
$u^2 + v^2 = 1$

FIGURE 2.1

Wrap this number line $u = 1$ around the circle $u^2 + v^2 = 1$ in both directions with the positive part of the number line going around counter-clockwise and the negative part clockwise, somewhat as an endless fishing line might be wound, both ways, around a reel.

In this process each point A with coordinate x on the number line is mapped onto a unique point $P\,(u, v)$ of the circle giving a function $W: x \rightarrow (u, v)$ called a *wrapping function* whose domain is the set of real numbers and whose range is the set of ordered pairs satisfying the equation $u^2 + v^2 = 1$.

2.1/The Sine and Cosine Functions

Since the circumference of a unit circle is of length 2π, this wrapping function maps points of the line that are 2π units apart onto the same point of the unit circle. Thus we have the following for points of the number line mapping onto points of the circle:

$$\left.\begin{array}{c} 0 \to (1,0) \\ 2\pi \to (1,0) \\ 4\pi \to (1,0) \end{array}\right\} \implies \begin{cases} W(0) = W(2\pi) \\ W(0) = W(4\pi) \end{cases}$$

$$\cdots \qquad\qquad \cdots$$

$$\text{and } \left.\begin{array}{c} -2\pi \to (1,0) \\ -4\pi \to (1,0) \end{array}\right\} \implies \begin{cases} W(0) = W(-2\pi) \\ W(0) = W(-4\pi) \end{cases}$$

$$\cdots \qquad\qquad \cdots$$

Similarly,

$$\left.\begin{array}{c} x \to (u,v) \\ x + 2\pi \to (u,v) \\ x + 4\pi \to (u,v) \end{array}\right\} \implies \begin{cases} W(x) = W(x + 2\pi) \\ W(x) = W(x + 4\pi) \end{cases}$$

$$\cdots \qquad\qquad \cdots$$

$$\left.\begin{array}{c} x - 2\pi \to (u,v) \\ x - 4\pi \to (u,v) \end{array}\right\} \implies \begin{cases} W(x) = W(x - 2\pi) \\ W(x) = W(x - 4\pi) \end{cases}$$

In general, for $n \in I$, $W(x + 2n\pi) = W(x)$. A function with this property is called *periodic*.

A function f is periodic with period $k \neq 0$ if, whenever x is in the domain of f, $x + k$ is also in the domain of f and $f(x + k) = f(x)$.

The smallest positive k satisfying the condition of this definition is called the *fundamental period* of f. Hence W is periodic with period 2π.

Our wrapping function $x \to (u,v)$ gives rise to two new functions called *circular functions*, namely the sine function

$$\sin: x \to v$$

and the cosine function

$$\cos: x \to u.$$

Hence $u = \cos x$ and $v = \sin x$. This fact is illustrated in Figure 2.2.

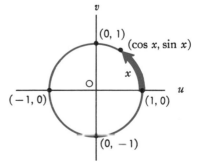

FIGURE 2.2

Since $u^2 + v^2 = 1$ we have the following.

$$\text{For all } x \in R, \cos^2 x + \sin^2 x = 1.$$

It follows immediately that the domain of cos and the domain of sin is the same as the domain of W, which is the set of real numbers R. To find the range of cos and sin we use the fact that $u^2 + v^2 = 1$. Hence, $|u| \le 1$ and $|v| \le 1$, that is, $|\cos x| \le 1$ and $|\sin x| \le 1$. Thus the range of cos and sin is the same, namely the set of numbers in the interval from -1 to 1 inclusive.

Because W is periodic with period 2π, the functions cos and sin are periodic with period 2π. Indeed, as you will show in the next exercise, 2π is the fundamental period so that the graphs of cos and sin repeat themselves at intervals of 2π.

In order to obtain enough information to graph the sin and cos functions we observe from Figure 2.3 that

$$\sin 0 = 0 \quad \sin \frac{\pi}{2} = 1 \quad \sin \pi = 0 \quad \sin \frac{3\pi}{2} = -1 \quad \sin 2\pi = 0$$

$$\cos 0 = 1 \quad \cos \frac{\pi}{2} = 0 \quad \cos \pi = -1 \quad \cos \frac{3\pi}{2} = 0 \quad \cos 2\pi = 1$$

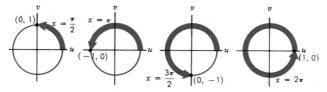

FIGURE 2.3

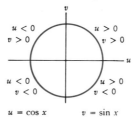

$$u = \cos x \qquad v = \sin x$$

FIGURE 2.4

Moreover, the following is clear from Figure 2.4.

$0 \le x \le \dfrac{\pi}{2}$	$\dfrac{\pi}{2} \le x \le \pi$	$\pi \le x \le \dfrac{3\pi}{2}$	$\dfrac{3\pi}{2} \le x \le 2\pi$
$0 \le \sin x \le 1$	$1 \ge \sin x \ge 0$	$0 \ge \sin x \ge -1$	$-1 \le \sin x \le 0$
$1 \ge \cos x \ge 0$	$0 \ge \cos x \ge -1$	$-1 \le \cos x \le 0$	$0 \le \cos x \le 1$

2.1/The Sine and Cosine Functions

This information together with the specific values of sin x and cos x that you are asked to complete in Exercise 2.1 is sufficient to permit accurate graphs of these functions to be sketched in the interval $0 \leq x \leq 2\pi$ using x and y axes. The graphs (Figure 2.5) are completed using the fact that each function has a period of 2π.

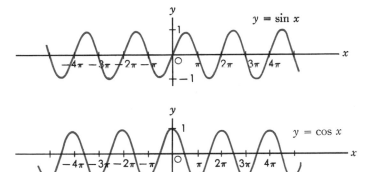

FIGURE 2.5

Exercise 2.1

B 1. (a) Draw a unit circle (radius 1) and a tangent line at (1,0).
  (b) Mark points along the tangent line at the following distances from (1,0).

   $\dfrac{\pi}{2}, 3\pi, \dfrac{3\pi}{4}, \dfrac{\pi}{4}, \dfrac{\pi}{6}$ (Use $\pi = 3.1$)

  (c) Mark the points on the circle into which the points in part (b) map.

2. Repeat Question 1 for points on the tangent line at the following distances from (1,0).

   $1, 2, \dfrac{1}{2}, 4, 12$

3. Show that the number $\dfrac{\pi}{4}$ on the tangent line to the unit circle of Question 1 maps onto the point $(\dfrac{1}{\sqrt{2}}, \dfrac{1}{\sqrt{2}})$.

4. Find the coordinates of the point on the unit circle that the number $\dfrac{3\pi}{4}$ on the tangent line of Question 1 maps.

5. Use the figure to complete the table.

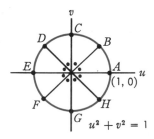

$$u^2 + v^2 = 1$$

Point			A	B	C	D	E	F	G	H	A
Coordinates of point	(u, v)	$(1, 0)$									
Arc length from A	x			$\dfrac{\pi}{4}$				$\dfrac{5\pi}{4}$			2π
1st coordinate	$\cos x$				0						
2nd coordinate	$\sin x$					$\dfrac{1}{\sqrt{2}}$					

6. Prove that $\sin \dfrac{\pi}{6} = \cos \dfrac{\pi}{3} = \dfrac{1}{2}$ and $\sin \dfrac{\pi}{3} = \cos \dfrac{\pi}{6} = \dfrac{\sqrt{3}}{2}$.

7. Graph $y = \cos x$ and $y = \sin x$ on the same coordinate axes for $-6\pi \le x \le 6\pi$ and find their points of intersection.

8. Use the accompanying figure and properties of reflection in the u axis to explain why

$\cos(-x) = \cos x$
$\sin(-x) = -\sin x$

Why are these statements true for all $x \in R$?

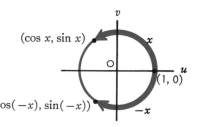

$(\cos x, \sin x)$

$(\cos(-x), \sin(-x))$

9. Use the accompanying figure and properties of reflection in the origin to explain why

$$\cos (\pi + x) = -\cos x$$
$$\sin (\pi + x) = -\sin x$$

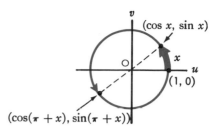

10. Use the accompanying figures and properties of reflection to prove the following

(a) $\cos (\pi - x) = -\cos x$
     $\sin (\pi - x) = \sin x$

(b) $\cos (2\pi - x) = \cos x$
     $\sin (2\pi - x) = -\sin x$

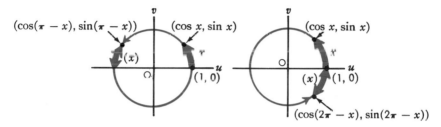

11. Do the equations in Questions 9 and 10 hold for all real values of x? Explain.

12. Verify the results of Questions 8, 9 and 10 using the graphs of Figure 2.5, page 41.

13. Use the accompanying diagram and properties of reflection in the line $u = v$ to verify that

$$\cos \left(\frac{\pi}{2} - x\right) = \sin x$$

$$\sin \left(\frac{\pi}{2} - x\right) = \cos x$$

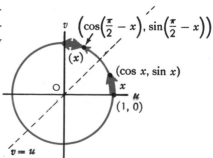

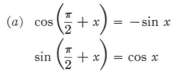

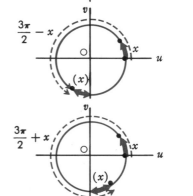

14. Use the accompanying diagrams and properties of reflection to prove the following.

(a) $\cos\left(\dfrac{\pi}{2} + x\right) = -\sin x$

$\sin\left(\dfrac{\pi}{2} + x\right) = \cos x$

(b) $\cos\left(\dfrac{3\pi}{2} - x\right) = -\sin x$

$\sin\left(\dfrac{3\pi}{2} - x\right) = -\cos x$

(c) $\cos\left(\dfrac{3\pi}{2} + x\right) = \sin x$

$\sin\left(\dfrac{3\pi}{2} + x\right) = -\cos x$

15. Verify the results of Questions 13 and 14 using the graphs of Figure 2.5, page 41.

16. If k is any period of cos then $\cos (x + k) = \cos x$ for each real number x.

(a) Prove that $\cos k = 1$ and hence $k = 2n\pi$.

(b) Use the results of part (a) to show that the cosine function has fundamental period 2π.

17. Show that the sine function has fundamental period 2π.

C 18. A function f is periodic with period $\dfrac{3}{4}$. If $f(1) = 3$ and $f\left(\dfrac{17}{12}\right) = -2$, find $f\left(\dfrac{2}{3}\right)$.

19. A function is periodic with period 2, $f(x) = x$ for $-1 < x < 1$ and $f(1) = 0$. Sketch the graph of f.

20. Show that there is no function h with period 2 such that $h(x) = x$ for $-1 \le x \le 1$.

2.2 The Tan, Csc, Sec and Cot Functions

Certain combinations of the sine and cosine arise in mathematics with sufficient frequency to have been given special names. These functions are the tangent (tan), cosecant (csc), secant (sec) and cotangent (cot) and are defined as follows.

$$\tan: x \rightarrow \tan x = \frac{\sin x}{\cos x}$$

$$\csc: x \rightarrow \csc x = \frac{1}{\sin x}$$

$$\sec: x \rightarrow \sec x = \frac{1}{\cos x}$$

$$\cot: x \rightarrow \cot x = \frac{\cos x}{\sin x}$$

To graph the tangent function we observe that $\tan 0 = 0$ since $\sin 0 = 0$. Moreover, since $\sin x$ and $\cos x$ are both positive for $0 < x < \frac{\pi}{2}$, so also $\tan x$ is positive. In the interval $\frac{\pi}{2} < x < \pi$, $\tan x$ is negative since $\sin x$ is positive and $\cos x$ is negative. Similarly $\tan x$ is positive in the interval $\pi < x < \frac{3\pi}{2}$, and $\tan x$ is negative in the interval $\frac{3\pi}{2} < x < 2\pi$. These facts, together with the knowledge that $\tan \pi = 0$, suggest that tan is periodic with period π.

Since $\sin \frac{\pi}{4} = \cos \frac{\pi}{4} = \frac{1}{\sqrt{2}}$, the value of $\tan \frac{\pi}{4} = 1$.

Since $\cos \frac{3\pi}{4} = \frac{-1}{\sqrt{2}}$ and $\sin \frac{3\pi}{4} = \frac{1}{\sqrt{2}}$, the value of $\tan \frac{3\pi}{4} = -1$.

Observe that $\tan \frac{\pi}{2}$ is not defined, since $\cos \frac{\pi}{2} = 0$.

However, when x is less than but close to $\frac{\pi}{2}$, $\sin x$ is close to 1 and $\cos x$ is close to 0 and the quotient $\frac{\sin x}{\cos x} = \tan x$ has a large positive value. Indeed the closer x is to $\frac{\pi}{2}$, the larger this value will be. In other words, the values of $\tan x$ become larger and larger, that is, increase without bound, as x approaches $\frac{\pi}{2}$ from the left. Similarly, the values of $\tan x$ decrease without bound as x approaches $\frac{\pi}{2}$ from the right.

The line $x = \frac{\pi}{2}$ is called a *vertical asymptote* of the graph of the function. Since $\cos x = 0$ for $x = (2n + 1)\frac{\pi}{2}$, $n \in I$, the tan function has infinitely many vertical asymptotes. These asymptotes are indicated in the graph in Figure 2.6 by dotted lines.

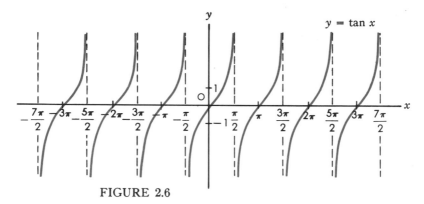

FIGURE 2.6

$$\tan: x \to \tan x = \frac{\sin x}{\cos x}$$

Since $\sin 0 = 0 = \sin n\pi$, for $n \in I$, the graph of the cot function $\left(\cot x = \frac{\cos x}{\sin x}\right)$ will have the vertical asymptotes at the points on the x axis where $x = n\pi$, $n \in I$. Since $\cos \frac{\pi}{2} = 0 = \cos (2n + 1)\frac{\pi}{2}$, $n \in I$, the graph of the cot function will cross the x axis at the points where $x = (2n + 1)\frac{\pi}{2}$, $n \in I$. As in the case of the tan function the cot function will have a value of 1 whenever $\cos x = \sin x$ and a value of -1 whenever $\cos x = -\sin x$. The graph of cot x is given in Figure 2.7.

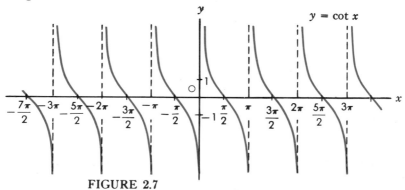

FIGURE 2.7

$$\cot: x \to \cot x$$
Cot is periodic with period π

2.2/The Tan, Csc, Sec and Cot Functions

The graphs of the cosecant and secant functions can be drawn by noting that

(1) The cosecant function has vertical asymptotes whenever $\sin x = 0$, while the secant function has vertical asymptotes whenever $\cos x = 0$.

(2) Since $|\sin x| \le 1$ and $|\cos x| \le 1$, then

$$|\csc x| = \left|\frac{1}{\sin x}\right| \ge 1 \text{ and } |\sec x| = \left|\frac{1}{\cos x}\right| \ge 1$$

The graphs of csc and sec are given in Figures 2.8 and 2.9.

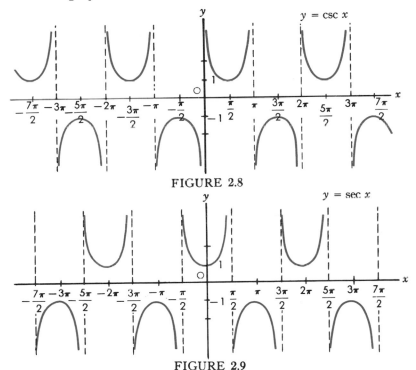

FIGURE 2.8

FIGURE 2.9

Both csc and sec are periodic with period 2π.

In the preceding discussion we have noted that $\sin x$ and $\cos x$ are positive when $0 < x < \frac{\pi}{2}$, that is, whenever the image $W(x)$ on the circle $u^2 + v^2 = 1$ lies in the first quadrant. For $W(x)$ in the second quadrant, for example, $\frac{\pi}{2} < x < \pi$, $\sin x$ is positive while $\cos x$ is negative. The chart in Figure 2.10 extends these results to include the six circular functions.

2.2/The Tan, Csc, Sec and Cot Functions

47

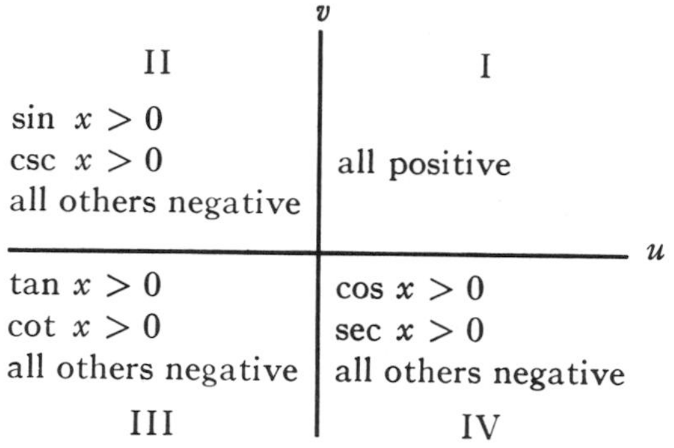

II	I
sin $x > 0$ csc $x > 0$ all others negative	all positive
tan $x > 0$ cot $x > 0$ all others negative	cos $x > 0$ sec $x > 0$ all others negative
III	IV

FIGURE 2.10

Example

If $\sin x = -\dfrac{1}{3}$ where $\pi < x < \dfrac{3\pi}{2}$, find the values of the other five circular functions.

Solution

Since $\pi < x < \dfrac{3\pi}{2}$, tan x and cot x are positive while the other function values are negative.

But
$$\because \ \sin^2 x + \cos^2 x = 1 \quad \text{(see page 40)}$$
$$\therefore \ \left(-\frac{1}{3}\right)^2 + \cos^2 x = 1$$
$$\therefore \ \cos^2 x = \frac{8}{9}$$
$$\therefore \ \cos x = \frac{\sqrt{8}}{3} \ \text{or} \ \cos x = -\frac{\sqrt{8}}{3}$$
$$\because \ \cos x < 0, \ \cos x = -\frac{\sqrt{8}}{3}$$
$$\therefore \ \tan x = \frac{\sin x}{\cos x} = \frac{-\dfrac{1}{3}}{-\dfrac{\sqrt{8}}{3}} = \frac{1}{\sqrt{8}}$$
$$\cot x = \frac{\cos x}{\sin x} = \sqrt{8}$$
$$\csc x = \frac{1}{\sin x} = -3$$
$$\sec x = \frac{1}{\cos x} = -\frac{3}{\sqrt{8}}$$

Exercise 2.2

B 1. Use Questions 5, 6, 14 of Section 2.1 to complete the following table.

x	0	$\dfrac{\pi}{6}$	$\dfrac{\pi}{4}$	$\dfrac{\pi}{3}$	$\dfrac{\pi}{2}$	$\dfrac{2\pi}{3}$	$\dfrac{3\pi}{4}$	$\dfrac{5\pi}{6}$	π
$\sin x$									
$\cos x$									
$\tan x$									
$\sec x$									
$\csc x$									
$\cot x$									

2. Use the fact that $\sin(\pi + x) = -\sin x$ and $\cos(\pi + x) = -\cos x$ and the table of Question 1 to complete the following table.

x	$\dfrac{7\pi}{6}$	$\dfrac{5\pi}{4}$	$\dfrac{4\pi}{3}$	$\dfrac{3\pi}{2}$	$\dfrac{5\pi}{3}$	$\dfrac{7\pi}{4}$	$\dfrac{11\pi}{6}$	2π
$\sin x$								
$\cos x$								
$\tan x$								
$\sec x$								
$\csc x$								
$\cot x$								

3. State the domain and range of the tan, cot, csc and sec functions.

4. (a) Using the same coordinate axes sketch the graphs of $y = \tan x$ and $y = \cot x$ for $-4\pi \le x \le 4\pi$.

   (b) List the points of intersection of the graphs in (a).

5. (a) Using the same coordinate axes sketch the graphs of $y = \sin x$ and $y = \csc x$ for $-4\pi \le x \le 4\pi$.

   (b) Using the same coordinate axes sketch the graphs of $y = \cos x$ and $y = \sec x$ for $-4\pi \le x \le 4\pi$.

6. Use the definitions of the circular functions to prove the following for all real x.

(a) $\sin^2 x + \cos^2 x = 1$
(b) $\sec^2 x = 1 + \tan^2 x$
(c) $\csc^2 x = 1 + \cot^2 x$

7. Find the values of the other five trigonometric functions in each of the following.

(a) $\sin x = \dfrac{3}{5}$, $\quad 0 < x < \dfrac{\pi}{2}$

(b) $\cos x = -\dfrac{12}{13}$, $\quad \dfrac{\pi}{2} < x < \pi$

(c) $\sin x = -\dfrac{5}{13}$, $\quad \pi < x < \dfrac{3\pi}{2}$

(d) $\cos x = \dfrac{1}{3}$, $\quad \dfrac{3\pi}{2} < x < 2\pi$

8. Use the graphs of the corresponding functions or the results of Questions 8 to 13 of Exercise 2.1, pages 42-43, to verify the following.

(a) $\tan(\pi + x) = \tan x$

(b) $\csc(-x) = -\csc x$

(c) $\cot\left(\dfrac{\pi}{2} - x\right) = \tan x$

(d) $\sec\left(\dfrac{3\pi}{2} + x\right) = \csc x$

(e) $\cot(2\pi - x) = -\cot x$

(f) $\sec(\pi - x) = -\sec x$

9. Show that the following are true.

(a) $\cot\left(\dfrac{\pi}{2} + x\right) = -\cot\left(\dfrac{\pi}{2} - x\right)$

(b) $\csc\left(\dfrac{\pi}{2} + x\right) = \csc\left(\dfrac{\pi}{2} - x\right)$

10. Describe transformations that will map the graphs of the circular functions as indicated.

(a) The graph of sin onto the graph of cos.
(b) The graph of tan onto the graph of cot.
(c) The graph of csc onto the graph of sec.

C 11. (a) Show that the fundamental period of tan and cot is π.
(b) Show that the fundamental period of csc and sec is 2π.

50

2.3 Period, Amplitude and Phase

The intensity of a radio wave of amplitude a, wavelength λ and velocity c is given by

$$y = a \sin \frac{2\pi}{\lambda} (x - ct)$$

where x measures distance and t the time. We shall study a mathematical counterpart of this equation, namely,

$$y = a \sin(kx + d).$$

Period

A function f is periodic if there exists a positive real number k such that for all x and $x + k$ in the domain of f

$$f(x + k) = f(x).$$

The fundamental period of the function f is the smallest positive number p such that for all $x \in R$

$$f(x + p) = f(x).$$

For example, W is periodic with fundamental period 2π because 2π is the smallest number for which

$$W(x + 2\pi) = W(x).$$

Whenever the word period is used, we shall mean the fundamental period unless stated otherwise.

$$\text{If} \qquad f(x) = a \sin(kx + d)$$
$$\text{then} \quad f(x + p) = a \sin(k(x + p) + d)$$
$$= a \sin(kx + d + kp)$$

$\because$ the period of the sine function is 2π,

$\therefore$ $f(x) = f(x + p)$ provided that $|kp| = 2\pi$.

$$\because \qquad\qquad\qquad p > 0$$
$$\therefore \qquad\qquad\qquad |k|p = 2\pi$$
$$p = \frac{2\pi}{|k|}$$
$$\therefore \qquad f(x) = f(x + p) \quad \text{if} \quad p = \frac{2\pi}{|k|}$$

Similarly, $g: x \to a \cos (kx + d)$ has period $\dfrac{2\pi}{|k|}$

$f: x \to a \sin (kx + d)$
$g: x \to a \cos (kx + d)$ are periodic with period $\dfrac{2\pi}{|k|}$.

Example 1

Find the period of the sine function $f: x \rightarrow \sin 3x$.

Solution 1

Let the period of f be p.

$$f(x) = \sin 3x$$
$$f(x + p) = \sin(3x + 3p)$$
$$\text{But} \quad \sin 3x = \sin(3x + 2\pi)$$
$$\text{for smallest positive } p, \ 3p = 2\pi$$
$$\therefore \quad p = \frac{2\pi}{3}$$

$\therefore$ the period of f is $\frac{2\pi}{3}$.

Solution 2

Compare f with $x \rightarrow a \sin(kx + d)$

$$a = 1, \quad k = 3, \quad d = 0$$

The period is given by $\frac{2\pi}{|k|}$.

$\therefore$ the period of f is $\frac{2\pi}{3}$.

Example 2

Find the period of $f: x \rightarrow 5 \cos(7x + 2)$.

Solution

Compare with $x \rightarrow a \cos(kx + d)$
$$a = 5, \quad k = 7, \quad d = 2$$
The period is given by $\frac{2\pi}{|k|}$

$\therefore$ period of f is $\frac{2\pi}{7}$.

Amplitude

When a periodic function has a *maximum value of M* and a *minimum value of m*, we define the *amplitude* to be $\frac{M - m}{2}$.

For $f: x \rightarrow \sin x$, $x \in R$ we know $-1 \le \sin x \le 1$

$\therefore \quad M = 1 \quad$ and $\quad m = -1$

$\therefore$ the amplitude is $\frac{M - m}{2} = \frac{1 + 1}{2} = 1$

Example 3

Find the amplitude of $f : x \to a \sin x$.

Solution

$$-1 \le \sin x \le 1$$

$\therefore \qquad M = |a|, \qquad m = -|a|$

$\therefore \quad$ amplitude is $\dfrac{M - m}{2} = \dfrac{|a| + |a|}{2} = |a|$

Figure 2.11 shows the period and amplitude of the functions defined by

$$y = \sin x \qquad y = \sin 2x \qquad y = 2 \sin x$$

Curve	Amplitude	Period
$y = \sin x$	1	2π
$y = \sin 2x$	1	π
$y = 2 \sin x$	2	2π

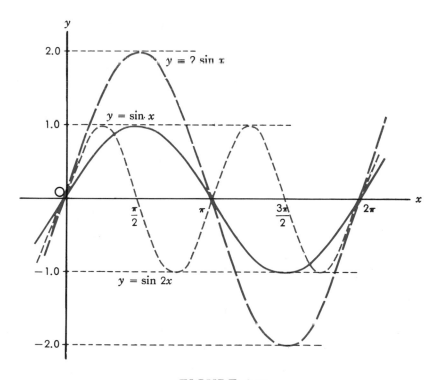

FIGURE 2.11

Observe that in the graph of $y = \sin 2x$, 2 wavelengths occur in the interval $0 < x < 2\pi$. How many wavelengths would occur in the interval $0 < x < 2\pi$ in the graph of $y = \sin 3x$?

$$y = \sin \frac{1}{2}x?$$

$$y = \sin kx, \; k > 0?$$

Example 4

Graph the function defined by

$$y = 3 \sin \left(2x + \frac{\pi}{3} \right).$$

Solution

Compare with $y = a \sin (kx + d)$ where $a = 3$, $k = 2$, and $d = \frac{\pi}{3}$.

The graph is a sine curve with amplitude 3 and period

$$\frac{2\pi}{|k|} = \frac{2\pi}{2} = \pi.$$

The zeros of the function are obtained by noting that

$$\sin 0 = \sin \pi = \sin 2\pi = \cdots = 0$$

If $2x + \frac{\pi}{3} = 0$	If $2x + \frac{\pi}{3} = \pi$	If $2x + \frac{\pi}{3} = 2\pi$
$x = -\frac{\pi}{6}$	$x = \frac{\pi}{3}$	$x = \frac{5\pi}{6}$

The maximum and minimum points may be obtained by noting that

for a maximum,	for a minimum,
$\sin \frac{\pi}{2} = 1$	$\sin \frac{3\pi}{2} = -1$
$\therefore \quad 2x + \frac{\pi}{3} = \frac{\pi}{2}$	$2x + \frac{\pi}{3} = \frac{3\pi}{2}$
$x = \frac{\pi}{12}$	$x = \frac{7\pi}{12}$

x	$-\frac{\pi}{6}$	$\frac{\pi}{3}$	$\frac{5\pi}{6}$	$\frac{\pi}{12}$	$\frac{7\pi}{12}$
$3 \sin \left(2x + \frac{\pi}{3} \right)$	0	0	0	3	-3

The complete graph of

$y = 3 \sin \left(2x + \dfrac{\pi}{3} \right)$ is obtained by

translating the graph (right) to the right and left in multiples of the period π. There are 2 wavelengths in the interval of 2π.

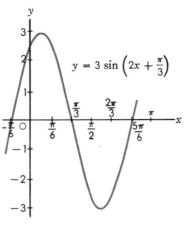

The graph of Example 4 is the same as that of $y = 3 \sin 2x$ except that it has been translated or shifted to the left $\dfrac{\pi}{6}$ units.

We call $-\dfrac{\pi}{6}$ the *phase shift*.

The graph of $y = 3 \sin \left(2x - \dfrac{\pi}{3} \right)$ would be translated $\dfrac{\pi}{6}$ units to the right.

For the graph of $y = a \sin(kx + d)$ a zero occurs when

$$kx + d = 0 \qquad \text{or} \qquad x = -\frac{d}{k}.$$

If $-\dfrac{d}{k} < 0$, the graph of $y = a \sin (k\theta + d)$ is translated $\left| \dfrac{d}{k} \right|$ to the

left and if $-\dfrac{d}{k} > 0$ the translation is $\left| \dfrac{d}{k} \right|$ to the right. The number $-\dfrac{d}{k}$ is called the *phase shift*.

Identical results are found for $y = a \cos (kx + d)$ when the graph is compared with that of $y = \cos x$.

For the functions $\{(x, y) \in R \times R \mid y = a \sin(kx + d)\}$
and $\{(x, y) \in R \times R \mid y = a \cos(kx + d)\}$

(1) the graph is sinusoidal,

(2) the amplitude is $|a|$,

(3) the period is $\dfrac{2\pi}{|b|}$, that is, $|k|$ wavelengths occur

in the interval $0 \le x \le 2\pi$,

(4) the phase shift is $-\dfrac{d}{k}$.

2.3/Period, Amplitude and Phase 55

Exercise 2.3

A

1. For each of the following functions state the amplitude, period and phase shift. In each case state an equation of the function to which it is related.

   (a) $\left\{(x, y) \,\middle|\, y = 2 \sin\left(2x + \dfrac{\pi}{2}\right)\right\}$

   (b) $\{(x, y) \,|\, y = \frac{1}{2} \sin(3x - \pi)\}$

   (c) $f: x \rightarrow 4 \sin\left(\dfrac{1}{3}x + \dfrac{\pi}{6}\right)$

   (d) $f: x \rightarrow \cos(3x + \pi)$

   (e) $\left\{(t, y) \,\middle|\, y = 3 \cos\left(\dfrac{1}{2}t - \dfrac{\pi}{3}\right)\right\}$

2. For each of the following state the equation of a sine wave with the given data.

   (a) period 2π, amplitude $= 3$ (d) period 3π, amplitude $= 5$
   (b) period 2π, amplitude $= \frac{1}{2}$ (e) period $\frac{1}{3}\pi$, amplitude $= 4$
   (c) period π, amplitude $= 2$

B

3. For each of the following functions determine the amplitude and period. Sketch the graph for two consecutive periods.

   (a) $\{(x, y) \,|\, y = 3 \sin x\}$ (d) $\{(x, y) \,|\, y = \frac{1}{2} \cos 2x\}$
   (b) $f: x \rightarrow \sin 3x$ (e) $\{(t, y) \,|\, y = 2 \sin \frac{1}{2}t\}$
   (c) $f: t \rightarrow \cos 3t$ (f) $f: x \rightarrow 4 \cos \frac{1}{3}x$

4. For each of the following functions determine the amplitude, period and phase shift. Sketch the graph.

   (a) $\left\{(x, y) \,\middle|\, y = 2 \cos\left(x + \dfrac{\pi}{2}\right)\right\}$ (d) $f: x \rightarrow \frac{1}{2} \sin(3x - \pi)$

   (b) $\{(x, y) \,|\, y = \cos(3x + \pi)\}$ (e) $f: t \rightarrow 3 \cos\left(\dfrac{1}{2}t - \dfrac{\pi}{3}\right)$

   (c) $\left\{(t, y) \,\middle|\, y = \sin\left(2t + \dfrac{\pi}{2}\right)\right\}$ (f) $f: x \rightarrow 4 \sin\left(\dfrac{1}{3}x + \dfrac{\pi}{6}\right)$

5. Write an equation of a sine wave given the data in each of the following. Repeat the question for a cosine wave.

   (a) period 2π, amplitude 3, phase shift $\dfrac{\pi}{6}$

   (b) period π, amplitude 5, phase shift $\dfrac{\pi}{3}$

(c)   period 3π, amplitude 2, phase shift $\dfrac{\pi}{4}$

(d)   period $\dfrac{\pi}{2}$, amplitude 7, phase shift $-\dfrac{\pi}{4}$

6. Use the idea of phase shift or translation to prove each of the following.

(a) $\sin x = \cos\left(x - \dfrac{\pi}{2}\right)$ (b) $\cos x = \sin\left(x + \dfrac{\pi}{2}\right)$

C

7. Explain how the graph of $y = \sec 2x$ would differ from the graph of $y = \sec x$.

8. Explain how the graph of $y = \tan 3x$ would differ from the graph of $y = \tan x$.

9. How do the graphs of $y = \csc\left(3x + \dfrac{\pi}{6}\right)$ and $y = \csc x$ compare?

10. How do the graphs of $y = \cot\left(2x - \dfrac{\pi}{4}\right)$ and $y = \cot x$ compare?

11. Graph each of the following functions by adding ordinates. State the period and amplitude of each function using your graph.

(a) $\{(x, y) \mid y = 3 + 2 \sin x\}$ (c) $\{(x,y) \mid y = \sin\frac{1}{2}x + 2\cos x\}$
(b) $\{(x, y) \mid y = \sin x + \cos x\}$ (d) $f : x \to \sin 4x + 3 \cos 2x$

2.4 The Inverse Circular Functions

Recall from Section 1.2 that

(1) $f = \{(x, y) \mid y = f(x)\}$ and
$f^{-1} = \{(x, y) \mid x = f(y)\}$ are
inverses,

(2) f and f^{-1} are mirror images
in the line $y = x$.

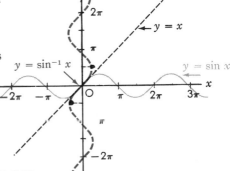

FIGURE 2.12

If sin $= \{(x, y) | y = \sin x\}$ is graphed, then the graph of its inverse is $\{(x, y) | x = \sin y\}$ and is obtained by finding the mirror image of the sine graph in the line $y = x$. The graph of the function sine and the inverse relation are given in Figure 2.12. Note that the vertical line test shows that the inverse of sine is *not* a function.

Consider a part of the inverse of sine that is a function. Restrict the y values of the inverse of sine so that for each x there is only one y by using only the **solid** colored portion of the curve shown in Figure 2.12. Call this function $\sin^{-1}$. Thus $\sin^{-1}$ has domain $-1 \leq x \leq 1$ and range $-\frac{\pi}{2} \leq y \leq \frac{\pi}{2}$.

Recall that f^{-1} has either $y = f^{-1}(x)$ or $x = f(y)$ as a defining equation. Thus we have the following.

For the function $\sin^{-1}$,

$$y = \sin^{-1}x \Leftrightarrow x = \sin y$$

where $-1 \leq x \leq 1$

$$-\frac{\pi}{2} \leq y \leq \frac{\pi}{2}.$$

Example 1

Find the value of the following.

(a) $\sin^{-1}\left(\frac{1}{2}\right)$

(b) $\sin^{-1}\left(-\frac{\sqrt{3}}{2}\right)$

Solution

(a) Let $\quad y = \sin^{-1}\left(\frac{1}{2}\right)$

Then $\quad \frac{1}{2} = \sin y$

But $\quad \frac{1}{2} = \sin \frac{\pi}{6}$

$\therefore y = \frac{\pi}{6} = \sin^{-1}\left(\frac{1}{2}\right)$

(b) Let $\quad y = \sin^{-1}\left(-\frac{\sqrt{3}}{2}\right)$

Then $\quad -\frac{\sqrt{3}}{2} = \sin y$

But $\quad -\frac{\sqrt{3}}{2} = \sin\left(-\frac{\pi}{3}\right)$

$\therefore \quad y = -\frac{\pi}{3} = \sin^{-1}\left(-\frac{\sqrt{3}}{2}\right)$

Note: There are other values of y besides $\frac{\pi}{6}$ for which $\sin y = \frac{1}{2}$, but y is restricted to the interval $-\frac{\pi}{2} \leq y \leq \frac{\pi}{2}$.

58

Figure 2.13 shows the graph of the function
cos $= \{(x, y) \mid y = \cos x\}$ and its inverse relation $\{(x, y) \mid x = \cos y\}$. To ensure that the inverse of cos is a function, only the solid colored portion of the mirror image in $y = x$ of the graph of cos is used. Thus we have the following.

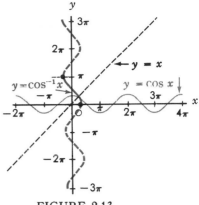

FIGURE 2.13

For the function $\cos^{-1}$,

$$y = \cos^{-1}x \Leftrightarrow x = \cos y$$

where

$$-1 \leq x \leq 1 \text{ and } 0 \leq y \leq \pi.$$

In Figure 2.14 the graph of tan $= \{(x, y) \mid y = \tan x\}$ and its inverse $\{(x, y) \mid x = \tan y\}$ are drawn. Only one portion of the mirror image of tan in the line $y = x$ is used to define $\tan^{-1}$.

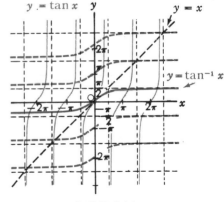

For the function $\tan^{-1}$,
$$y = \tan^{-1}x \Leftrightarrow x = \tan y$$
where
$$x \in R \text{ and } -\frac{\pi}{2} < y < \frac{\pi}{2}.$$

FIGURE 2.14

The functions $\csc^{-1}$, $\sec^{-1}$, and $\cot^{-1}$ are defined as follows:

$$\csc^{-1} = \left\{(x, y) \mid y = \sin^{-1}\left(\frac{1}{x}\right), \; |x| \geq 1, 0 < |y| \leq \frac{x}{2}\right\}$$

$$\sec^{-1} = \left\{(x, y) \mid y = \cos^{-1}\left(\frac{1}{x}\right), \; |x| \geq 1, 0 \leq y < \frac{\pi}{2} \text{ or } \frac{\pi}{2} < y \leq \pi\right\}$$

$$\cot^{-1} = \left\{(x, y) \mid y = \tan^{-1}\left(\frac{1}{x}\right), \; x \in R, 0 < y < \pi\right\}$$

Example 2

Evaluate $\sin\left[\cos^{-1}\left(\dfrac{3}{5}\right)\right]$.

Solution

Let $y = \cos^{-1}\left(\dfrac{3}{5}\right)$

$\therefore \dfrac{3}{5} = \cos y$ where $0 \le y \le \pi$

$\because \cos y > 0$, y must be further restricted to $0 \le y \le \dfrac{\pi}{2}$.

Now $\sin\left[\cos^{-1}\left(\dfrac{3}{5}\right)\right] = \sin y$ and $\sin^2 y + \cos^2 y = 1$

$\therefore \sin^2 y + \left(\dfrac{3}{5}\right)^2 = 1$

$\therefore \sin^2 y = \dfrac{16}{25}$

$\therefore \sin y = \dfrac{4}{5}\left(-\dfrac{4}{5}$ is not admissible, $\because 0 \le y \le \dfrac{\pi}{2}\right)$

$\therefore \sin\left[\cos^{-1}\left(\dfrac{3}{5}\right)\right] = \dfrac{4}{5}$

Since y in $x = \sin y$ can be represented as the length of an arc on a unit circle, the expression $y = \sin^{-1}x$ is sometimes written $y = \text{arc sin } x$, where arc sin x is read "arc sine of x." Thus the functions $\sin^{-1}$, $\cos^{-1}$, $\tan^{-1}$ can be named arc sin, arc cos and arc tan respectively.

Exercise 2.4

B

1. Sketch graphs of the inverse circular functions $\sin^{-1}$, $\cos^{-1}$, $\tan^{-1}$.

2. Sketch the graphs of the functions $\csc^{-1}$, $\sec^{-1}$, $\cot^{-1}$. List the domain and range of each function.

3. Evaluate.

(a) $\sin^{-1}\left(\dfrac{\sqrt{3}}{2}\right)$ (d) $\csc^{-1}\left(\sqrt{2}\right)$ (g) $\sin^{-1}\left(-\dfrac{1}{\sqrt{2}}\right)$

(b) $\cos^{-1}(-1)$ (e) $\sec^{-1}(1)$ (h) $\cos^{-1}\left(\dfrac{\sqrt{3}}{2}\right)$

(c) $\tan^{-1}(0)$ (f) $\cot^{-1}(1)$ (i) $\tan^{-1}(-\sqrt{3})$

4. Evaluate.

   (a) $\cos\,[\sin^{-1}\,(1)]$

   (b) $\sin\left[\cos^{-1}\left(-\dfrac{1}{2}\right)\right]$

   (c) $\tan\,[\tan^{-1}\,(-1)]$

   (d) $\sin^{-1}\left(\cos\,\dfrac{\pi}{3}\right)$

   (e) $\cos^{-1}\left(\tan\,\dfrac{\pi}{4}\right)$

   (f) $\tan^{-1}\left(\sin\,\dfrac{\pi}{2}\right)$

5. Evaluate.

   (a) $\sin\left[\cos^{-1}\left(\dfrac{1}{3}\right)\right]$

   (b) $\cos\left[\sin^{-1}\left(-\dfrac{5}{13}\right)\right]$

6. If $x = \sin^{-1}\left(\dfrac{1}{2}\right) + \tan^{-1}\,(1)$, find x.

7. If $|x| \leq 1$, does $\sin^{-1}(\sin x) = \sin\,(\sin^{-1}x)$ for every value of x? Explain.

8. Explain why $\tan(\tan^{-1}x) = x$ for all real x.

C

9. Graph the functions $\csc^{-1}$, $\sec^{-1}$ and $\cot^{-1}$.

10. (a) Prove that $\sin(\cos^{-1}x) = \sqrt{1-x^2}$.
    (b) Evaluate $\cos(\sin^{-1}x)$.

11. If $|x| < 1$ prove that $\sin^{-1}|x| = \sec^{-1}\dfrac{1}{\sqrt{1-x^2}}$.

12. Prove that $\cos[\tan^{-1}(\sin(\cot^{-1}x))] = \dfrac{\sqrt{x^2+1}}{\sqrt{x^2+2}}$.

2.5 Identities

An open sentence in one variable is an identity if the solution set and the domain of the variable are the same. For example, the following are identities.

   (1) for all $x \in R$, $x(x-1) = x^2 - x$

   (2) for all $x \in N$, $x > 0$

   (3) for all $x \in R$, $\tan x = \dfrac{\sin x}{\cos x}$, $\cos x \neq 0$

Here are the basic identities that are direct consequences of the definitions of the circular functions.

Reciprocal identities	Quotient identities	Pythagorean identities
$\csc x = \dfrac{1}{\sin x}$	$\tan x = \dfrac{\sin x}{\cos x}$	$\sin^2 x + \cos^2 x = 1$
$\sec x = \dfrac{1}{\cos x}$	$\cot x = \dfrac{\cos x}{\sin x}$	$\sec^2 x = 1 + \tan^2 x$
$\cot x = \dfrac{1}{\tan x}$		$\csc^2 x = 1 + \cot^2 x$

Ingenuity and perseverance are often required to prove an identity. Indeed, many methods must be devised to handle all the problems that arise. To prove simple identities you will find the following suggestions helpful.

(1) Simplify one side of an identity at a time, starting with the more complicated side first.
(2) Express csc x, sec x, tan x, cot x in terms of the sines and/or cosines of x.
(3) Simplify algebraically.
(4) If $\sin^2 x$, $\cos^2 x$, etc. appear, employ a Pythagorean relation if its use simplifies the expression.

Example 1

Prove that $(1 + \cot^2 x) \tan^2 x = \sec^2 x$.

Solution

$$\text{LS} = \csc^2 x \left(\frac{\sin x}{\cos x}\right)^2 \qquad\qquad \text{RS} = \left(\frac{1}{\cos x}\right)^2$$

$$= \frac{1}{\sin^2 x} \frac{\sin^2 x}{\cos^2 x}$$

$$= \frac{1}{\cos^2 x}$$

$$= \text{RS}$$

$$\therefore \ (1 + \cot^2 x) \tan^2 x = \sec^2 x$$

Example 2

Prove $\dfrac{1 + \cos x}{1 - \cos x} = \dfrac{\sec x + 1}{\sec x - 1}$, $\qquad \cos x \notin \{0, 1\}$

Solution

$$\text{RS} = \frac{\sec x + 1}{\sec x - 1}$$

$$= \frac{\dfrac{1}{\cos x} + 1}{\dfrac{1}{\cos x} - 1}$$

$$= \frac{1 + \cos x}{1 - \cos x}$$

$$\therefore \qquad \frac{1 + \cos x}{1 - \cos x} = \frac{\sec x + 1}{\sec x - 1}, \qquad \cos x \notin \{0, 1\}$$

Why is the restriction on $\cos x$ required?

Exercise 2.5

B 1. Prove the following identities.

    (a) $\sin x \sec x = \tan x$

    (b) $\sin y \sec y \cot y = 1$

    (c) $\cot z \sec z = \csc z$

    (d) $\dfrac{\cos y \csc y}{\cot y} = 1$

    (e) $\sec x(1 + \cos x) = 1 + \sec x$

    (f) $\sin x(1 + \csc x) = \sin x + 1$

    (g) $\tan x(1 + \cot x) = 1 + \tan x$

    (h) $\cos x(\sec x + 1) = \cos x + 1$

    (i) $\csc y(\sin y - 1) = 1 - \csc y$

    (j) $\cot z(1 - \tan z) = \cot z - 1$

  2. Prove.

    (a) $\sin y \tan^2 y \cot^3 y = \cos y$

    (b) $\sin^2 x \sec^2 x = \sec^2 x - 1$

    (c) $(1 + \tan^2 x)\cos^2 x = 1$

    (d) $(1 + \tan y)^2 = \sec^2 y + 2\tan y$

    (e) $(\cos x - \sin x)^2 = 1 - 2\sin x \cos x$

    (f) $(\sin y + \cos y)(\sin y - \cos y) = 1 - 2\cos^2 y$

    (g) $\cos^2 y - \sin^2 y = 1 - 2\sin^2 y$

    (h) $\csc^2 x\,(1 - \cos^2 x) = 1$

    (i) $(\cot y + 1)^2 = \csc^2 y + 2\cot y$

    (j) $\sec x - \cos x = \sin x \tan x$

  3. Prove.

    (a) $\tan y \sin y + \cos y = \sec y$

    (b) $\cot^2 x - \cos^2 x = \cos^2 x \cot^2 x$

    (c) $\cos^4 z - \sin^4 z = \cos^2 z - \sin^2 z$

    (d) $\dfrac{1 + \tan^2 x}{1 + \cot^2 x} = \tan^2 x$

(e) $\dfrac{\tan^2 x - 1}{\cot^2 x - 1} = 1 - \sec^2 x$

(f) $\dfrac{1}{1 + \tan^2 y} + \dfrac{1}{1 + \cot^2 y} = 1$

(g) $\dfrac{\tan^2 z}{1 + \tan^2 z} = \sin^2 z$

(h) $\dfrac{1 + \cos x}{1 - \cos x} = 1 + \dfrac{2 \cos x(1 + \cos x)}{\sin^2 x}$

(i) $\dfrac{\sec z}{\csc^2 z} = \sec z - \cos z$

(j) $\csc^2 y - \csc y \cot y = \dfrac{1}{1 + \cos y}$

4. Prove the following identities.

(a) $\dfrac{1 + \sin^2 x \sec^2 x}{1 + \cos^2 x \csc^2 x} = \sin^2 x \sec^2 x$

(b) $2 + \dfrac{\sin^4 y + \cos^4 y}{\sin^2 y \cos^2 y} = \sec^2 y \csc^2 y$

(c) $\dfrac{1 + \sin y}{\cos y} = \dfrac{\cos y}{1 - \sin y}$

(d) $\dfrac{1}{1 + \sin x} = \sec^2 x - \sec x \tan x$

(e) $\sqrt{\dfrac{1 - \cos z}{1 + \cos z}} = \left| \dfrac{1}{\csc z + \cot z} \right|$

(f) $(\tan x + \cot x)(\sec x - \cos x) = \sec x \tan x$

(g) $\sin^6 x + \cos^6 x = 1 - 3 \sin^2 x \cos^2 x$

(h) $(1 - \cos y)(1 + \sec y) = \sin y \tan y$

5. For $x, y \in R$, prove the following.

(a) $\tan^2 x + \sec^2 y = \sec^2 x + \tan^2 y$

(b) $\dfrac{\tan x + \cot y}{\cot x + \tan y} = \dfrac{\tan x}{\tan y}$

(c) $\sin^2 x \cos^2 y - \cos^2 x \sin^2 y = \sin^2 x - \sin^2 y$

(d) $\sec^2 x \tan^2 y - \tan^2 x \sec^2 y = \tan^2 y - \tan^2 x$

(e) $(\sin x \cos y + \cos x \sin y)^2 + (\cos x \cos y - \sin x \sin y)^2 = 1$

6. Explain why $\sin x = \sqrt{1 - \cos^2 x}$, $x \in R$ is not an identity.

2.6 Parametric Equations

We are accustomed to expressing the defining equation of a curve using two variables x and y. In some cases we can conveniently express the coordinates (x, y) of a point on the curves in terms of a third variable. For example,

$$x = 1 + t^2 \quad \text{or} \quad x = \cos\theta$$
$$y = t \qquad\qquad y = \sin\theta$$

This third variable is called a *parameter* and the two equations are called *parametric equations* of the curve. Parametric equations are especially useful when the parameter is time t, in which case the position of a point on the curve is known for any time t.

Example 1

Graph the curve whose parametric equations are

$$x = 1 + t^2$$
$$y = t.$$

Solution

To find values for x and y, we give t particular values and construct a table.

t	-3	-2	-1	0	1	2	3
x	10	5	2	1	2	5	10
y	-3	-2	-1	0	1	2	3

Plot the points (x, y) and join the points with a smooth curve.

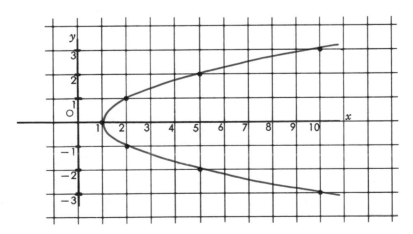

Example 2

For each of the given parametric equations of a curve, find a Cartesian equation of the curve.

(a) $x = 1 + t^2$
    $y = t$

(b) $x = \cos \theta$
    $y = \sin \theta$

Solution

In general the Cartesian equation is found by eliminating the parameter from the parametric equations.

(a) Substituting $y = t$ in the equation $x = 1 + t^2$ gives $x = 1 + y^2$. Thus, $y^2 = x - 1$ is the required equation.
(b) Recall the trigonometric identity $\sin^2\theta + \cos^2\theta = 1$. Find $\cos \theta$ and $\sin \theta$ in terms of x and y and substitute in the identity.
    $\because \sin \theta = y$ and $\cos \theta = x$
    $\therefore y^2 + x^2 = 1$ is the required equation.

Example 3

Two concentric circles have radii a and b respectively. Any radius cuts the two circles at A and B as shown.

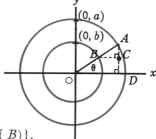

Find a Cartesian equation of the curve that results from the set of points
$T = \{(x \text{ coordinate of } A), (y \text{ coordinate of } B)\}$.

Solution

Let $C(x, y)$ be any point of the set T, and let $\angle AOD = \theta$.
$\therefore A$ is $(a \cos \theta, a \sin \theta)$
   B is $(b \cos \theta, b \sin \theta)$
Thus, the coordinates of C are $(a \cos \theta, b \sin \theta)$.
But the coordinates of C are (x, y)
$\therefore x = a \cos \theta, y = b \sin \theta$
$\therefore \cos \theta = \dfrac{x}{a}$ and $\sin \theta = \dfrac{y}{b}$
Substitute in $\cos^2\theta + \sin^2\theta = 1$
$\therefore \dfrac{x^2}{a^2} + \dfrac{y^2}{b^2} = 1$ is the required equation.

Example 4

The path of a point, P, on a wheel that rolls without slipping is called a *cycloid*. Find parametric equations of a cycloid.

Solution

Let P be a point on a circle of radius r which rolls along the x axis. Let the initial position of P be at the origin.

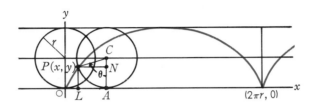

Consider the position of P after the circle has rolled a distance OA and a radius has rotated through an angle θ.

$\therefore\ \angle PCA = \theta$ (in radians).

$\therefore\ OA = r\theta$

$$x = OL = OA - LA$$
$$= OA - PN$$
$$= r\theta - r \sin \theta$$

$$y = PL = CA - CN$$
$$= r - r \cos \theta$$

$\therefore$ parametric equations of the cycloid are $x = r\theta - r \sin \theta$

$$y = r - r \cos \theta$$

Exercise 2.6

B

1. For each of the following parametric equations make a table of values and sketch the curve.

(a) $x = 3t$
  $y = 7t$

(b) $x = t$
  $y = \dfrac{1}{t}$

(c) $x = t^2$
  $y = t^3$

(d) $x = 3 \sin \theta$
  $y = 3 \cos \theta$

(e) $x = 4 \tan \theta$
  $y = 4 \sec \theta$

(f) $x = 4t$
  $y = 20 - 16t^2$

2. Show that $x = 2t$, $y = 5 - 6t$ are parametric equations of a straight line.

3. Show that $x = at^2$, $y = 2at$ are parametric equations of the parabola $y^2 = 4ax$.

2.6/Parametric Equations

67

4. Show that $x = \dfrac{2az}{1 + z^2}$, $y = \dfrac{a(1 - z^2)}{1 + z^2}$ are parametric equations of a circle.

5. Each of the following are parametric equations of a curve. Find the Cartesian equation of the curve.

(a) $x = a \sec \theta$
$y = b \tan \theta$

(b) $x = 3 \cos \theta + 4 \sin \theta$
$y = 3 \sin \theta - 4 \cos \theta$

6. A point P lies on the radius of a circle with centre C and radius r. Let $CP = a$, $(a < r)$. Find the parametric equations of the path of P if the circle rolls without slipping along a straight line. This curve is called a *curtate cycloid* or a *trochoid*.

Hint: $x = OL$
$\quad\quad = OA - PN$
$y = PL$
$\quad\quad = CA - CN$

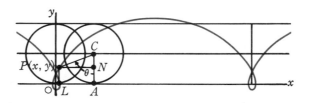

C 7. Repeat Question 6 where $CP = a$, $(a > r)$. The curve is called a *prolate cycloid* or a *trochoid*.

Hint:

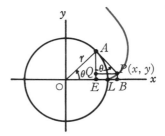

8. A string is wound about the circumference of a circle. One end is fastened to the circumference and the string is unwound. If the string is kept stretched, the curve traced by the free end of the string is called the *involute* of the circle. Find the involute of a circle with radius r.

Hint: arc $AL = AP$
$\quad\quad\quad\quad = r\theta$
$x = OE + QP$
$y = AE - AQ$

9. The path of a point, P, on a wheel that rolls without slipping along the circumference of another circle is called an *epicycloid*. Use the given diagram to show that parametric equations of the epicycloid are

$$x = (R + r) \cos \theta - r \cos \left(\frac{R + r}{r} \right) \theta$$

$$y = (R + r) \sin \theta - r \sin \left(\frac{R + r}{r} \right) \theta$$

Hint: arc AD = arc AP

$$R\theta = r\phi$$

$$\alpha = \frac{(R + r)\,\theta}{r} - 90$$

$$x = OM = OL + LM$$
$$= (R + r) \cos \theta + r \sin \alpha$$

$$y = PM = CL - CN$$
$$= (R + r) \sin \theta - r \cos \alpha$$

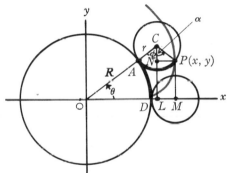

10. A ray from $A(-a, 0)$ cuts the y axis at C. Points P and P' are located on the ray so that $P'C = CP = OC$. Find the loci of P and P' combined. This curve is called a *strophoid*.

Hint: $OC = a \tan \theta$

$$x = CR$$
$$= CP \cos \theta$$

$$y = PM$$
$$= OC + PR$$
$$= OC + CP \sin \theta$$

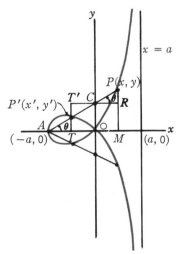

Review Exercise 2.7

B

1. Sketch the graphs of the 6 circular functions in the interval -4π to 4π.

2. Use your graphs of Question 1 as an aid to evaluate each of the following.

   (a) $\sin \pi$

   (b) $\cos \dfrac{\pi}{3}$

   (c) $\tan \dfrac{\pi}{4}$

   (d) $\sin \left(-\dfrac{\pi}{3}\right)$

   (e) $\cos \dfrac{5\pi}{4}$

   (f) $\tan \dfrac{11\pi}{6}$

   (g) $\csc \dfrac{\pi}{6}$

   (h) $\sec \left(-\dfrac{\pi}{6}\right)$

   (i) $\cot \dfrac{\pi}{4}$

3. Using the same axes, graph the functions defined by

   (a) $y = \cos x$

   (b) $y = 2 \cos x$

   (c) $y = \cos 2x$

4. For each of the following functions determine the amplitude, period and phase shift. Sketch the graph.

   (a) $\{(x, y) \,|\, y = 2 \sin x\}$

   (b) $\{(x, y) \,|\, y = \sin 2x\}$

   (c) $f: x \to 2 \sin 3x$

   (d) $f: t \to \frac{1}{3} \cos \frac{1}{2}t$

   (e) $\left\{(x, y) \,\middle|\, y = 5 \cos\left(x + \dfrac{\pi}{3}\right)\right\}$

   (f) $\left\{(t, y) \,\middle|\, y = 7 \sin\left(\dfrac{1}{3}t + \dfrac{\pi}{2}\right)\right\}$

   (g) $h: x \to -2 \cos 4x$

5. Use a unit circle to show that each of the following is true where $0 < x < \dfrac{\pi}{2}$.

   (a) $\sin x = \sin(\pi - x)$
   (b) $\sin x = -\sin(\pi + x)$

   (c) $\cos x = -\cos(\pi + x)$
   (d) $\cos(\pi - x) = \cos(\pi + x)$

6. (a) For $0 < x < \dfrac{\pi}{2}$, $\sin x = \dfrac{5}{13}$. Find $\cos x$, $\tan x$.

   (b) For $\dfrac{\pi}{2} < x < \pi$, $\cos x = -\dfrac{3}{5}$. Find $\sin x$, $\tan x$.

   (c) For $\pi < x < \dfrac{3\pi}{2}$, $\sin x = -\dfrac{1}{3}$. Find $\cos x$, $\cot x$.

   (d) For $\dfrac{3\pi}{2} < x < 2\pi$, $\cos x = \dfrac{2}{5}$. Find $\sin x$, $\cot x$.

7. Sketch the graphs of $\sin^{-1}$, $\cos^{-1}$, $\tan^{-1}$.

8. Sketch the graphs of $\csc^{-1}$, $\sec^{-1}$, $\cot^{-1}$.

9. Evaluate.

(a) $\sin^{-1}\left(-\dfrac{\sqrt{3}}{2}\right)$ (d) $\sin^{-1}\left(-\dfrac{1}{\sqrt{2}}\right)$ (g) $\sin^{-1}\left(\cos\dfrac{\pi}{2}\right)$

(b) $\cos^{-1}\left(\dfrac{1}{2}\right)$ (e) $\sec^{-1}\left(-\dfrac{2}{\sqrt{3}}\right)$ (h) $\cos\left[\sin^{-1}\left(-\dfrac{1}{2}\right)\right]$

(c) $\tan^{-1}\left(\dfrac{1}{\sqrt{3}}\right)$ (f) $\cot^{-1}(\sqrt{3})$ (i) $\cos\left[\tan^{-1}\left(\dfrac{4}{3}\right)\right]$

10. Prove the following identities.

(a) $\cos x \tan x = \sin x$

(b) $\sec x \cot x = \csc x$

(c) $(\tan y + \cot y) \sin y \cos y = 1$

(d) $(1 - \cos^2 x) \csc^2 x = 1$

(e) $\cot^2 y (1 - \cos^2 y) = \cos^2 y$

(f) $(1 + \tan^2 z) \cos^2 z = 1$

(g) $(1 - \cos^2 x)(1 + \tan^2 x) = \tan^2 x$

(h) $\sin^2 x \sec^2 x = \sec^2 x - 1$

(i) $\dfrac{\sin y + \cos y}{\sec y + \csc y} = \dfrac{\cos y}{\csc y}$

(j) $\cos t + \sin t = \dfrac{1 + \tan t}{\sec t}$

(k) $\dfrac{1}{1 - \sec x} + \dfrac{1}{1 + \sec x} = -2 \cot^2 x$

(l) $\dfrac{(\sin x + \cos x)^2}{(\sin x - \cos x)^2} = \dfrac{\sec^2 x + 2 \tan x}{\sec^2 x - 2 \tan x}$

(m) $\dfrac{1 - 2 \cos^2 A}{\sin A \cos A} = \tan A - \cot A$

(n) $1 - \dfrac{\cos^2 \theta}{1 + \sin \theta} = \sin \theta$

(o) $\dfrac{1}{1 - \sin A} + \dfrac{1}{1 + \sin A} = 2 \sec^2 A$

(p) $\dfrac{\sin \theta}{\sin \theta + \cos \theta} = \dfrac{\sec \theta}{\sec \theta + \csc \theta}$

(q) $\dfrac{\sin^3 \theta + \cos^3 \theta}{\sin \theta + \cos \theta} = 1 - \sin \theta \cos \theta$

3 / The Circular Functions of Number Combinations

In Chapter 2 we discovered many properties of the circular functions through their definitions. In this chapter we shall study the circular functions of the sum and difference of two numbers from which we can rediscover many of the known properties of these functions and also find many new ones.

The circular functions have as domain the set R of real numbers. We shall show the relation between these functions and the corresponding functions where the domain is the set of angles.

3.1 The Cosine Function for the Sum and Difference of Two Numbers

Given any two real numbers x and y, we shall obtain a formula for $\cos(x - y)$ in terms of $\cos x$, $\cos y$, $\sin x$, and $\sin y$. You have already met particular instances of the result we shall derive. For example,

$$\cos(x + 2\pi) = \cos x$$

and
$$\cos(x - \pi) = -\cos x.$$

Theorem

> For each $x, y \in R$,
> $$\cos(x - y) = \cos x \cos y + \sin x \sin y.$$

Consider a unit circle and the following points on it.

$A = W(0) = (1, 0)$
$B - W(x-y) = (\cos(x-y), \sin(x-y))$
$C = W(y) = (\cos y, \sin y)$
$D = W(x) = (\cos x, \sin x)$

Notice that arc AB = arc CD = $x - y$.

$\therefore \qquad AB = CD$

$$
\begin{aligned}
AB^2 &= [\cos(x - y) - 1]^2 + [\sin(x - y)]^2 \\
&= \cos^2(x - y) - 2\cos(x - y) + 1 + \sin^2(x - y) \\
&= [\cos^2(x - y) + \sin^2(x - y)] + 1 - 2\cos(x - y) \\
&= 2 - 2\cos(x - y)
\end{aligned}
$$

$$
\begin{aligned}
CD^2 &= (\cos x - \cos y)^2 + (\sin x - \sin y)^2 \\
&= (\cos^2 x + \sin^2 x) + (\cos^2 y + \sin^2 y) \\
&\qquad\qquad -2\cos x \cos y - 2\sin x \sin y \\
&= 2 - 2(\cos x \cos y + \sin x \sin y)
\end{aligned}
$$

$\because \qquad AB^2 = CD^2$

$\therefore \; 2 - 2\cos(x - y) = 2 - 2(\cos x \cos y + \sin x \sin y)$

$\therefore \qquad \cos(x - y) = \cos x \cos y + \sin x \sin y$

This is the required result for any pair of real numbers x and y.

$$\boxed{\cos(x - y) = \cos x \cos y + \sin x \sin y}$$

Example 1

Evaluate $\cos\left(\dfrac{\pi}{3} - \dfrac{\pi}{4}\right)$.

Solution

$$\cos(x - y) = \cos x \cos y + \sin x \sin y$$

Let $x = \dfrac{\pi}{3}$ and $y = \dfrac{\pi}{4}$

$$\therefore \cos\left(\frac{\pi}{3} - \frac{\pi}{4}\right) = \cos\frac{\pi}{3}\cos\frac{\pi}{4} + \sin\frac{\pi}{3}\sin\frac{\pi}{4}$$

$$= \frac{1}{2}\cdot\frac{\sqrt{2}}{2} + \frac{\sqrt{3}}{2}\cdot\frac{\sqrt{2}}{2}$$

$$= \frac{\sqrt{2} + \sqrt{6}}{4}$$

Example 2

Show that $\cos\left(\dfrac{\pi}{2} - y\right) = \sin y$.

Solution

$$\cos\left(\frac{\pi}{2} - y\right) = \cos\frac{\pi}{2}\cos y + \sin\frac{\pi}{2}\sin y$$

$$= 0\cdot\cos y + 1\cdot\sin y$$

$$= \sin y$$

Another important relationship can be obtained from Example 2 by substituting $\dfrac{\pi}{2} - x$ for y in

$$\cos\left(\frac{\pi}{2} - y\right) = \sin y.$$

$$\therefore \quad \cos\left(\frac{\pi}{2} - \left(\frac{\pi}{2} - x\right)\right) = \sin\left(\frac{\pi}{2} - x\right)$$

$$\therefore \qquad\qquad \cos x = \sin\left(\frac{\pi}{2} - x\right)$$

These important relationships between sine and cosine values are summarized below.

$$\sin\left(\frac{\pi}{2} - x\right) = \cos x$$

$$\cos\left(\frac{\pi}{2} - x\right) = \sin x$$

For any point $W(x)$, its image with respect to the horizontal axis is $W(-x)$.

If $W(x)$ has coordinates (a, b) then $W(-x)$ has coordinates $(a, -b)$. But

$$(a, b) = (\cos x, \sin x)$$
and $\quad (a, -b) = (\cos(-x), \sin(-x))$
$\therefore \quad \cos(-x) = \cos x$
and $\quad \sin(-x) = -\sin x.$

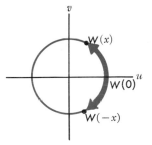

$$\cos(-x) = \cos x$$
$$\sin(-x) = -\sin x$$

Example 3

Prove that

$$\cos(x + y) = \cos x \cos y - \sin x \sin y.$$

Solution

By the previous theorem, for all real numbers a and b we have
$$\cos(a - b) = \cos a \cos b + \sin a \sin b.$$

Substitute $a = x$ and $b = -y$.
$$\therefore \ \cos[x - (-y)] = \cos x \cos(-y) + \sin x \sin(-y)$$
but $\cos(-y) = \cos y$ and $\sin(-y) = -\sin y$
$$\therefore \qquad \cos(x + y) = \cos x \cos y - \sin x \sin y.$$

Example 4

Show that $\cos\left(\dfrac{\pi}{2} + x\right) = -\sin x.$

Solution

$$\cos\left(\frac{\pi}{2} + x\right) = \cos\frac{\pi}{2}\cos x - \sin\frac{\pi}{2}\sin x$$

but $\quad \cos\dfrac{\pi}{2} = 0$ and $\sin\dfrac{\pi}{2} = 1$

$\therefore \quad \cos\left(\dfrac{\pi}{2} + x\right) = -\sin x.$

Compare the two formulas for the cosine of the sum and difference of two numbers.

$$\cos(x + y) = \cos x \cos y - \sin x \sin y$$
$$\cos(x - y) = \cos x \cos y + \sin x \sin y$$

Exercise 3.1

A 1. Express each of the following in terms of values of trigonometric functions in one number.

(a) $\cos(p - q)$
(b) $\cos(r + s)$
(c) $\cos(x + 2)$

(d) $\cos(y - 3)$
(e) $\cos(2x + 3y)$
(f) $\cos(4x - 5y)$

2. Express each of the following as a single trigonometric function value.

(a) $\cos 2x \cos x - \sin 2x \sin x$
(b) $\cos 4a \cos 4a - \sin 4a \sin 4a$
(c) $\cos x \cos x - \sin x \sin x$
(d) $\cos 3x \cos x + \sin 3x \sin x$
(e) $\cos(x + 2)\cos(y + 2) + \sin(x + 2)\sin(y + 2)$
(f) $\cos^2 2x + \sin^2 2x$

B 3. For each of the following use the sum or difference formula and simplify.

(a) $\cos\left(\dfrac{\pi}{2} - x\right)$

(b) $\cos(\pi - x)$

(c) $\cos\left(x - \dfrac{\pi}{2}\right)$

(d) $\cos(x - \pi)$

4. Given $\dfrac{5\pi}{12} = \dfrac{\pi}{4} + \dfrac{\pi}{6}$. Find $\cos\dfrac{5\pi}{12}$.

5. Given $\dfrac{\pi}{12} = \dfrac{\pi}{3} - \dfrac{\pi}{4}$. Find $\cos\dfrac{\pi}{12}$.

6. Given $\dfrac{2\pi}{3} = \dfrac{\pi}{2} + \dfrac{\pi}{6}$. Find $\cos\dfrac{2\pi}{3}$.

7. Find each of the following.

   (a) $\cos\dfrac{5\pi}{6}$

   (b) $\cos\dfrac{3\pi}{4}$

   (c) $\cos\dfrac{4\pi}{3}$

   (d) $\cos\dfrac{5\pi}{4}$

8. Prove the following identities.

   (a) $\cos(\pi + x) = -\cos x$

   (b) $\cos\left(\dfrac{3\pi}{2} - x\right) = -\sin x$

   (c) $\cos\left(\dfrac{3\pi}{2} + x\right) = \sin x$

   (d) $\cos(3\pi + x) = -\cos x$

9. Given $\sin x = \frac{4}{5}$ and $\cos y = -\frac{5}{13}$ where x and y lie in the interval $\dfrac{\pi}{2}$ to π. Find a value for each of the following.

   (a) $\cos(x + y)$ (b) $\cos(x - y)$ (c) $\cos(y - x)$

10. If $0 \le a \le \dfrac{\pi}{2}$ and $\dfrac{3\pi}{2} \le b \le 2\pi$ and $\cos a = \dfrac{4}{5}$, $\cos b = \dfrac{3}{5}$, find $\cos(a + b)$ and $\cos(a - b)$.

C 11. If $\sec x = \dfrac{17}{8}$, $\csc y = \dfrac{5}{3}$ and x, y lie in the interval 0 to $\dfrac{\pi}{2}$, find $\sec(x + y)$.

12. Prove the following formula.
    $$\cos x + \cos y = 2 \cos\dfrac{x + y}{2} \cos\dfrac{x - y}{2}$$

13. Prove the following identities.

    (a) $\dfrac{\cos(x - y)}{\cos x \sin y} = \cot y + \tan x$

    (b) $\cos(a + b)\cos(a - b) = \cos^2 a - \sin^2 b$

    (c) $2\cos\left(\dfrac{\pi}{4} + x\right)\cos\left(\dfrac{\pi}{4} - x\right) = \cos^2 x - \sin^2 x$

3.2 The Sine Function for the Sum and Difference of Two Numbers

The formulas of Section 3.1 are employed here to develop the formulas for the sine function of the sum of two numbers.

$$\therefore \quad \sin(x + y) = \cos\left[\frac{\pi}{2} - (x + y)\right]$$

$$= \cos\left[\left(\frac{\pi}{2} - x\right) - y\right]$$

$$= \cos\left(\frac{\pi}{2} - x\right)\cos y + \sin\left(\frac{\pi}{2} - x\right)\sin y$$

$$= \sin x \cos y + \cos x \sin y$$

In a similar way we may show that

$$\sin(x - y) = \sin x \cos y - \cos x \sin y.$$

$$\sin(x + y) = \sin x \cos y + \cos x \sin y$$
$$\sin(x - y) = \sin x \cos y - \cos x \sin y$$

The formulas we have developed for $\cos(x - y)$, $\cos(x + y)$, $\sin(x - y)$, and $\sin(x + y)$ are usually referred to collectively as the *Addition Formulas* for sine and cosine.

Example 1

Evaluate $\sin\dfrac{5\pi}{12}$.

Solution

$$\frac{5\pi}{12} = \frac{\pi}{4} + \frac{\pi}{6}$$

$$\sin\frac{5\pi}{12} = \sin\left(\frac{\pi}{4} + \frac{\pi}{6}\right)$$

$$= \sin\frac{\pi}{4}\cos\frac{\pi}{6} + \cos\frac{\pi}{4}\sin\frac{\pi}{6}$$

$$= \frac{\sqrt{2}}{2}\cdot\frac{\sqrt{3}}{2} + \frac{\sqrt{2}}{2}\cdot\frac{1}{2}$$

$$= \frac{\sqrt{6} + \sqrt{2}}{4}$$

Exercise 3.2

A 1. Use the Addition Formulas to obtain alternate expressions for each of the following.

(a) $\sin(a - b)$ (d) $\sin(y - 5)$

(b) $\sin(a + b)$ (e) $\sin(2x + 3y)$

(c) $\sin(x + 2)$ (f) $\sin(2x - 3y)$

2. Use the Addition Formulas to express each of the following as a single trigonometric function value.

(a) $\sin 3x \cos x + \cos 3x \sin x$

(b) $\sin 5a \cos 2a - \cos 5a \sin 2a$

(c) $\sin x \cos x + \cos x \sin x$

(d) $\sin 2y \cos y - \cos 2y \sin y$

(e) $\sin(x + 3) \cos(y + 3) - \cos(x + 3) \sin(y + 3)$

B 3. Given $\dfrac{\pi}{12} = \dfrac{\pi}{3} - \dfrac{\pi}{4}$, evaluate $\sin \dfrac{\pi}{12}$.

4. Given $\dfrac{2\pi}{3} = \dfrac{\pi}{2} + \dfrac{\pi}{6}$, evaluate $\sin \dfrac{2\pi}{3}$.

5. Evaluate each of the following.

(a) $\sin \dfrac{5\pi}{6}$ (c) $\cos \dfrac{4\pi}{3}$

(b) $\sin \dfrac{3\pi}{4}$ (d) $\cos \dfrac{5\pi}{4}$

6. Prove the following identities.

(a) $\sin\left(x + \dfrac{\pi}{2}\right) = \cos x$ (d) $\sin(\pi + x) = -\sin x$

(e) $\sin\left(\dfrac{3\pi}{2} + x\right) = -\cos x$

(b) $\sin\left(\dfrac{\pi}{2} - x\right) = \cos x$

(c) $\sin(\pi - x) = \sin x$ (f) $\sin\left(\dfrac{3\pi}{2} - x\right) = -\cos x$

7. Given $\sin x = \dfrac{3}{5}$ and $\cos y = \dfrac{12}{13}$ where x and y lie in the interval 0 to $\dfrac{\pi}{2}$. Find a value for each of the following.

(a) $\sin(x + y)$ (b) $\sin(x - y)$ (c) $\sin(y-x)$

8. Given $\sin a = \frac{3}{5}$, $\sin b = \frac{4}{5}$, and $\frac{\pi}{2} \le a \le \pi$, $\frac{\pi}{2} \le b \le \pi$. Find $\sin(a + b)$ and $\sin(a - b)$.

C 9. If $\sec x = \frac{17}{8}$, $\csc y = \frac{5}{3}$ and x, y lie in the interval 0 to $\frac{\pi}{2}$, find $\csc(x + y)$.

10. Prove the following identities. What values of the variables must be excluded from the domain for each?

(a) $\dfrac{\sin(x + y)}{\cos x \cos y} = \tan x + \tan y$

(b) $\dfrac{\sin(x - y)}{\sin x \sin y} = \cot y - \cot x$

(c) $\sin(a + b)\sin(a - b) = \cos^2 b - \cos^2 a$

(d) $\dfrac{\sin(y - z)}{\cos y \cos z} + \dfrac{\sin(z - x)}{\cos z \cos x} + \dfrac{\sin(x - y)}{\cos x \cos y} = 0$

11. Prove that the range of the function with values

$\sin x - \cos x$ is $\{y \in R \mid y^2 \le 2\}$. Hint: Use $\sin\left(x - \dfrac{\pi}{4}\right)$.

12. Prove the following.

(a) $\sin x + \sin y = 2 \sin \dfrac{x + y}{2} \cos \dfrac{x - y}{2}$

(b) $\sin x - \sin y = 2 \cos \dfrac{x + y}{2} \sin \dfrac{x - y}{2}$

(c) $\cos x - \cos y = -2 \sin \dfrac{x + y}{2} \sin \dfrac{x - y}{2}$

13. Prove the following.

(a) $2 \sin x \cos y = \sin(x + y) + \sin(x - y)$
(b) $2 \cos x \sin y = \sin(x + y) - \sin(x - y)$
(c) $2 \cos x \cos y = \cos(x + y) + \cos(x - y)$
(d) $-2 \sin x \sin y = \cos(x + y) - \cos(x - y)$

14. Show that $\cos(x + y + z) = \cos x \cos y \cos z - \cos x \sin y \sin z - \sin x \sin y \cos z - \sin x \cos y \sin z$.

3.3 The Addition Formulas for Tangent

We shall derive the formulas for $\tan(x+y)$ and $\tan(x-y)$ by using the fact that, if $\cos a \neq 0$, then

$$\tan a = \frac{\sin a}{\cos a}.$$

We wish to express $\tan(x+y)$ in terms of $\tan x$ and $\tan y$. Thus, none of the numbers $(x+y)$, x or y must be odd multiples of $\frac{\pi}{2}$.

$$\therefore \quad \tan(x+y) = \frac{\sin(x+y)}{\cos(x+y)}$$

$$= \frac{\sin x \cos y + \cos x \sin y}{\cos x \cos y - \sin x \sin y}$$

$\because$ neither x nor y is an odd multiple of $\frac{\pi}{2}$, then $\cos x \neq 0$, $\cos y \neq 0$ and $\cos x \cos y \neq 0$.

$$\tan(x+y) = \frac{(\sin x \cos y + \cos x \sin y) \cdot \dfrac{1}{\cos x \cos y}}{(\cos x \cos y - \sin x \sin y) \cdot \dfrac{1}{\cos x \cos y}}$$

$$= \frac{\dfrac{\sin x \cos y}{\cos x \cos y} + \dfrac{\cos x \sin y}{\cos x \cos y}}{\dfrac{\cos x \cos y}{\cos x \cos y} - \dfrac{\sin x \sin y}{\cos x \cos y}}$$

$$= \frac{\dfrac{\sin x}{\cos x} + \dfrac{\sin y}{\cos y}}{1 - \dfrac{\sin x}{\cos x} \cdot \dfrac{\sin y}{\cos y}}$$

$$= \frac{\tan x + \tan y}{1 - \tan x \tan y}$$

A similar method yields a similar formula for $\tan(x-y)$. The Addition Formulas for tangent follow.

For all $x, y \in R$, where x, y or $(x+y)$ are not odd multiples of $\frac{\pi}{2}$, $\quad \tan(x+y) = \dfrac{\tan x + \tan y}{1 - \tan x \tan y}$

For all $x, y \in R$, where x, y or $(x-y)$ are not odd multiples of $\frac{\pi}{2}$, $\quad \tan(x-y) = \dfrac{\tan x - \tan y}{1 + \tan x \tan y}$

Exercise 3.3

A 1. Use an addition formula to find another expression for each of the following.

    (a) $\tan(a + b)$ (c) $\tan(x + 2)$ (e) $\tan(2x + 3y)$

    (b) $\tan(a - b)$ (d) $\tan(x - 3)$ (f) $\tan(3x - 4y)$

2. Use an addition formula to find another expression for each of the following.

    (a) $\dfrac{\tan 2a + \tan a}{1 - \tan 2a \cdot \tan a}$ (b) $\dfrac{\tan 5x - \tan 2x}{1 + \tan 5x \tan 2x}$ (c) $\dfrac{\tan x + \tan x}{1 - \tan^2 x}$

B 3. Given $\dfrac{\pi}{12} = \dfrac{\pi}{3} - \dfrac{\pi}{4}$, find $\tan \dfrac{\pi}{12}$.

4. Given $\dfrac{5\pi}{12} = \dfrac{\pi}{4} + \dfrac{\pi}{6}$, find $\tan \dfrac{5\pi}{12}$.

5. Explain why the formula for $\tan(x + y)$ cannot be applied to $\tan\left(\dfrac{\pi}{2} + x\right)$.

6. Find each of the following.

    (a) $\tan \dfrac{5\pi}{6}$ (b) $\tan \dfrac{3\pi}{4}$ (c) $\tan \dfrac{4\pi}{3}$ (d) $\tan \dfrac{7\pi}{12}$

7. Prove the following identities.

    (a) $\tan(\pi - x) = -\tan x$ (b) $\tan(\pi + x) = \tan x$

8. Express $\cot(x + y)$ as the quotient of the cosine by the sine and show that $\cot(x + y) = \dfrac{\cot x \cot y - 1}{\cot x + \cot y}$.

9. Find a formula for $\cot(x - y)$ in terms of $\cot x$ and $\cot y$. State the restrictions on the variable.

10. Given $\tan x = \frac{3}{4}$ and $\cot y = \frac{12}{5}$ where x and y lie in the interval 0 to $\dfrac{\pi}{2}$, find each of the following.

    (a) $\tan(x + y)$ (b) $\tan(x - y)$ (c) $\tan(y - x)$

11. If $\tan x = \frac{5}{4}$ and $\tan y = -\frac{7}{15}$, find $\tan(x - y)$.

12. Prove that $\dfrac{\tan(a - b) + \tan b}{1 - \tan(a - b) \tan b} = \tan a$.

13. Without using tables, find the value of

$$\frac{\tan 62° - \tan 17°}{1 + \tan 62° \tan 17°}$$

14. If $3 \tan A = 2 \tan B$, prove that

$$\tan(A + B) = \frac{5 \tan B}{3 - 2 \tan^2 B} = \frac{5 \tan A}{2 - 3 \tan^2 A}$$

3.4 Double Angle Formulas

Some important trigonometric relationships may be found by employing the addition formulas to determine equivalent expressions or double angle formulas for sin $2x$, cos $2x$, and tan $2x$.

$$
\begin{aligned}
\sin 2x &= \sin(x + x) \\
&= \sin x \cos x + \cos x \sin x \\
&= 2 \sin x \cos x \\
\cos 2x &= \cos(x + x) \\
&= \cos x \cos x - \sin x \sin x \\
&= \cos^2 x - \sin^2 x \\
&\because \sin^2 x + \cos^2 x = 1 \\
\cos 2x &= \cos^2 x - \sin^2 x \\
&= 1 - \sin^2 x - \sin^2 x \\
&= 1 - 2 \sin^2 x \\
\text{and } \cos 2x &= \cos^2 x - \sin^2 x \\
&= \cos^2 x - (1 - \cos^2 x) \\
&= 2 \cos^2 x - 1 \\
\text{also } \tan 2x &= \frac{\tan x + \tan x}{1 - \tan x \tan x} \\
&= \frac{2 \tan x}{1 - \tan^2 x}
\end{aligned}
$$

$$
\begin{aligned}
\sin 2x &= 2 \sin x \cos x \\
\cos 2x &= \cos^2 x - \sin^2 x \\
&= 2 \cos^2 x - 1 \\
&= 1 - 2 \sin^2 x \\
\\
\tan 2x &= \frac{2 \tan x}{1 - \tan^2 x}
\end{aligned}
$$

Example 1

Given $\sin x = \dfrac{2}{3}, \dfrac{\pi}{2} < x < \pi$, find the following.

(a) $\sin 2x$ (b) $\cos 2x$ (c) $\tan 2x$

Solution

$\sin x = \dfrac{2}{3}$ and $\sin^2 x + \cos^2 x = 1$

$\therefore \dfrac{4}{9} + \cos^2 x = 1$

$\therefore \qquad \cos^2 x = \dfrac{5}{9}$

$\therefore \qquad \cos x = \dfrac{\sqrt{5}}{3}$ or $-\dfrac{\sqrt{5}}{3}$

$\because \qquad \cos x < 0$ for $\dfrac{\pi}{2} < x < \pi$

$\therefore \qquad \cos x = -\dfrac{\sqrt{5}}{3}$

(a) $\sin 2x = 2 \sin x \cos x$

$$= 2\left(\dfrac{2}{3}\right)\left(-\dfrac{\sqrt{5}}{3}\right)$$

$$= -\dfrac{4\sqrt{5}}{9}$$

(b) $\cos 2x$ may be found using any one of the three formulas

$$\cos 2x = 1 - 2 \sin^2 x$$

$$= 1 - 2\left(\dfrac{2}{3}\right)^2$$

$$= \dfrac{1}{9}$$

(c) $\tan 2x$ may be obtained as follows using the results of (a) and (b) or the formula for $\tan 2x$.

$$\tan 2x = \dfrac{\sin 2x}{\cos 2x} = \dfrac{\dfrac{-4\sqrt{5}}{9}}{\dfrac{1}{9}} = -4\sqrt{5}$$

or $\tan 2x = \dfrac{2 \tan x}{1 - \tan^2 x}$

$$= \dfrac{2\left(-\dfrac{2}{\sqrt{5}}\right)}{1 - \dfrac{4}{5}}$$

$$= -\dfrac{20}{\sqrt{5}} \text{ or } -4\sqrt{5}$$

Notice that if $\frac{\pi}{2} < x < \pi$, then $\pi < 2x < 2\pi$.

Since $\sin 2x < 0$ and $\cos 2x > 0$,

$\therefore \frac{3\pi}{2} < 2x < 2\pi.$

Example 2

Prove that $\dfrac{\sin 2x}{1 - \cos 2x} = \cot x.$

Solution

$$\frac{\sin 2x}{1 - \cos 2x} = \frac{2 \sin x \cos x}{1 - (1 - 2 \sin^2 x)}$$

$$= \frac{2 \sin x \cos x}{2 \sin^2 x}$$

$$= \frac{\cos x}{\sin x}$$

$$= \cot x$$

Note that the formula used in line 1 for $\cos 2x$ was the formula that enabled the *1 to be eliminated.*

Exercise 3.4

A 1. Apply a double angle formula to each of the following.

(*a*) $\sin 4x$ (*c*) $\tan 10y$ (*e*) $\cos 5a$
(*b*) $\cos 6a$ (*d*) $\sin 3x$ (*f*) $\tan 7y$

2. State the interval for $2x$ given the interval for x as in each of the following.

(*a*) $0 < x < \dfrac{\pi}{2}$ (*b*) $\pi < x < \dfrac{3\pi}{2}$

3. State the interval for x given the interval for $2x$ as in each of the following.

(*a*) $0 < 2x < \pi$ (*c*) $\pi < 2x < 2\pi$
(*b*) $0 < 2x < \dfrac{3\pi}{2}$ (*d*) $\dfrac{\pi}{2} < 2x < \dfrac{3\pi}{2}$

B 4. If $\sin x = -\dfrac{3}{5}$ and $\pi < x < \dfrac{3\pi}{2}$ find each of the following.

(*a*) $\sin 2x$ (*b*) $\cos 2x$ (*c*) $\tan 2x$

3.4/Double Angle Formulas   85

5. If $\cos \theta = -\dfrac{5}{13}$ and $\dfrac{\pi}{2} < \theta < \pi$, find each of the following.

    (a) $\sin 2\theta$ (b) $\cos 2\theta$ (c) $\tan 2\theta$

6. Prove the following for $0 < 2x < \dfrac{\pi}{2}$.

    (a) $\dfrac{\sin 2x}{1 + \cos 2x} = \tan x$

    (b) $\dfrac{1 - \cos 2x}{\sin 2x} = \tan x$

    (c) $|\,\sin 2x\,| = \dfrac{2}{\sqrt{1 + \tan^2 x}\ \sqrt{1 + \cot^2 x}}$

7. (a) Prove that $\sin^2 x = \dfrac{1 - \cos 2x}{2}$ and $\cos^2 x = \dfrac{1 + \cos 2x}{2}$

    (b) If $\cos 2x = \dfrac{3}{5}$ and $\dfrac{3\pi}{2} < 2x < 2\pi$, use the formulas of part (a) to find the value of $\sin x$ and $\cos x$.

8. If $\sin x = \dfrac{1}{3}$ for $\dfrac{\pi}{2} < x < \pi$, find the following.

    (a) $\cos x$ (b) $\cos 2x$ (c) $\sin 2x$

9. Prove the following identities stating any necessary restriction on the variable.

    (a) $\csc 2\theta = \dfrac{\sec \theta\, \csc \theta}{2}$ (d) $\cos 4x = 8 \cos^4 x - 8 \cos^2 x + 1$

    (b) $\cot 2x = \dfrac{1 + \cos 4x}{\sin 4x}$ (e) $\sin 4x$

                                      $= 8 \cos^3 x \sin x - 4 \cos x \sin x$

    (c) $\dfrac{\csc^2 x - 2}{\csc^2 x} = \cos 2x$ (f) $\dfrac{1 + \sec a}{\sec a} = 2 \cos^2 \dfrac{a}{2}$

10. Prove the following identity.

    $2 \sin (x + y) \sin (x - y) = \cos 2y - \cos 2x$

11. Prove the following.

    (a) $\dfrac{1 - \cos x}{\sin x} = \tan \dfrac{x}{2}$

    (b) $\dfrac{1 + \cos x}{\sin x} = \cot \dfrac{x}{2}$

C 12. Prove the following formulas.

    (a) $\sin \dfrac{\theta}{2} = \pm \sqrt{\dfrac{1 - \cos \theta}{2}}$

    (b) $\cos \dfrac{\theta}{2} = \pm \sqrt{\dfrac{1 + \cos \theta}{2}}$ (c) $\tan \dfrac{\theta}{2} = \pm \sqrt{\dfrac{1 - \cos \theta}{1 + \cos \theta}}$

3.4/Double Angle Formulas

13. If $\cos \theta = -\dfrac{5}{13}$ and $\pi < \theta < \dfrac{3\pi}{2}$ find the following.

    (a) $\sin \dfrac{\theta}{2}$ (b) $\cos \dfrac{\theta}{2}$ (c) $\tan \dfrac{\theta}{2}$

14. If $\sin \beta = -\dfrac{3}{5}$ and $\dfrac{3\pi}{2} < \beta < 2\pi$, find the value of $\cos \dfrac{\beta}{2}$ and $\sin \dfrac{\beta}{2}$.

15. Prove that, for any angle θ,

    (a) $\cos 3\theta = 4 \cos^3 \theta - 3 \cos \theta$
    (b) $\sin 3\theta = 3 \sin \theta - 4 \sin^3 \theta$

16. (a) Develop an expansion for $\tan(x + y + z)$ in terms of $\tan x$, $\tan y$, and $\tan z$.
    (b) By letting $x = y = z = \theta$, use the expansion of part (a) to show that

$$\tan 3\,\theta = \frac{3 \tan \theta - \tan^3 \theta}{1 - 3 \tan^2 \theta}.$$

3.5 Circular Functions of an Angle

The circular functions have domain R, the set of real numbers. We shall change the domain of these functions to a set of angles and give meaning to the functions through the *real number* x which is the *radian measure* of the angle.

Recall that 1 rad (radian) is defined as a sector angle whose sector arc is one radius, see Figure 3.1.

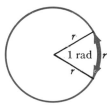
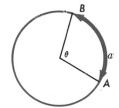

FIGURE 3.1   FIGURE 3.2

Radian measure provides a simple formula for the length of an arc of a circle. For example, in Figure 3.2, if the sector arc AB has length a and the sector angle is θ rad then the ratio of a to the circumference equals the ratio of θ to 2π.

$$\frac{a}{2\pi r} = \frac{\theta}{2\pi}$$
$$\therefore \quad a = r\theta$$

In the case of the winding function the radius of the circle was one. Thus, the arc length formula

$$a = r\theta$$
becomes
$$a = \theta$$
for the unit circle.

In the unit circle, the measure of the sector arc equals the measure of the sector angle in radians.
$$a = \theta$$

By winding a string about a disc we transfer a scale to the circumference. For the unit circle the scale gives the arc length from $W(0)$ to any other point $W(x)$.

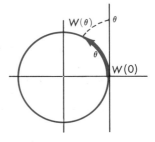

$$\therefore \quad \text{arc } W(0)W(\theta) = \theta$$
The number θ is also the measure of the sector angle whose sector arc is
$$\text{arc } W(0)W(\theta).$$

Associated to $W(\theta)$ are its coordinates $(\cos \theta, \sin \theta)$. The cos, sin, and tan are real valued functions of a real variable, that is functions from R to R. Symbols such as $\cos \angle ABC$, $\cos 50°$ require definition because $\angle ABC$, and $50°$ do not denote real numbers. However, the corresponding angle in each case has a radian measure a, say, where $a \in R$. Consequently, if we wish to speak of "the cosine of an angle" we must give such terms meaning through the real number a which is the radian measure of the angle.

The *degree measure* of a sector angle may be obtained by dividing the circumference into 360 equal parts. The length of the sector arc obtained by using the *number* of these new circumference divisions is called the *degree measure* of the central angle.

Recall the important relationship between degree measure and radian measure.

$$\pi \text{ rad} = 180°$$

3.5/Circular Functions of an Angle

Another familiar result may be obtained by considering two concentric circles, one of radius 1 and the other of radius r. Let the ray OP make an angle of θ rad with OX (Figure 3.3), that is, θ is in standard position.

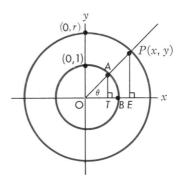

∵ arc BA is θ.
∴ the coordinates of A are
$(\cos \theta, \sin \theta)$.
Let the coordinates of P be (x, y).

$$\triangle OAT \sim \triangle OPE$$

∴ $\dfrac{AT}{PE} = \dfrac{OT}{OE} = \dfrac{OA}{OP}$

$$\dfrac{\sin \theta}{y} = \dfrac{\cos \theta}{x} = \dfrac{1}{r}$$

∴ $y = r \sin \theta$ and $x = r \cos \theta$

FIGURE 3.3

$\sin \theta = \dfrac{y}{r}$ and $\cos \theta = \dfrac{x}{r}$ where $x^2 + y^2 = r^2$

Since $\tan \theta = \dfrac{\sin \theta}{\cos \theta}$

$$\tan \theta = \dfrac{\dfrac{y}{r}}{\dfrac{x}{r}} = \dfrac{y}{x}$$

The following chart summarizes the familiar results for an angle θ in standard position, a point $P(x, y)$ on the terminal arm and the length $OP = r$.

$\sin \theta = \dfrac{y}{r}$	$\csc \theta = \dfrac{r}{y}$		$P(x, y)$
$\cos \theta = \dfrac{x}{r}$	$\sec \theta = \dfrac{r}{x}$	$x^2 + y^2 = r^2$	
$\tan \theta = \dfrac{y}{x}$	$\cot \theta = \dfrac{x}{y}$		

Note that all of the formulas for circular functions of a real number are also true when the domain of the variable is the set of angles measured in degrees or radians.

Example 1

Given $\sin \theta = \dfrac{3}{5}$ where $90° < \theta < 180°$. Find $\cos \theta$.

Solution

Since $\sin \theta = \dfrac{3}{5}$ and θ is in the second quadrant, we may select $y = 3$ and $r = 5$.

$\because x^2 + y^2 = r^2$

$\therefore x^2 + 9 = 25$

$\therefore x^2 = 16$

$\because x < 0, x = -4$

$\therefore \cos \theta = \dfrac{x}{r} = -\dfrac{4}{5}$

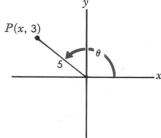

It is worthwhile recalling the following.

$$\sin 30° = \dfrac{1}{2} \qquad \sin 45° = \dfrac{1}{\sqrt{2}} \qquad \sin 60° = \dfrac{\sqrt{3}}{2}$$

$$\cos 30° = \dfrac{\sqrt{3}}{2} \qquad \cos 45° = \dfrac{1}{\sqrt{2}} \qquad \cos 60° = \dfrac{1}{2}$$

$$\tan 30° = \dfrac{1}{\sqrt{3}} \qquad \tan 45° = 1 \qquad \tan 60° = \sqrt{3}$$

Example 2

Use the sum formulas to find the value of $\sin 75°$ without using tables.

Solution

$$75° = 45° + 30°$$
$$\sin 75° = \sin (45° + 30°)$$
$$= \sin 45° \cos 30° + \cos 45° \sin 30°$$
$$= \dfrac{1}{\sqrt{2}} \cdot \dfrac{\sqrt{3}}{2} + \dfrac{1}{\sqrt{2}} \cdot \dfrac{1}{2}$$
$$= \dfrac{\sqrt{3} + 1}{2\sqrt{2}}$$

90   *3.5/Circular Functions of an Angle*

Exercise 3.5

A

1. Convert each of the following radian measures to degree measures.

(a) $\dfrac{\pi}{2}$ (d) $\dfrac{5\pi}{6}$ (g) $\dfrac{3\pi}{2}$

(b) $\dfrac{\pi}{3}$ (e) $-\dfrac{13\pi}{12}$ (h) $-\dfrac{11\pi}{6}$

(c) $-\dfrac{\pi}{4}$ (f) 3π (i) $\dfrac{5\pi}{3}$

2. Convert each of the following degree measures to radian measure.

(a) $210°$ (d) $60°$ (g) $-210°$
(b) $-120°$ (e) $150°$ (h) $390°$
(c) $-270°$ (f) $180°$ (i) $-330°$

3. Find the six circular function values at θ in each of the following.

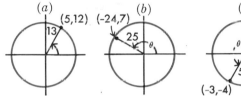 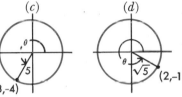

B

4. Given $0° < \theta < 90°$ and $\cos \theta = \dfrac{24}{25}$. Find the other five circular function values at θ.

5. Given $90° < \theta < 180°$ and $\tan \theta = -\dfrac{5}{3}$. Find the other five circular function values at θ.

6. Given $-90° > \alpha > -180°$ and $\sin \alpha = -\dfrac{5}{\sqrt{29}}$. Find the other five circular function values at α.

7. Given $-90° < \alpha < 0$ and $\sec \alpha = \dfrac{\sqrt{50}}{7}$. Find the other five circular function values at α.

8. Use an isosceles right-angled triangle to find the six circular function values of $45°$.

9. Employ an equilateral triangle and its altitude to determine the six circular functions of the following angles.

(a) $60°$ (b) $30°$

10. Evaluate the following without using tables.

(a) $\cos 15°$ (c) $\cos 165°$
(b) $\cos 105°$ (d) $\cos 195°$

11. Evaluate the following without using tables.

    (a) sin 15°   (c) sin (−15°)

    (b) sin 75°   (d) sin 105°

12. Find the length of the arc of a circle of radius 12 cm intercepted by a central angle of 1.5 rad.

13. Find the radian measure of the central angle that intercepts an arc of length 70 cm if the radius of the circle is 50 cm.

14. Find the radian measure of the angle through which the minute hand of a clock rotates in 10 min.

15. A Gemini satellite in a circular orbit takes 96 min for one complete orbit. Through how many degrees does the satellite turn in 1 h relative to the earth?

C 16. Use the formula $\cos 2x = 2\cos^2 x - 1$ with $x = 22\frac{1}{2}°$ to prove that $\cos 22\frac{1}{2}° = \sqrt{\dfrac{\sqrt{2}+1}{2\sqrt{2}}}$.

17. Use the formula for $\tan 2x$ where $x = 22\frac{1}{2}°$ to prove that $\tan 22\frac{1}{2}° = \sqrt{2} - 1$.

18. The angle measure used by artillery officers is based on a unit called a *mil*. This is obtained by dividing the circle circumference in 6400 equal parts.

    (a) If α is an angle of a rad, $d°$, and m mils, show that $a = \dfrac{\pi}{3200}m$ and $m = \dfrac{160}{9}d$.

    (b) What is the mil measure of an angle of 24°?

    (c) What is the degree measure of an angle of 1800 mils?

19. (a) If the circle in the figure has radius 1, express the coordinates of A and B in terms of sines and cosines of α and β.

    (b) Explain why $\overrightarrow{OA} = (\cos\theta, \sin\theta)$ and $\overrightarrow{OB} = (\cos\beta, \sin\beta)$.

    (c) Explain why $\angle AOB = \theta - \beta$.

    (d) Use the dot product of vectors to find $\cos(\theta - \beta)$.

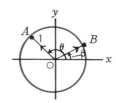

3.6 Angle Between Two Lines

Recall that to each non vertical line in the $R \times R$ plane we can assign a real number called the *slope of the line*.

Given any two points on a line L, the slope m of L is given by

$$m = \frac{y_2 - y_1}{x_2 - x_1}, \qquad x_1 \neq x_2.$$

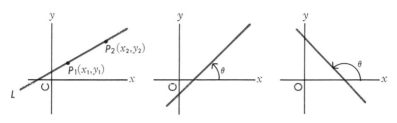

The slope of the line can also be obtained as the value of $\tan \theta$, where θ is the angle between the line and the positive direction of the x axis. Thus, for any non vertical line,

$$m = \tan \theta.$$

The angle between two intersecting lines L_1 and L_2 is defined as the smallest positive angle, θ, through which L_1 must be revolved about the point of intersection to coincide with L_2. Thus, $0 \leq \theta \leq \pi$.

Let L_1 have slope $m_1 = \tan \theta_1$ and L_2 have slope $m_2 = \tan \theta_2$

There are two cases that must be considered, namely $\theta_1 < \theta_2$ and $\theta_1 > \theta_2$.

Case 1: $\theta_1 < \theta_2$

θ_2 is an exterior angle of the triangle.

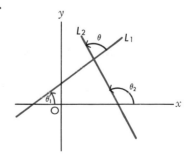

$$\therefore \qquad \theta_2 = \theta_1 + \theta$$
$$\therefore \qquad \theta = \theta_2 - \theta_1$$
$$\tan \theta = \tan(\theta_2 - \theta_1)$$
$$= \frac{\tan \theta_2 - \tan \theta_1}{1 + \tan \theta_2 \tan \theta_1}$$

Case 2: $\theta_1 > \theta_2$

θ_1 is an exterior angle of the triangle.

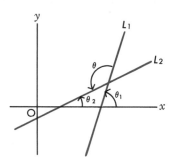

$$\therefore \qquad \theta_1 = \theta_2 + (\pi - \theta)$$
$$\therefore \quad \pi - \theta = \theta_1 - \theta_2$$
$$\therefore \quad \tan(\pi - \theta) = \tan(\theta_1 - \theta_2)$$
$$-\tan\theta = \frac{\tan\theta_1 - \tan\theta_2}{1 + \tan\theta_1 \tan\theta_2}$$
$$\therefore \quad \tan\theta = \frac{\tan\theta_2 - \tan\theta_1}{1 + \tan\theta_2 \tan\theta_1}$$

which is the same result as Case 1.

The angle, θ, between two lines with slopes m_1 and m_2 respectively is given by the formula

$$\tan\theta = \frac{m_2 - m_1}{1 + m_2 m_1}, \qquad 0 \le \theta \le \pi$$

In this formula $\tan\theta$ may be positive or negative. If $0 < \theta < \dfrac{\pi}{2}$, $\tan\theta > 0$. If $\dfrac{\pi}{2} < \theta < \pi$, $\tan\theta < 0$. Between two intersecting lines L_1 and L_2 there are four angles equal in pairs. Let θ be the acute angle from L_1 to L_2, and α be the obtuse angle from L_2 to L_1. But $\alpha + \theta = 180°$. Thus $\tan\alpha = -\tan\theta$. From these results we have the following.

The acute angle θ between two lines is given by

$$\tan\theta = \left| \frac{m_2 - m_1}{1 + m_2 m_1} \right|$$

A special case of the formula occurs when $\theta_1 = \theta_2$, that is, when the lines have the same slope and are parallel.

$$\therefore \quad \tan\theta = 0 \quad \text{and} \quad \theta = 0 \quad \text{or} \quad \pi$$

Another special case occurs if the lines are perpendicular. Then,

$\theta = \dfrac{\pi}{2}$ and $\tan\theta$ is undefined but $\cot\theta = 0$.

$$\therefore \quad 1 + \tan\theta_2 \tan\theta_1 = 0$$
$$\text{or} \qquad 1 + m_1 m_2 = 0$$
$$\text{or} \qquad m_1 m_2 = -1$$

Thus,

$$L_1 \parallel L_2 \Leftrightarrow \quad m_1 = m_2$$
$$L_1 \perp L_2 \Leftrightarrow m_1 m_2 = -1$$

Example 1

Find the angles of intersection of the lines
$$x - 2y + 2 = 0 \text{ and } 2x - y - 4 = 0.$$

Solution

Recall that the slope of a line $ax + by + c = 0$ is $-\dfrac{a}{b}$. The slopes of the given lines are $\dfrac{1}{2}$ and 2 respectively. Let $m_1 = \dfrac{1}{2}$ and $m_2 = 2$. The acute angle between the lines is given by

$$\tan \theta = \left| \frac{m_2 - m_1}{1 + m_2 m_1} \right|$$

$$\therefore \tan \theta = \left| \frac{2 - \dfrac{1}{2}}{1 + 2 \cdot \dfrac{1}{2}} \right|$$

$$= \frac{3}{4} = 0.75$$

$$\therefore \qquad \theta \doteq 37°$$

Thus one angle of intersection is 37°; the other angle is 143°.

Exercise 3.6

B 1. Find the acute angle of intersection of the lines given in each of the following.

(a) $3x + 4y = 12$, $6x - 7y = 0$
(b) $x + y - 3 = 0$, $x + 2y = 5$
(c) $x - y + 2 = 0$, $2x - 3y - 7 = 0$
(d) $x = 2$, $2x - y = 8$

2. Prove that the line through $(-3, 6)$ and $(9, 1)$ is perpendicular to the line through $(0, 0)$ and $(5, 12)$.

3. Prove that the triangle with vertices $(5, 0)$, $(8, 4)$, $(-4, 13)$ is right-angled and find its acute angles.

4. Find the angles of a triangle whose vertices are $(2, 6)$, $(6, 0)$, and $(-3, 8)$.

5. Find the slope of the line making an angle of $45°$ with the line $2x + y = 8$.

6. Find an equation of the line through $(-3, 2)$ that makes an angle of $135°$ with $3x - 2y = 12$.

7. The base of a triangle is the segment joining $(0, 0)$ to $(12, 0)$. The slopes of the other two sides are $\frac{3}{4}$ and $-\frac{2}{3}$. Find the measure of the angles of the triangle.

8. The slopes of two lines are -2 and 3. Find the slope of the line bisecting the angle between them.

3.7 Reduction Formulas

Many of the formulas we study in this section have already been developed in the exercises of Chapter 2 and can be obtained as applications of the sum and difference formulas. We shall show that the different formulas bear a simple relationship to one another. The formulas enable us to express a trigonometric function of any angle in terms of a trigonometric function of an acute angle.

We begin by determining the trigonometric function values of $\pi - x$, $\pi + x$ for any angle x, $x \in R$.

$$\begin{aligned}
\cos(\pi - x) &= \cos \pi \cos x + \sin \pi \sin x \\
&= -1 \cdot \cos x + 0 \cdot \sin x \\
&= -\cos x \\
\cos(\pi + x) &= \cos \pi \cos x - \sin \pi \sin x \\
&= -\cos x \\
\sin(\pi - x) &= \sin \pi \cos x - \cos \pi \sin x \\
&= 0 \cdot \cos x - (-1) \sin x \\
&= \sin x \\
\sin(\pi + x) &= \sin \pi \cos x + \cos \pi \sin x \\
&= -\sin x
\end{aligned}$$

$$\tan(\pi - x) = \frac{\sin(\pi - x)}{\cos(\pi - x)}, \qquad \tan(\pi + x) = \frac{\sin(\pi + x)}{\cos(\pi + x)}$$

$$= \frac{\sin x}{-\cos x} \qquad\qquad\qquad = \frac{-\sin x}{-\cos x}$$

$$= -\tan x \qquad\qquad\qquad = \tan x$$

Recalling that $\cos(-x) = \cos x$ and $\sin(-x) = -\sin x$ we can deduce that $\tan(-x) = -\tan x$.

To summarize, let us consider x to be an acute angle.

II		I
$\cos(\pi - x) = -\cos x$		$\cos x$
$\sin(\pi - x) = \sin x$		$\sin x$
$\tan(\pi - x) = -\tan x$		$\tan x$
$\cos(\pi + x) = -\cos x$	O	$\cos(-x) = \cos x$
$\sin(\pi + x) = -\sin x$		$\sin(-x) = -\sin x$
$\tan(\pi + x) = \tan x$		$\tan(-x) = -\tan x$
III		IV

The above identities are true for all x, even if x is not an acute angle, except for x an odd multiple of $\frac{\pi}{2}$ in the case of the tangent. These identities are often called *reduction formulas*.

The reduction formulas give a simple method for determining the trigonometric function value of an angle in any one of the four quadrants. First we consider the sign of the circular function values for angles in the various quadrants which is summarized below.

Function	Quadrant	I	II	III	IV
sin		$+$	$+$	$-$	$-$
cos		$+$	$-$	$-$	$+$
tan		$+$	$-$	$+$	$-$

S	A
T	C

A means all function values positive
S means sine positive
T means tangent positive
C means cosine positive

We shall refer to this summary as the *CAST rule*.

> To find the value of a trigonometric function of an angle θ,
>
> where $\frac{\pi}{2} < \theta < 2\pi$, $\theta \neq \pi$, $\theta \neq \frac{3\pi}{2}$, proceed as follows.
>
> (1) Express θ as $\pi - x$, $\pi + x$ or $2\pi - x$ where $0 < x \leq \frac{\pi}{2}$.
>
> (2) The value of the given function at θ is the positive or negative value of the same function at x.
>
> (3) The sign of the value is determined by the quadrant in which θ lies and the sign of the function value in that quadrant (CAST rule).

Example 1

Express $\tan 295°$ as a function of an acute angle.

Solution

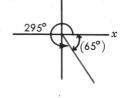

$295 = 360 - 65$
$295°$ is an angle in quadrant IV
$\therefore$ tan is negative in quadrant IV
$\therefore$ $\tan 295° = -\tan 65°$.

We shall now employ the Addition Formulas to find circular function values of $\left(\frac{\pi}{2} - x\right)$.

$$\sin\left(\frac{\pi}{2} - x\right) = \sin\frac{\pi}{2}\cos x - \cos\frac{\pi}{2}\sin x$$
$$= 1\cdot\cos x - 0\cdot\sin x$$
$$= \cos x$$

$$\cos\left(\frac{\pi}{2} - x\right) = \cos\frac{\pi}{2}\cos x + \sin\frac{\pi}{2}\sin x$$
$$= 0\cdot\cos x + 1\cdot\sin x$$
$$= \sin x$$

$$\tan\left(\frac{\pi}{2} - x\right) = \frac{\sin\left(\frac{\pi}{2} - x\right)}{\cos\left(\frac{\pi}{2} - x\right)}$$
$$= \frac{\cos x}{\sin x}$$
$$= \cot x$$

3.7/Reduction Formulas

Thus,

$$\sin\left(\frac{\pi}{2} - x\right) = \cos x$$

$$\cos\left(\frac{\pi}{2} - x\right) = \sin x$$

$$\tan\left(\frac{\pi}{2} - x\right) = \cot x, \quad x \neq n\pi, \quad n \in I$$

Since $\left(\frac{\pi}{2} - x\right)$ and x are complementary, that is, they have a sum of $\frac{\pi}{2}$, the functions sin and cos are called *complementary functions*, and are related by the formula

sine of an angle equals cosine of the complement of the angle

Similarly, tan and cot, sec and csc are complementary functions.

By taking the images of $C\left(\cos\left(\frac{\pi}{2} - x\right), \sin\left(\frac{\pi}{2} - x\right)\right)$ in the x axis, y axis and the origin we may obtain the remaining relationships between complementary functions.

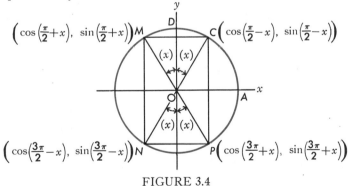

FIGURE 3.4

Compare the coordinates of C and M in Figure 3.4.

$$\cos\left(\frac{\pi}{2} + x\right) = -\cos\left(\frac{\pi}{2} - x\right) = -\sin x$$

$$\sin\left(\frac{\pi}{2} + x\right) = \sin\left(\frac{\pi}{2} - x\right) = \cos x$$

Compare the slopes of OC and OM.

$$\tan\left(\frac{\pi}{2} + x\right) = -\tan\left(\frac{\pi}{2} - x\right) = -\cot x$$

Similarly we may show the identities summarized in the following chart where x is considered to be an acute angle. These identities are called *reduction formulas* and are true even if x is not an acute angle.

S	A
T	C

$$\cos\left(\frac{\pi}{2}+x\right) = -\sin x \qquad\qquad \cos\left(\frac{\pi}{2}-x\right) = \sin x$$

$$\sin\left(\frac{\pi}{2}+x\right) = \cos x \qquad\qquad \sin\left(\frac{\pi}{2}-x\right) = \cos x$$

$$\tan\left(\frac{\pi}{2}+x\right) = -\cot x \qquad\qquad \tan\left(\frac{\pi}{2}-x\right) = \cot x$$

$$\cos\left(\frac{3\pi}{2}-x\right) = -\sin x \qquad\qquad \cos\left(\frac{3\pi}{2}+x\right) = \sin x$$

$$\sin\left(\frac{3\pi}{2}-x\right) = -\cos x \qquad\qquad \sin\left(\frac{3\pi}{2}+x\right) = -\cos x$$

$$\tan\left(\frac{3\pi}{2}-x\right) = \cot x \qquad\qquad \tan\left(\frac{3\pi}{2}+x\right) = -\cot x$$

The following indicates the method of finding the value of the function of an angle θ in terms of the acute angle between the terminal arm of θ and the y axis.

(1) Express θ as $\frac{\pi}{2} - x, \frac{\pi}{2} + x, \frac{3\pi}{2} - x, \frac{3\pi}{2} + x$ where $0 \le x \le \frac{\pi}{2}$.

(2) The value of the given function at θ is the positive or negative value of the *complimentary function* at x.

(3) The sign of the value is determined by the quadrant in which θ lies and the sign of the *given* function value in that quadrant (CAST rule).

Example 2

Express csc 310° as a function of an angle less than 45°.

Solution

$310 = 270 + 40$
310° is an angle in quadrant IV
csc is negative in quadrant IV
Since we measured the angle 40° to the y axis we must use the complementary function. $\csc 310° = -\sec 40°$.

3.7/Reduction Formulas

Exercise 3.7

A 1. Express each of the following angle measures as $180 + x$ or $180 - x$ where $0 < x < 90$.

(a) 120	(d) 260	(g) 150
(b) 110	(e) 190	(h) 210
(c) 200	(f) 170	(i) 178

2. State the quadrant in which the terminal arm of each of the following angles lies. State the acute angle between the terminal arm and the x axis.

(a) 135°	(d) −120°	(g) 480°
(b) 275°	(e) 405°	(h) −210°
(c) −300°	(f) −370°	(i) −720°

B 3. Express the following as a function value for an acute angle.

(a) sin 220°	(c) tan 296°	(e) csc 212°
(b) cos 163°	(d) sec 152°	(f) cot 260°

4. Express each of the following as a function value for an acute angle. Illustrate by means of a diagram.

(a) sin (−105°)	(c) tan (−295°)	(e) csc (−170°)
(b) cos (−210°)	(d) sec (−140°)	(f) cot (−240°)

5. Express the following as a function value for an angle, θ, where $0° < \theta < 45°$

(a) cos 260°	(d) sec 290°	(g) sin (−200°)
(b) sin 105°	(e) csc (−110°)	(h) tan (−95°)
(c) tan 160°	(f) cot (−150°)	(i) sec (−250°)

6. Express the sec, csc and cot function values for $(\pi - x)$, $(\pi + x)$ and $(-x)$ in terms of x.

7. Express the sec, csc and cot function values for $\left(\dfrac{\pi}{2} - x\right)$, $\left(\dfrac{\pi}{2} + x\right)$, $\left(\dfrac{3\pi}{2} - x\right)$ and $\left(\dfrac{3\pi}{2} + x\right)$, in terms of x.

8. Prove the following identities.

(a) $\cos x + \cos(\pi - x) = \cos(\pi + x) + \cos(-x)$

(b) $\tan x + \tan(\pi - x) + \cot\left(\dfrac{\pi}{2} + x\right) = \tan(2\pi - x)$

(c) $\dfrac{\sin(\pi - x)}{\tan(\pi + x)} \cdot \dfrac{\cot\left(\dfrac{\pi}{2} - x\right)}{\tan\left(\dfrac{\pi}{2} + x\right)} \cdot \dfrac{\cos(2\pi - x)}{\sin(-x)} = \sin x$

(d) $\dfrac{\sin(\pi + x)}{\cos(2\pi + x)} + \dfrac{\sec(\pi - x)}{\csc(2\pi - x)} = 0$

9. Given $0 < x < \dfrac{\pi}{2}$. Draw a unit circle and indicate the points $W(x)$, $W(\pi - x)$, $W(\pi + x)$, and $W(-x)$. Compare the coordinates of these points and determine the reduction formulas associated with $\pi - x$, $\pi + x$, and $-x$.

3.8 Reduction of $a \sin \theta + b \cos \theta$

An important application of the sum and difference formulas occurs in electronics and acoustics. Alternating current and sound waves can often be specified by means of the sin and cos functions. We shall study the sum of a sine and a cosine function with the same period.

Consider $\qquad f: \theta \rightarrow f(\theta) = 3 \sin \theta + 4 \cos \theta.$

We shall graph f by first graphing f_1 and f_2, where

$$f_1: \theta \rightarrow 3 \sin \theta$$
$$f_2: \theta \rightarrow 4 \cos \theta,$$

and then adding ordinates.

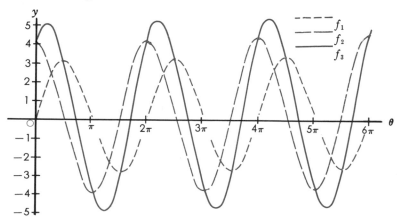

The graph of f appears to be sinusoidal. The period of f is 2π and there is a phase shift.

The graph suggests that $3 \sin \theta + 4 \cos \theta$ might be expressed as $A \sin(\theta + d)$, with $A > 0$.

If $A \sin(\theta + d) = 3 \sin \theta + 4 \cos \theta$ for all θ
$\therefore$ $A \sin \theta \cos d + A \cos \theta \sin d = 3 \sin \theta + 4 \cos \theta$

If $\theta = 0$ we have $A \sin d = 4$. If $\theta = \dfrac{\pi}{2}$ we have $A \cos d = 3$.

$\therefore$
$$(A \sin d)^2 + (A \cos d)^2 = 4^2 + 3^2$$
$$A^2(\sin^2 d + \cos^2 d) = 25$$
$$A^2 = 25$$
$\therefore$
$$A = 5$$
$\therefore$
$\therefore$
$$5 \sin d = 4 \text{ and } 5 \cos d = 3$$
$\therefore$
$$\sin d = \tfrac{4}{5} \text{ and } \cos d = \tfrac{3}{5}$$
$\therefore$
$$d \doteq 53° \doteq 0.93 \text{ (rad.)}$$
$\therefore$
$$3 \sin \theta + 4 \cos \theta = 5 \sin(\theta + 0.93)$$

Thus a defining equation for f is $y = 5 \sin(\theta + 0.93)$

Example 1

Express $\sqrt{3} \sin x + \sqrt{7} \cos x$ as $A \sin(x + \alpha)$ where $x \in R$.

Solution

Let $\sqrt{3} \sin x + \sqrt{7} \cos x = A \sin(x + \alpha)$

$\therefore$ $\sqrt{3} \sin x + \sqrt{7} \cos x = A(\sin x \cos \alpha + \cos x \sin \alpha)$ (1)
(1) is true for all values of x.

If $x = 0$, (1) becomes $\sqrt{3} \cdot 0 + \sqrt{7} \cdot 1 = A(0 \cdot \cos \alpha + 1 \cdot \sin \alpha)$
$$\therefore \sqrt{7} = A \sin \alpha \qquad (2)$$
If $x = \dfrac{\pi}{2}$, (1) becomes $\sqrt{3} \cdot 1 + \sqrt{7} \cdot 0 = A(1 \cdot \cos \alpha + 0 \cdot \sin \alpha)$
$$\therefore \sqrt{3} = A \cos \alpha \qquad (3)$$

Also, $(2)^2 + (3)^2$ gives $7 + 3 = A^2 \sin^2 \alpha + A^2 \cos^2 \alpha$
$$\therefore 10 = A^2(\sin^2 \alpha + \cos^2 \alpha)$$
$$\therefore 10 = A^2$$
$$\therefore A = \sqrt{10} \text{ or } -\sqrt{10}$$

Let $A = \sqrt{10}$, then from (2) and (3) we have
$$\sin \alpha = \frac{\sqrt{7}}{\sqrt{10}} \text{ and } \cos \alpha = \frac{\sqrt{3}}{\sqrt{10}}$$

From tables the smallest positive value for α satisfying (2) and (3) is $\alpha \doteq 57° = 0.99$ radians.

$$\therefore \sqrt{3} \sin x + \sqrt{7} \cos x = \sqrt{10} \sin (x + 0.99)$$

Note 1 α must be expressed in radians since x is a real number.

Note 2 If $a \sin x + b \cos x = A \sin (x + \alpha)$ then $A = \sqrt{a^2 + b^2}$.

Example 2

Express $2 \sin 2x - 3 \cos 2x$ as $A \cos(2x - \alpha)$.

Solution

Here $a = 2$, $b = 3$, $\qquad \therefore A = \sqrt{a^2 + b^2} = \sqrt{13}$

$$\therefore 2 \sin 2x - 3 \cos 2x = \sqrt{13} \cos (2x - \alpha)$$
$$= \sqrt{13} (\cos 2x \cos \alpha + \sin 2x \sin \alpha) \qquad (1)$$

Let $x = 0$, (1) gives $\cos \alpha = -\dfrac{3}{\sqrt{13}}$

Let $x = \dfrac{\pi}{4}$, (1) gives $\sin \alpha = \dfrac{2}{\sqrt{13}}$

From tables the smallest positive value of α satisfying these equations is $\alpha \doteq 146° \doteq 2.55$

$$\therefore 2 \sin 2x - 3 \cos 2x = \sqrt{13} \cos (2x - 2.55)$$

From Example 2 we see that the graph of $2 \sin 2x + 3 \cos 2x$ is sinusoidal with period π. The graph is congruent to $\sqrt{13} \cos 2x$ and is shifted 1.275 units to the right.

Exercise 3.8

A

1. For each of the following graphs state the amplitude, period and phase shift.

    (a) $y = 2 \sin 3x$ (c) $y = 3 \cos\left(x + \dfrac{\pi}{2}\right)$

    (b) $y = 5 \cos 2x$ (d) $y = 5 \sin\left(3x + \dfrac{\pi}{6}\right)$

B

2. Express each of the following in the form $A \sin(x + \alpha)$. State the amplitude and phase shift.

    (a) $3 \sin x + 4 \cos x$ (c) $B \sin x + B \cos x$, $B > 0$
    (b) $3 \sin x - 4 \cos x$ (d) $\sin x + 5 \cos x$

3. Express each of the following in the form $y = A \cos(x - \alpha)$.
   (a) $y = 4 \sin x + 3 \cos x$ (b) $y = 4 \sin x - 3 \cos x$

4. (a) Sketch the graph of the function defined by
   $y = 2 \sin 2x - \cos 2x$ by the method of adding ordinates.
   (b) Express $2 \sin 2x - \cos 2x$ as the value of a trigonometric function and thereby determine the amplitude and phase shift of $y = 2 \sin 2x - \cos 2x$.
   (c) Compare the results of part (b) with the graph of part (a).

5. Prove the following.
   (a) $a \sin \theta + b \cos \theta = \sqrt{a^2 + b^2} \sin (\theta + d)$ where $\tan d = \dfrac{b}{a}$.

   (b) $a \sin \theta + b \cos \theta = \sqrt{a^2 + b^2} \cos (\theta - \alpha)$ where $\cot \alpha = \dfrac{b}{a}$.

Review Exercise 3.9

B

1. Use sum and difference formulas to prove the following formulas. $x \in R$

   (a) $\sin x = \sin(\pi - x)$ (c) $\cos x = -\cos(\pi + x)$
   (b) $\sin x = -\sin(\pi + x)$ (d) $\cos(\pi - x) = \cos(\pi + x)$

2. Given that A and B are angles in the first quadrant with $\tan A = \frac{3}{4}$ and $\sin B = \frac{12}{13}$. Find each of the following.
   (a) $\sin(A + B)$ (d) $\cos(A + B)$
   (b) $\sin(A - B)$ (e) $\tan(A + B)$
   (c) $\cos(A - B)$ (f) $\tan(A - B)$

3. Find $\sin 15°$ and $\cos 15°$ from function values for $45°$ and $30°$.

4. Given $\cos x = -\dfrac{20}{29}$, $\dfrac{\pi}{2} < x < \pi$ and $\tan y = \dfrac{8}{15}$, $\pi < y < \dfrac{3\pi}{2}$.

   Find each of the following.
   (a) $\sin(x - y)$ (b) $\cos(x + y)$

5. Prove that $\tan\left(\dfrac{\pi}{4} + x\right) = \dfrac{1 + \tan x}{1 - \tan x}$.

6. Given $\sin x = \dfrac{12}{13}$, $\dfrac{\pi}{2} < x < \pi$ and $\sec y = \dfrac{5}{4}$, $\dfrac{3\pi}{2} < y < 2\pi$.

   Find each of the following.
   (a) $\sin(x - y)$ (b) $\cos(x + y)$

7. Given $\sin 18° = 0.309$, $\sin 15° = 0.259$, $\cos 18° = 0.951$, and $\cos 15° = 0.966$, find each of the following.

(a) $\sin 3°$ (b) $\cos 3°$ (c) $\sin 21°$

8. If $\sin x = -\dfrac{8}{17}$ and $\cos y = -\dfrac{5}{13}$, find two different values for $\sin (x + y)$. Examine all four cases.

9. Given $\tan x = \dfrac{3}{4}$, $0 < x < \dfrac{\pi}{2}$. Find each of the following.

(a) $\sin 2x$ (b) $\cos 2x$ (c) $\tan 2x$

10. Given $\sin x = \dfrac{5}{13}$, $\dfrac{\pi}{2} < x < \pi$, find $\cos 2x$. In what quadrant does $2x$ lie?

11. If $\tan x = \dfrac{1}{2}$, $\pi < x < \dfrac{3\pi}{2}$, find $\tan 2x$ and determine the quadrant in which $2x$ lies.

12. Given $\sin \dfrac{x}{2} = \dfrac{1}{2}$ and $0 < x < \dfrac{\pi}{2}$. Find each of the following.

(a) $\sin x$ (b) $\cos x$

13. Find the acute angle between each of the following pairs of lines.

(a) $x - 3y + 5 = 0$, $x + 3y - 6 = 0$
(b) $3x - 4y - 12 = 0$, $4x + 3y + 24 = 0$
(c) $2x + y + 7 = 0$, $4x + 2y + 3 = 0$
(d) $4x + 6y - 9 = 0$, $x - y + 3 = 0$

14. Find the equation of the line through $(5, 0)$ that makes an angle of $45°$ with $3x - 4y = 12$.

15. If $\cos 2x = \dfrac{24}{25}$ and $\dfrac{3\pi}{2} < 2x < 2\pi$, determine the following.

(a) $\sin x$ (b) $\cos x$ (c) $\tan x$

C   16. Prove the following identities.

(a) $\tan x = \csc 2x - \cot 2x$ (d) $\cos^4 x - \sin^4 x = \cos 2x$

(b) $\cot x = \csc 2x + \cot 2x$ (e) $\dfrac{2 \tan x}{1 + \tan^2 x} = \sin 2x$

(c) $2 - 2 \tan x \cot 2x = \sec^2 x$ (f) $\dfrac{1 - \sin 2\theta}{\cos 2\theta} = \dfrac{1 - \tan \theta}{1 + \tan \theta}$

17. Express $5 \sin 2x - 7 \cos 2x$ as $A \cos(ax + b)$.

18. Express $3 \sin x - 5 \cos x$ as $A \sin(x + b)$.

4 / Plane Transformations

4.1 Translations

One of the simplest rigid motion transformations is the *translation*. Every plane transformation is a 1:1 mapping of all the points of the $R \times R$ plane onto all or part of the points in the $R \times R$ plane. A transformation is defined whenever the image P' of a point P is given. P is often called the pre-image of P'. In the case of a translation, each point P is mapped into a different point P' such that the vector PP' equals a given vector. Thus under a transformation defined by a vector $\vec{a}$ (Figure 4.1), the point P maps onto the point P' such that $\overrightarrow{PP'} = \vec{a}$, that is, the length of segment $PP' = |a|$ and segment PP' is parallel to $\vec{a}$. If $\vec{a} = (4, 3)$ and P has coordinates

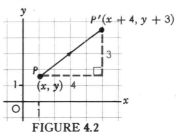

FIGURE 4.1   FIGURE 4.2

(x, y), then P' would be obtained from P by moving 4 units parallel to the positive x axis and then 3 units parallel to the positive y axis (Figure 4.2). Hence P' would have coordinates $(x + 4, y + 3)$. The translation defined by the vector $\vec{a} = (4, 3)$ is called a $(4, 3)$ translation. In general we have the following definition.

An (h, k) translation is a 1:1 mapping of a plane onto itself defined by the vector $\vec{a} = (h, k)$ such that the point

$$(x, y) \rightarrow (x + h, y + k).$$

In Exercise 4.1 you will show that a translation is a *rigid motion transformation* or an *isometry*.

> Suppose $A \rightarrow A'$ and $B \rightarrow B'$ under a certain transformation T. If $AB \cong A'B'$ then the transformation T is called a *rigid motion transformation* or an *isometry*.

In Example 1 we shall show that a line maps into a line under a translation. Hence under a translation isometry, triangles map onto congruent triangles so that it is easy to see that distances, angles, and shape are preserved.

Example 1

(a) Find an equation of the image of the line $y = mx + b$ under an (h, k) translation.

(b) Prove the given line of (a) is parallel to its image line.

Solution

(a) Under an (h, k) translation,
$(x, y) \rightarrow (x + h, y + k)$.
If (u, v) is any point on the image of $y = mx + b$,
then $\left. \begin{array}{l} u = x + h \\ v = y + k \end{array} \right\} \Rightarrow \left\{ \begin{array}{l} u - h = x \\ v - k = y \end{array} \right.$
Substituting in $y = mx + b$ we find
$$v - k = m(u - h) + b$$
$$v = mu + b - mh + k$$
The image curve is $\{(u, v) \,|\, v = mu + b - mh + k\}$,
which may be written $\{(x, y) \,|\, y = mx + b - mh + k\}$,
which is a straight line.

(b) The slope of the given line $y = mx + b$ is m.
The slope of the image line $y = mx + b - mh - k$ is also m.
Hence the given line and its image are parallel.

The example shows that a line AB maps onto a line $A'B'$.

> If $A \rightarrow A'$, $B \rightarrow B'$ under a translation, then $AB \,\|\, A'B'$

This property of translations is not common to all isometries.

Because a translation is a rigid motion, under a translation a circle maps onto another circle with the same radius, and a parabola maps onto a congruent parabola. In Examples 2 and 3 we shall find the new equations that a parabola and a circle have after they have been transformed by a translation.

Example 2

(a) Find an equation of the image of the parabola $y = x^2$ under a $(3, 5)$ translation.

(b) Graph the given curve and its image.

Solution

(a) Suppose a point $P(x, y)$ on the original curve $y = x^2$ maps onto a point $P'(u, v)$ on the image curve under the $(3, 5)$ translation. Thus $(x, y) \rightarrow (x + 3, y + 5) = (u, v)$

$\therefore \left. \begin{array}{l} u = x + 3 \\ v = y + 5 \end{array} \right\} \Rightarrow \left\{ \begin{array}{l} x = u - 3 \\ y = v - 5 \end{array} \right.$

But in the original parabola $y = x^2$
Substitute for x and y.
$\therefore \quad v - 5 = (u - 3)^2$
$\therefore \quad v - 5 = u^2 - 6u + 9$
$\therefore \qquad v = u^2 - 6u + 14$
The image curve is the set of points
$\{(u, v) \mid v = u^2 - 6u + 14\}$.
The more usual way to designate this set is
$\{(x, y) \mid y = x^2 - 6x + 14\}$.
Thus the image of the curve $y = x^2$ under a $(3, 5)$ translation is the curve $y = x^2 - 6x + 14$.

(b) The given curve is a parabola with vertex $(0, 0)$, opening on the positive y axis as axis of symmetry. We know the image curve is a parabola because translations preserve size and shape. The vertex of the image curve $y = x^2 - 6x + 14$ is the image of the vertex $(0, 0)$ of the original curve $y = x^2$. But $(0, 0) \rightarrow (3, 5)$ under the $(3, 5)$ translation. Thus $(3, 5)$ is the vertex of the curve $y = x^2 - 6x + 14$. The graph of $y = x^2 - 6x + 14$ is obtained by translating each point of $y = x^2$ to the right 3 units and 5 units up.

(Observe in Example 2 an x^2 term appears in the equations of both the given curve and the image curve, but a first degree term in x is introduced in the image equation.)

Example 3

Find an equation of the image of the circle $x^2 + y^2 = 4$ under the translations defined by $\vec{a} = (3, -1)$. Find the centre and radius of the image circle.

Solution

Suppose $P(x, y)$ is any point on the circle $x^2 + y^2 = 4$.

Let $P(x, y) \rightarrow P'(u, v)$ under the translation

$$(x, y) \rightarrow (x + 3, y - 1)$$

$$\therefore \left. \begin{array}{l} u = x + 3 \\ v = y - 1 \end{array} \right\} \Longrightarrow \left\{ \begin{array}{l} x = u - 3 \\ y = v + 1 \end{array} \right.$$

But on the original circle $x^2 + y^2 = 4$.

$$\therefore (u - 3)^2 + (v + 1)^2 = 4$$

$$\therefore u^2 - 6u + 9 + v^2 + 2v + 1 = 4$$

$$\therefore u^2 + v^2 - 6u + 2v + 6 = 0$$

Thus $\{(x, y) \,|\, x^2 + y^2 = 4\}$ maps onto

$$\{(u, v) \,|\, u^2 + v^2 - 6u + 2v + 6 = 0\}$$

which may be rewritten $\{(x, y) \,|\, x^2 + y^2 - 6x + 2y + 6 = 0\}$.

Thus the image of $x^2 + y^2 = 4$ is the circle

$$x^2 + y^2 - 6x + 2y + 6 = 0.$$

Since the centre of $x^2 + y^2 = 4$, namely $(0, 0)$ maps onto $(3, -1)$, the image curve has centre $(3, -1)$. Since lengths are preserved, the radius of the image circle is 2.

In Example 3 observe that the terms x^2 and y^2 still remain under the transformation, and that a first degree term in x and y has been introduced.

Under an (h, k) translation the point $P(x, y) \rightarrow P'(x + h, y + k)$. Observe that under an $(-h, -k)$ translation the point $P'(x + h, y + k) \rightarrow (x + h + (-h), y + k + (-k)) = (x, y)$, that is, $P' \rightarrow P$. An (h, k) translation and a $(-h, -k)$ translation are called *inverse translations*.

Suppose $(x, y) \rightarrow (u, v)$ under an (h, k) translation, then

$$u = x + h$$
$$v = y + k$$

Note the image coordinates occur on the left and the pre-image coordinates on the right. Algebraically these equations may be rewritten

$$x = u - h$$
$$y = v - k.$$

110

The latter set of equations could also have been obtained by realizing that $(u, v) \rightarrow (x, y)$ by the translation inverse to the (h, k) translation, namely, the $(-h, -k)$ translation. Thus considering (u, v) to be the pre-image and (x, y) the image, we have

$$x = u + (-h) = u - h$$
$$y = v + (-k) = v - k.$$

Exercise 4.1

A

1. State the image of the point $(5, -2)$ under the translations defined by the following vectors.

   (a) $\vec{a} = (1, 2)$ (b) $\vec{b} = (-3, 4)$ (c) $\vec{c} = (-5, 2)$

2. Determine the translations that map the point (a, b) onto each of the following points.

   (a) $(a + 1, b + 3)$ (c) $(a - 2, b - 6)$
   (b) $(a + 4, b - 5)$ (d) $(a + t, b - m)$

3. Is any point of the plane invariant under a translation, that is, does any point map onto itself?

4. A line has slope $\frac{2}{3}$. What is the slope of an image line under a translation?

5. Which of the following congruent figures can be images of each other under a translation?

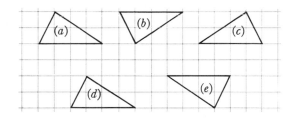

6. For each of the following translations describe the inverse translation.

   (a) $(2, 3)$ translation
   (b) $(-4, 6)$ translation
   (c) $(-5, -8)$ translation
   (d) the translation defined by $\vec{a} = (7, -6)$
   (e) the translation defined by $\vec{b} = (-9, 2)$
   (f) the translation defined by $\vec{c} = (m, t)$

B 7. Determine the images of the given points under a $(-4, 3)$ translation.

    (a) $A(0, 0)$ (b) $B(-12, 5)$ (c) $C(-2, -3)$ (d) $D(-3, -2)$

8. Describe the translation that maps the first point onto the second or image point.

    (a) $A(0, 0) \rightarrow A'(3, 4)$ (c) $C(2, 1) \rightarrow C'(3, 5)$
    (b) $B(0, 0) \rightarrow B'(-9, -4)$ (d) $D(4, -2) \rightarrow D'(-6, -4)$

9. For each part of Question 8 find the translation that maps the image back onto the pre-image point.

10. Under a $(3, 4)$ translation the points $P_1(1, 2)$ and $P_2(-4, 5)$ map onto P_1' and P_2' respectively.

    (a) Find the coordinates of P_1' and P_2'.
    (b) Prove that $P_1P_2 \cong P_1'P_2'$.

11. Under an (h, k) translation the points $P_1(x_1, y_1)$ and $P_2(x_2, y_2)$ map onto P_1' and P_2' respectively.

    (a) Find the coordinates of P_1' and P_2'.
    (b) Prove that $P_1P_2 \cong P_1'P_2'$, hence that a translation is a rigid motion.

12. A straight line having positive slope makes an angle of $45°$ with the positive x axis. The line is translated so that $(3, 5)$ lies on the image line. Find an equation of the image line.

13. The straight line joining the points $A(-2, 3)$ and $B(9, -1)$ is translated so that the point $C'(-5, -6)$ lies on the image line. Find an equation of the image line.

14. Find an equation of the line through the point $(4, 5)$ which maps onto itself under a $(1, -3)$ translation.

15. A line L through the point $A(6, 2)$ is mapped onto a line M through the point $(8, 3)$ by a translation defined by the vector $\vec{a} = (3, 4)$. Find an equation for L.

16. (a) Find an equation of the image under the translation $(x, y) \rightarrow (x + 2, y + 4)$ of the circle $x^2 + y^2 = 25$.
    (b) Find the centre and radius of the image circle.
    (c) Graph the given circle and its image.

17. (a) Find an equation of the image under the translation
$(x, y) \rightarrow (x - 3, y + 2)$ of the parabola $y = -x^2$.
(b) Find the vertex and axis of symmetry of the image curve.
(c) Sketch the parabola and its image.

18. (a) Show that the circle $x^2 + y^2 = r^2$ maps onto the circle
$(x - h)^2 + (y - k)^2 = r^2$ under an (h, k) translation.
(b) State the centre and radius of the circle
$(x - h)^2 + (y - k)^2 = r^2$.

19. (a) Show that the parabola $y = ax^2$ maps onto the parabola
$y = a(x - h)^2 + k$ under an (h, k) translation.
(b) Give the coordinates of the vertices and an equation of the
axis of symmetry of the parabola $y = a(x - h)^2 + k$.

20. A line segment AB of length 2 is translated so that A maps onto
the origin $(0, 0)$. If $B \rightarrow B'$, describe the set of points consisting
of all possible positions of B'.

C
21. Find an equation of the line through the point $(1, 3)$ that is
carried the greatest possible distance under the translation
$(x, y) \rightarrow (x + 3, y + 4)$.

22. Show that the result of an (h_1, k_1) translation followed by an
(h_2, k_2) translation is $(x, y) \rightarrow (x + h_1 + h_2, y + k_1 + k_2)$. Deduce that the composition of translations (by performing them
in succession) is commutative, that is, the order in which the
translations are performed is immaterial.

23. Translation T_1 carries (a, b) onto (c, d). Translation T_2 carries
(e, f) onto (g, h). Find the point onto which (x, y) is carried after
both translations.

24. Show that the composition of a translation and its inverse is
defined by the zero vector.

25. (a) Can a figure map onto itself under a translation?
(b) Can an infinite strip pattern map onto itself under a translation?

4.2 Rotations

According to the ancients, the sun and stars rotated around the earth.

"The ancient philosophers affirm the earth to be at rest at the centre of the universe, and doubtless to maintain itself there. But, if anyone holds that the earth rotates, he affirms at any rate that the motion is natural . . . ."

Copernicus, de Revolutionibus
Orbium Caelestium

Nicolaus Copernicus (1473–1543) was the first of the Renaissance scholars who realized that the stars may be regarded as fixed so that the earth undergoes a continual rotation relative to the celestial universe.

The nature of rotation transformations or *rotations*, and many of their properties, can be deduced from rotations in a plane. Every rotation is defined by naming the point about which the rotation is made (the *centre*), and giving the measure of the angle of rotation. Let us consider a rotation about the origin through an angle θ.

Under this transformation the point $P(x, y)$ has as image the point $P'(u, v)$ constructed as follows. (Figure 4.3)

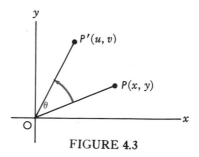

(i) $\angle POP' = \theta$
(ii) $OP \cong OP'$

If the rotation is counter-clockwise, then $\theta > 0$.
If the rotation is clockwise, then $\theta < 0$.
Thus we have the following definition.

FIGURE 4.3

> A rotation about a point O of an angle θ is a 1:1 mapping of a plane onto itself where if each point P maps onto a point P' then $\angle POP' = \theta$ and $OP \cong OP'$.

You will be given the opportunity in the exercise that follows (Question 19) to show that a *rotation is a rigid motion*. We shall now find the relationship between the coordinates (x, y) of a point P and the coordinates (u, v) of its image P' under a rotation θ about the origin $(0, 0)$.

114

Example 1

If $P(x, y) \rightarrow P'(u, v)$ under a rotation θ about the point $(0, 0)$, find the value of u and v in terms of x, y, θ.

Solution

Let $OP = r$ and the angle OP makes with the positive x axis be α.
$\therefore \angle POA = \alpha$, $OP' = r$, and $\angle P'OA = \alpha + \theta$

By definition: $\cos \alpha = \dfrac{x}{r}$, and $\cos (\alpha + \theta) = \dfrac{u}{r}$

$$\sin \alpha = \dfrac{y}{r}, \text{ and } \sin (\alpha + \theta) = \dfrac{v}{r}$$

But $\cos (\alpha + \theta) = \cos \alpha \cos \theta - \sin \alpha \sin \theta$

$\therefore \dfrac{u}{r} = \dfrac{x}{r} \cos \theta - \dfrac{y}{r} \sin \theta$

$\therefore u = x \cos \theta - y \sin \theta$

Also $\sin (\alpha + \theta) = \sin \alpha \cos \theta + \cos \alpha \sin \theta$

$\therefore \dfrac{v}{r} = \dfrac{y}{r} \cos \theta + \dfrac{x}{r} \sin \theta$

$\therefore v = y \cos \theta + x \sin \theta$

or $v = x \sin \theta + y \cos \theta$

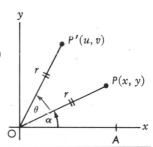

If $(x, y) \rightarrow (u, v)$ under a rotation θ about the point $(0, 0)$,
then
$$u = x \cos \theta - y \sin \theta$$
$$v = x \sin \theta + y \cos \theta$$

Note 1 The image coordinates (u, v) appear on the left side of these equations, while the pre-image coordinates (x, y) appear on the right.
Note 2 In the diagram α and θ are shown as acute angles. However the same proof holds for arbitrary angles α and θ.
Note 3 These important formulas can be better understood if we consider certain particular cases. For example, if $\theta = 0$ we have a rotation through the angle zero which must be the identity transformation

$$u = x \cos 0 - y \sin 0, \qquad v = x \sin 0 + y \cos 0$$
$$= x \cdot 1 - y \cdot 0 \qquad\qquad = x \cdot 0 + y \cdot 1$$
$$= x \qquad\qquad\qquad\qquad = y$$

This special case helps one to remember that in the general equations for a rotation of angle θ, the cosine is the coefficient of x in the first equation and of y in the second.

4.2/Rotations 115

Example 2

Find the image of $P(x, y)$ under a rotation of $\theta = \dfrac{\pi}{2}$ rad about the origin.

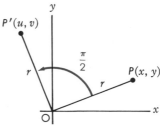

Solution

$$\text{Let } P(x, y) \rightarrow P'(u, v)$$

$$\because \theta = \frac{\pi}{2}$$

$$\therefore u = x \cos \frac{\pi}{2} - y \sin \frac{\pi}{2} \qquad v = x \sin \frac{\pi}{2} + y \cos \frac{\pi}{2}$$

$$= x \cdot 0 - y \cdot 1 \qquad\qquad\quad = x \cdot 1 + y \cdot 0$$

$$= -y \qquad\qquad\qquad\qquad = x$$

$\therefore P(x, y) \rightarrow P'(-y, x)$ under a rotation of $\dfrac{\pi}{2}$ about the origin.

Example 3

Determine the image of $P(x, y)$ under a rotation $\theta = \dfrac{\pi}{4}$ rad about the origin.

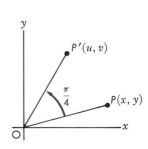

Solution

$$\text{Let } P(x, y) \rightarrow P'(u, v)$$

$$\because \theta = \frac{\pi}{4}$$

$$\therefore u = x \cos \frac{\pi}{4} - y \sin \frac{\pi}{4} \qquad v = x \sin \frac{\pi}{4} + y \cos \frac{\pi}{4}$$

$$= x \cdot \frac{1}{\sqrt{2}} - y \cdot \frac{1}{\sqrt{2}} \qquad\quad = x \cdot \frac{1}{\sqrt{2}} + y \cdot \frac{1}{\sqrt{2}}$$

$$= \frac{x - y}{\sqrt{2}} \qquad\qquad\qquad = \frac{x + y}{\sqrt{2}}$$

$\therefore P(x, y) \rightarrow P'\left(\dfrac{x - y}{\sqrt{2}}, \dfrac{x + y}{\sqrt{2}}\right)$ under a rotation of $\dfrac{\pi}{4}$ about the origin.

116

Example 4

The plane is rotated about the origin through an angle of $-150°$. Find the coordinates of the image of the point (x, y).

Solution

Let $P(x, y) \rightarrow P'(u, v)$ under $\theta = -150°$ about the origin.

$$\therefore u = x \cos(-150°) - y \sin(-150°)$$
$$= x(-\cos 30°) - y(-\sin 30°)$$
$$= -x \cos 30° + y \sin 30°$$
$$= -x \cdot \frac{\sqrt{3}}{2} + y \cdot \frac{1}{2}$$
$$= \frac{-x\sqrt{3} + y}{2}$$

$$v = x \sin(-150°) + y \cos(-150°)$$
$$= x(-\sin 30°) + y(-\cos 30°)$$
$$= -x \sin 30° - y \cos 30°$$
$$= -x \cdot \frac{1}{2} - y \cdot \frac{\sqrt{3}}{2}$$
$$= \frac{-x - y\sqrt{3}}{2}$$

$\therefore$ the coordinates of the image of (x, y) under a rotation of $-150°$ about the origin are $\left(\dfrac{-x\sqrt{3} + y}{2}, \dfrac{-x - y\sqrt{3}}{2} \right)$.

Exercise 4.2

A

1. Which points of the plane remain fixed under a rotation about the origin through an acute angle?

2. Are there any rotations about the origin in which more than one point is mapped onto itself? If so, describe the angle of such a rotation.

3. Under a rotation about the origin, the image of $(1, 0)$ is $(-1, 0)$. Find the angle of this rotation.

4. For which pairs of figures can one figure be superimposed upon the other by a suitable translation followed by a rotation?

(a)   (b)   (c)

B 5. Find the images of the given points under a rotation of $\frac{\pi}{2}$ rad (a quarter-turn) in the counter-clockwise sense.

(a) (0, 1)   (c) (1, 0)   (e) (1, 1)
(b) (0, 3)   (d) (2, 0)   (f) (3, −4)

How could this question be done without using the rotation formulas?

6. Without using the formulas for the image of a point under a rotation, determine the coordinates of the following points under a rotation of 180° (a half-turn) about (0, 0).

(a) (2, 0)   (b) (0, −4)   (c) (4, 3)   (d) (x, y)

Check your result for (d) by using the rotation formulas.

7. Determine the images of the following under a rotation of $\frac{\pi}{3}$ rad in the counter-clockwise sense.

(a) (1, 0)   (c) (2, 5)   (e) (1, −2)
(b) (0, 3)   (d) (−1, 1)   (f) (0, 0)

8. Find the images of $A(1, 0)$ and $B(4, 3)$ under the rotations specified by each of the given angles θ (in radians).

(a) $\frac{\pi}{4}$ (b) $\frac{\pi}{3}$ (c) $\frac{\pi}{2}$ (d) $\frac{\pi}{6}$

9. Use the fact that a rotation is a rigid motion to find the distance between the images of A and B obtained in each part of Question 8.

10. By comparing with the general equations for a rotational angle about the origin, where $0 \le \theta < 2\pi$, find the angle θ of the rotation transformations given.

(a) $(x, y) \rightarrow (\frac{1}{2}(\sqrt{3}x - y), \frac{1}{2}(x + \sqrt{3}y))$.

(b) $(x, y) \rightarrow \left(\frac{-x + y}{\sqrt{2}}, \frac{-x - y}{\sqrt{2}} \right)$

11. Find the image of $(4, 3)$ under the rotation about the origin that maps $(1, 0)$ onto $(0, 1)$.

12. Under a rotation of 30° about the origin the point $P(x, y)$ maps onto the point $P'(u, v)$.

(a) Under what rotation about the origin will the point $P'(u, v)$ map back onto $P(x, y)$?

118   *4.2/Rotations*

(b) Use your result of part (a) and the formulas for rotation with $P'(u, v)$ as the pre-image point to express each of x and y in terms of u and v.

13. Under a rotation of θ about the origin the point $P(x, y)$ maps onto the point $P'(u, v)$.

(a) Under what rotation about the origin will the point $P'(u, v)$ map back onto $P(x, y)$?

(b) Use your result of part (a) and the formulas for rotation with $P'(u, v)$ as the pre-image point to express each of x and y in terms of u and v.

14. The hyperbola $3x^2 - 4y^2 = 12$ is rotated about the origin through an angle of $90°$. State an equation of the image hyperbola. (It is not necessary nor advisable to use the rotation formulas.)

15. The straight line joining $(1, 0)$ and $(4, 1)$ is rotated about the origin through an angle of $\frac{\pi}{2}$ rad. Find an equation of the image line.

16. Is there a rotation about $(0, 0)$ mapping the point $(3, 2)$ onto the point $(-1, 4)$? Justify your answer.

17. A line segment AB of length 3 is rotated about the origin so that A maps onto the point $A'(2, 0)$. If B maps onto B' describe the set of points consisting of all possible positions of B'.

18. An angle between two lines L and M is α. Under a rotation about the origin the line L maps onto the line L' and M onto M'. Prove that an angle between L' and M' is α.

19. Let (u_1, v_1) and (u_2, v_2) be the images under a rotation of angle θ about the origin of (x_1, y_1) and (x_2, y_2) respectively. From the Cartesian equations of the rotation show directly that

$$(u_1 - u_2)^2 + (v_1 - v_2)^2 = (x_1 - x_2)^2 + (y_1 - y_2)^2.$$

How does this show that the rotation is a rigid motion?

C 20. Prove that a line maps onto a line under a rotation of θ about the origin by showing that the image of $y = mx + b$ is a straight line. (Hint: Substitute for x and y in terms of u and v using the formulas of Question 13 (b).)

21. (a) Find the image Q of $P(2, 3)$ under a $(-5, -1)$ translation.
    (b) Find the image R of Q of part (a) under the rotation $\theta = \dfrac{\pi}{2}$ about $(0, 0)$ and hence about the point $(5, 1)$.
    (c) Find the image P' of R of part (b) under a $(5, 1)$ translation.
    (d) Why is P' the image of P under a rotation of $\dfrac{\pi}{2}$ about the point $(5, 1)$?
    (e) Find equations defining a rotation through the angle about the centre (a, b). (Hint: First translate (a, b) to the origin.)

22. Given $A(1, 0)$, $B(2, 0)$, $A'(0, 4)$, and $B'(0, 5)$, the segment AB is mapped onto the segment $A'B'$ in the following two ways where A is mapped onto A' and B mapped onto B'.

    (1) AB is rotated through an angle θ about the origin, and its image is then translated so as to lie on $A'B'$.

    (2) AB is translated to a position from which a rotation about the origin then maps AB onto $A'B'$.

    (a) Are the rotations about the origin in (1) and (2) the same?
    (b) Are the translations in (1) and (2) the same?

23. Prove that the mapping $(x, y) \rightarrow \left(\dfrac{3}{5}x - \dfrac{4}{5}y, \dfrac{4}{5}x + \dfrac{3}{5}y \right)$ is a rotation and find the angle of rotation θ.

4.3 Reflections

If a point P is reflected in a mirror line, then the mirror line is the perpendicular bisector of the line segment joining P to its image P'. This fact leads to the definition of another rigid motion transformation called reflection.

> A reflection in a line m is a 1:1 mapping of a plane onto itself such that the line m is the perpendicular bisector of the line segment joining each point to its image.

The line of reflection is called the *mirror line*. Recall that the points $P(x, y)$ and $A(x, -y)$ are symmetrical about the x axis, while the points $P(x, y)$ and $B(-x, y)$ are symmetrical about the y axis (Figure 4.4), and the points $P(x, y)$ and $C(y, x)$ are symmetrical about the line $y = x$. We shall use these facts to define the following reflection transformations.

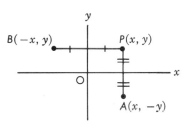

FIGURE 4.4

Reflection in the x axis is defined by $(x, y) \rightarrow (x, -y)$.
Reflection in the y axis is defined by $(x, y) \rightarrow (-x, y)$.
Reflection in the line $y = x$ is defined by $(x, y) \rightarrow (y, x)$.

Note that each reflection has an infinite number of *invariant* or *fixed* points, that is, points each of which maps onto itself. These invariant points lie on the mirror line.

You will be given the opportunity in the exercise that follows to show that *reflection is a rigid motion*. Figure 4.5 shows that sense is not preserved under a reflection, for the sense of the image points P', Q', R' is different from that of P, Q, R. The sense of P, Q, R, is *clockwise*, while the sense of P', Q', R' is *counter-clockwise*.

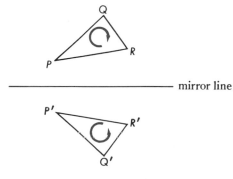

FIGURE 4.5

Example

Find an equation of the image of the parabola $y = 2x^2$ under reflection in the x axis.

Solution

If $P(x, y) \to P'(u, v)$ under a reflection in the x axis, then
$$\left. \begin{array}{l} u = x \\ v = -y \end{array} \right\} \Longrightarrow \left\{ \begin{array}{l} x = u \\ y = -v \end{array} \right.$$
For any point on the given curve
$y = 2x^2$
Substitute for x and y
$\therefore \quad -v = 2(u)^2$
$\therefore \quad v = -2u^2$
Thus the curve $y = 2x^2$ maps onto the curve $v = -2u^2$ or $y = -2x^2$ under a reflection in the x axis.

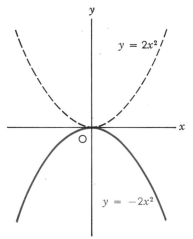

Exercise 4.3

A

1. If the mirror line of a reflection is given, describe how a point and its image under the reflection are related.

2. What is the location of the mirror line of a reflection with respect to the straight line joining any point to its image point?

3. Which points in the plane remain invariant under a reflection transformation.

4. State the effect on the clockwise or counter-clockwise order of points in a figure under each of the following transformations.

   (a) translation   (b) rotation   (c) reflection

5. State the image of each of the following under a reflection in the x axis.

   (a) $(1, 2)$ (c) $(-2, 4)$ (e) $(0, 1)$ (g) $(0, 0)$
   (b) $(1, 0)$ (d) $(-3, -5)$ (f) $(5, -2)$ (h) (a, b)

6. Repeat Question 5 for reflection in the y axis and reflection in the line $y = x$.

$4.3/Reflections$

B 7. Given the points $P(3, 5)$ and $Q(-1, 2)$.

  (a) Find the images P' and Q' of P and Q under reflection in the x axis.

  (b) Calculate and compare the distances PQ and $P'Q'$.

  (c) Repeat parts (a) and (b) for reflection in the y axis.

  (d) Repeat parts (a) and (b) for reflection in the line $y = x$.

8. Given the points $P(x_1, y_1)$ and $Q(x_2, y_2)$.

  (a) Repeat parts (a), (b), (c) and (d) of Question 7.

  (b) Explain why you can say that reflection is a rigid motion.

9. Find the reflection image of the point $P(2, 3)$ in each of the following mirror lines.

  (a) $x = 1$
  (c) $y = 1$
  (e) $y = -3$
  (b) $x - 4$
  (d) $y = 4$
  (f) $y = -x$

10. Find equations of the images of the parabola $y = x^2 + 4$ in the following lines of reflection. Sketch the parabola and its images.

  (a) the x axis
  (b) the y axis
  (c) the line $y = x$

11. Find equations of the images of the parabola $y = 3(x - 2)^2 + 5$ in the following lines of reflections. Sketch the curve and its images.

  (a) the x axis
  (b) the y axis
  (c) the line $y - x$

12. Determine and describe the transformations that result from performing in the order given the two reflections listed in each case.

  (a) Reflection in the y axis followed by reflection in the line $x = 1$.

  (b) Reflection in the x axis followed by reflection in the line $y = -3$.

  (c) Reflection in the x axis followed by reflection in the y axis.

C 13. (a) Given two straight lines L_1 and L_2 find a geometric construction for the transformation obtained by reflection first with L_1 as mirror and second with L_2 as mirror.

  (b) Show that if L_1 and L_2 are parallel, the transformation is a translation of length twice the distance between L_1 and L_2 and in a direction perpendicular to L_1 and L_2.

  (c) Show that if L_1 and L_2 intersect at O, the transformation is a rotation about O through twice the directed angle from L_1 to L_2.

4.4 Dilatations and Other Non-Isometries

> "The Guard was looking at her, first through a telescope, then through a microscope, and then through an opera glass. At last he said, 'You're travelling the wrong way'."

> *(Through the Looking Glass)*

The transformations we have encountered so far have been distance-preserving, that is, isometries. These transformations map given figures onto congruent figures. Now, however, we shall introduce some transformations under which distances are not preserved.

The first of these is a type of transformation under which all distances are changed in the same ratio. This type of transformation is called a *dilatation* (to dilate is to enlarge). Here we shall consider only dilatations under which the origin is fixed; these are sometimes called central dilatations.

A dilatation of factor k is a 1:1 mapping of the plane onto itself such that the point (x, y) maps onto the point (kx, ky), $k \in R$. That is,

$$(x, y) \rightarrow (kx, ky)$$

Consider $\triangle ABC$ in Figure 4.6. Under a dilatation of factor 2

$A(1, 1) \rightarrow A'(2, 2)$
$B(3, 4) \rightarrow B'(6, 8)$
$C(-1, 5) \rightarrow C'(-2, 10)$

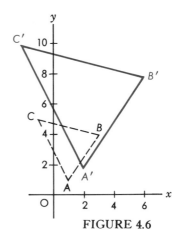

FIGURE 4.6

Observe the following.

(1) The origin O, the point A, and its image A' are collinear.
(2) $A'B' \parallel AB$, $B'C' \parallel BC$, $A'C' \parallel AC$.
Thus a line and its image are parallel lines.

124   *4.4/Dilatations and other Non-Isometries*

(3) $A'B' = 2 \times AB$
$A'C' = 2 \times AC$
$B'C' = 2 \times BC$
Thus, lengths are doubled by this dilatation.

(4) $\triangle ABC \backsim \triangle A'B'C'$

The following examples generalize these results.

Example 1

Under the dilatation $(x, y) \rightarrow (kx, ky)$ with centre $O(0, 0)$, a point P, its image P', and O are collinear.

Solution

If $P(x, y) \rightarrow P'(kx, ky)$

slope $OP = \dfrac{y - 0}{x - 0} = \dfrac{y}{x}$

slope $OP' = \dfrac{ky - 0}{kx - 0} = \dfrac{ky}{kx} = \dfrac{y}{x}$

$\therefore OP \parallel OP'$

$\therefore O, P, P'$ are collinear.

Example 2

Under a dilatation of factor k with centre the origin, the line $y = mx + b$ and its image are parallel.

Solution

If $P(x, y) \rightarrow P'(u, v)$ under a dilatation of factor k about the origin, then

$$\left.\begin{array}{l} u = kx \\ v = ky \end{array}\right\} \implies \left\{\begin{array}{l} x = \dfrac{u}{k} \\ y = \dfrac{v}{k} \end{array}\right.$$

Let $P(x, y)$ be on the original line $y = mx + b$.
Substituting for x and y,

$$\frac{v}{k} = m\frac{u}{k} + b$$
$$v = mu + bk$$

Thus the image of $y = mx + b$ has equation $v = mu + bk$, which may be written $y - mx + bk$.

Since $y = mx + bk$ is a linear equation, a line maps onto a line under a dilatation. Since the slopes of $y = mx + b$ and its image $y = mx + bk$ are each m, a line maps onto a parallel line under a dilatation.

Example 3

Show that under a dilatation of factor k the length of a line segment is multiplied by a factor $|k|$.

Solution

Consider the segment joining $P(a, b)$ and $Q(c, d)$.

$P \rightarrow P'$ with coordinates (ka, kb)
$Q \rightarrow Q'$ with coordinates (kc, kd)

$$PQ = \sqrt{(\Delta x)^2 + (\Delta y)^2}$$
$$= \sqrt{(c - a)^2 + (d - b)^2}$$
$$P'Q' = \sqrt{(\Delta x)^2 + (\Delta y)^2}$$
$$= \sqrt{(kc - ka)^2 + (kd - kb)^2}$$
$$= \sqrt{k^2(c - a)^2 + k^2(d - b)^2}$$
$$= \sqrt{k^2} \sqrt{(c - a)^2 + (d - b)^2}$$
$$= \sqrt{k^2} \times PQ$$
$$= |k| \times PQ \qquad \text{(Why is } \sqrt{k^2} = |k| \text{?)}$$

Thus the length of line segments is multiplied by a factor $|k|$ under a dilatation of factor k. Distance is not invariant under a dilatation. *A dilatation is not an isometry.*

The fact that every triangle is mapped onto a similar triangle under a dilatation of factor k follows immediately from Example 3, since the lengths of the corresponding sides of the triangles will be proportional to k.

It is worthwhile noting (Figure 4.7) that under a dilatation of factor -2,

$A(1, 1) \rightarrow A'(-2, -2)$
$B(3, 4) \rightarrow B'(-6, -8)$
$C(-1, 5) \rightarrow C'(2, -10)$

Again, each point, its image, and the origin are collinear, but a point and its image are *on opposite sides* of the origin. Check the other properties.

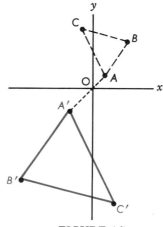

FIGURE 4.7

4.4/Dilatations and other Non-Isometries

The following summarizes the results for a dilatation.

Properties of a dilatation with factor k

(1) If $A \rightarrow A'$ then there exists a point O, called the centre of the dilatation, such that $A' \in$ line OA.
If $k > 0$, then A and A' are on the same side of O.
If $k < 0$, then A and A' are on opposite sides of O.
(2) A line and its image are parallel lines.
(3) Lengths of segments are multiplied by a factor $|k|$.
(4) A triangle maps onto a similar triangle.
(5) The origin is the centre of the dilatation
$(x, y) \rightarrow (kx, ky)$

Dilatations are not the only non-rigid transformations. In the exercise that follows you will be given the opportunity to discover some of the properties of the following transformations that do *not* preserve distances.

Transformation	*Mapping*
stretch in x direction	$(x, y) \rightarrow (ax, y)$
stretch in y direction	$(x, y) \rightarrow (x, by)$
two-way stretch	$(x, y) \rightarrow (ax, by)$
shear in x direction	$(x, y) \rightarrow (x + ky, y)$
shear in y direction	$(x, y) \rightarrow (x, kx + y)$

Example 4

Find an equation of the image of the circle $x^2 + y^2 = 2$ under the dilatation $(x, y) \rightarrow (3x, 3y)$.

Solution

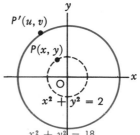

If $P(x, y) \rightarrow P'(u, v)$ under the dilatation

of factor 3, then $\left. \begin{matrix} u = 3x \\ v = 3y \end{matrix} \right\} \rightarrow \left\{ \begin{matrix} x = \dfrac{u}{3} \\ y = \dfrac{v}{3} \end{matrix} \right.$

On the given curve $x^2 + y^2 = 2$,

Substituting for x and y, $\left(\dfrac{u}{3}\right)^2 + \left(\dfrac{v}{3}\right)^2 = 2$

$$u^2 + v^2 = 18$$

The image of the circle $x^2 + y^2 = 2$ under a dilatation of factor 3 is the circle $u^2 + v^2 = 18$, that is, $x^2 + y^2 = 18$. The original circle has radius $\sqrt{2}$ and the image circle has radius $3\sqrt{2}$, hence the circle has been magnified by a factor of 3.

Example 5

Find an equation of the image of the circle $x^2 + y^2 = 1$ under the stretch $(x, y) \rightarrow (3x, y)$ parallel to the x axis. Sketch the image curve.

Solution

If $P(x, y) \rightarrow P'(u, v)$ under the given stretch then

$$\left. \begin{matrix} u = 3x \\ v = y \end{matrix} \right\} \Rightarrow \left\{ \begin{matrix} x = \dfrac{u}{3} \\ y = v \end{matrix} \right.$$

On the given curve $x^2 + y^2 = 1$

$$\frac{u^2}{9} + v^2 = 1$$

Therefore, the equation of the image of the circle $x^2 + y^2 = 1$ under the one-way stretch is $\dfrac{u^2}{9} + v^2 = 1$ or $u^2 + 9v^2 = 9$ which may be written $x^2 + 9y^2 = 9$. The image curve is called an *ellipse*.

Exercise 4.4

A

1. State the coordinates of the image of the points $P(2, -3)$, $Q(1, 5)$ and $R(-4, -2)$ under each of the following transformations.

    (*a*) a dilatation of factor 4
    (*b*) a dilatation of factor 3
    (*c*) a stretch of factor 2 parallel to the y axis

2. State the coordinates of the image of the points $A(4, 1)$ and $B(-3, 2)$ under each of the following transformations.

    (*a*) $(x, y) \rightarrow (3x, y)$
    (*b*) $(x, y) \rightarrow (x, 2y)$
    (*c*) $(x, y) \rightarrow (5x, -4y)$
    (*d*) $(x, y) \rightarrow (x, 3x + y)$

3. Name the transformation in each part of Question 2.

4.4/Dilatations and other Non-Isometries

B

4. Given the points $A(1, 2)$, $B(4, 6)$, $C(7, 1)$ and a dilatation of factor -3 such that $A \rightarrow A'$, $B \rightarrow B'$, $C \rightarrow C'$.

   (a) Find the coordinates of A', B', and C'.
   (b) Calculate the lengths of AB, BC, AC, $A'B'$, $B'C'$, $A'C'$. How do the lengths of a segment and its image compare?
   (c) Prove that $AB||A'B'$, $BC||B'C'$ and $AC||A'C'$.

5. Given the points $P(2, 0)$, $Q(-1, 0)$, $R(0, -3)$, $T(0, 6)$ and the stretch $(x, y) \rightarrow (4x, y)$ such that $P \rightarrow P'$, $Q \rightarrow Q'$, $R \rightarrow R'$, $T \rightarrow T'$.

   (a) Find the coordinates of P', Q', R', T'.
   (b) Calculate the lengths of PQ, RT, $P'Q'$, $R'T'$. Draw conclusions. Test your conclusions with other points.
   (c) Why is the transformation called a one-way stretch?

6. Repeat Question 5 (a) and (b) for the stretch $(x, y) \rightarrow (x, -3y)$.

7. Repeat Question 5 (a) and (b) for the two-way stretch $(x, y) \rightarrow (2x, 5y)$.

8. Find equations of the images of the circle $x^2 + y^2 = 1$ under the following transformations. Sketch the circle and its image in each case.

   (a) $(x, y) \rightarrow (2x, 2y)$
   (b) $(x, y) \rightarrow (x, 3y)$
   (c) $(x, y) \rightarrow (3x, 2y)$

9. Prove that the stretch $(x, y) \rightarrow (ax, y)$ stretches a line segment that is parallel to the x axis by a factor of $|a|$.

10. Prove that the stretch $(x, y) \rightarrow (x, by)$ stretches a line segment that is parallel to the y axis by a factor $|b|$.

11. Prove that the two-way stretch $(x, y) \rightarrow (ax, by)$ stretches a line segment that is parallel to the x axis by a factor of $|a|$ and a line segment that is parallel to the y axis by a factor of $|b|$.

12. Given the points $A(0, 0)$, $B(1, 0)$, $C(1, 2)$, $D(2, 2)$ and the shear $(x, y) \rightarrow (x + 3y, y)$ where A, B, C, D map onto A', B', C', D' respectively.

    (a) Find the coordinates of A', B', C', D'.
    (b) Draw the quadrilateral $ABCD$ and its image $A'B'C'D'$ using the same coordinate axes.
    (c) Is a shear parallel to the x axis a rigid motion?

4.4/Dilatations and other Non-Isometries   129

13. (a) Repeat Question 12 (a), (b) for the shear $(x, y) \rightarrow (x, 2x + y)$.
    (b) Is a shear parallel to the y axis a rigid motion?

14. Show that the two-way stretch $(x, y) \rightarrow (5x, 3y)$ can be expressed as the composition of a dilatation followed by a one-way stretch.

C 15. Express the effect of a dilatation $(x, y) \rightarrow (ax, ay)$ followed by a second dilatation $(x, y) \rightarrow (bx, by)$.

16. Find the non-trivial dilatation which, when applied twice in succession, gives the identity transformation. By what other name is this transformation also known?

17. (a) Conjecture how the area of a given figure is altered by a dilatation $(x, y) \rightarrow (ax, ay)$.
    (b) Prove your conjecture for a square of your choice.

18. Describe as a single transformation the resulting effect of a stretch $(x, y) \rightarrow (ax, y)$ followed by a stretch $(x, y) \rightarrow (x, by)$.

19. Find the stretch parallel to the y axis that is not equal to the identity transformation $(x, y) \rightarrow (x, y)$ but if applied twice gives the identity transformation. By what other name is this transformation known?

20. (a) Conjecture how the area of a given figure is altered by the stretch $(x, y) \rightarrow (x, by)$.
    (b) Prove your conjecture for a rectangle of your choice.

21. Given the segment OP, where O is the origin and P the point (a, b). Let P' be the image of P under the transformation $(x, y) \rightarrow (3x, 5y)$. Show that

$$3 \, OP \leq OP' \leq 5 \, OP.$$

Discuss the position of P if equality holds on either side.

22. Find the image under $(x, y) \rightarrow (ax, by)$ of the square $|x| \leq 1$, $|y| \leq 1$. How does the area of the square behave under the transformation?

23. Find the image of the rectangle $|x| \leq 1$, $|y| \leq 2$ under the shear $(x, y) \rightarrow (x + ky, y)$. How is the area of the rectangle affected under the transformation?

4.4/Dilatations and other Non-Isometries

4.5 Matrices and Transformations

A transformation is a mapping of the plane onto itself. All of the transformations we have considered are 1:1. To emphasize the mapping idea we frequently make use of the function notation of mapping. If a reflection R_1 in the x axis maps a point $P(x, y)$ onto the point $P'(u, v)$, we may write $R_1:P \rightarrow R_1 (P)$ where $R_1 (P)$ is read "R_1. image of P." Thus $R_1 (P) = (x, -y)$.

Another notation employed often helps to unify the concept of transformation. This notation is the matrix notation. An array such as the following is called a *matrix*.

$\begin{bmatrix} 2 & 1 \\ 0 & 3 \end{bmatrix}$ is an example of a 2 × 2 matrix.

$\begin{bmatrix} 2 \\ 4 \end{bmatrix}$ is an example of a 2 × 1 matrix or column matrix.

In matrix notation we use the word *row* to describe the set of numerals displayed horizontally, and the word *column* to describe the set of numerals listed vertically.

First Column   Second Column

First Row
Second Row

$$\begin{bmatrix} 2 & 1 \\ 0 & 3 \end{bmatrix}$$

An operation, called multiplication, can be performed between a 2 × 2 matrix and a 2 × 1 matrix as follows.

If $A = \begin{bmatrix} 2 & 1 \\ 0 & 3 \end{bmatrix}$ and $P = \begin{bmatrix} x \\ y \end{bmatrix}$

then the product AP is written as $\begin{bmatrix} 2 & 1 \\ 0 & 3 \end{bmatrix}\begin{bmatrix} x \\ y \end{bmatrix}$

and is defined as $\begin{bmatrix} 2 \cdot x + 1 \cdot y \\ 0 \cdot x + 3 \cdot y \end{bmatrix} = \begin{bmatrix} 2x + y \\ 3y \end{bmatrix}$.

Observe that the product is a 2 × 1 matrix.

In general the product of the 2 × 2 matrix $\begin{bmatrix} a & b \\ c & d \end{bmatrix}$

and the 2 × 1 matrix $\begin{bmatrix} x \\ y \end{bmatrix}$ is a 2 × 1 matrix given by the following.

$$\begin{bmatrix} a & b \\ c & d \end{bmatrix}\begin{bmatrix} x \\ y \end{bmatrix} = \begin{bmatrix} ax + by \\ cx + dy \end{bmatrix}$$

Notice that the 2 × 2 matrix occurs on the left in the product, while the 2 × 1 matrix occurs on the right. There is no matrix multiplication defined for a 2 × 1 matrix on the left and a 2 × 2 matrix on the right.

If we write the coordinates of a point $P(x, y)$ in column vector form $\begin{bmatrix} x \\ y \end{bmatrix}$, we can use matrix notation for various transformations.

Reflections in the line $y = x$:

$$\begin{bmatrix} x \\ y \end{bmatrix} \rightarrow \begin{bmatrix} y \\ x \end{bmatrix} = \begin{bmatrix} 0 \cdot x + 1 \cdot y \\ 1 \cdot x + 0 \cdot y \end{bmatrix} = \begin{bmatrix} 0 & 1 \\ 1 & 0 \end{bmatrix} \begin{bmatrix} x \\ y \end{bmatrix}$$

Reflections in the x axis:

$$\begin{bmatrix} x \\ y \end{bmatrix} \rightarrow \begin{bmatrix} x \\ -y \end{bmatrix} = \begin{bmatrix} 1 \cdot x + & 0 \cdot y \\ 0 \cdot x + (-1) \cdot y \end{bmatrix} = \begin{bmatrix} 1 & 0 \\ 0 & -1 \end{bmatrix} \begin{bmatrix} x \\ y \end{bmatrix}$$

Dilatation of factor k:

$$\begin{bmatrix} x \\ y \end{bmatrix} \rightarrow \begin{bmatrix} kx \\ ky \end{bmatrix} = \begin{bmatrix} k \cdot x + 0 \cdot y \\ 0 \cdot x + k \cdot y \end{bmatrix} = \begin{bmatrix} k & 0 \\ 0 & k \end{bmatrix} \begin{bmatrix} x \\ y \end{bmatrix}$$

There is a very simple way to remember these matrices. Under reflection in the line $y = x$ $\quad (1, 0) \rightarrow (0, 1)$
$$(0, 1) \rightarrow (1, 0)$$
Note that the matrix for reflection in $y = x$ is

$$\begin{bmatrix} 0 & 1 \\ 1 & 0 \end{bmatrix} = \begin{bmatrix} \begin{pmatrix} \text{image} \\ \text{of} \\ (1, 0) \end{pmatrix} & \begin{pmatrix} \text{image} \\ \text{of} \\ (0, 1) \end{pmatrix} \end{bmatrix}$$

The same is true for reflection in the x axis for $\quad (1, 0) \rightarrow (1, 0)$
$$(0, 1) \rightarrow (0, -1)$$

and its matrix is $\begin{bmatrix} 1 & 0 \\ 0 & -1 \end{bmatrix} = \begin{bmatrix} \begin{pmatrix} \text{image} \\ \text{of} \\ (1, 0) \end{pmatrix} & \begin{pmatrix} \text{image} \\ \text{of} \\ (0, 1) \end{pmatrix} \end{bmatrix}$

Under a dilatation of factor k $\quad (1, 0) \rightarrow (k, 0)$
$$(0, 1) \rightarrow (0, k)$$

which produces $\begin{bmatrix} k & 0 \\ 0 & k \end{bmatrix}$, the correct matrix.

According to this we should be able to determine easily the matrices for rotations such as $\frac{1}{2}$ turn or $\frac{1}{8}$ turn.

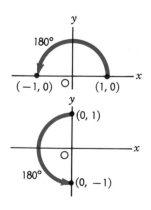

Under a rotation of 180° about $(0, 0)$
$(1, 0) \rightarrow (-1, 0)$
$(0, 1) \rightarrow (0, -1)$
so the matrix for a half-turn should be $\begin{bmatrix} -1 & 0 \\ 0 & -1 \end{bmatrix}$.

For an eighth-turn, $\theta = 45°$

$(1,0) \rightarrow \left(\dfrac{1}{\sqrt{2}}, \dfrac{1}{\sqrt{2}}\right)$

$(0,1) \rightarrow \left(-\dfrac{1}{\sqrt{2}}, \dfrac{1}{\sqrt{2}}\right)$

so its matrix is given by $\begin{bmatrix} \dfrac{1}{\sqrt{2}} & \dfrac{-1}{\sqrt{2}} \\ \dfrac{1}{\sqrt{2}} & \dfrac{1}{\sqrt{2}} \end{bmatrix}$

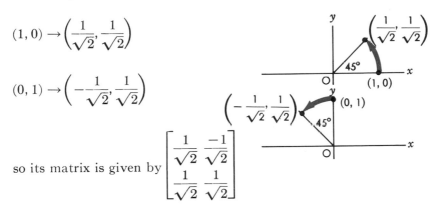

You will be given an opportunity in the exercise that follows to show that these matrices are correct and to verify the following rule for other transformations.

If $(1,0) \rightarrow (a,b)$
and $(0,1) \rightarrow (p,q)$
then the matrix for this transformation is
$$\begin{bmatrix} a & p \\ b & q \end{bmatrix}$$

Note the effect of the matrix $I = \begin{bmatrix} 1 & 0 \\ 0 & 1 \end{bmatrix}$ on the column matrix $\begin{bmatrix} x \\ y \end{bmatrix}$

$$\begin{bmatrix} 1 & 0 \\ 0 & 1 \end{bmatrix}\begin{bmatrix} x \\ y \end{bmatrix} = \begin{bmatrix} 1 \cdot x + 0 \cdot y \\ 0 \cdot x + 1 \cdot y \end{bmatrix} = \begin{bmatrix} x \\ y \end{bmatrix}$$

Since $\begin{bmatrix} x \\ y \end{bmatrix} \rightarrow \begin{bmatrix} x \\ y \end{bmatrix}$ under I, the matrix I is called the *unit* matrix or *identity* for matrix multiplication.

Combining matrix notation and functional notation we have the following:

function: $A : P \rightarrow A(P)$
matrix: $\quad A : P \rightarrow AP$

Thus for a transformation defined by a matrix A, the image $A(P)$ is given by AP.

4.5/Matrices and Transformations

Example 1

What 2×2 matrix corresponds to the transformation

$$(x, y) \rightarrow (2x - 3y, 5x + y)?$$

Solution

Let the matrix be $\begin{bmatrix} a & b \\ c & d \end{bmatrix}$.

$\therefore \quad \begin{bmatrix} x \\ y \end{bmatrix} \rightarrow \begin{bmatrix} a & b \\ c & d \end{bmatrix} \begin{bmatrix} x \\ y \end{bmatrix} = \begin{bmatrix} ax + by \\ cx + dy \end{bmatrix}$

But $\begin{bmatrix} x \\ y \end{bmatrix} \rightarrow \begin{bmatrix} 2x - 3y \\ 5x + y \end{bmatrix}$

$\therefore \quad \begin{matrix} ax + by = 2x - 3y \\ cx + dy = 5x + y \end{matrix} \Bigg\} \Rightarrow \begin{bmatrix} a & b \\ c & d \end{bmatrix} = \begin{bmatrix} 2 & -3 \\ 5 & 1 \end{bmatrix}$

Example 2

A transformation is defined by the matrix $\begin{bmatrix} 2 & -1 \\ 3 & 1 \end{bmatrix}$.
Find the image $A'B'C'D'$ of the square $ABCD$ where
$A = (-1, -1)$, $B = (2, -1)$, $C = (2, 2)$, $D = (-1, 2)$.

Solution

$A' = \begin{bmatrix} 2 & -1 \\ 3 & 1 \end{bmatrix} \begin{bmatrix} -1 \\ -1 \end{bmatrix} = \begin{bmatrix} (2)(-1) + (-1)(-1) \\ (3)(-1) + (1)(-1) \end{bmatrix} = \begin{bmatrix} -1 \\ -4 \end{bmatrix}$

$B' = \begin{bmatrix} 2 & -1 \\ 3 & 1 \end{bmatrix} \begin{bmatrix} 2 \\ -1 \end{bmatrix} = \begin{bmatrix} (2)(2) + (-1)(-1) \\ (3)(2) + (1)(-1) \end{bmatrix} = \begin{bmatrix} 5 \\ 5 \end{bmatrix}$

$C' = \begin{bmatrix} 2 & -1 \\ 3 & 1 \end{bmatrix} \begin{bmatrix} 2 \\ 2 \end{bmatrix} = \begin{bmatrix} (2)(2) + (-1)(2) \\ (3)(2) + (1)(2) \end{bmatrix} = \begin{bmatrix} 2 \\ 8 \end{bmatrix}$

$D' = \begin{bmatrix} 2 & -1 \\ 3 & 1 \end{bmatrix} \begin{bmatrix} -1 \\ 2 \end{bmatrix} = \begin{bmatrix} (2)(-1) + (-1)(2) \\ (3)(-1) + (1)(2) \end{bmatrix} = \begin{bmatrix} -4 \\ -1 \end{bmatrix}$

The effect of this transformation is shown in the following figure.

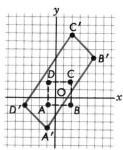

Is this transformation either a rigid motion or a similarity?

Exercise 4.5

B

1. Express each of the following matrix products as a 2 × 1 matrix.

(a) $\begin{bmatrix} 1 & 2 \\ 3 & 1 \end{bmatrix} \begin{bmatrix} x \\ y \end{bmatrix}$

(e) $\begin{bmatrix} 4 & 3 \\ 1 & 0 \end{bmatrix} \begin{bmatrix} 2 \\ 3 \end{bmatrix}$

(b) $\begin{bmatrix} 3 & -1 \\ 4 & 0 \end{bmatrix} \begin{bmatrix} x \\ y \end{bmatrix}$

(f) $\begin{bmatrix} 1 & 0 \\ 0 & -1 \end{bmatrix} \begin{bmatrix} 4 \\ -5 \end{bmatrix}$

(c) $\begin{bmatrix} 2 & 0 \\ 0 & 2 \end{bmatrix} \begin{bmatrix} x \\ y \end{bmatrix}$

(g) $\begin{bmatrix} 3 & 2 \\ 1 & -1 \end{bmatrix} \begin{bmatrix} -6 \\ 2 \end{bmatrix}$

(d) $\begin{bmatrix} -2 & 8 \\ 6 & -1 \end{bmatrix} \begin{bmatrix} x \\ y \end{bmatrix}$

(h) $\begin{bmatrix} 0 & 1 \\ 4 & 3 \end{bmatrix} \begin{bmatrix} -1 \\ -4 \end{bmatrix}$

2. For each of the following transformations name the type of transformation and find the matrix that defines the transformations. Check to see what matrices conform to the rule suggested on page 133.

   (a) $(x, y) \rightarrow (ax, y)$

   (b) $(x, y) \rightarrow (x, by)$

   (c) $(x, y) \rightarrow (ax, by)$

   (d) $(x, y) \rightarrow (x + ky, y)$

   (e) $(x, y) \rightarrow (x, kx + y)$

   (f) $(x, y) \rightarrow (-x, y)$

3. Find the image of the square $A(-1, -1)$, $B(-1, 1)$, $C(1, 1)$, $D(1, -1)$ under the transformations defined by each of the following matrices. In each case draw $ABCD$ and its image $A'B'C'D'$.

   (a) $\begin{bmatrix} -1 & 0 \\ 0 & -1 \end{bmatrix}$

   (b) $\begin{bmatrix} -2 & 0 \\ 0 & -2 \end{bmatrix}$

   (c) $\begin{bmatrix} 2 & 1 \\ -3 & 1 \end{bmatrix}$

4. (a) Find the image P' of the point $P(x, y)$ under the transformation defined by the matrix $A = \begin{bmatrix} 2 & 5 \\ 1 & 3 \end{bmatrix}$.

   (b) Find the image P'' of the point P' of (a) under the transformation defined by $B = \begin{bmatrix} 3 & -5 \\ -1 & 2 \end{bmatrix}$.

   (c) How are the transformations defined by A and B related? Matrices A and B are called *inverse matrices*.

5. Find the image $A'B'C'D'$ of the square $A(-2, -2)$, $B(-2, 2)$, $C(2, 2)$, $D(2, -2)$ under the transformations defined by each of the following matrices. In each case describe the geometric effect of the transformation on the square $ABCD$.

   (a) $\begin{bmatrix} 0 & -1 \\ 1 & 0 \end{bmatrix}$

   (b) $\begin{bmatrix} -1 & 0 \\ 0 & -1 \end{bmatrix}$

   (c) $\begin{bmatrix} 0 & 1 \\ -1 & 0 \end{bmatrix}$

4.5/Matrices and Transformations

135

6. (a) Find the matrix defining a rotation θ about the origin.
   (b) Use your result of part (a) to find the matrix corresponding to a half turn and a full turn. Verify that these matrices follow the rule suggested on page 133.

7. Show that the matrix corresponding to a rotation of 360° about the origin is the unit matrix.

8. (a) What transformation is the inverse of a rotation of θ about the origin?
   (b) Write the matrix defining the inverse of a rotation of θ about the origin.

9. (a) The matrix A is such that $A:P \rightarrow A(P) = P'$. If matrix B is the inverse of matrix A then describe the point $B(P')$.
   (b) Describe the transformation defined by $A = \begin{bmatrix} -1 & 0 \\ 0 & 1 \end{bmatrix}$.
   (c) Describe the inverse of the transformation in (b).
   (d) Write the inverse of matrix A of part (b).
   (e) Name other matrices that are their own inverses.

C

10. If matrix $M = \begin{bmatrix} a \\ b \end{bmatrix}$ and matrix $N = \begin{bmatrix} c \\ d \end{bmatrix}$ then $M + N$ is defined as the 2 X 1 matrix $\begin{bmatrix} a + c \\ b + d \end{bmatrix}$.
   (a) Given the matrix $A = \begin{bmatrix} h \\ k \end{bmatrix}$ and the matrix $P = \begin{bmatrix} x \\ y \end{bmatrix}$ show that the transformation $T:P \rightarrow T(P)$ where $T(P) = P + A$ is a translation.
   (b) Show that $T(P)$ cannot be written as the product of a 2 X 2 matrix B and the matrix $P = \begin{bmatrix} x \\ y \end{bmatrix}$.

11. (a) Find the images of $(1,0)$ and $(0,1)$ under a reflection in the origin.
   (b) Write the matrix corresponding to a reflection in the origin.
   (c) Find the image of the point (x, y) under a reflection in the origin.

12. Show that the matrix corresponding to a rotation of 180° about the origin is the same as the matrix corresponding to a reflection in the origin.

4.5/Matrices and Transformations

Transformation	*Image of point* (x, y)	*Matrix*
rotation	$(x \cos \theta - y \sin \theta,$ $x \sin \theta + y \cos \theta)$	$\begin{bmatrix} \cos \theta & -\sin \theta \\ \sin \theta & \cos \theta \end{bmatrix}$
reflection in x axis	$(x, -y)$	$\begin{bmatrix} 1 & 0 \\ 0 & -1 \end{bmatrix}$
reflection in y axis	$(-x, y)$	$\begin{bmatrix} -1 & 0 \\ 0 & 1 \end{bmatrix}$
reflection in line $y = x$	(y, x)	$\begin{bmatrix} 0 & 1 \\ 1 & 0 \end{bmatrix}$
half-turn	$(-x, -y)$	$\begin{bmatrix} -1 & 0 \\ 0 & -1 \end{bmatrix}$
quarter-turn	$(-y, x)$	$\begin{bmatrix} 0 & -1 \\ 1 & 0 \end{bmatrix}$
dilatation	(kx, ky)	$\begin{bmatrix} k & 0 \\ 0 & k \end{bmatrix}$
stretch in x direction	(ax, y)	$\begin{bmatrix} a & 0 \\ 0 & 1 \end{bmatrix}$
stretch in y direction	(x, by)	$\begin{bmatrix} 1 & 0 \\ 0 & b \end{bmatrix}$
two-way stretch	(ax, by)	$\begin{bmatrix} a & 0 \\ 0 & b \end{bmatrix}$
shear in x direction	$(x + ky, y)$	$\begin{bmatrix} 1 & k \\ 0 & 1 \end{bmatrix}$
shear in y direction	$(x, kx + y)$	$\begin{bmatrix} 1 & 0 \\ k & 1 \end{bmatrix}$
(h, k) translation	$(x + h, y + k)$	None

Note that all of the above matrices can be obtained using the rule,

$$\text{matrix} = \left[\begin{pmatrix} \text{image of} \\ (1, 0) \end{pmatrix} \begin{pmatrix} \text{image of} \\ (0, 1) \end{pmatrix} \right].$$

4.6 Composition of Transformations

Suppose $\triangle ABC$ of Figure 4.8 is mapped onto $\triangle STV$ by a reflection M_x in the x axis. Then suppose $\triangle STV$ is mapped onto $\triangle A'B'C'$ by a rotation R_{270} about the origin O. The successive transformations are illustrated in Figure 4.9.

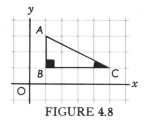

FIGURE 4.8

The transformation of $\triangle ABC$ onto $\triangle A'B'C'$ where $A \rightarrow A'$, $B \rightarrow B'$, $C \rightarrow C'$ is called the *composition* of the two transformations, R_{270} and M_x, and is described by the notation $R_{270} \circ M_x$. The notation indicates that the composition transformation is obtained by performing the transformation M_x first and then the transformation R_{270}. Thus, $R_{270} \circ M_x$ can be read "R_{270} *follows* M_x." You should notice carefully the order in which the transformations R_{270} and M_x are performed in $R_{270} \circ M_x$. Which transformation would be performed first in the composition transformation $M_x \circ R_{270}$?

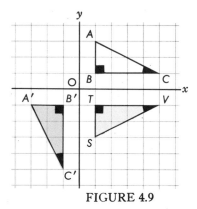

FIGURE 4.9

The composition of transformations can also be studied using the matrices that define a transformation.

The matrix for reflection in the x axis is $M_x = \begin{bmatrix} 1 & 0 \\ 0 & -1 \end{bmatrix}$

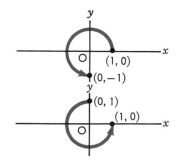

The matrix for a rotation of 270° about O is

$$R_{270} = \left[\begin{pmatrix} \text{image of} \\ (1,0) \end{pmatrix} \begin{pmatrix} \text{image of} \\ (0,1) \end{pmatrix} \right] = \begin{bmatrix} 0 & 1 \\ -1 & 0 \end{bmatrix}$$

4.6/Composition of Transformations

Consider the effect of M_x and R_{270} in turn on the point $P(x, y)$.

Under M_x, $\begin{bmatrix} x \\ y \end{bmatrix} \rightarrow \begin{bmatrix} 1 & 0 \\ 0 & -1 \end{bmatrix} \begin{bmatrix} x \\ y \end{bmatrix} = \begin{bmatrix} x \\ -y \end{bmatrix}$

Under R_{270}, $\begin{bmatrix} x \\ -y \end{bmatrix} \rightarrow \begin{bmatrix} 0 & 1 \\ -1 & 0 \end{bmatrix} \begin{bmatrix} x. \\ -y \end{bmatrix} = \begin{bmatrix} -y \\ -x \end{bmatrix}$

Thus under $R_{270} \circ M_x$ $\begin{bmatrix} x \\ y \end{bmatrix} \rightarrow \begin{bmatrix} -y \\ -x \end{bmatrix}$

or $P(x, y) \rightarrow P'(-y, -x)$.

Observe that this checks with Figure 4.9 where, under $R_{270} \circ M_x$

$$A(1, 3) \rightarrow A'(-3, -1)$$
$$B(1, 1) \rightarrow B'(-1, -1)$$
$$\text{and } C(6, 1) \rightarrow C'(-1, -6)$$

Since $\begin{bmatrix} -y \\ -x \end{bmatrix} = \begin{bmatrix} 0 & -1 \\ -1 & 0 \end{bmatrix} \begin{matrix} x \\ y \end{matrix}$ the composite transformation $R_{270} \circ M_x$

has $\begin{bmatrix} 0 & -1 \\ -1 & 0 \end{bmatrix}$ as its defining matrix.

Using function notation we can write

$$M_x: P \rightarrow M_x(P) = Q$$
$$R_{270}: Q \rightarrow R_{270}(Q) = P'$$
$$M_x \circ R_{270}: P \rightarrow P' = R_{270}(Q)$$
$$= R_{270}(M_x(P)) \quad (1)$$

We shall agree to denote the matrix of the transformation $R_{270} \circ M_x: P \rightarrow P'$ by the symbol $R_{270}M_x$ and shall write
$$P' = R_{270}M_x(P) \quad (2)$$
Thus, (2) and (1) indicate that

$$P' = R_{270}(M_x(P)) = R_{270}M_x(P).$$

This last equation is of basic importance, for it is the definition of what we mean by the product matrix $R_{270}M_x$.

According to this definition the product matrix $R_{270}M_x$ is the matrix that defines the composite transformation obtained by applying the matrix M_x to a column vector $\begin{bmatrix} x \\ y \end{bmatrix}$ and then applying the

matrix R_{270} to the result. In general, the product AB of the 2 × 2 matrices A and B is the 2 × 2 matrix corresponding to the composite transformation $A \circ B$ in which B is applied first then A. (Figure 4.10)

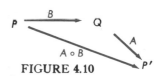

FIGURE 4.10

Example 1

Find the product matrix AB corresponding to the transformations whose matrices are $A = \begin{bmatrix} -1 & 0 \\ 0 & 1 \end{bmatrix}$ and $B = \begin{bmatrix} 1 & 2 \\ 0 & 1 \end{bmatrix}$

Solution

AB is the matrix of the composite transformation $A \circ B$. Consider the image of a point $P(x, y)$

under B:
$$\begin{bmatrix} x \\ y \end{bmatrix} \rightarrow \begin{bmatrix} 1 & 2 \\ 0 & 1 \end{bmatrix}\begin{bmatrix} x \\ y \end{bmatrix} = \begin{bmatrix} x + 2y \\ y \end{bmatrix}$$

under A:
$$\begin{bmatrix} x + 2y \\ y \end{bmatrix} \rightarrow \begin{bmatrix} -1 & 0 \\ 0 & 1 \end{bmatrix}\begin{bmatrix} x + 2y \\ y \end{bmatrix} = \begin{bmatrix} -x - 2y \\ y \end{bmatrix}$$

But
$$\begin{bmatrix} -x - 2y \\ y \end{bmatrix} = \begin{bmatrix} -1 & -2 \\ 0 & 1 \end{bmatrix}\begin{bmatrix} x \\ y \end{bmatrix}$$

$\therefore AB$
$$= \begin{bmatrix} -1 & -2 \\ 0 & 1 \end{bmatrix}$$

In Example 1, A defines a reflection in the y axis and B defines a shear of factor 2 in the y direction. There is no special name for the transformation defined by AB. Check to see if $AB = BA$.

Example 2

Use transformations to find the product CD of the 2×2 matrices,

$C = \begin{bmatrix} 1 & 2 \\ -3 & 6 \end{bmatrix}$ and $D = \begin{bmatrix} 4 & -1 \\ 5 & 2 \end{bmatrix}$

Solution

Matrix CD corresponds to the composite transformation $C \circ D$. Consider the effect of $C \circ D$ on the point (x, y)

under D:
$$\begin{bmatrix} x \\ y \end{bmatrix} \rightarrow \begin{bmatrix} 4 & -1 \\ 5 & 2 \end{bmatrix}\begin{bmatrix} x \\ y \end{bmatrix} = \begin{bmatrix} 4x - y \\ 5x + 2y \end{bmatrix}$$

under C:
$$\begin{bmatrix} 4x - y \\ 5x + 2y \end{bmatrix} \rightarrow \begin{bmatrix} 1 & 2 \\ -3 & 6 \end{bmatrix}\begin{bmatrix} 4x - y \\ 5x + 2y \end{bmatrix}$$
$$= \begin{bmatrix} (1)(4x - y) + 2(5x + 2y) \\ -3(4x - y) + 6(5x + 2y) \end{bmatrix}$$
$$= \begin{bmatrix} 14x + 3y \\ 18x + 15y \end{bmatrix}$$

4.6/Composition of Transformations

Thus under $C \circ D \begin{bmatrix} x \\ y \end{bmatrix} \rightarrow \begin{bmatrix} 14x + 3y \\ 18x + 15y \end{bmatrix} = \begin{bmatrix} 14 & 3 \\ 18 & 15 \end{bmatrix} \begin{bmatrix} x \\ y \end{bmatrix}$

Thus the product matrix $CD = \begin{bmatrix} 14 & 3 \\ 18 & 15 \end{bmatrix}$.

Exercise 4.6

B

1. Write the matrix corresponding to each of the following transformations.

(a) $\begin{bmatrix} x \\ y \end{bmatrix} \rightarrow \begin{bmatrix} 2x - 3y \\ 4x + y \end{bmatrix}$ (c) $\begin{bmatrix} x \\ y \end{bmatrix} \rightarrow \begin{bmatrix} -4x + 7y \\ -3x - 5y \end{bmatrix}$

(b) $\begin{bmatrix} x \\ y \end{bmatrix} \rightarrow \begin{bmatrix} x \\ 3x + 5y \end{bmatrix}$ (d) $\begin{bmatrix} x \\ y \end{bmatrix} \rightarrow \begin{bmatrix} x - 4y \\ x \end{bmatrix}$

2. Find the product matrix AB for each of the following.

(a) $A = \begin{bmatrix} 1 & 0 \\ 2 & 1 \end{bmatrix}$ (b) $A = \begin{bmatrix} 1 & 3 \\ 2 & 0 \end{bmatrix}$ (c) $A = \begin{bmatrix} -1 & -2 \\ 3 & 4 \end{bmatrix}$

    $B = \begin{bmatrix} 1 & 0 \\ 0 & -1 \end{bmatrix}$ $B = \begin{bmatrix} 5 & 0 \\ 1 & 2 \end{bmatrix}$ $B = \begin{bmatrix} 5 & 1 \\ -6 & 3 \end{bmatrix}$

3. Find the product matrix BA for each part of Question 2. Draw conclusions.

4. Find the matrix that represents a rotation through $180°$ about $(0, 0)$ followed by a reflection in the line $y = x$.

5. Find the matrix that represents a reflection in the y axis followed by a shear of factor k parallel to the x axis.

6. Find the matrix that represents a dilatation of factor k followed by a reflection in the x axis.

7. Find the matrix that represents a two-way stretch followed by a rotation of $45°$ about the origin.

8. Find the matrix R that corresponds to a rotation of $30°$ about $(0, 0)$ followed by a rotation of $60°$ about $(0, 0)$. What single transformation is defined by R?

9. Let R be a reflection in the line $y = x$ and M_y a reflection in the y axis. Find the matrix corresponding to the composition transformation $M_y \circ R$.

10. If $A = \begin{bmatrix} -1 & 0 \\ 0 & 1 \end{bmatrix}$, and $B = \begin{bmatrix} 0 & -1 \\ 1 & 0 \end{bmatrix}$, find the transformations

corresponding to the matrices AB and BA.

11. (a) If T is a $(4, 5)$ translation and M_x is a reflection in the
x axis, find the image of the point (x, y) under the composite transformation $T \circ M_x$.
(b) Repeat part (a) for the transformation $M_x \circ T$.

12. If T is an (h, k) translation and S is a shear of factor a parallel
to the x axis find the image of the point (x, y) under the following transformations.

(a) $T \circ S$ (b) $S \circ T$

C 13. (a) If $A = \begin{bmatrix} a & b \\ c & d \end{bmatrix}$ and $B = \begin{bmatrix} u & v \\ w & t \end{bmatrix}$ find AB.

(b) Prove $BA \neq AB$.

14. (a) Find the matrix that represents a rotation through an
angle θ_1 about $(0, 0)$ followed by a rotation through an
angle θ_2 about $(0, 0)$.
(b) By equating the matrix of (a) to the matrix that represents
a rotation of the angle $(\theta_1 + \theta_2)$ about $(0, 0)$ deduce the
formulas for the sine and cosine of the sum of two angles.

15. (a) Find the image P' of $P(x, y)$ under the transformation
defined by the matrix $A = \begin{bmatrix} 2 & 1 \\ 7 & 4 \end{bmatrix}$

(b) Find the matrix B that defines the transformation that
maps P' of (a) back onto P.
(c) A and B are called inverse matrices. Explain.

16. Use the method of Question 15 to find the inverse of each of
the following matrices.

(a) $A = \begin{bmatrix} 2 & 3 \\ 1 & 2 \end{bmatrix}$ (b) $B = \begin{bmatrix} 1 & 2 \\ 0 & 1 \end{bmatrix}$ (c) $C = \begin{bmatrix} 3 & 0 \\ 0 & 3 \end{bmatrix}$

How could you have predicted your result for 16 (c)?

17. (a) Find the inverse of matrix $A = \begin{bmatrix} a & b \\ u & w \end{bmatrix}$

(b) Under what conditions does A not have an inverse matrix?

Review Exercise 4.7

A

1. Explain what is meant by a rigid motion transformation. Give another name for such a transformation.

2. (a) Name the rigid motion transformations studied in this chapter.
   (b) Name the transformations studied in this chapter that are not isometries.

3. (a) State the coordinates of the image of the point (x, y) under the various isometries studied in this chapter.
   (b) State the coordinates of the image of the point (x, y) under the various non-rigid motion transformations studied in this chapter.

B

4. (a) Prove that a dilatation of factor k is not a rigid motion.
   (b) Prove that under a dilatation of factor k,

   (i) lengths of segments are multiplied by a factor $|k|$,
   (ii) a line maps onto a parallel line,
   (iii) the measure of an angle is preserved.

5. Name the transformations under which lines map onto parallel lines.

6. Describe the translations that map the origin onto each of the given points.

   (a) $(2, -7)$ (b) $(-1, -5)$ (c) (a, b)

7. Find the image of (x, y) under the translation for which the image of $(1, 2)$ is the point given in each case.

   (a) $(1, 3)$ (b) $(0, 0)$ (c) $(6, -3)$

8. Determine the translations that are inverses of the following translations.

   (a) $(x, y) \rightarrow (x + 3, y + 2)$
   (b) the translation defined by $\vec{a} = (-4, 5)$
   (c) an (m, s) translation.

9. Under a translation the point $P(-2, 3)$ maps onto the point $P'(7, -5)$. Determine the translation that maps P' back onto P.

10. Find the mirror image of the point (x, y) under each of the following mirror lines.

    (a) $x = 2$ (b) $y = -3$ (c) $x = a, a \in R$ (d) $y = b, b \in R$

11. Find an equation of the image of the line of $x - 2y + 6 = 0$ under the translation defined by $\vec{a} = (-4, 1)$.

12. Without using the formulas for rotation find the image of the following points under a rotation of $90°$ about $(0, 0)$.

    (a) $(2, 0)$ (b) $(0, -3)$ (c) $(4, 3)$ (d) $(-5, -6)$

13. Repeat Question 12 for a rotation of $180°$ about $(0, 0)$.

14. Determine the image of each of the given points under a rotation of $\frac{\pi}{4}$ rad about the origin.

    (a) $(1, 0)$ (c) $(1, 1)$ (e) (x, y)
    (b) $(0, 1)$ (d) $(-1, 1)$ (f) $(a + b, a - b)$

15. Find the images of the given points under a rotation of $\frac{\pi}{3}$ rad.

    (a) $(1, 0)$ (b) $(0, 3)$ (c) $(-1, -1)$ (d) $(-3, 4)$

16. Find the image of the point (x, y) under rotations about the origin through each of the given angles measured in radians.

    (a) $\frac{\pi}{2}$ (c) $\frac{\pi}{4}$ (e) $-\frac{\pi}{2}$

    (b) π (d) $\frac{\pi}{6}$ (f) $-\frac{3\pi}{4}$

17. Under a rotation of $\frac{\pi}{3}$ rad about the origin the point $P(x, y)$ maps onto the point $P'(u, v)$.

    (a) Express each of u and v in terms of x and y.
    (b) Under what rotation about $(0, 0)$ will the point $P'(u, v)$ map back onto the point $P(x, y)$?
    (c) Use your results of part (b) and the formulas for rotation to express each of x and y in terms of u and v.

18. Under a rotation θ about $(0, 0)$, $P(x, y) \rightarrow P'(u, v)$. Use the fact that $P'(u, v) \rightarrow P(x, y)$ under a rotation of $-\theta$ about $(0, 0)$ to express each of x and y in terms of u, v, and θ.

19. Explain why the point $A(2, 3)$ cannot be mapped onto the point $B(-3, 4)$ by a rotation about the point $C(1, 2)$.

20. Find the equations of the images of the circle $x^2 + y^2 = 4$ and the parabola $y = x^2$ under the translation $(x, y) \rightarrow (x - 2, y + 3)$. Sketch the curves and their images.

21. Find an equation for the image of the circle $x^2 + y^2 = 4$ under the two-way stretch $(x, y) \rightarrow (2x, 3y)$. Sketch the circle and its image.

22. State the coordinates of the images of points $A(3, -2)$ and $B(-6, 4)$ under each of the following transformations.

(a) $(x, y) \rightarrow (x, 2y)$ (c) $(x, y) \rightarrow (6x, -3y)$
(b) $(x, y) \rightarrow (4x, 4y)$ (d) $(x, y) \rightarrow (x + 2y, y)$

23. Describe each of the transformations in Question 22.

24. Prove that a two-way stretch is not an isometry.

25. Given the one-way stretch (x, y) › (x, by), where $b \neq 1$.

(a) Distances parallel to what axis are invariant under this stretch?
(b) Distances parallel to what direction are most greatly changed under this stretch?
(c) If all distances are either unchanged or else increased by the stretch, what condition is satisfied by b?

26. Under the transformation $(x, y) \rightarrow (ax, by)$ distances parallel to the x axis are increased by a factor of 4 whereas distances parallel to the y axis are decreased by a factor of 2.

(a) If no figure is reversed, find the values of a and b.
(b) If lengths inclined at angle θ to the x axis are invariant, find $\tan \theta$.

27. Express each of the following matrix products as a 2×1 matrix.

(a) $\begin{bmatrix} 1 & 3 \\ 2 & -1 \end{bmatrix} \begin{bmatrix} x \\ y \end{bmatrix}$ (b) $\begin{bmatrix} 2 & 1 \\ 0 & -2 \end{bmatrix} \begin{bmatrix} x \\ y \end{bmatrix}$ (c) $\begin{bmatrix} m & t \\ s & p \end{bmatrix} \begin{bmatrix} x \\ y \end{bmatrix}$

28. Write the matrix corresponding to each of the following transformations.

(a) a rotation of $45°$ about $(0, 0)$
(b) a rotation of $270°$ about $(0, 0)$
(c) a reflection in the line $y = x$
(d) a shear parallel to the y axis of factor -4
(e) a dilatation of factor 6
(f) $\begin{bmatrix} x \\ y \end{bmatrix} \rightarrow \begin{bmatrix} 2x + 7y \\ -4x \end{bmatrix}$
(g) $\begin{bmatrix} x \\ y \end{bmatrix} \rightarrow \begin{bmatrix} x - 3y \\ 8x + y \end{bmatrix}$

29. Under a transformation with matrix $\begin{bmatrix} 1 & b \\ a & -2 \end{bmatrix}$, the point $(-4, 1)$ is mapped onto the point $(6, 3)$. Find a and b.

30. A transformation is defined by the matrix $A = \begin{bmatrix} 2 & -4 \\ 1 & 3 \end{bmatrix}$. Find the image of the square $P(-2, -2)$, $Q(2, -2)$, $R(2, 2)$, $S(-2, 2)$ under this transformation. Sketch $PQRS$ and its image $P'Q'R'S'$ on the same axes of reference.

31. If A and B are matrices defining transformations A and B, explain the relationship between the matrix product AB and the composite transformation $A \circ B$.

32. Find the product matrix AB for each of the following.

(a) $A = \begin{bmatrix} -1 & 0 \\ 0 & -1 \end{bmatrix}$ (b) $A = \begin{bmatrix} 1 & 2 \\ 0 & 1 \end{bmatrix}$ (c) $A = \begin{bmatrix} 2 & -1 \\ 1 & 3 \end{bmatrix}$

$B = \begin{bmatrix} 3 & 0 \\ 0 & 3 \end{bmatrix}$ $B = \begin{bmatrix} 0 & -1 \\ -1 & 0 \end{bmatrix}$ $B = \begin{bmatrix} 1 & 4 \\ 0 & 5 \end{bmatrix}$

33. Find the matrix that defines a rotation of $90°$ about $(0, 0)$ followed by a reflection in the x axis.

34. Find the matrix that defines a shear of factor 3 parallel to the y axis followed by a shear of factor -2 parallel to the x axis.

35. For each of the following find the matrix that is the inverse of the given matrix.

(a) $\begin{bmatrix} 2 & 0 \\ 0 & 2 \end{bmatrix}$ (b) $\begin{bmatrix} -1 & 0 \\ 0 & -1 \end{bmatrix}$ (c) $\begin{bmatrix} 1 & 2 \\ 0 & 1 \end{bmatrix}$ (d) $\begin{bmatrix} 2 & 1 \\ 3 & 2 \end{bmatrix}$

36. Show that the composition of a reflection in the x axis followed by a reflection in the y axis is equivalent to a rotation of $180°$ about $(0, 0)$.

37. A and B are two points such that $AB = 4$.
If $(x, y) \rightarrow (2x + y, -x + 2y)$ and $A \rightarrow A'$, $B \rightarrow B'$, determine the distance between A' and B'.

5 / The Conics

The conic sections are so named because they are the shapes of the sections made by a plane cutting a cone. Apollonius of Perga, in the second century B.C. produced a systematic treatise on the conic sections that included all that was previously known about them, but greatly extended the knowledge on the subject. So good were the methods of Apollonius that they were to remain a model of mathematical reasoning for over eighteen centuries.

Many other mathematicians added to his work. One was Pappus of Alexandria, in the third century A.D., who first gave the definition of conics by means of focus and directrix. Not until the seventeenth century do we find further significant work on the conics, when Girard G. Desargues, Blaise Pascal, and René Descartes made contributions to the subject.

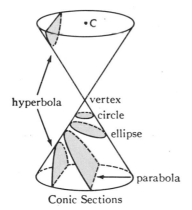

Conic Sections

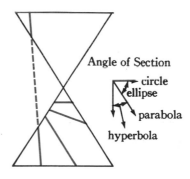

Angle of Section of the Cone

The conic sections were given the names *parabola*, *ellipse* and *hyperbola* by Apollonius. We conjecture that he obtained these names by referring to the slant or slope of the cone because *parabole* was a word used to mean "equal", *ellipsis* meant "left short" and *hyperbole* meant "exceeding."

There are three other types of cross sections; one is a point, one is a straight line, and the other is two intersecting lines. Can you decide how to cut a cone to obtain these three figures as cross sections?

5.1 The Circle

The circle is a curve or locus of points equidistant from a fixed point.

Example 1

Find an equation of a circle with centre $(0, 0)$ and radius 3.

Solution

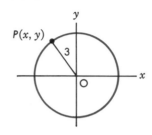

The circle is the locus of points distant 3 from $(0, 0)$.
Let $P(x, y)$ be any point on the locus.

$$OP = 3$$
$$\therefore \quad OP^2 = 9$$
$$\therefore \quad (x - 0)^2 + (y - 0)^2 = 9$$
$$\therefore \quad x^2 + y^2 = 9 \text{ is an equation of the required circle.}$$

In general an equation of a circle with centre at $(0, 0)$ and radius r is $x^2 + y^2 = r^2$.

For circles with centres at points other than the origin, we may use translations to obtain their equations.

Example 2

Find an equation of a circle with centre (h, k) and radius r.

Solution

An equation of the circle with centre $(0, 0)$ and radius r is $x^2 + y^2 = r^2$.

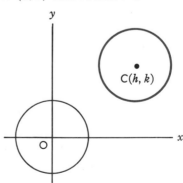

We need to find an equation of the circle under the translation
$$(x, y) \rightarrow (x + h, y + k).$$

If (u, v) is a point on the image circle, then

$$\begin{rcases} u = x + h \\ v = y + k \end{rcases} \Rightarrow \begin{cases} x = u - h \\ y = v - k \end{cases}$$

Substitute in $x^2 + y^2 = r^2$
$$(u - h)^2 + (v - k)^2 = r^2$$
or $u^2 + v^2 - 2hu - 2kv + h^2 + k^2 = r^2$
which may be expressed as $x^2 + y^2 - 2hx - 2ky + h^2 + k^2 - r^2 = 0$

Notice that the coefficients of the x^2 and y^2 terms are the same.

Can we tell the centre and radius of a circle from its equation? For example, what is the centre and radius of the circle

$$x^2 + y^2 - 6x + 8y - 24 = 0?$$

Compare with $x^2 + y^2 - 2hx - 2ky + h^2 + k^2 - r^2 = 0$.

$$\text{Here } -2h = -6 \qquad -2k = 8$$
$$\therefore \ h = 3 \qquad\qquad k = -4$$
$$\therefore \ \text{the centre is } (3, -4).$$
$$\text{Also} \qquad h^2 + k^2 - r^2 = -24$$
$$\therefore \ 9 + 16 - r^2 = -24$$
$$\therefore \ r^2 = 49$$
$$\therefore \ r = 7 \qquad (\because r > 0)$$

In general a circle with equation $x^2 + y^2 + ax + by + c = 0$ has

centre $\left(-\dfrac{a}{2}, -\dfrac{b}{2}\right)$ and radius $\sqrt{\left(\dfrac{a}{2}\right)^2 + \left(\dfrac{b}{2}\right)^2 - c}$

Notice the following.

When the coefficients of x^2 and y^2 are 1 in the equation of the circle:

1. The centre is $[-(\frac{1}{2} \text{ coefficient of } x), -(\frac{1}{2} \text{ coefficient of } y)]$.

2. The radius is

$$\sqrt{(x \text{ of centre})^2 + (y \text{ of centre})^2 - \text{constant term.}}$$

Example 3

Find the centre and radius of each of the following circles.
(a) $x^2 + y^2 - 8x + 4y - 44 = 0$
(b) $3x^2 + 3y^2 + 8x - 4y - 27 = 0$

Solution

(a) Centre is $\left(-\left(\dfrac{1}{2} \times (-8)\right), -\left(\dfrac{1}{2} \times 4\right)\right)$

$$= (4, -2)$$

Radius is $\sqrt{4^2 + (-2)^2 - (-44)}$

$$= \sqrt{64}$$
$$= 8$$

(b) To make the coefficients of x^2 and y^2 equal to 1, we rewrite the equation as

$$x^2 + y^2 + \frac{8}{3}x - \frac{4}{3}y - 9 = 0$$

$$\text{Centre is} \left(-\left(\frac{1}{2} \times \frac{8}{3} \right), -\left(\frac{1}{2} \times \left(-\frac{4}{3} \right) \right) \right)$$

$$= \left(-\frac{4}{3}, \frac{2}{3} \right)$$

$$\text{Radius is} \sqrt{ \left(-\frac{4}{3} \right)^2 + \left(\frac{2}{3} \right)^2 - (-9) }$$

$$= \sqrt{ \frac{16}{9} + \frac{4}{9} + 9 }$$

$$= \sqrt{ \frac{101}{9} } = \frac{1}{3} \sqrt{101}$$

Exercise 5.1

B

1. Find an equation of each of the following circles.
   - (a) centre $(5, 8)$, radius 8
   - (b) centre $(5, -12)$, radius 13
   - (c) centre $(-6, 0)$, radius 6
   - (d) centre $(-3, -3)$, radius 4

2. Find an equation of each of the following circles.
   - (a) tangent to the y axis, radius 10 y coordinate of the centre is -8
   - (b) tangent to both axes, radius 5, centre in the second quadrant
   - (c) passing through $(0, 0)$, centre $(-3, 4)$
   - (d) diameter has end points $(12, 6)$, $(-8, 4)$
   - (e) passing through the points $(0, 0)$, $(8, 0)$, $(0, -4)$
   - (f) tangent to the x axis and with y-intercepts 2 and 8

3. Find the centre and radius of each of the following circles.
   - (a) $x^2 + y^2 - 6x - 10y - 66 = 0$
   - (b) $x^2 + y^2 + 12x - 16y = 0$
   - (c) $2x^2 + 2y^2 - 9x = 0$
   - (d) $x^2 + y^2 + 12x - 8y + 3 = 0$
   - (e) $4x^2 + 4y^2 + 4x - 3 = 0$

4. By finding the radius of a circle show that each of the following equations defines a single point.

(a) $x^2 + y^2 - 8x + 6y + 25 = 0$
(b) $x^2 + y^2 + 2x - 2y + 2 = 0$
(c) $x^2 + y^2 + 14y + 49 = 0$

Why might these be called *point circles*?

5. By finding the radius of a circle show that each of the following equations defines no point.

(a) $x^2 + y^2 - 18x + 8y + 98 = 0$
(b) $x^2 + y^2 + 8x + 25 = 0$

Why might these be called *imaginary circles*?

6. Find equations of the following circles.

(a) tangent to the negative y axis and the line $y = -7$, centre in the fourth quadrant and radius 3.
(b) tangent to both axes, centre on the line $x = y$ and radius 7.
(c) tangent to the x axis with centre on the line $x - 2y = 0$ and radius 4.
(d) centre on the x axis, radius 3 and passing through the point $(2, 2\sqrt{2})$.

7. Find an equation of the circle passing through the points $(0, 2)$ and $(-1, 1)$ and having its centre on the x axis.

8. A circle has its centre on the y axis and the line $x - 5y - 15 = 0$. If the circle passes through the point $(4, 2)$, find its equation.

9. Two circles touch both the x axis and the y axis and pass through the point $(9, 8)$. Find equations for the circles.

10. Find an equation of the circle that passes through the points $(-2, 5)$, $(8, 5)$ and $(-6, 9)$.

11. Find an equation of the circle that passes through the points $A(-4, 1)$, $B(3, 0)$, $C(5, 4)$. (Hint: Find equations for the perpendicular bisectors of AB and AC. The point of intersection of these lines is the centre of the circle.)

12. Find an equation of the circle that passes through the points $(10, 9)$, $(4, -5)$, $(0, 5)$.

13. Find an equation of the diameter of the circle
$$x^2 + y^2 - 4x + 6y - 1 = 0$$
that passes through the point $(0, -2)$.

14. Show that the centres of the three circles
$$x^2 + y^2 - 2x - 6y + 1 = 0$$
$$x^2 + y^2 - 2y - 4 \quad\;\; = 0$$
$$x^2 + y^2 + 4x + 6y + 3 = 0$$
are collinear.

C 15. Find an equation of the circle passing through the points $(-1, 1)$ and $(6, 0)$ that has its centre on the line $x + 3y + 7 = 0$.

16. Find equations for the two circles, each of which has centre 9 units to the right of the y axis and radius $2\sqrt{5}$, that are tangent to the line $2x + y - 10 = 0$.

17. (a) Show that $(2x + y - 3)^2 + (x - 2y + 1)^2 = 20$ represents a circle and find its centre and radius.

   (b) What relationship do the lines $2x + y - 3 = 0$ and $x - 2y + 1 = 0$ have with each other and the circle in (a)?

18. Use the following to prove that an angle inscribed in a semi-circle is a right angle.

   (a) Find the coordinates of A_1 and A_2.
   (b) Find the slopes of P_1A_1 and P_1A_2.
   (c) Prove $P_1A_1 \perp P_1A_2$.

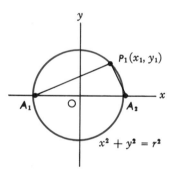

19. Use the following to prove that the angles inscribed in the same segment of a circle are congruent.

   (a) Find the slopes of P_1A and P_1B.
   (b) Find $\tan \angle AP_1B$ in terms of the slopes of P_1A and P_1B.
   (c) Show that $\tan \angle AP_1B = \dfrac{c}{d}$ and hence is a constant.
   (d) Show that the measure of $\angle AP_1B$ is fixed and does not depend on the position of P_1.

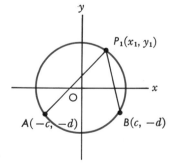

5.2 Stretching the Circle

It is easy to imagine a one-way stretch of the circle. The image curve obtained is a familiar one called an ellipse.

Example 1

Given the circle $x^2 + y^2 = 25$.

(a) Find an equation of the image of the circle under the one-way stretch

$$(x, y) \rightarrow (x, \frac{3}{5}y)$$

(b) Graph the circle and its image.

Solution

(a) For $(x, y) \rightarrow (x, \frac{3}{5}y) = (u, v)$

$$\left. \begin{array}{l} u = x \\ v = \frac{3}{5}y \end{array} \right\} \Rightarrow \left\{ \begin{array}{l} x = u \\ y = \frac{5}{3}v \end{array} \right.$$

Substitute in $x^2 + y^2 = 25$

An equation of the image curve is $u^2 + \frac{25}{9}v^2 = 25$

or $9u^2 + 25v^2 = 225$

which can be expressed as $9x^2 + 25y^2 = 225$

(b)

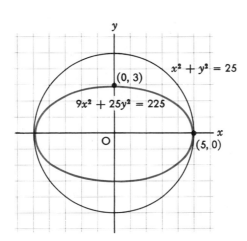

The image curve has the shape of an ellipse. Notice that the coefficients of x^2 and y^2 are different.

An ellipse can be drawn using two tacks and a loop of string. Notice that the sum of the distances of the pencil point to the two tacks is a constant. We shall use this property to find an equation of an ellipse.

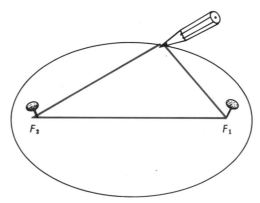

Example 2

Find a defining equation of the ellipse that is the locus of all points the sum of whose distances from $F_1(4, 0)$ and $F_2(-4, 0)$ is 10.

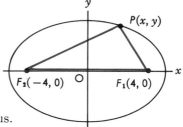

Solution

Let $P(x, y)$ be any point in the locus.

$$\therefore PF_1 + PF_2 = 10$$

or $\sqrt{(x - 4)^2 + y^2} + \sqrt{(x + 4)^2 + y^2} = 10$

$$\sqrt{(x + 4)^2 + y^2} = 10 - \sqrt{(x - 4)^2 + y^2}$$

Squaring,

$$x^2 + 8x + 16 + y^2 = 100$$
$$- 20\sqrt{(x - 4)^2 + y^2} + x^2 - 8x + 16 + y^2$$
$$\therefore \qquad 16x - 100 = -20\sqrt{(x - 4)^2 + y^2}$$
$$4x - 25 = -5\sqrt{(x - 4)^2 + y^2}$$

Squaring, $\qquad 16x^2 - 200x + 625 = 25x^2 - 200x + 400 + 25y^2$
$$225 = 9x^2 + 25y^2$$

$\therefore$ an equation of the ellipse is $9x^2 + 25y^2 = 225$.

The equations in Example 1 and Example 2 are identical! This illustrates that a stretch image of a circle is in fact an ellipse.

From the equation $9x^2 + 25y^2 = 225$ we can show that (page 117) the ellipse is symmetrical about the x and y axes. The ellipse

5.2/Stretching the Circle

has x-intercepts 5 and -5, and y-intercepts 3 and -3. The segment joining $(5, 0)$ and $(-5, 0)$ contains the foci and is called the *major axis*. The segment joining $(0, 3)$ and $(0, -3)$ is called the *minor axis*. The points $(5, 0)$ and $(-5, 0)$ are the ends of the major axis and are called the *vertices* of the ellipse.

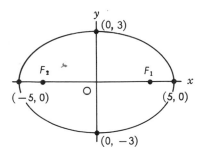

Notice again that in an equation of the ellipse the coefficients of x^2 and y^2 are different.

The segments PF_2 and PF_1 are called focal radii of the ellipse. In general, a *focal radius* of a conic is defined as a segment with one end point a focus and the other end point a point on the conic. For an ellipse, the sum of the focal radii for any point on the ellipse is a constant.

Exercise 5.2

A

1. To make an elliptical flower bed a string is tied to two pegs A and B as illustrated.

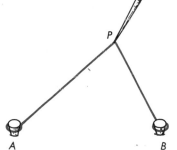

   (a) Describe the different shapes of the ellipse as A and B are placed closer together.

   (b) Describe the different shapes of the ellipse as A and B are placed farther apart.

2. How many axes of symmetry does an ellipse have?

B

3. Square each of the following

   (a) $\sqrt{(x + 3)^2 + y^2}$

   (b) $\sqrt{x^2 + y^2}$

   (c) $10 - \sqrt{(x - 2)^2 + y^2}$

   (d) $3 - \sqrt{(x + 1)^2 + y^2}$

4. Find an equation of the image of $x^2 + y^2 = 100$ under each of the following transformations. Graph the circle and image curve in each case.

   (a) $(x, y) \rightarrow \left(\dfrac{1}{2}x, y\right)$

   (b) $(x, y) \rightarrow (x, 2y)$

   (c) $(x, y) \rightarrow \left(\dfrac{1}{2}x, 2y\right)$

   (d) $(x, y) \rightarrow \left(\dfrac{4}{5}x, \dfrac{3}{5}y\right)$

5. (a) Find the axes of symmetry for each ellipse in Question 4.
   (b) Find the length of the major and minor axes of each ellipse.
   (c) Compare the axis lengths with the diameter of the circle and stretch factors.

6. (a) Find an equation of the image of $x^2 + y^2 = 25$ under the one-way stretch $(x, y) \rightarrow \left(x, \frac{4}{5}y\right)$.
   (b) Sketch the circle and its image.
   (c) Find an equation of the ellipse that is the locus of the points the sum of whose distances from $F_1(-3, 0)$ and $F_2(3, 0)$ is 10.
   (d) How are the ellipses in (a) and (c) related?
   (e) Find the lengths of the axes of the ellipse.
   (f) How is the length of the major axis related to the sum of the distances in part (c)?
   (g) Find the x-intercepts of the ellipse.
   (h) How are the x-intercepts related to the sum of the distances in part (c)?

7. (a) Find an equation of the image of the circle $x^2 + y^2 = 25$ under a one-way stretch $(x, y) \rightarrow \left(\frac{4}{5}x, y\right)$.
   (b) Sketch the circle and its image.
   (c) Find an equation of the ellipse that is the locus of points the sum of whose distances from $F_1(0, 3)$ and $F_2(0, -3)$ is 10.
   (d) How are the ellipses in (a) and (c) related?
   (e) Find the length of the axes of the ellipse.
   (f) How is the length of the major axis related to the sum of the distances in (c)?
   (g) Find the y-intercepts of the ellipse.
   (h) How are the y-intercepts related to the sum of the distances in part (c)?

8. Under the stretch transformation $(x, y) \rightarrow (x, ky)$, $k > 0$, the circle $x^2 + y^2 = 100$ maps onto an ellipse.
   (a) Find an equation of each ellipse for $k = \frac{1}{2}$ and $k = 2$.
   (b) Sketch each ellipse in (a).
   (c) What range of values of k give an image ellipse with major axis along the x axis?
   (d) What range of values of k give an image ellipse with major axis along the y axis?

9. Let $PF_1 + PF_2 = 2a$, $F_1F_2 = 2c$

   (a) Find A_1A_2
   (b) If $OB_1 = b$, show that $a^2 = b^2 + c^2$

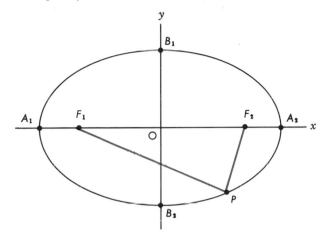

10. (a) Find an equation of the image curve of $x^2 + y^2 = a^2$ under a one-way stretch $(x, y) \rightarrow \left(x, \dfrac{b}{a}y \right)$.

    (b) Find an equation of the locus of points the sum of whose distances from $F_1(-c, 0)$ and $F_2(c, 0)$ is $2a$. Let $a^2 - c^2 = b^2$.

11. (a) Find an equation of the image of $x^2 + y^2 - a^2$ under a one-way stretch $(x, y) \rightarrow \left(\dfrac{b}{a}x, y \right)$.

    (b) Find an equation of the locus of points the sum of whose distances from $F_1(0, -c)$ and $F_2(0, c)$ is $2a$. Let $a^2 - c^2 = b^2$.

12. Show that the image of the ellipse $x^2 + 9y^2 = 81$ under the stretch $(x, y) \rightarrow \left(\dfrac{1}{3}x, y \right)$ is a circle.

13. Find the stretch that transforms the ellipse $x^2 + 9y^2 = 81$ into the circle $x^2 + y^2 = 81$.

14. Show that the image of the ellipse $4x^2 + 9y^2 = 36$ under the stretch $(x, y) \rightarrow (2x, 3y)$ is a circle.

15. Find the stretch that transforms the ellipse $4x^2 + 9y^2 = 36$ into the circle $x^2 + y^2 = 100$.

16. Given three pegs placed at the vertices of an equilateral triangle with sides 8 units long. A loop of string with length 26 units is placed around the pegs. A pencil is placed in the loop. Pull the loop taut and trace out a curve. Describe the curve.

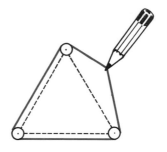

17. Repeat Question 16 for a square with sides 8 units long and a string loop of 34 units in length.

18.

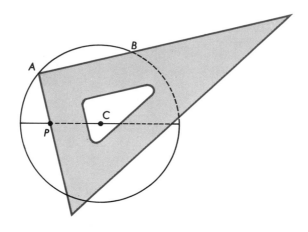

(a) Draw a large circle and draw any diameter.
(b) Mark a point P anywhere in the diameter.
(c) Use a set square to draw chords AB such that $AB \perp AP$.
(d) Draw at least 24 such chords.
(e) What curve do the chords outline?

C 19. Sam is 9 m up a ladder that is 12 m long. The ladder slips at the bottom and Sam takes a "gentle" ride on it to the ground. Sam's feet trace out a path. Find an equation of the curve along which the path lies. (The French call such a locus a *sliding curve* or *glissette*.)

"Comical" my foot; it's "conical".

5.2/Stretching the Circle

5.3 The Ellipse

Before we proceed let us summarize some of the properties and facts we have learned about an ellipse.

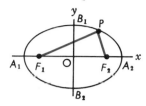

(1). An ellipse has two axes of symmetry, A_1A_2 and B_1B_2.
$A_1A_2 \perp B_1B_2$

(2) An ellipse is a locus of points P such that
$PF_1 + PF_2 = 2a$ (a constant), $a > 0$.

(3) A_1 and A_2 are called *vertices* and $A_1A_2 = 2a$.

(4) O is called the *centre* of the ellipse because O is the midpoint of all chords of the ellipse that pass through O.

(5) Each of F_1 and F_2 is called a *focus* of the ellipse (plural *foci*) and the foci lie on the major axis and $F_1F_2 = 2c$.

(6) OA_2 is called the *semi-major axis* of the ellipse and $OA_2 = a$. OB_1 is called the *semi minor axis* of the ellipse and $OB_1 = b$.

(7) Triangle B_1OF_2 is an *abc* triangle, and $a^2 = b^2 + c^2$.

Example 1

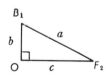

Given the ellipse $x^2 + 25y^2 = 25$

(a) Find the length of the semi-major and semi-minor axes.

(b) Find the coordinates of the foci.

Solution

(a) The longer axis is the major axis. To find the length of the axes we need the x- and y-intercepts.

x-intercepts	y-intercepts
Let $y = 0$ in $x^2 + 25y^2 = 25$	Let $x = 0$ in $x^2 + 25y^2 = 25$
$\therefore x^2 = 25$	$\therefore y^2 = 1$
$\therefore x = 5$ or -5	$\therefore y = 1$ or -1
The length of the axis along the x axis is 10.	The length of the axis along the y axis is 2.

The longer axis, the major axis, is along the x axis and has length 10. Thus the semi-major axis has length 5, that is, $a = 5$. The minor axis is along the y axis. Thus the semi-minor axis has length 1, that is, $b = 1$.

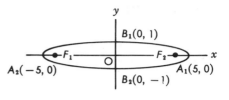

(b) From (a) we have $a = 5$, $b = 1$
$\because a^2 = b^2 + c^2$
$\therefore 25 = 1 + c^2$
$\therefore c^2 = 24$
$\therefore c = 2\sqrt{6}$ or $-2\sqrt{6}$
   Since the foci lie on the longer axis,
$\therefore F_1$ is $(-2\sqrt{6}, 0)$ and F_2 is $(2\sqrt{6}, 0)$

Ellipses have equations of the form $px^2 + qy^2 = t$. The x-intercepts are obtained from the equation

$$px^2 + q(0) = t$$
$$x^2 = \frac{t}{p}$$
$$x = \sqrt{\frac{t}{p}} \text{ or } -\sqrt{\frac{t}{p}}$$

Similarly, the y-intercepts are $\sqrt{\frac{t}{q}}$ or $-\sqrt{\frac{t}{q}}$.

For these intercepts to be real, the numbers p, q and t must have the same sign.

Notice that $\qquad px^2 + qy^2 = t$

can be rewritten as $\dfrac{px^2}{t} + \dfrac{qy^2}{t} = 1$

or $\dfrac{x^2}{\left(\dfrac{t}{p}\right)} + \dfrac{y^2}{\left(\dfrac{t}{q}\right)} = 1$

or $\dfrac{x^2}{\left(\sqrt{\dfrac{t}{p}}\right)^2} + \dfrac{y^2}{\left(\sqrt{\dfrac{t}{q}}\right)^2} = 1$

This leads to the observation that

$$\frac{x^2}{(x\text{-intercept})^2} + \frac{y^2}{(y\text{-intercept})^2} = 1$$

is an equation of an ellipse.

Exercise 5.3

A

1. In the figure an ellipse is given with axes along the coordinate axes.

    (a) Name the vertices.
    (b) On what axes are the foci?
    (c) Name the centre.
    (d) What is the length of the semi-major axis?
    (e) What is the length of the semi-minor axis?
    (f) What is the sum of the distances from P to the foci?
    (g) Give a, b.

    (h) How is c calculated?
    (i) What are the x-intercepts of the ellipse?
    (j) What are the y-intercepts of the ellipse?
    (k) How are the intercepts related to a and b?

2. Given the ellipse $4x^2 + 9y^2 = 36$.

    (a) Find the x- and y-intercepts.
    (b) State the coordinates of the vertices.
    (c) Give the values of a and b.
    (d) On which axis do the foci lie?

B

3. An ellipse has foci on the x axis, centre at $(0, 0)$ and $a = 5, b = 3$.

    (a) On which axis does the major axis lie?
    (b) Name the x- and y-intercepts.
    (c) Suggest an equation for the ellipse.
    (d) From the abc triangle relationship calculate c.
    (e) Name the coordinates of the foci.

4. Repeat Question 3 for an ellipse with foci on the y axis and $a = 13, b = 5$.

5. In each of the following ellipses, find the x- and y-intercepts. Hence determine the values of a, b and c. Sketch the ellipse and mark the foci.

    (a) $\dfrac{x^2}{25} + \dfrac{y^2}{16} = 1$ (d) $x^2 + 25y^2 = 25$

    (b) $\dfrac{x^2}{144} + \dfrac{y^2}{169} = 1$ (e) $9x^2 + 4y^2 = 36$

    (c) $x^2 + 4y^2 = 100$ (f) $7x^2 + 16y^2 = 448$

6. Find an equation of the ellipse with centre the origin and foci on the x axis for each of the following cases.

   (a) major axis 6, minor axis 4
   (b) $a = 17$, $c = 15$
   (c) a focus at $(5, 0)$, $b = 12$

7. (a) Find the distances from the foci of the ellipse $16x^2 + 25y^2 = 400$ to a point on the curve whose x coordinate is 2.
   (b) Compare the sum of the distances with the length of the major axis.

C 8. (a) Find an equation of a circle with centre $(3, 4)$ and radius 8.
   (b) Find an equation of the image of the circle under a stretch
   $$(x, y) \to \left(x, \frac{y}{2}\right)$$
   (c) Find a and b for the ellipse.
   (d) Sketch the circle and ellipse.

9. Find an equation for each of the following ellipses.

   (a) centre $(2, 3)$, $a = 6$, $b = 3$, major axis parallel to the x axis
   (b) centre $(-2, -7)$, $a = 8$, $b = 2$, major axis parallel to the x axis
   (c) centre $(-4, 6)$, $a = 9$, $b = 3$, major axis parallel to the y axis
   (d) centre $(3, -5)$, $a = 6$, $b = 4$, major axis parallel to the y axis

10. Find an equation of the locus of a point P such that the distance of P from $(-4, 0)$ is half the distance from P to the line $x = -16$.

11. The base of a triangle is 12 units long. The product of the tangents of the base angles is $\frac{9}{16}$. Find an equation of the locus of the vertex of this triangle.

12. (a) Describe the possible sections of the surface of a right circular cylinder made by a plane.
   (b) Show that the section of a right circular cylinder of radius 5, made by a plane making a 45° angle with the axis of the cylinder, is an ellipse.
   (c) Find the major and minor axis of the ellipse in (b).

5.4 The Parabola

Figures and their images under a dilatation are said to be similar. For this reason, all circles are similar. We shall show that all parabolas are similar.

Example 1

Show that any parabola is similar to the basic parabola $y = x^2$.

Solution

We may commence with any parabola, P.

Let the origin be at the vertex of P, and let the y axis fall along the axis of P. (The x axis must lie in the plane of P.)

The equation of P will then be of the form $y = ax^2$ $(a \neq 0)$.

Now, apply the dilatation
$(x, y) \rightarrow (ax, ay) = (u, v)$.

$$\therefore x = \frac{u}{a}, y = \frac{v}{a}$$

Substitute in $y = ax^2$.

$$\therefore \frac{v}{a} = a\left(\frac{u}{a}\right)^2 \Leftrightarrow v = u^2 \text{ or } \boxed{y = x^2}$$

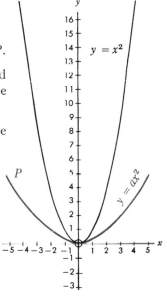

Example 1 illustrates that any given parabola can be transformed into the basic parabola $y = x^2$ by means of a *dilatation*. Thus we may say that all parabolas are similar.

Is it possible that a parabola can be obtained as the image of some other curve? For example, can the parabola be the image of an ellipse under some transformation? An ellipse is a closed curve, whereas a parabola is not. Yet, if you are prepared to use your intuition and imagination you will see that such a transformation can be accomplished.

If one vertex and the nearer focus of an ellipse are kept fixed, and the major axis is allowed to become large beyond all bound, the ellipse will become a parabola!

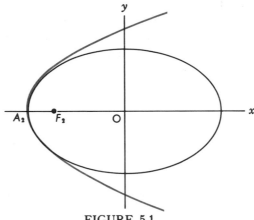

FIGURE 5.1

To prove this unusual property we proceed as follows using Figure 5.1. Let the ellipse equation be $b^2x^2 + a^2y^2 = a^2b^2$ and let $A_2F_2 = p$ (a constant).

A_2 has coordinates $(-a, 0)$.

Translate the ellipse so that the image of A_2 is at $(0, 0)$.

The translation is

$$(x, y) \rightarrow (x + a, y) = (u, v)$$

$$\left. \begin{matrix} u = x + a \\ v = y \end{matrix} \right\} \Rightarrow \begin{cases} x = u - a \\ y = v \end{cases}$$

Substituting in $b^2x^2 + a^2y^2 = a^2b^2$

$\therefore b^2(u - a)^2 + a^2v^2 = a^2b^2$

or $b^2(x - a)^2 + a^2y^2 = a^2b^2$ is an equation of the image curve.

The equation may be written as

$$b^2x^2 + a^2y^2 - 2ab^2x = 0$$

$$\text{or } y^2 = \frac{2b^2}{a}x - \frac{b^2}{a^2}x^2 \tag{1}$$

Since $A_2F_2 = a - c = p$

and $a^2 - c^2 = b^2$

we have $b^2 = a^2 - c^2$

$$= (a - c)(a + c)$$

$$= p(2a - p)$$

$$= 2ap - p^2$$

Substituting for b^2 in (1) we obtain the equation

$$y^2 = \frac{2(2ap - p^2)}{a}x - \frac{(2ap - p^2)x^2}{a^2}$$

$$\text{or } y^2 = \left(4p - \frac{2p^2}{a}\right)x - \left(\frac{2p}{a} - \frac{p^2}{a^2}\right)x^2$$

To make the major axis become very large we let a become very large. Remember p is fixed in value. As a becomes very large $\dfrac{2p^2}{a}$ approaches zero as do the values of $\dfrac{2p}{a}$ and $\dfrac{p^2}{a^2}$. Thus as a becomes large without bound the ellipse approaches the curve given by
$$y^2 = (4p - 0)x - (0 - 0)x^2$$
or $y^2 = 4px$

We recognize $y^2 = 4px$ as an equation of a parabola. The point $(p, 0)$ is called the *focus* of the parabola and $A_2\,(0, 0)$ is called the *vertex*.

Example 2

Show that the locus of the points that are the same distance from the point $(p, 0)$ as from the line $x = -p$ is a parabola.

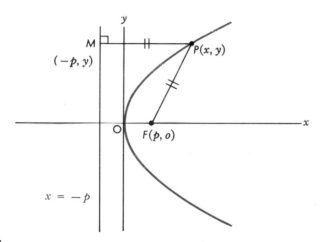

Solution

Let $P(x, y)$ be any point on the locus.

∴ $PF = PM$

or $(PF)^2 = (PM)^2$

∴ $(x - p)^2 + y^2 = (x + p)^2$

∴ $x^2 - 2px + p^2 + y^2 = x^2 + 2px + p^2$

or $y^2 = 4px$, which defines a parabola.

The point $(p, 0)$ is the focus and the line with equation $x = -p$ is called the *directrix*.

Using the method of Example 2 you can show that a parabola with focus $(0, p)$ and directrix $y = -p$ has defining equation $x^2 = 4py$.

PARABOLAS with vertices at the origin.

Equation	$y^2 = 4ax$	$x^2 = 4ay$
Focus	$(a, 0)$	$(0, a)$
Directrix	$x = -a$	$y = -a$
Axis of Symmetry	x axis	y axis
Shape		

Exercise 5.4

A

1. State an equation of the parabola in each of the following.

    (*a*) vertex $(0, 0)$ and focus $(5, 0)$

    (*b*) vertex $(0, 0)$ and directrix $x = -3$

    (*c*) focus $(4, 0)$ and directrix $x + 4 = 0$

2. Given $y^2 = 4x$, $y^2 = 12x$, $y^2 = -10x$.
   For each parabola state the following.

    (*a*) the coordinates of the focus

    (*b*) an equation of the directrix

    (*c*) the coordinates of the point on the parabola with y coordinate 6

B

3. (*a*) Find an equation of the image of the parabola $y^2 = 8x$ under reflection in the line $y = x$.

    (*b*) Sketch the parabola and its image.

    (*c*) Find the coordinates of the focus of the given parabola and its image.

4. Describe the transformation that maps $y^2 = 4x$ into a parabola in each of the following positions.

    (*a*)   (*b*)   (*c*)

5. Find an equation for each image in Question 4. Sketch and mark the focus for each.

6. Each of the following parabolas is congruent to the parabola $y^2 = 10x$. Give an equation for each.

(a)   (b)   (c)   (d)

7. Write an equation of a parabola satisfying the following data.
   (a) directrix $y = 4$, focus $(0, -4)$
   (b) vertex $(0, 0)$, axis of symmetry along a coordinate axis, one point of the curve is $(10, -10)$. (2 answers)
   (c) vertex $(0, 0)$ directrix $y = -6$

8. Find the focus and directrix of the parabola whose defining equation is given in each of the following.

   (a) $y^2 = 12x$ (d) $2y^2 + 7x = 0$
   (b) $x^2 = -8y$ (e) $5y^2 - 3x - 0$
   (c) $3x^2 = 2y$ (f) $3x^2 - 17y = 0$

9. Find an equation of the image of the parabola $y^2 = 8x$ under each of the following stretches.
   (a) $(x, y) \rightarrow (2x, y)$
   (b) $(x, y) \rightarrow \left(x, \dfrac{y}{2} \right)$
   (c) $(x, y) \rightarrow \left(2x, \dfrac{y}{3} \right)$

10. (a) Find an equation of the image of the parabola $y = x^2$ under the stretch $(x, y) \rightarrow (kx, y)$.
    (b) For $k > 1$ compare the image parabola to the original parabola as k increases.
    (c) How is the position of the foci of the parabolas in (b) affected as k increases?
    (d) For $0 < k < 1$, compare the image parabola with the original parabola as k decreases.
    (e) How is the position of the foci of the parabolas in (d) affected as k decreases?

11. A parabola has vertex at $(3, 5)$ and its directrix is the line $x = -1$.

   (a) Find the focus.

   (b) Use the method of Example 2 to find an equation of the parabola.

   (c) Find an equation of the image of the parabola in (b) under a translation that carries the vertex to $(0, 0)$ and the focus onto the x axis.

C 12. Show that, as the ellipse $b^2x^2 + a^2y^2 = a^2b^2$ is stretched as on page 164, so that a increases without bound, the value of b increases without bound. (Hint: Express b^2 in terms of a and c and note that $a - c$ is constant)

13. The roadway of a bridge is supported by a parabolic steel arch 18 m in height and 60 m in horizontal length.

   (a) Find an equation of the parabola.

   (b) Determine the length of a horizontal girder stretching across the arch 8 m below the vertex.

14. A cable of a suspension bridge hangs in the form of a parabola. There are two towers 420 m apart that support the cable. The lowest point of the cable is 70 m below the top of the tower.

   (a) Find an equation for the parabola using the road as the x axis.

   (b) Find the length of a vertical steel rod, which supports the roadway, 105 m from the tower.

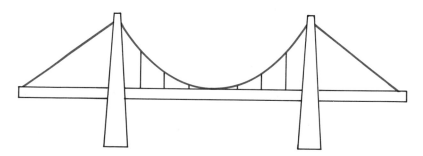

   (c) Find the length of a steel rod 50 m from the centre.

15. A ball is thrown from a height of 5 m above the ground. The ball attains its maximum height of 30 m above the ground when it has travelled a horizontal distance of 50 m. Assuming that the shape of the path of the ball is a parabola determine the height of the ball after it has gone a horizontal distance of 60 m.

16. A roadway that is 4 m wide has a cross section in the shape of a parabola. The sides of the road are 10 cm lower than the crest, which is in the middle of the road. How much lower than the crest are points on the road 1 m from the middle of the road?

17. A cement bridge over a river has an arch with a parabolic shape. The arch has a width of 30 m at water level and a width of 20 m at points 10 m above water level. Find the height of the arch above water level at its highest point.

18. The *latus rectum* of a parabola is the length of the chord of the parabola that passes through its focus and is perpendicular to its axis of symmetry. Find the *latus rectum* of the following parabolas.

    (*a*) $y^2 = 16x$ (*b*) $y^2 = 4ax$ (*c*) $x^2 = 4ay$

19. Prove that the length of the focal radius of the point (x_1, y_1) on the parabola $y^2 = 4ax$ is $\left| y_1 + a \right|$.

20. The ends of the base of a triangle are $(a, 0)$ and $(-a, 0)$. Find the locus of the opposite vertex if the ratio of the length of the base to that of the altitude is equal to the slope of the median to the base.

21. Draftsmen use an *ellipsograph* to draw an ellipse. Two pins A and B are adjustable on a rod. Pin A is allowed to slide along the x axis and pin B along the y axis. Prove that P traces out an ellipse.

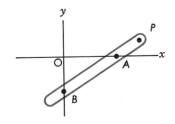

22. In Question 21, calculate the positions of pins A and B to draw an ellipse with $a = 5$ and $b = 3$.

5.4/The Parabola   169

5.5 The Hyperbola

The hyperbola, although a conic section, seems to be somewhat unrelated to both ellipse and parabola, in that it has two branches. In later sections we shall see that a hyperbola becomes a parabola in a limiting situation. The hyperbola can best be illustrated using the graph $xy = 1$.

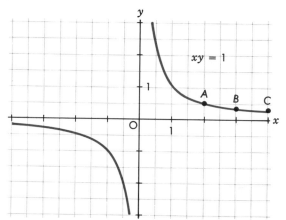

Notice the following characteristics.

1. A hyperbola consists of two *branches* and the branches extend to infinity.

2. Each branch "sweeps" towards both axes. Consider, for example, the coordinates of A, B and C which are $(2, \frac{1}{2})$, $(3, \frac{1}{3})$, $(4, \frac{1}{4})$. The y coordinate is the distance of the point to the x axis. As we continue along this branch of the curve we reach the points $\left(10, \frac{1}{10}\right), \left(100, \frac{1}{100}\right), \left(1000, \frac{1}{1000}\right), \cdots$. Notice that the distance between points (x, y) on the curve and the x axis decreases as we let x get larger. The distance is never zero but becomes smaller and smaller and gets closer and closer to zero. When a curve "sweeps" towards a line in this way, we call the line an *asymptote*. In a similar way we can show that the y axis is an asymptote.

Example 1

Find an equation of the image of the hyperbola $xy = 1$ under a rotation of $45°$ clockwise.

5.5/The Hyperbola

Solution

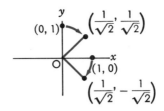

Find the images of $(1, 0)$ and $(0, 1)$ to get the rotation matrix $\begin{bmatrix} \dfrac{1}{\sqrt{2}} & \dfrac{1}{\sqrt{2}} \\ -\dfrac{1}{\sqrt{2}} & \dfrac{1}{\sqrt{2}} \end{bmatrix}$

$$\therefore \quad (x, y) \rightarrow \begin{bmatrix} \dfrac{1}{\sqrt{2}} & \dfrac{1}{\sqrt{2}} \\ -\dfrac{1}{\sqrt{2}} & \dfrac{1}{\sqrt{2}} \end{bmatrix} \begin{bmatrix} x \\ y \end{bmatrix} = \left(\dfrac{x}{\sqrt{2}} + \dfrac{y}{\sqrt{2}}, -\dfrac{x}{\sqrt{2}} + \dfrac{y}{\sqrt{2}} \right)$$

$$\therefore \quad \left.\begin{aligned} u &= \frac{x}{\sqrt{2}} + \frac{y}{\sqrt{2}} \\ v &= -\frac{x}{\sqrt{2}} + \frac{y}{\sqrt{2}} \end{aligned}\right\} \Rightarrow \left\{\begin{aligned} x &= \frac{u\sqrt{2} - v\sqrt{2}}{2} \\ y &= \frac{u\sqrt{2} + v\sqrt{2}}{2} \end{aligned}\right.$$

Substituting in $xy = 1$

we get $\quad \dfrac{2u^2 - 2v^2}{4} = 1$

or $\qquad u^2 - v^2 = 2$

This equation can be rewritten as $x^2 - y^2 = 2$ to give the required equation.

The asymptotes of the original hyperbola are the x and y axes. Under the rotation, the images of the lines $y = 0$ and $x = 0$ are the lines $y = x$ and $y = -x$. Thus the lines $y = x$ and $y = -x$ are asymptotes of the image hyperbola.

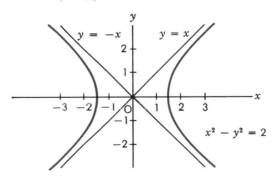

Thus, $x^2 - y^2 = 2$ is a hyperbola with asymptotes $y = x$ and $y = -x$. Notice that if the asymptotes are rewritten as $x - y = 0$ and $x + y = 0$ their equations correspond to the factors of $x^2 - y^2$.

To obtain a more general hyperbola we apply a two-way stretch to our hyperbola.

Example 2

Find an equation of the image of $x^2 - y^2 = 2$ under the two-way stretch $(x, y) \rightarrow \left(\dfrac{a}{\sqrt{2}} x, \dfrac{b}{\sqrt{2}} y \right)$.

Solution

Let $(x, y) \rightarrow (u, v)$.

$$\therefore \quad \left. \begin{array}{l} u = \dfrac{a}{\sqrt{2}} x \\[3mm] v = \dfrac{b}{\sqrt{2}} y \end{array} \right\} \Rightarrow \left\{ \begin{array}{l} x = \dfrac{u\sqrt{2}}{a} \\[3mm] y = \dfrac{v\sqrt{2}}{b} \end{array} \right.$$

Substituting in $\qquad x^2 - y^2 = 2$

we get $\qquad \dfrac{2u^2}{a^2} - \dfrac{2v^2}{b^2} = 2$

or $\qquad \dfrac{u^2}{a^2} - \dfrac{v^2}{b^2} = 1$

which may be rewritten as $\dfrac{x^2}{a^2} - \dfrac{y^2}{b^2} = 1$.

Under the transformation the asymptotes $x + y = 0$ and $x - y = 0$ become $\dfrac{x}{a} + \dfrac{y}{b} = 0$ and $\dfrac{x}{a} - \dfrac{y}{b} = 0$.

Notice again the relationship between the asymptote equations and the factors of $\dfrac{x^2}{a^2} - \dfrac{y^2}{b^2}$.

Example 3

Find an equation of the locus of points the difference of whose distances from $F_1(5, 0)$ and $F_2(-5, 0)$ is 6.

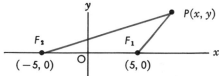

172

Solution

Let $P(x, y)$ be any point on the locus.

Then either $PF_2 - PF_1 = 6$

or $PF_2 - PF_1 = -6$

∴ $\sqrt{(x + 5)^2 + y^2} - \sqrt{(x - 5)^2 + y^2} = \pm 6$

∴ $\sqrt{(x + 5)^2 + y^2} = \pm 6 + \sqrt{(x - 5)^2 + y^2}$

Squaring, $x^2 + 10x + 25 + y^2 = 36 \pm 12 \sqrt{(x - 5)^2 + y^2}$
$$+ x^2 - 10x + 25 + y^2.$$
$$20x - 36 = \pm 12 \sqrt{(x-5)^2 + y^2}$$
$$5x - 9 = \pm 3 \sqrt{(x-5)^2 + y^2}$$

Squaring, $25x^2 - 90x + 81 = 9(x^2 - 10x + 25 + y^2)$

$16x^2 - 9y^2 = 144$ is the required equation.

The equation for Example 3 can be rewritten as $\dfrac{x^2}{9} - \dfrac{y^2}{16} = 1$, which is an equation of the hyperbola with asymptotes $\dfrac{x}{3} - \dfrac{y}{4} = 0$ and $\dfrac{x}{3} + \dfrac{y}{4} = 0$.

Example 4

Graph the relation $H = \{(x, y) \in R \times R \mid 16x^2 - 9y^2 = 144\}$

Solution

1. For the x-intercepts let $y = 0$
$$16x^2 = 144$$
$$x = 3 \text{ and } -3$$

   For the y-intercepts let $x = 0$
$$-9y^2 = 144$$
$$y^2 = -16$$
   There are no real values that satisfy the equation.
   ∴ there are no y-intercepts.

2. The graph is symmetric about the x and y axes.

3. $$\because 16x^2 - 9y^2 = 144$$

$$y^2 = \frac{16x^2 - 144}{9}$$
$\because y \subset R, 16x^2 - 144 \geq 0$
∴ $x^2 \geq 9$
∴ $x \geq 3$ or $x \leq -3$

$$x^2 = \frac{9y^2 + 144}{16}$$
$\because x \in R, 9y^2 + 144 \geq 0$
which is true of all real values of y.

∴ the domain of $H = \{x \in R \mid x \geq 3 \text{ or } x \leq -3\}$ and the range of H is R.

4. The asymptotes are $16x^2 - 9y^2 = 0$
   or $4x - 3y = 0$ and $4x + 3y = 0.$

5. Select a point on the curve.

   If $x = 5 \qquad y = \dfrac{16}{3}$ or $-\dfrac{16}{3}$

   $x = -5 \quad y = \dfrac{16}{3}$ or $-\dfrac{16}{3}$

   $\therefore \quad \left(5, \dfrac{16}{3}\right), \left(5, -\dfrac{16}{3}\right), \left(-5, \dfrac{16}{3}\right) \left(-5, -\dfrac{16}{3}\right)$ are points on the curve.

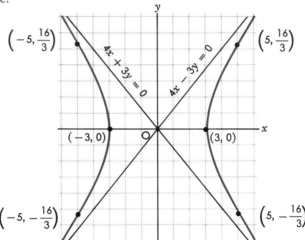

Exercise 5.5

A 1. Name the intercepts of each of the following hyperbolas.
   (a) $\{(x, y) \mid 4x^2 - 9y^2 = 36\}$
   (b) $\{(x, y) \mid x^2 - 4y^2 = -16\}$
   (c) $\{(x, y) \mid 16x^2 - 25y^2 = 400\}$

B 2. Graph each of the following hyperbolas. Determine the intercepts, symmetry, the domain and range of the relations. Find the asymptotes where they exist.
   (a) $A = \{(x, y) \mid x^2 - y^2 = 4\}$
   (b) $B = \{(x, y) \mid 16x^2 - y^2 = 64\}$
   (c) $C = \{(x, y) \mid 4x^2 - 9y^2 = -36\}$
   (d) $D = \{(x, y) \mid x^2 - y^2 = -1\}$
   (e) $E = \{(x, y) \mid 4x^2 - 9y^2 = 0\}$

3. Given $16x^2 + ky^2 = 16$. Discuss the nature of the x-intercepts, y-intercepts, domain, range, and type of conic for each of the following cases.

   (a) $k > 0$ (b) $k = 0$ (c) $k < 0$ (d) $|k|$ large

4. Given $16x^2 - y^2 = k$. Discuss the nature of the x-intercepts, y-intercepts, domain, range and type of conic for each of the following cases.

   (a) $k > 0$ (b) $k = 0$ (c) $k < 0$ (d) $|k|$ large

5. (a) Find an equation of the locus of points the difference of whose distances from $(13, 0)$ and $(-13, 0)$ is 10.
   (b) Graph the curve.

6. (a) Find an equation of the locus of points the difference of whose distances from $(0, 5)$ and $(0, -5)$ is 8.
   (b) Graph the curve.

5.6 Focus-Directrix-Eccentricity Definitions of the Conics

In this section we shall give a definition using focus and directrix, as in the case of the parabola, for all conics. This definition emerged in the course of five centuries of study by Greek geometers. The first person to state this definition explicitly was Pappus of Alexandria who ranks after Archimedes, Apollonius, and Euclid as one of the four greatest geometers of antiquity.

Associated with any conic is a special line, which the Greeks called the *directrix* and a special point called the *focus* (Figure 5.2).

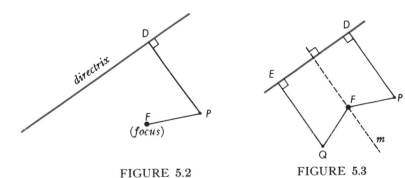

FIGURE 5.2   FIGURE 5.3

Pappus required that PF be a constant multiple of PD. The constant is called the *eccentricity* and we shall denote it by e, where $e > 0$. We are thus led to consider the set

$$C = \{P \mid PF = e \cdot PD, e > 0\}.$$

That is, the set of points, P, such that the ratio $PF : PD$ is a constant equal to e, the eccentricity of the conic.

In Section 5.4 we showed that the locus of points equidistant from a point and a line is a parabola. Thus, a parabola is conic for which $e = 1$. For example, in the diagram $PF = PD$. The locus is the parabola $y^2 = 12x$, where $p = 3$.

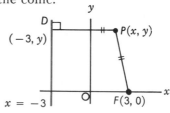

Notice that $(0, 0)$ is on the parabola and is the point of the parabola nearest to the directrix. Recall that the point $(0, 0)$ is called the *vertex* of the parabola.

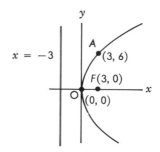

We shall now consider an example of a conic whose eccentricity is less than one.

Example 1

Find the defining equation of the conic with directrix $x = -12$, focus $(-3, 0)$ and with eccentricity $\frac{1}{2}$.

Solution

Let $P(x, y)$ be any point on the required conic.

$\therefore$ $\quad\quad\quad PF = \frac{1}{2} PD$

$\therefore$ $\quad\quad\quad 4(PF)^2 = (PD)^2$

$\because$ $\quad$ the coordinates of D are $(-12, y)$

$\therefore$ $\quad\quad 4[(x + 3)^2 + y^2] = (x + 12)^2$

$\therefore$ $\quad\quad\quad 3x^2 + 4y^2 = 108$

Thus, the defining equation of the conic is

$\quad\quad\quad 3x^2 + 4y^2 = 108.$

The conic in Example 1 is an ellipse.

(1) The x-intercepts are 6 and -6. Thus $a = 6$.

   The y-intercepts are $3\sqrt{3}$ and $-3\sqrt{3}$. Thus, $b = 3\sqrt{3}$.

(2) The graph is symmetric about the x and y axes.

The graph is also symmetric about the origin. Hence, the origin bisects every chord that passes through it, and is therefore called the *centre of the curve*. The curve is called a *central conic* with *centre at the origin*.

(3) The domain of C is $\{x \mid -6 \leq x \leq 6\}$.

   The range of C is $\{y \mid -3\sqrt{3} \leq y \leq 3\sqrt{3}\}$.

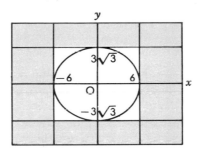

This example illustrates that a conic with eccentricity $e < 1$ is an ellipse.

Example 2

Given a conic with focus $(9, 0)$, directrix $x = 0$ and eccentricity $e = 2$.

(a) Find an equation of the conic.

(b) Show that the conic intersects the x axis in two points that lie on opposite sides of the directrix.

(c) Show that the conic has no points in common with the directrix.

(d) Explain why the conic can not be a parabola or ellipse.

Solution

(a) Let $P(x, y)$ be any point on the conic.

$\therefore \qquad PF = 2PD$

$\therefore \qquad (PF)^2 = 4(PD)^2$

$\therefore \qquad (x - 9)^2 + y^2 = 4x^2$

$\therefore \qquad x^2 - 18x + 81 + y^2 = 4x^2$

$\therefore \qquad 3x^2 - y^2 + 18x - 81 = 0$

is an equation of the conic.

(*b*) To obtain the *x*-intercepts, set $y = 0$

$$\therefore \quad 3x^2 + 18x - 81 = 0$$
$$x^2 + 6x - 27 = 0$$
$$(x + 9)(x - 3) = 0$$
$$\therefore \quad\quad\quad x = -9 \text{ or } x = 3$$

$\therefore$ the conic intersects the *x* axis at $A(3, 0)$ and $B(-9, 0)$. *A* and *B* lie on opposite sides of the *y* axis which is the directrix of the conic. *A* and *B* are called vertices of the conic.

(*c*) Since the directrix has equation $x = 0$, we can find the common points to directrix and conic by setting $x = 0$ in the equation of the conic.

$$\therefore \quad 0 - y^2 + 0 - 81 = 0$$
$$\therefore \quad\quad\quad\quad y^2 = -81$$

Since the roots of this equation are non-real, we conclude that the directrix and conic do not have points in common.

(*d*) A parabola has only one intersection with its axis of symmetry. Since the given conic has two points of intersection with its axis we can conclude that this conic is not a parabola.

Since an ellipse is closed, bounded, and connected, any line, perpendicular to its axis between the vertices, intersects the ellipse in two points. This given conic has no points in common with the directrix which lies between the vertices. Thus, the given conic is not an ellipse.

To determine the type of conic we have in Example 2 we might consider translating the curve so that the origin bisects the distance between the vertices $A(3, 0)$ and $B(-9, 0)$. The midpoint is $(-3, 0)$.

Thus, translate using $(x, y) \rightarrow (x + 3, y)$ and find an equation of the image of the conic $3x^2 - y^2 + 18x - 81 = 0$.

Let $(x + 3, y) = (u, v)$

$\therefore \quad x = u - 3, y = v.$

Substitute in the conic equation

$$3(u - 3)^2 - v^2 + 18(u - 3) - 81 = 0$$
$$\text{or} \quad\quad\quad\quad 3u^2 - v^2 - 108 = 0$$

which may be rewritten as $3x^2 - y^2 = 108$.

This is an equation of a hyperbola.

Let us now consider how the value of *e* affects the conic. For example, consider a conic with *y* axis at the directrix and $(f, 0)$ as the focus and with eccentricity *e*. How do the *x*-intercepts of the conic depend on *e*?

Let $P(x, 0)$ be a point in the conic.

$$\therefore \qquad PF = e \cdot PD, \qquad e > 0, \quad PD > 0$$

$$\therefore \qquad |f - x| = e|x|$$

$$\therefore \qquad f - x = ex \text{ or } f - x = -ex$$

$$\therefore \qquad x = \frac{f}{1 + e} \text{ or } x = \frac{f}{1 - e}$$

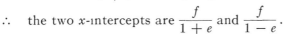

$\therefore$ the two x-intercepts are $\dfrac{f}{1 + e}$ and $\dfrac{f}{1 - e}$.

If $0 < e < 1$, the two intercepts are positive.

If $e = 1$, there is only one x-intercept.

If $e > 1$, one intercept is positive and the other negative.

We summarize this section by giving a definition of a conic.

Given a line l, called the *directrix*, a point $F \notin l$, called the focus, and a real number $e > 0$, called the eccentricity. A conic C is defined by

$$C = \{P \mid PF = e \cdot PD\}$$

where PD is the perpendicular distance from P to l.

The conic C is $\begin{cases} \text{a parabola if } e = 1 \\ \text{an ellipse if } e < 1 \\ \text{a hyperbola if } e > 1 \end{cases}$

Exercise 5.6

B

1. Find an equation of the conic with directrix $x = 2$, focus $(-2, 0)$, and eccentricity 1. Graph the conic.

2. (a) Find a defining equation of the conic with eccentricity $\frac{4}{5}$, focus at $(4, 0)$, and directrix $x = \frac{25}{4}$. Sketch the graph of the conic.

   (b) Find a defining equation of the conic with eccentricity $\frac{4}{5}$, focus at $(-4, 0)$, and directrix $x = -\frac{25}{4}$. Sketch the graph of the conic.

   (c) Give the two foci and two directrices of the ellipse defined by
   $$9x^2 + 25y^2 = 225.$$

3. (a) Find a defining equation of the conic whose focus is $(9, 0)$, directrix $x = 4$ and eccentricity $e = \frac{3}{2}$. Sketch the graph of the conic.

   (b) Find a defining equation of the conic whose focus is $(-9, 0)$, directrix $x = -4$ and eccentricity $e = \frac{3}{2}$. Sketch the graph of the conic.

(c) What are the two foci and two directrices of the hyperbola $5x^2 - 4y^2 = 180$?

4. Find a defining equation of a conic with eccentricity $\frac{1}{2}$, focus at $(6, 0)$ and directrix the y axis.

5. Find a defining equation of a conic with eccentricity $\frac{3}{2}$, focus at $(5, -2)$ and directrix the y axis.

6. Find the x-intercepts of the conic with focus $(12, 0)$, directrix the y axis, and eccentricity 3.

7. Given a conic with directrix $x = 0$ and focus $(6, 0)$.

    (a) If the eccentricity is 1, prove that there is only one point of intersection of the conic and the x axis.

    (b) If the eccentricity is $\frac{1}{2}$, prove that there are two points of intersection of the conic and the x axis.

    (c) If the eccentricity is $\frac{3}{2}$, prove that there are two points of intersection of the conic and the x axis. Does this conic intersect the y axis?

8. (a) Find a defining equation of a conic with eccentricity $\frac{3}{5}$, focus at $(0, -8)$ and directrix the x axis.

    (b) Find the y-intercepts of the conics.

    (c) Find the length of the major axis.

    (d) Find the centre of the conic.

    (e) Find the length of the minor axis.

    (f) Sketch the graph of the conic.

9. (a) Find a defining equation of a conic with focus at $(10, 0)$, eccentricity $\frac{2}{3}$ and directrix the y axis.

    (b) Find the x-intercepts of the conic.

    (c) Find a translation that moves the mid-point between the x-intercepts to the origin.

    (d) Find an equation of the image of the conic under the translation in (c).

    (e) Name the image curve and sketch it.

    (f) Sketch the conic given in (a).

C 10. (a) Find an equation of the conic with focus at $(f, 0)$, eccentricity e and directrix the y axis.

    (b) Show that the x-intercepts of the conic are

$$\frac{f}{1 - e}, \frac{f}{1 + e}$$

    (c) If $f = 10$ and $e = 2$, name the conic and sketch its graph.

(d) Complete the following table.

	Intercepts	
e	$\dfrac{f}{1+e}$	$\dfrac{f}{1-e}$
$1\frac{1}{2}$		
$1\frac{1}{4}$		
$1\frac{1}{10}$		
$1\frac{1}{100}$		
$1\frac{1}{1000}$		

(e) Describe what happens to the vertices of the hyperbola if $e > 1$ and e takes on values closer and closer to 1.

(f) What does the equation in (a) become if $e = 1$? Name the conic.

(g) Suggest how a parabola may be obtained from a hyperbola by "stretching the imagination."

11. (a) Repeat Question 10 for an ellipse. That is, for $e < 1$, let e take on values closer and closer to 1.

(b) Discuss the characteristics of the conic as e gets larger and larger, starting at 0.

5.7 The Ellipse and Hyperbola

By means of analytic geometry let us study the set, C, defined by Pappus in the case $e < 1$ or $e > 1$. We again take the axis of the conic as the x axis. This is accomplished by taking the focus on the x axis and directrix parallel to the y axis. We shall choose the position of the origin so that the origin is the midpoint of the segment joining the vertices. If the origin lies to the left of both focus $(c, 0)$ and directrix, $x = d$, then $c > 0$ and $d > 0$. Since the focus cannot lie on the directrix, $c \neq d$.

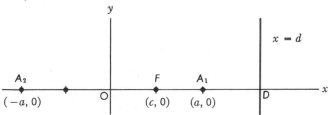

For an ellipse or hyperbola, the conic has two vertices. Let the vertices be placed at $A_1(a, 0)$ and $A_2(-a, 0)$, where $a > 0$.

$$\therefore \qquad FA_1 = a - c \quad \text{and} \quad FA_2 = a + c$$
$$A_1D = d - a \qquad\qquad A_2D = d + a$$
$$\text{But} \qquad FA_1 = eA_1D \quad \text{and} \quad FA_2 = eA_2D$$
$$\therefore \quad a - c = e(d - a) \quad \text{and} \quad a + c = e(d + a)$$

adding

$$2a = 2ed$$

$$\therefore \ a = ed \quad \text{or} \quad d = \frac{a}{e}$$

Substitute $d = \dfrac{a}{e}$ in $a - c \ = \ e(d - a)$

We get $a - c = a - ae$

$$\therefore \qquad c = ae$$

For both ellipse and hyperbola with centre $(0, 0)$, $e \neq 1$ and

$$d = \frac{a}{e} \quad \text{and} \quad c = ae$$

Example 1

Find an equation of the conic with eccentricity e, focus at $(ae, 0)$ and directrix $x = \dfrac{a}{e}$.

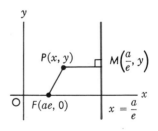

Solution

If $P(x, y)$ is any point on the conic then $PF = ePM$.
$(PF)^2 = e^2(PM)^2$

$$(x - ae)^2 + y^2 = e^2\left(\left(x - \frac{a}{e}\right)^2 + 0^2\right)$$
$$x^2 - 2aex + a^2e^2 + y^2 = a^2 - 2aex + e^2x^2$$
$$x^2(1 - e^2) + y^2 = a^2(1 - e^2)$$

Thus $\dfrac{x^2}{a^2} + \dfrac{y^2}{a^2(1 - e^2)} = 1$ is an equation of the conic.

The conic in Example 1 is symmetric about the x and y axes.
The x-intercepts are a and $-a$.
The y-intercepts are $a\sqrt{1 - e^2}$ and $-a\sqrt{1 - e^2}$

182

For an ellipse $e < 1$, and the ellipse has real x- and y-intercepts.

For a hyperbola, $e > 1$, and the hyperbola has real x-intercepts only.

Notice that for $e = 0$, the equation of the conic becomes

$$x^2 + y^2 - a^2 = 0$$

which is the defining equation of a circle.

Ellipse

For the ellipse, $e < 1$ and $a^2(1 - e^2) > 0$.

Let $\qquad\qquad a^2(1 - e^2) = b^2$ where $b > 0$.

The equation of the ellipse becomes

$$\frac{x^2}{a^2} + \frac{y^2}{b^2} = 1$$

Here a and $-a$ are the x-intercepts, and b and $-b$ are the y-intercepts, also $c = ae$ and

$$b^2 = a^2(1 - e^2)$$
$$b^2 = a^2 - a^2e^2$$
$$b^2 = a^2 - c^2$$
$$\therefore \quad a^2 = b^2 + c^2$$

Standard Form of Ellipse Equation

$$\frac{x^2}{a^2} + \frac{y^2}{b^2} = 1$$

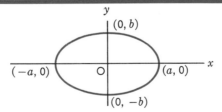

The points $(a, 0)$ and $(-a, 0)$ are the *vertices* of the ellipse.

The segment from $(0, 0)$ to $(a, 0)$ is called the *semi-major axis* and has length a. The segment from $(0, 0)$ to $(0, b)$ is called the *semi-minor axis* and has length b.

Since $a^2 = b^2 + c^2$, we may conclude $c < a$. Thus, the focus, $(c, 0)$, of the ellipse lies in the major axis of the ellipse. Since $c = e^2 d$, we conclude that $c < d$ and the foci of an ellipse lie between the directrices.

Hyperbola

We shall now consider the hyperbola and its equation

$$\frac{x^2}{a^2} + \frac{y^2}{a^2(1 - e^2)} = 1 \qquad \text{where } e > 1$$

$$\because \qquad e > 1$$

$$\therefore \quad a^2(1 - e^2) < 0.$$

Let $\qquad a^2(1 - e^2) = -b^2 \qquad \text{where } b > 0.$

The equation of the hyperbola becomes

$$\frac{x^2}{a^2} - \frac{y^2}{b^2} = 1.$$

Since $c = ae$ and $-b^2 = a^2(1 - e^2)$

$$-b^2 = a^2 - c^2$$

$$\therefore \qquad c^2 = a^2 + b^2$$

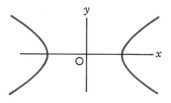

The hyperbola is symmetric about the x and y axes. The x-intercepts are a and $-a$. There are no y-intercepts. The points $(a, 0)$ and $(-a, 0)$ are called vertices of the hyperbola. The segment joining the two vertices is called the *transverse axis* and has length $2a$.

Since the y axis is an axis of symmetry, the segment joining $(0, b)$ to $(0, -b)$ is called the *conjugate axis* and has length $2b$.

Since $c = ae$, then $c > a$ and the vertices lie between the foci. Since $c = e^2d$, then $c > d$ and the foci lie outside the directrices.

Standard Form of Hyperbola Equation

$$\frac{x^2}{a^2} - \frac{y^2}{b^2} = 1$$

All the previous work could be repeated for conics with foci on the y axis. The simple transformation of reflection in the line $y = x$ makes such work unnecessary.

Recall that an equation of the image of a curve under reflection in the line $y = x$ may be obtained by interchanging the x and y in the defining equation of the curve.

Example 2

Find an equation of the image of each of the following conics under reflection in the line $y = x$.

(a) $3x^2 + 4y^2 = 48$

(b) $9x^2 - 25y^2 = 225$

(c) $\dfrac{x^2}{16} + \dfrac{y^2}{9} = 1$

(d) $\dfrac{x^2}{25} - \dfrac{y^2}{16} = 1$

5.7/The Ellipse and Hyperbola

Solution

(a) $3x^2 + 4y^2 = 48$ becomes $3y^2 + 4x^2 = 48$

or $4x^2 + 3y^2 = 48$

(b) $9x^2 - 25y^2 = 225$ becomes $9y^2 - 25x^2 = 225$

or $25x^2 - 9y^2 = -225$

(c) $\dfrac{x^2}{16} + \dfrac{y^2}{9} = 1$ becomes $\dfrac{x^2}{9} + \dfrac{y^2}{16} = 1$

(d) $\dfrac{x^2}{25} - \dfrac{y^2}{16} = 1$ becomes $\dfrac{x^2}{16} - \dfrac{y^2}{25} = -1$

Since an image and a figure are congruent under reflection, the values and relationships among a, b, c, d, e remain unchanged.

The following chart summarizes the information we now have about central ellipses and hyperbolas whose axes lie in the x and y axes.

	Ellipse		Hyperbola	
Foci on	x axis	y axis	x axis	y axis
Equation	$\dfrac{x^2}{a^2} + \dfrac{y^2}{b^2} = 1$	$\dfrac{x^2}{b^2} + \dfrac{y^2}{a^2} = 1$ $a > b$	$\dfrac{x^2}{a^2} - \dfrac{y^2}{b^2} = 1$	$\dfrac{x^2}{b^2} - \dfrac{y^2}{a^2} = -1$ a not necessarily greater than b
Foci	$(c, 0)$, $(-c, 0)$	$(0, c)$, $(0, -c)$	$(c, 0)$, $(-c, 0)$	$(0, c)$, $(0, -c)$
Axes	major $2a$ minor $2b$		transverse conjugate	
abc	$a^2 = b^2 + c^2$		$c^2 = a^2 + b^2$	
Eccentricity	$e = \dfrac{c}{a}$			
Directrices	$x = d$ $y = d$ and $x = -d$ and $y = -d$	$d = \dfrac{a}{e}$	$x = d$ $y = d$ and $x = -d$ and $y = -d$	
Focal Radii	$PF_1 + PF_2 = 2a$		$\lvert PF_1 - PF_2 \rvert = 2a$	

Example 3

(a) Graph the ellipse defined by $25x^2 + 9y^2 = 225$.
(b) Find the coordinates of the foci.
(c) Find the length of the major axis.
(d) Find e and an equation of a directrix.

Solution

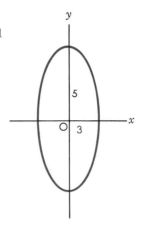

(a) $25x^2 + 9y^2 = 225$ becomes $\dfrac{x^2}{9} + \dfrac{y^2}{25} = 1$

The x-intercepts are 3, -3.
The y-intercepts are 5, -5.
∴ the major axis lies along the y axis.
∴ $a = 5, b = 3$.

(b) ∵ $a^2 = b^2 + c^2$, we get $c = 4$
∴ the foci are $(0, 4)$ and $(0, -4)$

(c) The major axis is $2a = 10$.

(d) $e = \dfrac{c}{a} = \dfrac{4}{5}$

$d = \dfrac{a}{e} = 5 \div \dfrac{4}{5} = \dfrac{25}{4}$

∴ an equation of a directrix is $y = \dfrac{25}{4}$

Exercise 5.7

A

1. State the values of a and b for the ellipse defined by each of the following.

(a) $\dfrac{x^2}{100} + \dfrac{y^2}{25} = 1$ (d) $9x^2 + y^2 = 36$

(b) $\dfrac{x^2}{36} + \dfrac{y^2}{9} = 1$ (e) $9x^2 + 4y^2 = 144$

(c) $\dfrac{x^2}{16} + \dfrac{y^2}{49} = 1$ (f) $x^2 + 2y^2 = 72$

2. State the equation of the ellipse that is a central conic with focus on an axis and semi-axes of length as given in each of the following.

Focus on x axis	Focus on y axis
(a) $a = 4, b = 3$	(c) $a = 6, b = 4$
(b) $a = 9, b = 5$	(d) $a = 5, b = 3$

3. State the values of a and b for the hyperbola defined by each of the following.

(a) $\dfrac{x^2}{64} - \dfrac{y^2}{9} = 1$ (d) $9x^2 - 4y^2 = -36$

(b) $\dfrac{x^2}{4} - \dfrac{y^2}{25} = 1$ (e) $x^2 - 9y^2 = 36$

(c) $x^2 - \dfrac{y^2}{36} = -1$ (f) $2x^2 - 3y^2 = -72$

B   4.   For the ellipse defined by $x^2 + 4y^2 = 16$ determine the following.

   (a)   the lengths of the semi-axes
   (b)   the coordinates of the vertices
   (c)   the coordinates of the foci
   (d)   the eccentricity
   (e)   equations of the directrices
   (f)   sketch the graph of the ellipse

5.   Repeat Question 4 for the ellipse defined by each of the following equations.

   (a) $9x^2 + 16y^2 = 144$
   (b) $3x^2 + 4y^2 = 12$
   (c) $16x^2 + 4y^2 = 64$
   (d) $4x^2 + 3y^2 = 12$

6.   For the hyperbola defined by $9x^2 - 4y^2 = 144$ determine the following.

   (a)   the lengths of the semi-transverse and semi-conjugate axes
   (b)   the coordinates of the vertices
   (c)   the coordinates of the foci
   (d)   the eccentricity
   (e)   equations of the directrices
   (f)   sketch the graph

7.   Repeat Question 6 for the hyperbola defined by each of the following.

   (a) $9x^2 - 16y^2 = 144$ (c) $x^2 - y^2 = -25$
   (b) $x^2 - 2y^2 = 36$ (d) $x^2 - 2y^2 = -36$

8.   What is the eccentricity of the ellipse whose major axis is twice as long as its minor axis?

9.   Find a defining equation of the ellipse with centre at the origin in each of the following.

   (a)   one vertex $(8, 0)$, minor axis 8
   (b)   major axis 12, one focus $(0, 3)$
   (c)   minor axis 10, one focus $(5, 0)$
   (d)   focus at $(4, 0)$, $e = \frac{1}{2}$
   (e)   one vertex at $(0, 6)$, $e = \frac{2}{3}$

10.   Find an equation of the ellipse whose eccentricity is $\frac{1}{2}$ and whose directrices are $x = 4$ and $x = -4$.

5.7/The Ellipse and Hyperbola   187

11. Find a defining equation of the hyperbola with centre at the origin and transverse axis along the x axis, given each of the following.

(a) $a = 3, b = 5$
(b) $a = 4, c = 5$
(c) $b = 6, c = 9$
(d) $a = 5, e = \sqrt{2}$

(e) $c = 8, e = \frac{4}{3}$
(f) $b = 4, e = \frac{4}{3}$
(g) $c = 6, e = \frac{3}{2}$
(h) $a = 6, b = 2$

12. Find a defining equation of the hyperbola satisfying each of the following conditions.

(a) vertices at $(6, 0)$ and $(-6, 0)$, $e = \frac{3}{2}$
(b) y-intercepts 4 and -4, foci at $(0, 5)$, $(0, -5)$
(c) foci at $(8, 0)$ and $(-8, 0)$, $e = 2$
(d) centre at $(0, 0)$, focus at $(0, 5)$, $e = \frac{5}{3}$

13. Find a defining equation of the set of points each of which is twice as far from $(0, 12)$ as from the line $y = 3$.

14. Find an equation of the ellipse whose foci are the points $(-3, 0)$, $(3, 0)$ and whose major axis is twice the minor axis.

15. The foci of an ellipse subtend a right angle at either extremity of the minor axis. Find the eccentricity.

16. The ellipse $\dfrac{x^2}{a^2} + \dfrac{y^2}{b^2} = 1$ and its

directrices are shown in the diagram.

(a) State equations of the directrices.
(b) Express PF_1 in terms of e and PD_1.
(c) Express PF_2 in terms of e and PD_2.
(d) Find $PF_1 + PF_2$ and show that the sum is $2a$.
(e) Express PD_1 and PD_2 in terms of $\dfrac{a}{e}$ and the x coordinate of P.
(f) Show that $PF_1 = a - ex$ and $PF_2 = a + ex$.

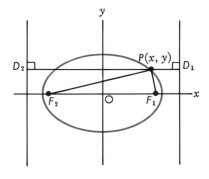

17. An eavestrough has the cross section of a semi-ellipse with a width at the top 24 cm and depth 20 cm. The ends of the trough are blocked off and water flows into the trough until it reaches the focus of the semi-ellipse. Find the depth of the water and the width of the trough at water level.

18. The arch of a bridge over a river is in the form of a semi-ellipse above the water level. The span of the bridge at water level is 40 m. The arch clearance at mid-span is 10 m.

    (a) Find an equation of the semi-ellipse using the water level as x axis and its axis of symmetry as y axis.

    (b) Determine the clearance under the bridge at a point 10 m from the axis of symmetry of the semi-ellipse.

C 19. Find an equation of the ellipse that passes through the point $(2, 1)$ and whose vertices are the points $(-3, 0)$, $(3, 0)$.

20. Find an equation of the ellipse with centre at the origin and foci on the y axis, if it passes through $(3, 4)$ and has eccentricity $\frac{3}{4}$.

21. Find an equation of the ellipse, having foci on the x axis, that passes through the points $(-2, 2)$ and $(-3, 1)$ and whose centre is at the origin.

22. Find a defining equation of the hyperbola with centre at the origin and transverse axis along the x axis, passing through the given points.

    (a) $(4, 0)$ and $(8, -6)$ (b) $(6, 6)$ and $(-4, 1)$

23. Show that the hyperbola $9x^2 - 16y^2 = 144$ and the ellipse $3x^2 + 4y^2 = 300$ are confocal (have the same focus).

24. Prove that the hyperbola with eccentricity 2 has vertices that bisect the segment from the centre to the focus.

25. Given the ellipse $b^2x^2 + a^2y^2 = a^2b^2$.

    (a) Find the relationship between a and b if $c = 0$.
    (b) Determine the corresponding equation of the ellipse.
    (c) Find the coordinates of the foci.
    (d) Draw a conclusion.

Note on the sections of a cone

Suppose the plane M cuts only one *nappe* of the cone C as in Figure 5.4. Consider two spheres inscribed in the cone that are tangent to the plane M. Each sphere intersects the cone in a circle lying in a plane perpendicular to the axis of the cone. Let the points of tangency of the spheres with M be F_1 and F_2.

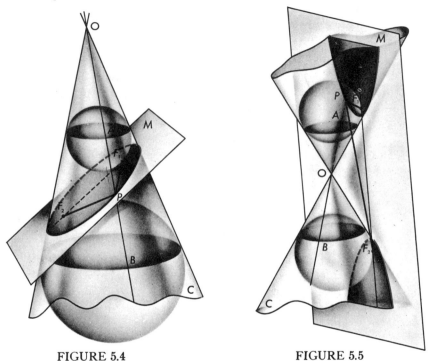

FIGURE 5.4   FIGURE 5.5

Let P be any point on the curve of intersection of the cone and the plane M. Join OP. Thus, $OAPB$ is a generator as in Figure 5.4. Join P, F_1 and P, F_2.

∵ all tangents from an external point to a sphere are equal in length,

∴ $PF_1 = PA$ and $PF_2 = PB$

∴ $PF_1 + PF_2 = PA + PB = AB$

Since AB is the length of the segment intercepted by the circle through A on the cone and the circle through B. Thus, AB is a constant, say $2a$.

∴ $PF_1 + PF_2 = 2a$

for all P on the curve of intersection of the plane M and the cone. Thus $\{P \mid P \in M \cap C\}$ is an ellipse.

190   *5.7/The Ellipse and Hyperbola*

In Figure 5.5 a plane M cuts both nappes of the cone. Two spheres are tangent to the plane M at F_1 and F_2. Take any point P on the intersection of the plane M and the cone.

∵ PA, PB, PF_1, and PF_2 are tangents to a sphere

$$PF_1 = PA \quad \text{and} \quad PF_2 = PB$$
$$PF_2 - PF_1 = PB - PA$$
$$= AB$$

but AB is a constant.

Thus $\{P \mid P \in M \cap C\}$ is a hyperbola.

If the plane is parallel to a generator of the cone we obtain Figure 5.6.

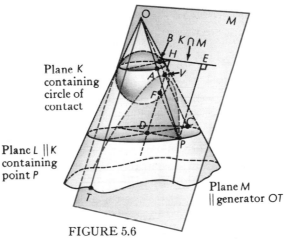

Plane K containing circle of contact

Plane L ‖ K containing point P

Plane M ‖ generator OT

FIGURE 5.6

$HEPD$ is a rectangle in the plane of section.
$HD \,\|\, OT$ and $BH \,\|\, DC$.

∵ PF and PA are tangents to a sphere

$$PF = PA$$
$$\text{but} \quad PA = BC$$
$$\therefore \quad BH \,\|\, DC$$
$$\therefore \quad \frac{BC}{HD} = \frac{BV}{VH}$$

∵ $\triangle BVH$ is isosceles
∴ $BV = VH$
∴ $BC = HD$
but $BC = PF$ and $HD = PE$
∴ $PF = PE$

This is the condition for a parabola.

Thus, the intersection of a cone with a plane parallel to a generator is a parabola.

Review Exercise 5.8

1. Find the centre and radius of each of the following circles.

   (a) $x^2 + y^2 - 10x + 12y + 2 = 0$
   (b) $x^2 + y^2 - 6x - 8y = 0$
   (c) $2x^2 + 2y^2 - 7y + 1 = 0$

2. Find an equation of the following circles.

   (a) centre at $(-2, 3)$ and radius 4
   (b) centre at $(-6, 3)$ and tangent to the x axis
   (c) centre at $(-3, 5)$ and passing through $(2, 1)$
   (b) tangent to both axes, radius 3, centre in the third quadrant

3. Each of the following equations defines a conic. Describe each conic as fully as possible.

   (a) $y^2 = 12x$ (e) $x^2 - 4y = 0$
   (b) $x^2 + y^2 = 25$ (f) $9x^2 + 4y^2 = 36$
   (c) $\dfrac{x^2}{16} + \dfrac{y^2}{9} = 1$ (g) $x^2 - y^2 = -1$
   (d) $9x^2 - 25y^2 = -225$ (h) $x^2 + 4y^2 = 0$

4. For each of the following parabolas find the coordinates of the focus and an equation of the directrix.

   (a) $y^2 = 8x$ (b) $x^2 = -20y$ (c) $3y^2 + 16x = 0$

5. State a defining equation of the parabola with focus at $(0, -5)$ and directrix $y = 5$.

6. State an equation of the ellipse whose semi-major axis is 7 and semi-minor axis is 3 and whose foci lie on the y axis.

7. State the values of a, b, c and e for the conic defined by each of the following equations.

   (a) $\dfrac{x^2}{9} + \dfrac{y^2}{6} = 1$ (c) $\dfrac{x^2}{25} - \dfrac{y^2}{64} = -1$ (e) $9x^2 + 4y^2 = 144$

   (b) $\dfrac{x^2}{4} + \dfrac{y^2}{9} = 1$ (d) $\dfrac{x^2}{16} - \dfrac{y^2}{4} = -1$ (f) $4x^2 - y^2 = 16$

8. Given the data in each of the following, find a defining equation of the ellipse with centre at the origin and foci on the y axis.

   (a) $a = 7, b = 3$
   (b) vertices at $(0, 5)$ and $(0, -5)$, minor axis 6
   (c) major axis 16 and minor axis 10
   (d) $c = 8, e = \frac{4}{5}$

9. Given the data in each of the following, find a defining equation of the hyperbola with centre at the origin and transverse axis along the y axis.

   (a) $a = 9, b = 5$
   (b) $a = 2, b = 7$
   (c) vertices at $(0, 6)$ and $(0, -6)$, conjugate axis with length 8
   (d) $b = 6, c = 9$

10. State an equation of the hyperbola whose foci are at $(5, 0)$ and $(-5, 0)$ and whose transverse axis has length 8.

11. Find the length of the segment joining the points which have x coordinates 4 and -6 and which lie on the parabola $x^2 = -8y$.

12. For the ellipse defined by $4x^2 + 3y^2 = 12$ determine each of the following.

    (a) length of the semi-axes   (d) the eccentricity
    (b) the coordinates of the foci (e) the equation of a directrix
    (c) the vertices

13. Find a defining equation of an ellipse for which $a = 8$ and the distance between the foci equals the minor axis.

14. (a) A conic has eccentricity $\frac{2}{3}$, focus at $(2, 0)$ and directrix with equation $x = 5$. Find an equation of the conic.
    (b) A conic has eccentricity 3, focus at $(-4, 0)$ and directrix with equation $x = -2$. Find an equation of the conic.

15. An arch in the form of a parabola is 40 m across the bottom and has its highest point 25 m above its base. What is the length of a beam placed horizontally in the arch 9 m below the top?

16. An arch of a bridge is in the form of a semi-ellipse. If the arch has a span of 100 m and a height of 21 m, find the following.

    (a) the position of the foci, and the eccentricity of the ellipse
    (b) an equation of the ellipse
    (c) the height at a point 25 m measured horizontally from the centre

17. M.I.T. Passer can throw a football along a parabolic arc so that it rises to a height of 20 m and travels a distance of 60 m. How far should M.I.T. stand from a flagpole 15 m in height if he wishes to hit a person sitting on top of the pole?

5.8/Review Exercise   193

18. A bridge is supported by an arch in the form of an arc of the rectangular hyperbola $x^2 - y^2 = -100$. If the width at the base of the arch is 40 m, find the height of the arch at its centre.

19. Describe the effect on the circle $x^2 + y^2 = 1$ of each of the given transformations.

    (a) $(x, y) \rightarrow (x, 2y)$ (c) $(x, y) \rightarrow (x, \frac{1}{4}y)$
    (b) $(x, y) \rightarrow (3x, y)$ (d) $(x, y) \rightarrow (\frac{1}{2}x, y)$

20. Describe the effect on the parabola $y = x^2$ of each of the given transformations.

    (a) $(x, y) \rightarrow (x, 2y)$ (b) $(x, y) \rightarrow (x, -y)$

21. Describe the effect on the straight line $y = x$ of each of the given transformations.

    (a) $(x, y) \rightarrow (x, 3y)$ (b) $(x, y) \rightarrow (5x, y)$

22. Graph each of the given curves and their images under the stretch $(x, y) \rightarrow (x, 2y)$.

    (a) $x^2 + y^2 = 4$ (d) $y^2 = 4x$
    (b) $4x^2 - y^2 = 4$ (e) $x^2 = y$
    (c) $4x^2 + 9y^2 = 36$ (f) $3x + 4y + 12 = 0$

23. Find equations of the images of each of the given curves under the stretch $(x, y) \rightarrow (-\frac{1}{3}x, y)$.

    (a) $x^2 + y^2 = 1$ (c) $x^2 - 4y = 36$
    (b) $x^2 + 9y^2 + 2x = 0$ (d) $y^2 = 12x$

24. Given the ellipse $4x^2 + y^2 = 16$, determine the stretch that transforms the given ellipse into each of the following circles.

    (a) $x^2 + y^2 = 16$ (b) $x^2 + y^2 = 4$

25. Find an equation of the images of the given curves under the transformation $(x, y) \rightarrow (3x, 5y)$. Sketch the curves and their images.

    (a) $x^2 + y^2 = 1$ (b) $9x^2 + 25y^2 = 1$

26. Find the equations of the image of the circle $x^2 + y^2 = 25$ under the following transformations.

    (a) $(x, y) \rightarrow (2x, 3y]$ (c) $(x, y) \rightarrow (4x, -3y)$
    (b) $(x, y) \rightarrow (-x, \frac{1}{2}y)$ (d) $(x, y) \rightarrow (-3x, -4y)$

27. For the transformation $(x, y) \rightarrow (ax, by)$ where $a \neq b$, a certain line segment is parallel to its image. Show the line segment is parallel to one of the coordinate axes.

28. Determine the two-way stretch that transforms each given curve into the circle $x^2 + y^2 = 1$.
    (a) $16x^2 + 36y^2 = 1$
    (b) $9x^2 + 25y^2 = 16$
    (c) $4x^2 + y^2 = 1$
    (d) $25x^2 + 4y^2 = 36$

29. What kind of conic is defined by $\dfrac{x^2}{50 - k} + \dfrac{y^2}{150 - k} = 1$ when $k = 25$? $k = 75$?

30. Determine a defining equation of an ellipse confocal with the ellipse $9x^2 + 16y^2 = 144$ and having eccentricity $\frac{1}{2}$.

31. Find a defining equation of the parabola with vertex at $(0, 0)$, foci on the y axis, and passing through the point $(3, 4)$.

32. Prove that for an ellipse each of the following is true.
    (a) $\dfrac{b}{a} = \sqrt{1 - e^2}$
    (b) $c = \dfrac{bc}{\sqrt{1 - e^2}}$

33. Find a defining equation of the hyperbola with foci at $(3, 0)$ and $(-3, 0)$ for which $a = b$.

34. Find a defining equation of $\{ P \mid PF_1 - PF_2 - 24 \}$ where F_1 is at $(0, 13)$ and F_2 is at $(0, -13)$.

35. Find a defining equation of $\{P \mid PF_1 + PF_2 - 8\}$ where F_1 is at $(0, 3)$ and F_2 is at $(0, -3)$.

36. Find a defining equation of the set of points where the product of the slopes of the lines from each point to the points $(6, 0)$ and $(-6, 0)$ is 4.

37. Prove that the conics defined by $x^2 + 3y^2 = 24$ and $3x^2 - y^2 = 12$ are confocal.

38. The earth moves around the sun in an elliptic orbit with the sun at one focus. The shortest distance and longest distance from earth to sun are in the ratio $29 : 30$. Find the eccentricity of the orbit.

39. In the Loran navigation system, two transmitters are 200 km apart. The difference in time taken to reach a ship by corresponding pulses sent out by the transmitters determines that the ship is 60 km further from one transmitter than the other. Find an equation of a hyperbola on which the ship is located using the positions of the transmitter as foci.

6 / Properties of Conics

The conics have many applications in engineering and science. Some of these applications are revealed through a study of intersection of lines with conics and of conics with conics.

We shall show that tangents to a conic can be found in the same way as tangents to a circle. Of special interest are the asymptotes to a hyperbola which can be regarded as special kinds of tangents. We shall also illustrate, through the use of mirror lines, how a set of tangent lines can *envelope* a curve.

6.1 Lines and Conics

You have had considerable practice in determining the intersection points of pairs of lines. We shall use similar methods to find the points of intersection of lines and conics.

Example 1

If $M = \{(x, y) \,|\, y^2 = 4x\}$ and $N = \{(x, y) \,|\, 2x + y - 4 = 0\}$ find $M \cap N$.

Solution

Consider the defining equations. The intersection point (x, y) satisfies

$$\text{(1)} \qquad y^2 = 4x$$

and (2) $\qquad 2x + y - 4 = 0$

From (2) $\qquad x = \dfrac{4 - y}{2}$

Substitute in (1) $\qquad y^2 = 4\left(\dfrac{4 - y}{2}\right)$

$$\therefore \qquad y^2 + 2y - 8 = 0$$
$$\therefore \qquad (y + 4)(y - 2) = 0$$
$$\therefore \qquad y = -4 \text{ or } y = 2$$
$$\because \qquad x = \dfrac{4 - y}{2}$$

When $\qquad y = -4,\ x = 4$

When $\qquad y = 2,\ x = 1$

$\therefore \qquad M \cap N = \{(1, 2), (4, -4)\}.$

196

Example 1 illustrates the use of the method of *solving a system of equations*.

We know that each equation in Example 1 defines an infinite set of points. Finding the intersection of the two sets corresponds to finding an ordered pair (x, y) that satisfies both equations *simultaneously*. The two given equations (1) $y^2 = 4x$ and (2) $2x+y-4=0$ are often called a pair of *simultaneous equations*.

It may happen that there is no common point, one, several, or an infinite number.

Example 2

Solve the system of equations,

$$(1)\ x^2 + 4y^2 = 20$$
$$(2)\ \ x + 4y = 10$$

Solution

If (x, y) is a solution then (x, y) satisfies both equations.

From (2) $\qquad\qquad\qquad\qquad\qquad x = 10 - 4y$

substitute in (1) $\quad\therefore\qquad\qquad (10 - 4y)^2 + 4y^2 = 20$

$$100 - 80y + 16y^2 + 4y^2 = 20$$
$$y^2 - 4y + 4 = 0$$
$$(y - 2)(y - 2) = 0$$
$$\therefore\qquad\qquad y = 2 \text{ or } y = 2$$
$$\because\qquad\qquad x = 10 - 4y$$
$$\therefore\qquad\qquad (y = 2) \Rightarrow (x = 2)$$

There is only *one* solution, $\{2, 2)\}$.

The result of Example 2 is illustrated in Figure 6.1.

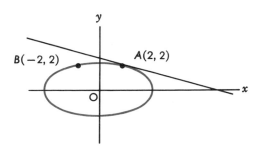

FIGURE 6.1

The line is *tangent* to the ellipse. Notice in the solution of Example 2 the occurrence of the *perfect square quadratic* results in only one solution. Perfect square quadratics such as $y^2 - 4y + 4 = 0$ have two equal roots and the solution set contains only one element.

Notice also that there are two points with y coordinate 2, A and B, on the ellipse; whereas, there is only one such point, A, on the line. Since A is the required point, the answer is obtained directly by substituting in the linear equation. If we had substituted in the quadratic equation we would have encountered the additional problem of deciding whether the coordinates of A or of B satisfied the system of equations.

Example 3

Solve the simultaneous equations,

$$(1) \quad 4x^2 - 9y^2 = 36$$
$$(2) \qquad x = y$$

Solution

Substitute $x = y$ in (1).
$$\therefore \quad 4y^2 - 9y^2 = 36$$

$$y^2 = -\frac{36}{5}$$

but $y \in R$, $\therefore y^2 \geq 0$

$\therefore$ there is no solution. Thus, there are no points $(x, y) \in R \times R$ satisfying $4x^2 - 9y^2 = 36$ and $x = y$ simultaneously.

The graph in Figure 6.2 shows that the hyperbola and the line do not intersect.

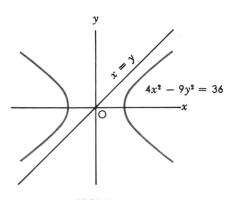

FIGURE 6.2

Example 4

Determine the slopes of the lines through $(0, 0)$ that do not intersect the hyperbola defined by $9x^2 - 16y^2 = 144$.

Solution

Let the defining equation of one of the required lines be

$$y = mx$$

Solve with $\qquad 9x^2 - 16y^2 = 144$

$\therefore \qquad\qquad 9x^2 - 16m^2x^2 = 144$

$\therefore \qquad\qquad x^2(9 - 16m^2) = 144$

$\because x \in R, x \neq 0$ then $x^2 > 0$.

$\therefore$ the equation can be satisfied only if $9 - 16m^2 > 0$. Thus, there will be no point of intersection if

$$9 - 16m^2 \leq 0$$

That is, if $\qquad\qquad m^2 \geq \tfrac{9}{16}$

or $\qquad\qquad |m| \geq \tfrac{3}{4}.$

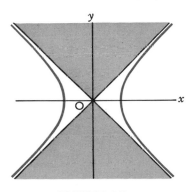

FIGURE 6.3

From the graph in Figure 6.3 it is apparent that any line through the origin and passing through the shaded region will not cut the hyperbola. Any line with slope between $-\tfrac{3}{4}$ and $\tfrac{3}{4}$ will cut the hyperbola. The two lines with slopes $\tfrac{3}{4}$ and $-\tfrac{3}{4}$ do not intersect the hyperbola but form a "boundary" between those lines that do and those that do not. These two boundary lines through the centre of the hyperbola are the *asymptotes* of the hyperbola.

The equations of the two asymptotes are

$$3x + 4y = 0 \qquad \text{and} \qquad 3x - 4y = 0.$$

Recall from Section 5.5 that defining equations of the pair of asymptote lines may be obtained from $9x^2 - 16y^2 = 0$.

Exercise 6.1

B

1. Solve each of the following systems.

   (a) $x^2 + y^2 = 25$
       $3x + 4y = 25$

   (b) $x^2 + y^2 = 25$
       $3x + 4y = 0$

   (c) $x^2 + y^2 = 25$
       $3x + 4y = 50$

2. Graph the relations corresponding to the equations in Question 1. State the relationship between the number of solutions and the quadratic used in the solutions.

3. Solve each of the following systems of equations, and graph the corresponding relations.

   (a) $x^2 = -9y$
       $x + y + 10 = 0$

   (c) $y^2 - 11x^2 = 5$
       $x + y - 5 = 0$

   (b) $3x^2 + 5y^2 = 32$
       $3x + y + 8 = 0$

   (d) $xy = 1$
       $3x + 3y = 10$

4. Solve the following systems.

   (a) $x^2 = -y$
       $x + y + 2 = 0$

   (c) $3x^2 - y^2 = 2$
       $3x + 2y - 1 = 0$

   (b) $2x^2 + 3y^2 = 35$
       $x + y - 5 = 0$

   (d) $xy = 8$
       $x + y = 4$

5. Prove that the line $25x - 12y + 45 = 0$ is tangent to the hyperbola $25x^2 - 9y^2 = 225$. Find the point of contact.

6. Use the method of Example 4 to find the asymptotes of the hyperbola $9x^2 - y^2 = 36$.

7. Prove that any line through $(0, 0)$ and with slope m, $|m| \geq \dfrac{b}{a}$, does not intersect the hyperbola $b^2x^2 - a^2y^2 = a^2b^2$.

C

8. Determine the value of t for which the line $y = 3x + t$ is tangent to the parabola $y^2 = 12x$.

9. Find the value of a for which the conic

$$a^2x^2 + 25y^2 = 3600$$

touches the line $4x - 5y - 100 = 0$.

6.2 Tangents to a Parabola

We shall utilize the idea of Section 6.1 in which we illustrated that a tangent has only one point in common with a conic and that the algebra yields only one solution because a perfect square quadratic is involved.

Example 1

Find the equation of the tangent to the parabola $y^2 = 8x$ having slope -2.

Solution

Let the equation of the tangent be

$$y = -2x + k.$$

If (x, y) is the point of tangency it satisfies both of the equations $y = -2x + k$ and $y^2 = 8x$.

$$\therefore \quad y^2 = 8\left(\frac{k - y}{2}\right)$$

$$y^2 + 4y - 4k = 0$$

For tangency only one solution exists.
Thus, $y^2 + 4y - 4k = 0$ must have equal roots.
That is, $y^2 + 4y - 4k$ is a perfect square and the discriminant, $b^2 - 4ac$, must be zero.
Here $a = 1$, $b = 4$, $c = -4k$.

$$\therefore \quad 16 - 4(1)(-4k) = 0$$
$$\therefore \qquad\qquad k = -1$$

$\therefore$ the equation of the tangent is
$$y = -2x - 1$$

Example 2

Find the equation of the tangents from the point $(3, 7)$ to the parabola $y^2 = 8x$.

Solution

Let the slope of a tangent be m.
$\therefore \quad y - 7 = m(x - 3)$ is the equation of the tangent.

If (x, y) is the common point of tangent and parabola then it satisfies

(1) $y - 7 = m(x - 3)$ and   (2) $y^2 = 8x$

from (1)
$$x = \frac{y - 7}{m} + 3$$

substitute in (2)
$$y^2 = 8\left(\frac{y - 7}{m} + 3\right)$$
$$\therefore \qquad my^2 - 8y + 56 - 24m = 0$$

For tangency we must have a perfect square quadratic equation.
$$\therefore \qquad\qquad b^2 - 4ac = 0$$

Here $a = m$, $b = -8$, $c = 56 - 24m$.
$$\therefore \qquad 64 - 4(m)(56 - 24m) = 0$$
$$\therefore \qquad 3m^2 - 7m + 2 = 0$$
$$\therefore \qquad (3m - 1)(m - 2) = 0$$
$$\therefore \qquad m = \tfrac{1}{3} \text{ or } m = 2$$

Thus, the equations of the two tangents from $(3, 7)$ to the parabola $y^2 = 8x$ are
$$x - 3y + 18 = 0$$
$$\text{and} \qquad 2x - y + 1 = 0$$

These tangents are illustrated in Figure 6.4.

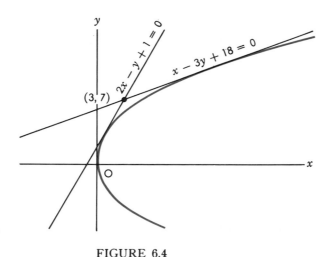

FIGURE 6.4

Example 2 illustrates a method for finding the equations of tangents from a point in the exterior region of a parabola.

6.2/Tangents to a Parabola

Example 3

Find the equation of the tangent to the parabola $y^2 = 8x$ at the point $(2, 4)$.

Solution

Let the slope of a tangent be m.

$\therefore$ $y - 4 = m(x - 2)$ is the equation of the tangent.

If (x, y) is the point of contact, then (x, y) satisfies both

$$\text{(1)} \qquad y - 4 = m(x - 2)$$
$$\text{and} \quad \text{(2)} \qquad y^2 = 8x$$
$$\text{from} \quad \text{(1)} \qquad x = \frac{y - 4}{m} + 2$$

substitute in (2) $\qquad y^2 = 8\left(\frac{y - 4}{m} + 2\right)$

$\therefore \qquad my^2 - 8y + 32 - 16m = 0$

For tangency this must be a perfect square quadratic equation. Thus, $b^2 - 4ac = 0$.

Here $a = m$, $b = -8$, $c = 32 - 16m$.

$$\therefore \qquad 64 - 4(m)(32 - 16m) = 0$$
$$m^2 - 2m + 1 = 0$$
$$(m - 1)(m - 1) = 0$$
$$\therefore \qquad m = 1$$

Thus, the equation of the tangent is $x - y + 2 = 0$.

Notice that $(2, 4)$ is on the parabola $y^2 = 8x$. Example 3 illustrates that the tangent at a point on a parabola is a unique line.

Exercise 6.2

B

1. Use the method of Example 1 to find an equation of the tangent with slope $\frac{2}{3}$ to the parabola $y^2 = 16x$.

2. Find an equation of the tangent with slope 1 to the parabola $x^2 - 20y = 0$.

3. Find an equation of the tangent to the parabola $y^2 = 4x$ from the point $(5, 6)$.

4. Find an equation of the tangent to $x^2 = -6y$ from the point $(2, 2)$.

5. Find an equation of the tangent to the curve at the given point in each of the following.

(a) $y^2 = 12x$, (3, 6)
(b) $y^2 = -5x$, (-5, 5)
(c) $x^2 = 8y$, (-4, 2)
(d) $x^2 = -4y$, (6, -9)

6. Given the parabola $y^2 = 12x$.

(a) Show that $4x - 3y = 12$ is a focal chord (a secant through the focus).
(b) Find the end points of the chord.
(c) Find the tangents at the points in (b).
(d) Show that the tangents intersect on the directrix of the parabola.
(e) Find the angle between the tangents in (c).

7. Given the parabola $y^2 = 12x$.
(a) Find an equation of the tangent at $P(3, 6)$ on the parabola.
(b) Find an equation of the image parabola under the stretch $(x, y) \rightarrow (x, \frac{1}{2}y)$.
(c) Find the image point of $P(3, 6)$ under the same stretch. Is this image point on the image parabola?
(d) Find an equation of the tangent to the image parabola at the image point of P.
(e) Find an equation of the image of the tangent line in (a) under the same stretch.
(f) Conjecture a tangency property under a stretch.

8. Repeat Question 7 for the parabola $x^2 = 8y$ and the point $(-4, 2)$ on the parabola for the stretch $(x, y) \rightarrow (\frac{1}{2}x, \frac{1}{2}y)$

C 9. The line drawn through the point of contact of a tangent and a curve at right angles to the tangent is called a *normal*. Given the parabola $y^2 = 6x$.

(a) Find an equation of the tangent at $P(6, 6)$.
(b) Find an equation of the normal PC.
(c) Find the length AB.
(d) Find the length BC.
(e) Join PF. If $PE \| AX$ show that $\triangle APF$ is isosceles and that $\angle APF = \angle TPE$.

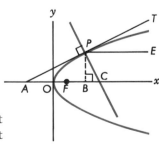

10. Select any point P on line l.

   (a) Draw the perpendicular bisector of PF as a colored line. (Use compasses or a mirror.)

   (b) Repeat (a) for at least 10 other points on the line l.

   (c) What curve do the lines in (b) seem to envelope?

   (d) Draw a line perpendicular to l at P of part (a).

   (e) Let the intersection of the lines in (a) and (d) be Q. Show that Q is on the parabola with focus F and directrix l.

   (f) Prove that the perpendicular bisector of FP is a tangent to the parabola by showing that it meets the parabola in only one point. (Use an indirect proof.)

6.3 Tangents to Ellipse and Hyperbola

We employ the same technique in dealing with tangents to an ellipse as with tangents to a parabola.

Example 1

Find an equation of the tangents with slope $\frac{1}{2}$ to the ellipse $x^2 + 4y^2 = 8$.

Solution

Let the tangent equation be

$$y = \tfrac{1}{2}x + k, \qquad k \in R.$$

Solve with

$$x^2 + 4y^2 = 8$$
$$x^2 + 4(\tfrac{1}{2}x + k)^2 = 8$$
$$2x^2 + 4kx + 4k^2 - 8 = 0$$

For tangency, $b^2 - 4ac = 0$.

Here $a = 2$, $b = 4k$, $c = 4k^2 - 8$.

$$\therefore \qquad 16k^2 - 4(2)(4k^2 - 8) = 0$$
$$\therefore \qquad k^2 = 4$$
$$\therefore \qquad k = 2 \text{ or } -2.$$

$\therefore$ the two tangents are $y = \tfrac{1}{2}x + 2$
and $y = \tfrac{1}{2}x - 2$.

Example 2

Find equations of tangents with slope 2 to the hyperbola
$$64x^2 - 25y^2 = 1600$$

Solution

Let the tangent equation be
$$y = 2x + k, \qquad k \in R.$$

Solve with
$$64x^2 - 25y^2 = 1600$$
$$\therefore \qquad 64x^2 - 25(2x + k)^2 = 1600$$
$$\therefore \; 36x^2 + 100kx + 25k^2 + 1600 = 0$$

For tangency, $b^2 - 4ac = 0$.

$$\therefore \qquad 10\,000k^2 - 4(36)(25k^2 + 1600) = 0$$
$$100k^2 - 36(k^2 + 64) = 0$$
$$64k^2 = 36 \times 64$$
$$k = 6 \text{ or } k = -6$$

$\therefore \quad$ the tangents are $\qquad y = 2x + 6$

and $\qquad\qquad\qquad y = 2x - 6.$

Exercise 6.3

B

1. Given the ellipse $9x^2 + 4y^2 = 72$. Find equations of the tangents with slope $\frac{3}{2}$.

2. For the hyperbola $16x^2 - 9y^2 = 112$ find equations of the tangents with slope $-\frac{16}{9}$.

3. For the ellipse $x^2 + 9y^2 = 52$ find equations of the tangents with slope $\frac{2}{9}$.

4. For the hyperbola $4x^2 - y^2 = 80$ find equations of the tangents with slope 3.

5. Find equations of the tangents with slope $-\frac{1}{8}$ to the hyperbola $x^2 - 4y^2 + 60 = 0$.

6. Find equations of the tangents with slope 2 to the hyperbola $xy = 10$. Illustrate your result with a diagram.

7. Show that the slope of the tangent to the ellipse $9x^2 + 16y^2 = 145$ at $(3, 2)$ on the ellipse is $-\frac{27}{32}$.

6.3/Tangents to Ellipse and Hyperbola

C 8. Given the circle $x^2 + y^2 = 25$.

(a) Find an equation of the tangent to the circle at the point $(3, 4)$. (Find the slope of the radius first.)

(b) Find an equation of the image of the circle under the stretch $(x, y) \rightarrow (x, \frac{1}{2}y)$.

(c) Find the image of $(3, 4)$ under the stretch.

(d) Find an equation of the tangent to the image curve in (b) at the image point in (c).

(e) Find an equation of the image of the tangent line in (a) under the stretch.

(f) Conjecture a tangency property under a stretch.

9. Find an equation of the tangent to the ellipse $4x^2 + 9y^2 = 40$ at $(1, -2)$ on it.

10. Find an equation of the tangent to the hyperbola $2x^2 - y^2 = 14$ at the point $(3, -2)$ on it.

11. (a) Draw a circle with centre F_1 and radius 6 cm.

(b) Join F_1 to any point P on the circle.

(c) Draw the perpendicular bisector (using compasses or mirrors) of PF_2, where F_2 is a point inside the circle and $F_2 \neq F_1$.

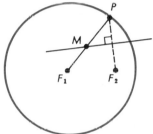

(d) Repeat (b) and (c) for 10 other points on the circle.

(e) What curves do the lines in (d) seem to envelope?

(f) In parts (b) and (c) let the point of intersection of PF_1 and the perpendicular bisector be M. Prove that
$$MF_1 + MF_2 = PF_1 = 6.$$

(g) Name the curve on which all the points in (d) lie.

(h) Describe the position of the curve.

(i) Prove that the perpendicular bisector of PF_2 is tangent to the ellipse by showing that it meets the ellipse in only one point. (Use an indirect proof).

12. (a) Repeat Question 11 (a), (b), (c), (d), (e) for a point F_2 outside the circle.

(b) Prove that $| MF_1 - MF_2 | = 6$, where M is the intersection of PF_1 and the perpendicular bisector of PF_2.

(c) Prove that the perpendicular bisector of PF_2 is tangent to the hyperbola by showing that it meets the hyperbola in only one point. (Use an indirect proof.)

6.4 Reflector Properties of Conics

Parabolic surfaces are frequently used as reflectors for light in headlights of cars, flashlights, and telescopes. In electronics and in radio astronomy the parabolic antenna has opened up new fields.

We shall try to illustrate the reflector properties of the conics by utilizing some properties of light. In general, light travels in straight lines. Indeed the concept of straightness of a line is derived from visual properties of rays of light.

If two points are given, the shortest journey from one point to the other in a homogeneous medium is by means of the straight line joining the two points. Thus, light travelling from one point to another travels along paths of minimum length.

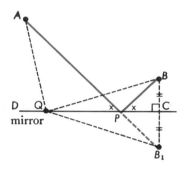

From physics we know that if an object B is viewed from a point A in a mirror the object would appear to be behind the mirror at a point B_1. The line of the mirror is the perpendicular bisector of BB_1.

We also learned that $\angle APD = \angle BPC$. This has the consequence that APB_1 is straight and that $AP + PB = AB_1$. We may prove that this actual path of light is shorter than any other path. If Q is any point in the mirror other than P, then join AQ, QB, and QB_1 as in the diagram.

$$\because \quad DC \text{ is the right bisector of } BB_1$$
$$\therefore \quad QB = QB_1 \text{ and } PB = PB_1$$

From $\triangle AQB_1$,

$$AQ + QB_1 > AB_1$$
$$\therefore \quad AQ + BQ > AP + PB_1$$
$$\therefore \quad AQ + QB > AP + PB$$

Since light travels at uniform speed in a given medium, we see it takes longer to go from A to B via Q than via its actual path through P. This property is called *Fermat's Principle** for a plane mirror and we shall assume it in proving the reflector properties of the conics.

---

*E. Whittaker—A History of Aether and Electricity (London 1951). In 1657 Fermat wrote a letter outlining his Principle of Least Time. "Nature always acts by the shortest course."

6.4/Reflector Properties of Conics

Consider a parabola, its focus F and any point A in the interior region. If the parabola is a reflector, then a fine beam of light emanating from F will be reflected from the mirror surface. We shall show that in travelling from F to A the reflected beam will take minimum time for PA parallel to the x axis. From the definition of a parabola we know

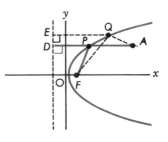

$$PF = PD.$$

If $\qquad PA \parallel x$ axis

$$\therefore \ PF + PA = DA$$

Take any other point Q on the parabola.

$$QF = QE$$
$$\therefore \ QF + QA = QE + QA$$
$$\text{but } QE + QA > DA$$

$\therefore \ PF + PA$ is a minimum when PA is parallel to the x axis.

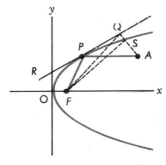

FIGURE 6.5

Thus, the path of a reflected ray requiring minimum time from F to A is through a point P on the parabola such that $PA \parallel x$ axis.

Consider the tangent to the parabola at P where $PA \parallel x$ axis. See Figure 6.5. Let Q be any point on the tangent. Join A, Q, meeting the parabola at S. Join F, S. By the previous argument

$$SA + FS \geq PF + PA$$
$$\text{Now} \qquad FQ + QS \geq FS$$
$$\text{and} \qquad FQ + QA = FQ + QS + SA$$
$$\therefore \ FQ + QS + SA \geq SA + FS$$
$$\therefore \qquad FQ + QA \geq PF + PA$$

Thus, if Q varies on the tangent, the distance from A to F via Q is a minimum when $Q = P$. Therefore, by our discussion of the plane mirror, it follows that the actual path of light reflected by the parabola is such that $\angle RPF = \angle APQ$. Thus, the parabola reflects "locally" as though it were a plane mirror tangent to the parabola. This is a very natural result. If we had started by assuming it, we could have proved the validity of Fermat's principle for a parabola just as we did for a plane mirror.

A polished reflector, like the reflector of a headlight of a car or searchlight, is made in the form of a paraboloid of revolution, that is, a surface generated by a parabola which is revolved about its axis. A light source placed at the focus will produce a set of reflected rays that are parallel to the axis of the parabola.

Consider a parabolic reflector aimed at the sun. The sun's rays are practically parallel to each other and to the axis of the reflector. The rays upon reflection all pass through the focus and on a bright day a combustible object would burst into flames if placed at the focus. It is to this property that the word *focus* owes its name; the Latin word focus meaning hearth or fireplace. The term was introduced into science by the astronomer Kepler in 1604. Parabolic mirrors have been used for solar furnaces.

In the ellipse, for any point P on the ellipse $PF_1 + PF_2 = 2a$. Draw a tangent to the ellipse at P. The tangent touches the ellipse at only one point. Take any other point Q on the tangent. Join Q, F_2 cutting the ellipse at S. Join Q, F_1, S, F_1.

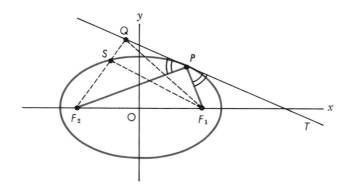

In $\triangle QSF_1$, $QF_1 + QS \geq F_1S$, with equality only if $Q = P$.

But $\qquad\qquad F_1S + F_2S = 2a$

$\therefore\qquad QF_1 + QS + F_2S \geq 2a$

$\therefore\qquad\qquad QF_1 + QF_2 \geq 2a$

6.4/Reflector Properties of Conics

$\therefore$ $QF_1 + QF_2$ is a minimum when $Q = P$. Thus, as in the case of the plane mirror, it follows that $\angle QPF_2 = \angle TPF_1$. But P is any point on the ellipse. Therefore, if the ellipse were a reflector, light from F_2 would, on reflection from *any* point on the ellipse, pass through F_1.

This property is exemplified in the famous elliptical "Whispering Gallery" in which a faint whisper at one focus of the gallery can be heard distinctly by a person standing at the other.

For a hyperbolic reflector we can show that if the path of a reflected ray from a focus is F_1PA then the line AP passes through the other focus F_2, as in Figure 6.6.

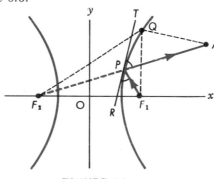

FIGURE 6.6

Is $PF_1 + PA$ a minimum?

Select any other point Q, on the hyperbola, Figure 6.6.
In $\triangle F_2QA$

$$QF_2 + QA \geq F_2A$$

and $$F_2A = PF_2 + PA$$

But for the hyperbola $$PF_2 = 2a + PF_1$$

and $$QF_2 = 2a + QF_1$$

$\because$ $$QF_2 + QA \geq PF_2 + PA$$

$\therefore$ $$2a + QF_1 + QA \geq 2a + PF_1 + PA$$

$\therefore$ $$QF_1 + QA \geq PF_1 + PA$$

$\therefore$ the path $PF_1 + PA$ is minimum. By Fermat's principle it must be the path actually followed by a ray of light passing from F_1 to A.

As in the previous cases, we can show that the incident and reflected rays make equal angles with the tangent at the point of reflection. In Figure 6.6, $\angle RPF_1 = \angle TPA$.

Exercise 6.4

B 1. (a) If a light source is placed at the centre of a circular reflector, how will the reflected ray behave?

(b) Explain why a sphere is sometimes placed on the outside of a light source as shown in the diagram.

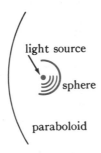

2. Illustrate, by means of a diagram, the reflection of a light beam from a convex hyperbolic reflector with a light source at the focus of the hyperbola. For example, in Figure 6.6, let F_2 be the source and the ray reflect at the point P.

3. Use Figure 6.6 to prove that for any point, V, on the tangent $F_1V + VA$ is a minimum only if $V = P$.

4. Use the reflector property of the parabola, ellipse, and hyperbola to describe a method of constructing a tangent to each conic.

6.5 Intersection of Conics

Recall from Section 6.1 that the intersection of a line and a conic gives three different kinds of solutions as illustrated in Figure 6.7.

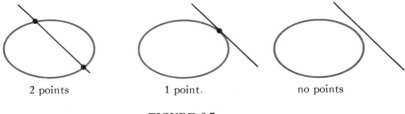

FIGURE 6.7

There are many more possible cases involved in the intersection of two distinct conics. In Figure 6.8 we illustrate the six different cases.

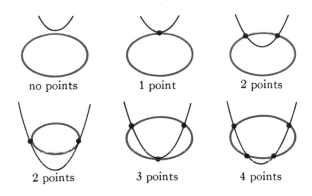

| no points | 1 point | 2 points |

| 2 points | 3 points | 4 points |

FIGURE 6.8

The most general case of the intersection of two conics is usually difficult to solve. By restricting ourselves to the conics with axes along the coordinate axes the problem is considerably simplified.

Example 1

Find $\{(x, y) \mid 2x^2 - y^2 = 1\} \cap \{(x, y) \mid y^2 = x + 2\}$.

Solution

The coordinates of each intersection point satisfy both the equations

$$2x^2 - y^2 = 1 \qquad (1)$$

and $\qquad y^2 = x + 2 \qquad (2)$

From (2) $\qquad y^2 = x + 2$

substitute for y^2 in (1) $\qquad 2x^2 - (x + 2) = 1$

$$\therefore \quad 2x^2 - x - 3 = 0$$

$$(2x - 3)(x + 1) = 0$$

$$x = \tfrac{3}{2} \text{ or } x = -1.$$

Substitute $x = \tfrac{3}{2}$ in (2).

$$\therefore \quad y^2 = \tfrac{7}{2}$$

$$\therefore \quad y = \sqrt{\tfrac{7}{2}} \text{ or } y = -\sqrt{\tfrac{7}{2}}$$

Substitute $x = -1$ in (2).

$$\therefore \quad y^2 = 1$$

$$y = 1 \quad \text{or} \quad y = -1$$

$\therefore$ the intersection set is

$$\left\{ \left(\tfrac{3}{2}, \sqrt{\tfrac{7}{2}}\right), \left(\tfrac{3}{2}, -\sqrt{\tfrac{7}{2}}\right), (-1, 1), (-1, -1) \right\}.$$

Example 2

Solve the system of equations

(1) $\quad x^2 + y^2 = 4$

(2) $4x^2 + 9y^2 = 36$

Solution

$$9 \times (1) \qquad\qquad 9x^2 + 9y^2 = 36$$
$$(2) \qquad\qquad\qquad 4x^2 + 9y^2 = 36$$

subtract $\qquad\qquad\qquad 5x^2 \qquad\quad = 0$

$$\therefore \quad x = 0$$

substitute $x = 0$ in (1).

$$\therefore \quad y^2 = 4$$
$$y = 2 \text{ or } -2$$

$\therefore \quad$ the solution set is $\{(0, 2), (0, -2)\}$.

Example 3

Find the points of intersection of the circle $x^2 + y^2 = 10$ and the hyperbola $xy = 9$.

Solution

If (1) $x^2 + y^2 = 10$, (2) $xy = 9$

From (2) $\qquad\qquad\qquad y = \dfrac{9}{x}$

Substitute $y = \dfrac{9}{x}$ in (1)

$$\therefore \quad x^2 + \left(\frac{9}{x}\right)^2 = 10$$

$$x^4 - 10x^2 + 81 = 0$$

The discriminant is $10^2 - 4(81)$ which is negative.
Thus there are no real values of x^2 that satisfy $x^4 - 10x^2 + 81 = 0$.
$\therefore$ there are no points of intersection.

The space program gives many illustrations of the applications of conics.

Due to the attraction of Earth, a bullet fired horizontally would drop a distance, $4.9t^2$ (in metres). If the bullet were travelling at a sufficiently high speed, the drop due to gravity would equal the falling away of the earth due to curvature. The velocity at which this occurs is 7.9 km/s or about 28 000 km/h. If there were no air resistance,

214 $\qquad\qquad\qquad\qquad\qquad$ *6.5/Intersection of Conics*

then a projectile fire horizontally at 28 000 km/h would theoretically never hit the earth.

A satellite travelling at 7.9 km/s will have a circular orbit. If the speed decreases the satellite will fall to earth. If the speed is increased the orbit becomes an ellipse with the centre of the earth as one focus. As the speed is increased the major axis of the ellipse increases in length. At a speed of 11.2 km/s the orbit changes to a parabola. Satellites travelling at 11.2 km/s or about 40 000 km/h will never return to earth unless they change course.

One of the most intricate problems involving space vehicles is that of bringing two of them together in space. That this problem has been solved in the case of manned vehicles is illustrated by the successful docking of the lunar module *Eagle* with the command module *Columbia*, following the historic moon landing in July, 1969.

The Mariner program involved placing a satellite in space so that its orbit would enable it to land on Mars. Thus, scientists had to know the orbit of Mars to a high degree of accuracy; then they had to calculate the orbit of the satellite so that the two orbits intersected; and finally they had to launch the satellite at the proper time in order to ensure that Mars and the satellite reached the point of intersection of orbits simultaneously.

Contrary to popular belief the path of a projectile such as a football is *not exactly a parabola*. The football is not travelling at 40 000 km/h, which is the speed necessary for a parabolic orbit! The path is really an ellipse with the centre of the earth at one focus. The elliptical path of the football intersects the earth. Since the ellipse has a very long major axis and a very short minor axis the parabolic approximation of the path is frequently adequate for ballistic calculations.

Exercise 6.5

B
1. Solve the following systems of equations. Sketch the corresponding graphs to illustrate your answer.

   (a) $x^2 + y^2 = 16$
   $9x^2 + 16y^2 = 144$

   (c) $x^2 - y^2 = 64$
   $9x^2 + 16y^2 = 144$

   (b) $x^2 + y^2 = 25$
   $x^2 - y^2 = 7$

   (d) $x^2 + y^2 = 25$
   $y = x^2 + 5$

2. Sketch a set of diagrams as in Figure 6.8 to show that there are 6 different cases of the intersection of a pair of intersecting straight lines and a circle.

3. Find $\{(x, y) \,|\, x^2 - 2xy = 0\} \cap \{(x, y) \,|\, 4x^2 + 9y^2 = 225\}$.

6.5/Intersection of Conics   215

4. Solve each of the following systems of equations and sketch the corresponding graphs.

(a) $3x^2 + y^2 = 28$
$x^2 - y^2 = 8$

(b) $3x^2 - 5y^2 = 63$
$xy = 18$

5. (a) Show that the equation $x^2 - 6xy + 8y^2 = 0$ represents two straight lines.

(b) Find the points of intersection of the ellipse $x^2 + 4y^2 = 4$ and the lines $x^2 - 6xy + 8y^2 = 0$.

(c) Illustrate your answer to (b) by graphing the ellipse and lines.

6. Find the points of intersection of the curves
$$x^2 - 3xy - 4y^2 = 0$$
and $$2x^2 - y^2 = 4.$$

7. (a) Find the points of intersection of the conics
$$x^2 + 4y^2 = 4$$
and $$2x^2 - y^2 = -1.$$

(b) Illustrate your answer to (a) by sketching the conics.

8. Find the points of intersection of the following pairs of conics.

(a) $x^2 + 4y^2 = 4$
$4x^2 + y^2 = 4$

(b) $9x^2 - 16y^2 = -144$
$16x^2 - 9y^2 = 144$

(Hint: Add the two equations)

9. Find the points of intersection of the parabolas.
$$y = x^2 + 2x - 3$$
$$y = -x^2 - x + 6$$

10. Find the points of intersection of the circles.
$$x^2 + y^2 - 2x - 4y - 20 = 0$$
$$x^2 + y^2 - 14x - 16y + 100 = 0$$

6.6 Relations Involving Inequalities

In this section we shall study combinations of two or more relations. The symbol $\wedge$ is used to mean "and" throughout this section.

Example 1

Graph the region $F = \{ (x, y) \mid (x^2 + y^2 < 5) \wedge (x + y - 1 \le 0) \}$.

Solution

$x^2 + y^2 < 5$ defines the region in the interior of the circle $x^2 + y^2 = 5$.

$x + y - 1 \leq 0$ is equivalent to $y \leq 1 - x$ and defines the region below and including the line $y = 1 - x$.

The points of intersection of line and circle are $(-1, 2)$ and $(2, -1)$.

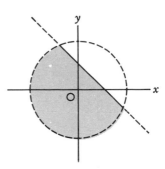

$\therefore\ F = \{(x, y) \mid x^2 + y^2 < 5\} \cap \{(x, y) \mid x + y - 1 \leq 0\}$ is the shaded area.

Example 2

Graph the region
$H = \{ (x, y) \mid (x^2 + y^2 \leq 25)$
  or $(x \geq 4) \}$.

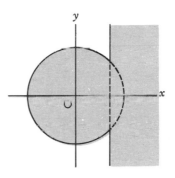

Solution

$A = \{(x, y) \mid x^2 + y^2 \leq 25 \}$
is the region inside and including the circle $x^2 + y^2 = 25$.
$B = \{ (x, y) \mid x \geq 4 \}$ is the region to the right and on the line $x = 4$.
$H = A \cup B$.

Exercise 6.6

B 1. In the accompanying diagrams the graphs of $x^2 + y^2 = 25$, $3x^2 + 16y = 0$ and $x - 3y = 5$ are shown.
(a) Find the points of intersections of these graphs.
(b) Describe, as sets, the regions shaded. Exclude the boundary lines.

(i)

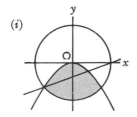

(ii)

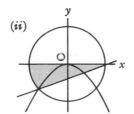

(iii)

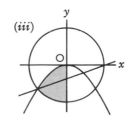

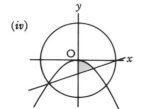 (iv)

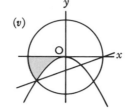 (v)

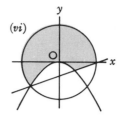 (vi)

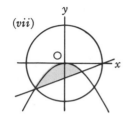 (vii)

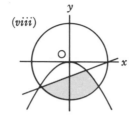 (viii)

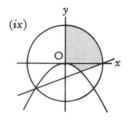 (ix)

2. Graph each of the following.

(a) $\{(x, y) \mid (x^2 + y^2 \geq 4) \wedge (x^2 + y^2 \leq 25)\}$

(b) $\{(x, y) \mid (x^2 + y^2 \geq 9) \wedge (x^2 + 9y^2 > 36)\}$

(c) $\{(x, y) \mid (16x^2 + 9y^2 \leq 144) \wedge (y > x)\}$

(d) $\{(x, y) \mid y^2 \leq 4x\} \cap \{(x, y) \mid 2x - y - 4 \leq 0\}$

(e) $\{(x, y) \mid 9x^2 - 16y^2 \leq 144\} \cap \{(x, y) \mid x^2 - y^2 \geq 9\}$

(f) $\{(x, y) \mid (9x^2 + 16y^2 \leq 144) \wedge (x^2 - y^2 \leq 9)\}$

3. Given $A = \{(x, y) \mid x \geq 0\}$
$B = \{(x, y) \mid y \leq 0\}$
$C = \{(x, y) \mid x - y \geq 4\}$
$D = \{(x, y) \mid x^2 + y^2 \leq 16\}$

Use the same axis and graph the sets in each of the following.

(a) $C \cup D$ (c) $A \cup D$ (e) $C \cap D$

(b) $(D \cap A) \cap B$ (d) $B \cap C$

6.7 Envelopes

If the coordinates of a point satisfy an algebraic relationship, the point is not free to move at random, but is one of an infinite set of points that form a curve called the *locus* of the point.

If the two constants a and b of a straight line $ax + by + 1 = 0$ satisfy an algebraic relationship, the line is not free to move at random, but is one of an infinite set, S, of lines. Indeed, it is possible to

218

find a curve such that each line of S is a tangent to this curve. This curve is called the *envelope* of the set of lines. Envelopes are the curves produced in *curve stitching*.

As an example, we shall find the envelope of the set or family of lines satisfying the condition that the sum of the intercepts of each line is a constant k.

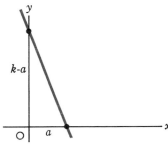

Let a be the x-intercept of one line of the family.

$\therefore$ $k - a$ is the y-intercept.

It can readily be shown that
$$x(k - a) + ay = a(k - a)$$
is an equation of the given family of lines.

Suppose two tangents TP and TQ intersect at T. As TQ moves closer to TP, then T moves nearer and nearer to the curve. In the limit, T is a point on the curve! That is, if the two tangents coincide, the point of intersection of the tangent lines is *on* the curve. Note also, that two tangents, drawn from an external point of a curve, will coincide when the point is on the curve.

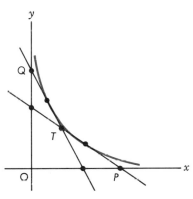

Rewrite the family equation $x(k - a) + ay = a(k - a)$
$$\text{as } a^2 + a(y - x - k) + kx = 0$$

This equation is quadratic in a and for each pair of values (x, y) has two solutions corresponding to the lines TP and TQ. If these lines are tangent to some curve E then the point (x, y) corresponds to the point T above. If T is outside the curve E, we expect two values of a which are real and distinct. If T is on the curve E, we expect one value of a. What do we expect if T is inside the curve?

$\therefore$ If $T(x, y)$ is on the curve E, our quadratic has equal roots.

$\therefore$ $$b^2 - 4ac = 0$$
$\therefore$ $$(y - x - k)^2 - 4kx = 0$$
or $(y - x)^2 - 2k(y - x) + k^2 - 4kx = 0$
or $$(y - x)^2 = 2k(y + x) - k^2$$

This equation is the condition for equal roots for coordinates (x, y) of a point T on the curve E and is therefore an equation of E. Since the second degree terms form a perfect square, E is a parabola.

Exercise 6.7

B 1. Find an equation of the envelope of the family of lines given by

$$y = mx + \frac{5}{m}.$$

2. Prove the following. If the difference of the intercepts made on the axes by each member of a family of lines is constant, then the family will envelope a parabola.

3. Find an equation of the envelope of the family of lines,

$$2ky = 2x + k^2.$$

4. Find an equation of the envelope of the family of lines whose x and y-intercepts have a constant product k.

5. P is any point on the parabola $y^2 = 4ax$ with vertex A. Complete the rectangle $ANPM$. Prove that the envelope of the family of lines MN is the parabola $y^2 + 16ax = 0$.

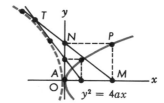

6. The middle point of a chord of a circle $x^2 + y^2 = r^2$ is on a fixed straight line $x = a$, $0 < a < r$. Prove that the envelope of the family of such chords is a parabola.

7. Each member of a family of circles has centre on the parabola $y = x^2$ and is tangent to the x axis. Find an equation of the envelope of the family of circles.

8. The point $(a, 0)$ is reflected in a mirror line so that its image falls on the y axis. Find an equation of the envelope of the family of mirror lines.

9. Show that the envelope of the family of circles $(x - a)^2 + y^2 = 1$ is the pair of lines $y = 1$ and $y = -1$.

C 10. Find the envelope of the family of circles each member of which has centre on the hyperbola $xy = 1$, and passes through $(0, 0)$.

11. If the corner of a rectangular piece of paper is folded down so that the sum of the edges left unfolded is constant, then the crease will envelope a parabola. Prove.

Review Exercise 6.8

B

1. Solve each of the following systems. Graph the corresponding relations and check your results.

   (a) $x^2 + y^2 = 5$
   $$x + y = 3$$
   (b) $x^2 - y^2 = 16$
   $$5x - 2y = 19$$

   (c) $y^2 = 4x$
   $$y - x + 1 = 0$$
   (d) $3x^2 + 7y^2 = 55$
   $$3x + y - 11 = 0$$

2. Solve the following systems.

   (a) $xy = 8$
   $$x + y = 4$$
   (b) $x^2 + 4y^2 = 32$
   $$x - 2y = -8$$

3. Find an equation of the tangent with slope 1 to the parabola $y^2 = 4x$ and find the point of contact.

4. Find an equation of the tangent with slope $-\dfrac{3}{4}$ to the parabola $y^2 = 12x$.

5. Find equations of the tangents from $(4, 1)$ to the parabola $y^2 = 12x$.

6. Find an equation of the tangent to the parabola $y^2 = -12x$ at the point $(-3, 6)$.

7. Find equations of the tangents with slope -1 to the ellipse $2x^2 + 6y^2 = 6$.

8. For the ellipse $x^2 + 2y^2 = 72$ find equations of the tangents with slope 2.

9. For the ellipse $x^2 + 4y^2 = 100$ find equations of the tangents with slope $\dfrac{2}{3}$.

10. Find equations of the tangents with slope 5 to the hyperbola $9x^2 - y^2 = 9$.

11. Show that $3x + y = 7$ is a defining equation of a tangent to the hyperbola $2x^2 - y^2 = 14$.

12. Find equations of the tangents with slope $-\dfrac{1}{2}$ to the hyperbola $xy = 18$.

13. Show that $x + 2y = 12$ is a defining equation of a tangent to the hyperbola $xy = 18$.

14. Solve the following systems of equations. Graph the corresponding conics to verify your answer.

(a) $x^2 - y^2 = 16$
      $2x^2 - 5y^2 = 5$

(b) $x^2 + y^2 = 97$
      $xy = 36$

(c) $x^2 + y^2 = 20$
      $y = x^2$

(d) $x^2 - 7y^2 = 9$
      $5x^2 + y^2 = 81$

15. Graph the regions in each of the following.

(a) $\{(x, y) \mid (3x^2 + y^2 \leq 13) \land (x^2 - y^2 < 5)\}$
(b) $\{(x, y) \mid (x^2 + y^2 > 89) \land (xy < 40)\}$

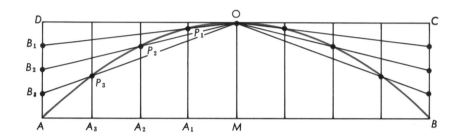

16. $ABCD$ is a rectangle. Divide AD and AM into the same number of equal parts. Call the points of division $A_1, A_2, A_3, \cdots$ and $B_1, B_2, B_3 \cdots$ as indicated in the diagram. The midpoint of DC is O. Join $OB_1, OB_2, OB_3, \cdots$. Erect perpendiculars to AB at $A_1, A_2, A_3, \cdots$. Let the point of intersection of $OB_1, OB_2, OB_3, \cdots$ with the perpendiculars be $P_1, P_2, P_3, \cdots$. Show that the locus of all the P_i's is a parabola.

17. In the same diagram graph the curves and regions defined as as follows:

(a) $x^2 + y^2 = 100$
(b) $(x - 5)^2 + y^2 \leq 4$
(c) $(x + 5)^2 + y^2 \leq 4$
(d) $(y \geq 5) \land (x^2 + y^2 \leq 100)$
(e) $(y = 5) \land (-12 \leq x \leq 12)$
(f) $x^2 + (y + 5)^2 \leq 1$
(g) $(|x| \leq 3) \land (-8 \leq y \leq -7)$

18. In the same diagram, graph the following relations.

(a) $\{(x, y) \mid (1 \leq y \leq 2) \land (x \in \{1, 2, 3, 4, 5\})\}$
(b) $\{(x, y) \mid (2 \leq x \leq 3) \land (y = 1)\}$
(c) $\{(x, y) \mid (4 \leq x \leq 5) \land (y = 1)\}$
(d) $\{(x, y) \mid (2 \leq x \leq 3) \land (y = 2)\}$

19. In the accompanying diagrams the graphs of $x^2 + 4y^2 = 20$, $4x^2 + y^2 = 20$ and $y^2 = 2x$ are shown.

    (a) Find the points of intersection of these graphs.

    (b) Describe as sets, the region shaded. Exclude the boundary lines.

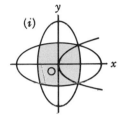 (i)

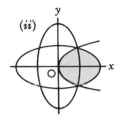 (ii)

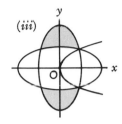 (iii)

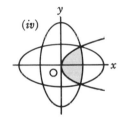 (iv)

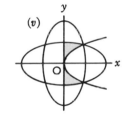 (v)

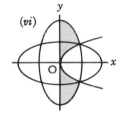 (vi)

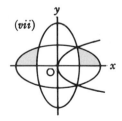 (vii)

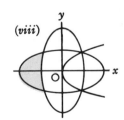 (viii)

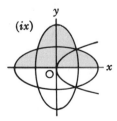 (ix)

20. Find equations of the tangents to the hyperbola $xy = 10$ from the point $(5, 1)$.

21. Find an equation of the tangent to the hyperbola $xy = 18$ at the point $(6, 3)$.

6.8/Review Exercise

223

$7 \, / \,$ Transformations and Conics

In the preceding chapters we have graphed simple quadratic equations in x and y and found that they represent conics. In this chapter we shall use transformations to graph more complicated quadratic equations. We shall find that a suitable transformation can reduce a general equation of the second degree in x and y to an equation having one of the standard forms. The graph of the original equation can be obtained by graphing the corresponding standard equation and then applying the inverse transformation.

7.1 Equations of Image Curves Under Translations

In Section 4.1 you learned how to obtain an equation of the translation image of a curve. In this section we shall do more such examples and try to discover what effect the translation has on the equation of the original curve.

Example 1

(a) Find an equation of the image of the ellipse $9x^2 + 25y^2 = 225$ under the translation $(x, y) \rightarrow (x - 8, y - 7)$.

(b) Find the centre, foci, vertices and axes of symmetry of the image curve.

(c) Graph the given curve and its image.

Solution

(a) Suppose $P(x, y)$ is any point on the original ellipse $9x^2 + 25y^2 = 225$. Let $P(x, y) \rightarrow P'(u, v)$ under the translation $(x, y) \rightarrow (x - 8, y - 7)$.

$$\begin{rcases} u = x - 8 \\ v = y - 7 \end{rcases} \Rightarrow \begin{cases} x = u + 8 \\ y = v + 7 \end{cases}$$

But on the original ellipse

$$9x^2 + 25y^2 - 225$$

Substituting for x and y we get

$$9(u + 8)^2 + 25(v + 7)^2 = 225$$
$$9u^2 + 25v^2 + 144u + 350v + 1576 = 0$$

Thus the ellipse $\{(x, y) \mid 9x^2 + 25y^2 = 225\}$ maps onto the ellipse $\{(u, v) \mid 9u^2 + 25v^2 + 144u + 350v + 1576 = 0\}$ which may be rewritten $\{(x, y) \mid 9x^2 + 25y^2 + 144x + 350y + 1576 = 0\}$

Thus the image of $9x^2 + 25y^2 = 225$ has equation

$9x^2 + 25y^2 + 144x + 350y + 1576 = 0$.

Observe that terms in x and y have been introduced by the translation.

(b) For the curve $9x^2 + 25y^2 = 225$ or $\dfrac{x^2}{25} + \dfrac{y^2}{9} = 1$,

$$a^2 = 25, \ b^2 = 9, \ c^2 = a^2 - b^2 = 16.$$

Thus the foci $(c, 0)$ and $(-c, 0)$ are $(4, 0)$, $(-4, 0)$. The centre is $(0, 0)$, the vertices $(a, 0)$ and $(-a, 0)$ are $(5, 0)$, $(-5, 0)$. The axes of symmetry are $x = 0$, $y = 0$.

Under the $(-8, -7)$ translation,
$$(0, 0) \rightarrow (-8, -7)$$
$$(4, 0) \rightarrow (-4, -7)$$
$$(-4, 0) \rightarrow (-12, -7)$$
$$(5, 0 \rightarrow (-3, -7)$$
$$(-5, 0) \rightarrow (-13, -7)$$
$$x = 0 \rightarrow u + 8 = 0 \text{ or } u = -8$$
$$y = 0 \rightarrow v + 7 = 0 \text{ or } v = -7$$

Thus the image ellipse has centre at $(-8, -7)$, foci at $(-4, -7)$, $(-12, -7)$, vertices at $(-3, -7)$ and $(-13, -7)$, and axes of symmetry $u = -8$ and $v = -7$, that is, $x = -8$ and $y = -7$.

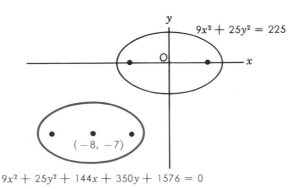

$$9x^2 + 25y^2 + 144x + 350y + 1576 = 0$$

(c) The curve $9x^2 + 25y^2 = 225$ is graphed first. This graph is translated 8 units left and 7 units down to obtain the graph of $9x^2 + 25y^2 + 144x + 350y + 1576 = 0$.

This example suggests that conics in standard form have images under translation with equations of the form

$$ax^2 + by^2 + 2gx + 2fy + c = 0, \qquad (1)$$

where $a, b, c, f, g \in R$.

Because this equation (1) does not contain any multiple of the product xy, it is not the most general equation of the second degree. We shall study the general equation later; let us for the present note that the given equation can represent a circle, ellipse, parabola, or hyperbola.

Exercise 7.1

A

1. State the values of a, b, c, g, f in $ax^2 + by^2 + 2gx + 2fy + c = 0$ to give the following equations.

(a) $x^2 + y^2 - 100 = 0$ (d) $x^2 - 4y + 8 = 0$
(b) $y^2 - 8x = 0$ (e) $4x^2 + 5y^2 - 20 = 0$
(c) $x^2 - 3y^2 - 18 = 0$

B

2. (a) Find an equation of the image under the translation $(x, y) \rightarrow (x + 7, y - 4)$ of the ellipse $4x^2 + 9y^2 = 36$.
    (b) Find the vertices, centre, foci, and axes of the image ellipse.

3. (a) Find an equation of the image under the translation $(x, y) \rightarrow (x - 5, y - 3)$ of the hyperbola $9x^2 - 16y^2 = 144$.
   (b) Find the vertices, centre, foci, and axes of the image hyperbola.
   (c) Sketch the hyperbola and its image.

4. For each of the following curves:

   (i) determine an equation of its image under the given translation

   (ii) name the type of curve

   (iii) sketch the *image* curve and *then* the given curve.

Curve	Translation
(a) $x^2 - 4y + 8 = 0$	$(x, y) \rightarrow (x, y - 2)$
(b) $x^2 + y^2 - 4x + 6y - 12 = 0$	$(x, y) \rightarrow (x - 2, y + 3)$
(c) $2x^2 + y - 8x = 0$	$(x, y) \rightarrow (x - 2, y - 8)$
(d) $4x^2 + 9y^2 - 24x - 72y + 36 = 0$	$(x, y) \rightarrow (x - 3, y - 4)$
(e) $x^2 - 4y^2 + 6x - 16y - 3 = 0$	$(x, y) \rightarrow (x + 3, y + 2)$

5. Regarding each of the equations in Questions 2, 3, 4 as an example of the general equation $ax^2 + by^2 + 2gx + 2fy + c = 0$, show that the sign of ab is invariant under translation. How could you use this fact to determine the *type of curve* in each part of Question 4 without actually performing the translation?

6. For each of the given curves, find the image under the translation $(x, y) \rightarrow (x + 6, y + 3)$. List all vertices, foci, and axes of symmetry for each conic that is not a circle. Sketch each curve and its image.

   (a) $4x^2 + y^2 - 4 = 0$ (d) $9x^2 + 4y^2 = 36$
   (b) $y^2 + 16x = 0$ (e) $4x^2 - y^2 = -4$
   (c) $x^2 = 8y$ (f) $x^2 + y^2 = 81$

7. (a) Find an equation of the image under the translation $(x, y) \rightarrow (x + 4, y - 3)$ of the hyperbola $xy = 12$.
   (b) Find the centre and asymptotes of the image hyperbola.
   (c) Sketch the hyperbola and its image.

8. (a) Find the image under the translation $(x, y) \rightarrow (x - 6, y + 2)$ of the second degree relation defined by $4x^2 - y^2 = 0$.
   (b) Graph the relation and its image.

9. By means of a translation find an equation of the parabola with vertex $(-3, 1)$ and focus $(-1, 1)$.

7.1/Equations of Image Curves Under Translations   227

10. What is the graph of $xy = 0$? Find an equation of the graph obtained under the translation $(x, y) \rightarrow (x - 2, y + 3)$ of the graph of $xy = 0$. Describe the translated graph.

C

11. Show that under the translation $(x, y) \rightarrow (x + h, y + k)$ the image of the second degree curve $ax^2 + by^2 + d = 0$ can be written in the form $ax^2 + by^2 + 2gx + 2fy + c = 0$. Hence prove the sign of ab is invariant under a translation.

12. (a) Under the translation $(x, y) \rightarrow (x + h, y + k)$ the line $3x + 4y - 12 = 0$ is its own image. Find a condition satisfied by h and k.

    (b) Repeat part (a) if the line $ax + by + c = 0$ is its own image under $(x, y) \rightarrow (x + h, y + k)$.

13. Find the translation under which the image of the vertex of the parabola $y = x^2 + x$ is the origin.

14. Find the translation under which the maximum point of the curve $y = 2x - x^2$ is mapped into its mirror image in the y axis.

7.2 Graphing Second Degree Equations Using Translations

We have now learned that when an ellipse, parabola, or hyperbola in standard position relative to the Cartesian axes is translated, the equation of the translated curve is of the form

$$ax^2 + by^2 + 2gx + 2fy + c = 0, \quad (1)$$

where a, b, g, f, $c \in R$.

We have also seen that several curves having equations similar to (1), can be transformed so that their equations have one of the three standard forms,

$$ax^2 + by^2 + c = 0, \ y^2 = 4px, \ x^2 = 4py. \quad (2)$$

Indeed we can show that any curve with an equation similar to (1) can be translated so that its image equation is one of the standard forms (2). But each of the equations (2) can be readily graphed, as in Chapter 5. Hence, by applying a suitable translation we will be able to graph any equation of form (1). In Question 5, Exercise 7.1, we also discovered that the sign of the product ab does not change, that is, is invariant under a translation. If $ax^2 + by^2 + c = 0$ is a circle, then $a = b$. If $ax^2 + by^2 + c = 0$ is an ellipse then either a and b are both positive or both negative so that $ab > 0$. If $ax^2 + by^2 + c = 0$ is a hyperbola then the signs of a and b are opposite so that $ab < 0$.

For the standard parabolas $y^2 = 4px$ and $x^2 = 4py$, one of a and b equals zero; hence, $ab = 0$.

In each of these cases it is possible for the conic to be a degenerate conic, that is, 2 lines for a hyperbola, a point for an ellipse or circle, and a single line for a parabola. We summarize these results as follows:

$$\text{Graph of } ax^2 + by^2 + 2gx + 2fy + c = 0$$
$$\text{ellipse} \Leftrightarrow ab > 0$$
$$\text{hyperbola} \Leftrightarrow ab < 0$$
$$\text{parabola} \Leftrightarrow ab = 0$$
$$\text{circle} \Leftrightarrow a = b$$

Example 1

Given the curve $4x^2 + 9y^2 - 8x + 36y + 4 = 0$.

(a) Name the type of conic.

(b) Find the translation that changes the given equation into standard form.

(c) Graph the given curve.

Solution

(a) Here $a = 4$, $b = 9$
$\therefore ab = 36 > 0$
$\therefore$ the curve is an ellipse.

(b) *Solution 1* (Completing the Squares)
We can find a translation image of the ellipse so that its defining equation is in standard form by completing the squares of the terms in x and the terms in y.
$\because \qquad 4x^2 + 9y^2 - 8x + 36y + 4 = 0$
$\therefore \qquad 4(x^2 - 2x) + 9(y^2 + 4y) = -4$
$\therefore \ 4(x^2 - 2x + 1) + 9(y^2 + 4y + 4) = -4 + 4 + 36$
$\therefore \qquad 4(x - 1)^2 + 9(y + 2)^2 = 36$
$\qquad \text{Let } x - 1 = u \text{ and } y + 2 = v$
$\therefore \qquad\qquad\qquad 4u^2 + 9v^2 = 36$

Thus the $(-1, 2)$ translation $(x, y) \to (x - 1, y + 2) = (u, v)$ maps $4x^2 + 9y^2 - 8x + 36y + 4 = 0$ into the standard form
$$4u^2 + 9v^2 = 36$$
which may be written $4x^2 + 9y^2 = 36$.

Solution 2

Let the required (h, k) translation be

$$(x, y) \to (u, v) \text{ where}$$

$$\left.\begin{array}{l} u = x + h \\ v = y + k \end{array}\right\} \Rightarrow \left\{\begin{array}{l} x = u - h \\ y = v - k \end{array}\right.$$

Since $\qquad\qquad 4x^2 + 9y^2 - 8x + 36y + 4 = 0$

$\therefore\ 4(u - h)^2 + 9(v - k)^2 - 8(u - h) + 36(v - k) + 4 = 0$

$\therefore\ 4(u^2 - 2hu + h^2) + 9(v^2 - 2vk + k^2)$

$$- 8u + 8h + 36v - 36k + 4 = 0$$

$\therefore\ 4u^2 + 9v^2 + u(-8h - 8) + v(-18k + 36)$

$$+ 4h^2 + 9k^2 + 8h - 36k + 4 = 0 \quad (1)$$

Equation (1) represents an ellipse in standard form if and only if there are no first degree terms in u and v. That is, if and only if the coefficients of u and v are each zero.

$\therefore \qquad\qquad \left.\begin{array}{l} -8h - 8 = 0 \\ -18k + 36 = 0 \end{array}\right\} \Rightarrow \left\{\begin{array}{l} h = -1 \\ k = 2 \end{array}\right.$

Substituting these values for h and k in equation (1) we obtain

$4u^2 + 9v^2 + u \cdot 0 + v \cdot 0 + 4(1) + 9(4) + 8(-1)$

$$- 36(2) + 4 = 0$$

or $\qquad 4u^2 + 9v^2 - 36 = 0.$

Thus the $(-1, 2)$ translation $(x, y) \to (x - 1, y + 2) = (u, v)$ maps the ellipse $4x^2 + 9y^2 - 8x + 36y + 4 = 0$ onto the image ellipse with equation in the standard form $4u^2 + 9v^2 = 36$ which may be written $4x^2 + 9y^2 = 36$.

(c) In order to graph the original curve

$$4x^2 + 9y^2 - 8x + 36y + 4 = 0$$

(1) graph $4x^2 + 9y^2 = 36$

(2) apply the translation inverse to the $(-1, 2)$ translation to the graph in (1).

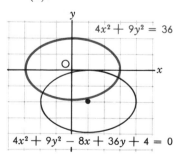

The graph shows $4x^2 + 9y^2 = 36$, an ellipse with centre $(0, 0)$ and x- and y-intercepts 3, -3 and 2, -2 respectively. The graph of $4x^2 + 9y^2 - 8x + 36y + 4 = 0$ is the graph of $4x^2 + 9y^2 = 36$ translated by the inverse translation $(1, -2)$, that is, each point of $4x^2 + 9y^2 = 36$ is moved one unit right and two units down.

Observe that the *method of completing of squares* was used in Solution 1 of part (b) of Example 1. Recall that a second degree expression such as $x^2 + kx$ becomes a perfect square if $\left(\dfrac{k}{2}\right)^2$ is added to it, that is, $x^2 + kx + \left(\dfrac{k}{2}\right)^2 = \left(x + \dfrac{k}{2}\right)^2$. Thus when the coefficient of x^2 is 1, the number used to complete the square is given by [half the coefficient of x]^2.

Example 2

Given the conic $y^2 - 4x + 6y + 1 = 0$.

(a) Determine the type of conic.

(b) Find a translation that transforms the given equation into standard form.

(c) Graph the given equation.

Solution

(a) Here $a = 0$, $b = 1$, $\therefore$ $ab = 0$. The conic is a parabola.

(b) We shall complete the square.
$$\because \qquad y^2 - 4x + 6y + 1 = 0$$
$$\therefore \qquad y^2 + 6y = 4x - 1$$
$$y^2 + 6y + 9 = 4x - 1 + 9$$
$$(y + 3)^2 = 4(x + 2)$$
Let $\qquad x + 2 = u$ and $y + 3 = v$
$$\therefore \qquad v^2 = 4u$$
which may be written $y^2 = 4x$
Thus under the $(2, 3)$ translation $(x, y) \rightarrow (x + 2, y + 3)$, the image of $y^2 - 4x + 6y + 1 = 0$ is the parabola $y^2 = 4x$.

(c) The graph of $y^2 = 4x$ is a parabola opening to the right with vertex at $(0, 0)$ and axis of symmetry along the x axis. The graph of $y^2 - 4x + 6y + 1 = 0$ is obtained by applying the *inverse* translation $(-2, -3)$ to the graph of $y^2 = 4x$ by moving each point 2 units to the left and 3 units down.

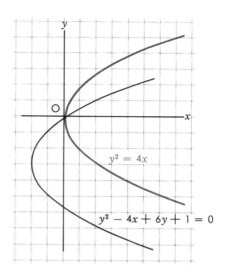

$y^2 = 4x$

$y^2 - 4x + 6y + 1 = 0$

Example 3

Given the curve $x^2 - 4y^2 + 6x - 16y - 3 = 0$.

(a) Determine the type of conic.

(b) Find the translation that transforms the given curve into standard form.

(c) Graph the given curve and find its centre.

Solution

(a) Here $a = 1$, $b = -4$, hence $ab = -4 < 0$. The curve is a hyperbola.

(b) We shall complete the squares.

$$\therefore \qquad x^2 - 4y^2 + 6x - 16y - 3 = 0$$
$$\therefore \qquad (x^2 + 6x) - 4(y^2 + 4y) = 3$$
$$\therefore \quad (x^2 + 6x + 9) - 4(y^2 + 4y + 4) = 3 + 9 - 16$$
$$\therefore \qquad (x + 3)^2 - 4(y + 2)^2 = -4$$

Let $\qquad x + 3 = u$ and $y + 2 = v$

$$\therefore \qquad u^2 - 4v^2 = -4$$

Thus the $(3, 2)$ translation $(x, y) \to (x + 3, y + 2)$ changes $x^2 - 4y^2 + 6x - 16y - 3 = 0$ into the standard form $u^2 - 4v^2 = -4$, which may be written $x^2 - 4y^2 = -4$.

(c) The graph of $x^2 - 4y^2 = -4$ is a hyperbola with centre $(0, 0)$ intersecting the y axis at $(0, 1)$ and $(0, -1)$. The graph of $x^2 - 4y^2 + 6x - 16y - 3 = 0$ is obtained by applying the

7.2/Graphing Second Degree Equations Using Translations

inverse translation $(-3, -2)$ to the graph of $x^2 - 4y^2 = -4$. The centre of $x^2 - 4y^2 + 6x - 16y - 3 = 0$ is the image of the centre $(0, 0)$ of $x^2 - 4y^2 = -4$, that is, $(-3, -2)$.

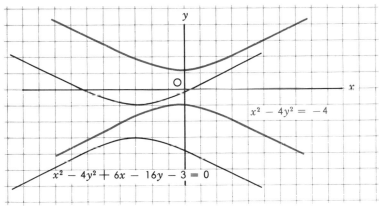

Exercise 7.2

A

1. By noting the coefficients of the second degree terms, state whether each of the following curves is a circle, an ellipse, a parabola, or a hyperbola.

   (a) $x^2 + y^2 - 4x - 12 = 0$ (d) $2x^2 - y^2 + 4x - 2y = 0$
   (b) $2x^2 + y^2 + 4x + 2y - 20 = 0$ (e) $x^2 + 3x + 4y - 6 = 0$
   (c) $x^2 - 3y^2 - 2x - 6y - 18 = 0$ (f) $y^2 - 2x - 4y + 1 = 0$

B

2. For each of the given equations find a translation that transforms it into standard form. In each case sketch the graph of the image of the given equation, and then the given curve.

   (a) $x^2 + y^2 - 2x + 4y - 4 = 0$
   (b) $4x^2 - 4y^2 + 8x - 16y + 13 = 0$
   (c) $x^2 + 2y^2 + 4x - 8y + 3 = 0$
   (d) $x^2 + 12x + 16y + 24 = 0$

3. For each of the given equations, find a translation that transforms it into standard form. In each case, graph the given equation.

   (a) $x^2 + 2x + 4y - 19 = 0$
   (b) $x^2 + 9y^2 - 6x + 18y + 9 = 0$
   (c) $4x^2 - y^2 - 8x - 4y - 1 = 0$
   (d) $y^2 + 4x - 12y + 4 = 0$
   (e) $3x^2 + 4y^2 + 12x - 8y + 4 = 0$
   (f) $2x^2 - 3y^2 - 12x - 12y - 6 = 0$

7.2/*Graphing Second Degree Equations Using Translations*   233

4. Using the same axes, plot the loci having the equations given.

(a) $x^2 + y^2 - 6x = 0$ (c) $x^2 + y^2 - 2x = 0$
(b) $x^2 + y^2 - 4x = 0$ (d) $x^2 + y^2 = 0$

5. Using the same axes, plot the curves listed.

(a) $x^2 - y^2 = 0$ (c) $x^2 - y^2 + 4x = 0$
(b) $x^2 - y^2 + 2x = 0$ (d) $x^2 - y^2 + 6x = 0$

6. Given the curve $4x^2 - y^2 + 2x + y = 0$.

(a) Find the translation that transforms the curve to standard position.
(b) Describe the graph of the given equation using the result of (a).
(c) Show that $2x + y$ is a factor of the left side of the given equation and hence verify your conclusion in (b).
(d) State the values of the coefficients a and b of the general equation for this case. Interpret the result as a special case of a hyperbola by considering the sections of a cone by a plane.

7. Graph each of the following conics. Determine the centre, vertices and axes of symmetry of each.

(a) $x^2 - y^2 + 2x + 2y + 1 = 0$
(b) $4x^2 + 9y^2 + 24x - 72y + 144 = 0$

8. Find the coordinates of the vertex and focus for each of the given parabolas.

(a) $6x^2 + 12x - y = 0$ (b) $y^2 - 4x + 8y - 12 = 0$

C 9. Find the coordinates of the centre and lengths of the semi-axes of each given curve.

(a) $x^2 + y^2 + 2ax - 2ay + a^2 = 0$
(b) $x^2 + 2y^2 - 4ax + 4ay + 2a^2 = 0$
(c) $\dfrac{x^2}{a^2} + \dfrac{y^2}{b^2} + \dfrac{2x}{a} - \dfrac{2y}{b} + 1 = 0$
(d) $x^2 - y^2 - 2ax + 2ay - 1 = 0$

10. Given a circle with equation $x^2 + y^2 + 2gx + 2fy + c = 0$.

(a) Show that the origin lies inside, on, or outside the circle when $c < 0$, $c = 0$, or $c > 0$, respectively.
(b) What condition on g, f, and c ensures that the locus is a single point? Is imaginary?

11. If $a > 0$, $b > 0$, show that $ax^2 + by^2 + 2gx + 2fy + c = 0$ represents an ellipse only if $\frac{g^2}{a} + \frac{f^2}{b} \geq c$. Describe the nature of the locus if this inequality is not satisfied.

12. If $a > 0$, $b < 0$, show that $ax^2 + by^2 + 2gx + 2fy + c = 0$ represents a hyperbola with principal axis directed as follows.

    (a) If $\frac{g^2}{a} + \frac{f^2}{b} > c$, principal axis parallel to x axis.

    (b) If $\frac{g^2}{a} + \frac{f^2}{b} < c$, principal axis parallel to y axis.

13. Describe the locus of Question 12 if $\frac{g^2}{a} + \frac{f^2}{b} = c$.

7.3 Equations of Image Curves Under a Rotation

If $P(x, y) \rightarrow P'(u, v)$ under a rotation of angle θ about $(0, 0)$ (Figure 7.1) then $u = x \cos \theta - y \sin \theta$
$$v = x \sin \theta + y \cos \theta$$

Observe that the image coordinates are on the left side of the equation and the pre-image coordinates are on the right side. Under the *inverse transformation*, a rotation of angle $-\theta$ about $(0, 0)$,

$$P'(u, v) \rightarrow P(x, y). \text{ (Figure 7.2)}$$

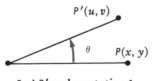

P → P' under rotation θ

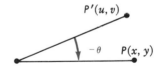

P' → P under rotation $-\theta$

FIGURE 7.1   FIGURE 7.2

Since $P(x, y)$ is the image and $P'(u, v)$ the pre-image under the rotation of $-\theta$, (x, y) must occur on the left side and (u, v) on the right side of the transformation equations.

Thus we have $x = u \cos (-\theta) - v \sin (-\theta)$
                   $y = u \sin (-\theta) + v \cos (-\theta)$

These equations may be further simplified, if desired, by recalling that
$$\cos (-\theta) = \cos \theta$$
$$\sin (-\theta) = -\sin \theta.$$

Example 1

(a) Find an equation of the image of the ellipse $3x^2 + y^2 = 12$ under a rotation through an angle $\frac{\pi}{4}$ rad about the origin.

(b) Graph the given curve and its image.

Solution

(a) Suppose $P(x, y)$ on the original curve maps onto $P'(u, v)$ on the image curve by the rotation of $\frac{\pi}{4}$ rad about $(0, 0)$, then $P'(u, v) \rightarrow P(x, y)$ under the *inverse rotation of* $-\frac{\pi}{4}$ about $(0, 0)$. Thus,

$$\left.\begin{array}{l} x = u \cos\left(-\dfrac{\pi}{4}\right) - v \sin\left(-\dfrac{\pi}{4}\right) \\[2mm] y = u \sin\left(-\dfrac{\pi}{4}\right) + v \cos\left(-\dfrac{\pi}{4}\right) \end{array}\right\} \Rightarrow$$

$$\left\{\begin{array}{l} x = u\left(\dfrac{1}{\sqrt{2}}\right) - v\left(-\dfrac{1}{\sqrt{2}}\right) = \dfrac{u + v}{\sqrt{2}} \\[3mm] y = u\left(-\dfrac{1}{\sqrt{2}}\right) + v\left(\dfrac{1}{\sqrt{2}}\right) = \dfrac{-u + v}{\sqrt{2}} \end{array}\right.$$

But in the original ellipse

$$3x^2 + y^2 = 12$$

Substituting for x and y we have

$$3\left(\frac{u + v}{\sqrt{2}}\right)^2 + \left(\frac{-u + v}{\sqrt{2}}\right)^2 = 12$$

$$\therefore \quad 3\left(\frac{u^2 + 2uv + v^2}{2}\right) + \frac{u^2 - 2uv + v^2}{2} = 12$$

$$\therefore \qquad\qquad u^2 + uv + v^2 = 6.$$

Thus the ellipse $\{(x, y) \mid 3x^2 + y^2 = 12\}$ maps onto the curve $\{(u, v) \mid u^2 + uv + v^2 = 6\}$ which may be written $\{(x, y) \mid x^2 + xy + y^2 = 6\}$.

Since rotation is a rigid motion, size and shape are preserved, thus the image is an ellipse and $x^2 + xy + y^2 = 6$ is an equation of the ellipse.

(b) The original curve $3x^2 + y^2 = 12$ has x-intercepts $2, -2$ and y-intercepts $\sqrt{12}, -\sqrt{12}$. This curve is graphed first, then rotated through an angle of $\frac{\pi}{4}$ rad about $(0, 0)$ to obtain the graph of $x^2 + xy + y^2 = 6$.

7.3/*Equations of Image Curves Under a Rotation*

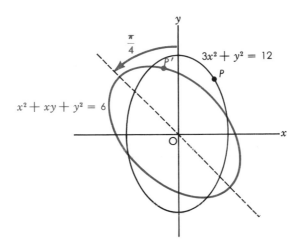

$x^2 + xy + y^2 = 6$

$3x^2 + y^2 = 12$

$\dfrac{\pi}{4}$

In Example 1 note that the coefficient of x^2 has changed and an xy term has been introduced.

Example 2

(a) Find an equation of the image of the hyperbola $x^2 - 2y^2 = 1$ under a rotation of $\dfrac{\pi}{3}$ rad about the origin.

(b) Graph the given curve and its image.

Solution

(a) Under a rotation of $\dfrac{\pi}{3}$ rad about $(0,0)$ any point $P(x, y)$ on $x^2 - 2y^2 = 1$ maps onto a point $P'(u, v)$ on the image curve.

Hence under the *inverse rotation* of $-\dfrac{\pi}{3}$ rad about $(0, 0)$

$P'(u, v) \rightarrow P(x, y)$

$$\left. \begin{array}{l} \therefore \ x = u \cos\left(-\dfrac{\pi}{3}\right) - v \sin\left(-\dfrac{\pi}{3}\right) \\[2mm] y = u \sin\left(-\dfrac{\pi}{3}\right) + v \cos\left(-\dfrac{\pi}{3}\right) \end{array} \right\} \Rightarrow$$

$$\left\{ \begin{array}{l} x = u\left(\dfrac{1}{2}\right) - v\left(-\dfrac{\sqrt{3}}{2}\right) = \dfrac{u + v\sqrt{3}}{2} \\[3mm] y = u\left(-\dfrac{\sqrt{3}}{2}\right) + v\left(\dfrac{1}{2}\right) = \dfrac{-u\sqrt{3} + v}{2} \end{array} \right.$$

But on the original curve $x^2 - 2y^2 = 1$
Substituting for x and y we have

$$\left(\frac{u + v\sqrt{3}}{2}\right)^2 - 2\left(\frac{-u\sqrt{3} + v}{2}\right)^2 = 1$$

$$\therefore \frac{u^2 + 2\sqrt{3}uv + 3v^2}{4} - 2\left(\frac{3u^2 - 2\sqrt{3}uv + v^2}{4}\right) = 1$$

$$\therefore \quad u^2 + 2\sqrt{3}uv + 3v^2 - 6u^2 + 4\sqrt{3}uv - 2v^2 = 4$$

$$\therefore \qquad\qquad 5u^2 - 6\sqrt{3}uv - v^2 = -4$$

Hence under a rotation of $\frac{\pi}{3}$ rad about the origin the

hyperbola $x^2 - 2y^2 = 1$

maps onto the hyperbola $5x^2 - 6\sqrt{3}xy - y^2 = -4$.

(b) The original hyperbola
$x^2 - 2y^2 = 1$ intersects the
x axis at $(1, 0)$ and $(-1, 0)$
and has centre at $(0, 0)$. The
graph of the image curve
$5x^2 - 6\sqrt{3}xy - y^2 = -4$
is obtained by rotating the
graph of $x^2 - 2y^2 = 1$

through $\frac{\pi}{3}$ rad about $(0, 0)$.

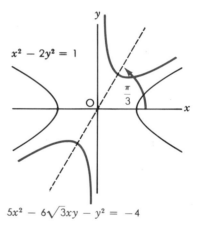

$5x^2 - 6\sqrt{3}xy - y^2 = -4$

Note once again that the rotation has introduced a term containing
the product xy.

The equation found in these two examples are instances of the
second degree equation

$$ax^2 + 2hxy + by^2 + c = 0.$$

Any curve represented by this type of equation is symmetric with
respect to the origin. That is, if (x, y) lies on the curve, then $(-x, -y)$
also lies on the curve. For

$$a(-x)^2 + 2h(-x)(-y) + b(-y)^2 + c = ax^2 + 2hxy + by^2 + c = 0$$

so the equation of the curve is satisfied by the coordinates $(-x, -y)$.

Is this curve symmetric with respect to the x axis? The y axis?
What is the condition for such symmetry? The curve would be symmetric about the x axis and the y axis if $h = 0$. When $h \neq 0$, we see
that the curve is not symmetric about the x axis or about the y axis.

Example 3

(a) Find an equation of the parabola obtained by rotating the parabola $y^2 = 4x$ through an angle of $135°$ about the origin.

(b) Graph the given equation and its image.

(c) Find an equation of the axis of symmetry of the image curve.

Solution

(a) Under a rotation of $135°$ about the origin any point $P(x, y)$ on $y^2 = 4x$ maps onto a point $P'(u, v)$ on the image curve. Thus under the inverse rotation of $-135°$ about the origin $P'(u, v) \rightarrow P(x, y)$

$$\left. \begin{array}{l} \therefore \ x = u \cos (-135°) - v \sin (-135°) \\ \\ y = u \sin (-135°) + v \cos (-135°) \end{array} \right\} \Rightarrow$$

$$\begin{cases} x = u\left(-\dfrac{1}{\sqrt{2}}\right) - v\left(-\dfrac{1}{\sqrt{2}}\right) = \dfrac{-u + v}{\sqrt{2}} \\ \\ y = u\left(-\dfrac{1}{\sqrt{2}}\right) + v\left(-\dfrac{1}{\sqrt{2}}\right) = \dfrac{-u - v}{\sqrt{2}} \end{cases}$$

On the original curve $\qquad y^2 = 4x$

$$\left(\dfrac{-u - v}{\sqrt{2}}\right)^2 = 4\left(\dfrac{-u + v}{\sqrt{2}}\right)$$

$$\therefore \qquad \dfrac{u^2 + 2uv + v^2}{2} = -2\sqrt{2}u + 2\sqrt{2}v$$

$$\therefore \ u^2 + 2uv + v^2 + 4\sqrt{2}u - 4\sqrt{2}v = 0$$

Thus under a rotation of $-135°$ about the origin, the parabola $y^2 = 4x$ maps onto the parabola

$$x^2 + 2xy + y^2 + 4\sqrt{2}x - 4\sqrt{2}y = 0.$$

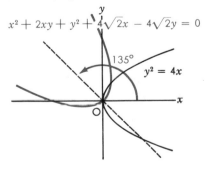

(b) The graph of $y^2 = 4x$ is a parabola with vertex at $(0, 0)$ opening along the positive x axis as axis of symmetry. The graph of $x^2 + 2xy + y^2 + 4\sqrt{2}x - 4\sqrt{2}y = 0$ is obtained by rotating the graph of $y^2 = 4x$ through $135°$ about $(0, 0)$.

(c) The axis of symmetry of the image curve is the image of the
   x axis under this rotation, namely, the line $y = -x$.
   The xy term is again present in Example 3, but the curve is not
symmetrical with respect to the origin. The image curve
$x^2 + 2xy + y^2 + 4\sqrt{2}x - 4\sqrt{2}y = 0$ has the form
$ax^2 + 2hxy + by^2 + 2gx + 2fy + c = 0$, where $a = 1$, $h = 1$, $b = 1$
and $ab = 1$. For the original curve $y^2 = 4x$, $a = 0$, $h = 0$, $b = 1$ and
$ab = 0$. Note that the sign of ab is *not* invariant under a rotation.
It can be shown that the sign of the expression $ab - h^2$ is invariant.
For a parabola, $ab - h^2 = 0$.

Exercise 7.3

A
1. What does the presence of an xy term in an equation of a conic
   signify about the axis of the conic?

B
2. Find an equation of the image of the parabola $y^2 = 4x$ under a
   rotation of $\frac{\pi}{6}$ rad about the origin. Graph the given curve and
   its image.

3. Find an equation of the image of the ellipse $4x^2 + y^2 = 4$ under
   a rotation of $45°$ about the origin. Graph the given curve and
   its image.

4. Find an equation of the image of the hyperbola $x^2 - 3y^2 = 12$
   under a rotation of $\frac{\pi}{3}$ rad about the origin. Graph the given
   curve and its image.

5. For each of the given curves determine an equation of its image
   under a rotation about the origin of the angle indicated. Graph
   the image curve and then the original curve.

Curve	Angle of rotation
(a) $xy = 1$	$\frac{\pi}{4}$ rad
(b) $3x^2 + 2\sqrt{3}xy + 5y^2 - 36 = 0$	$\frac{\pi}{6}$ rad
(c) $x^2 + 2xy + y^2 - 16\sqrt{2}y + 16\sqrt{2}x = 0$	$45°$

6. (a) Regarding each of the equations in Questions 2 to 5 as an
       example of the equation
       $$ax^2 + 2hxy + by^2 + 2gx + 2fy + c = 0$$
       find the sign of $ab - h^2$ for each conic and its image.

(b) The result of part (a) implies that the sign of $ab - h^2$ is invariant under a rotation about the origin. How could you use this fact to determine the type of curve in each part of Question 5 without actually performing the rotation?

7. Without using the formulas of rotation find an equation of the image of the line $x + y = 0$ under a rotation of $\frac{\pi}{4}$ rad about the origin. Graph the given line and its image.

8. Find equations of the curves formed by rotating each of the following curves through an angle of $\frac{\pi}{2}$ rad about the origin. It is not necessary to use the rotation formulas.

(a) $x^2 - y^2 = 3$ (c) $4x^2 - 3y^2 = 6$
(b) $x^2 + 2y^2 = 4$ (d) $x^2 + y^2 = 3$

9. Find equations of the curves formed by rotating each of the specified curves through an angle of $\frac{\pi}{4}$ rad about the origin.

(a) $x^2 - y^2 = 1$ (c) $x^2 = 16y$
(b) $4x^2 + 9y^2 = 1$ (d) $3x^2 - 2y^2 = 6$

10. Determine equations of the curves formed by rotating the given curves through an angle of $\frac{\pi}{3}$ rad about the origin.

(a) $\sqrt{3}x - y = 0$ (c) $x^2 - 3y^2 = 1$
(b) $x^2 + y^2 - 4 = 0$ (d) $2x^2 + 6y^2 = 3$

7.4 Graphing Second Degree Equations Using Rotations

In Section 7.3 we saw that the general equation of the second degree in x and y represents a conic. This equation is

$$ax^2 + 2hxy + by^2 + 2gx + 2fy + c = 0. \qquad (1)$$

In Exercise 7.3, Question 6, you were given the opportunity to check that the sign of the expression $ab - h^2$ is invariant under a rotation about the origin for curves whose equations are of the form of equation (1). It can be shown that $ab - h^2$ is invariant for all curves with second degree equations under a rotation. Now a second degree curve in standard position with $h = 0$ is an ellipse if $ab > 0$, $ab - h^2 > 0$; a hyperbola if $ab < 0$, $ab - h^2 < 0$; and a parabola if $ab = 0$, $ab - h^2 = 0$. Since $ab - h^2$ is invariant under a rotation, equation (1) represents an ellipse if $ab - h^2 > 0$, a hyperbola if $ab - h^2 < 0$, and a parabola if $ab - h^2 = 0$. In each case it is possible for the conic to be a degenerate conic as mentioned in Section 7.2, page 229. This result can be summarized as follows.

Graph of $ax^2 + 2hxy + by^2 + 2gx + 2fy + c = 0$

ellipse $\quad\Leftrightarrow ab - h^2 > 0$

hyperbola $\Leftrightarrow ab - h^2 < 0$

parabola $\quad\Leftrightarrow ab - h^2 = 0$

Example 1

Classify the following curves.

(a) $2x^2 + xy + y^2 - 1 = 0$

(b) $x^2 + 2xy + y^2 + 4\sqrt{2}x - 4\sqrt{2}y = 0$

(c) $x^2 + 3xy + 2y^2 - 1 = 0$

Solution

	a	b	h	$ab - h^2$	Type
(a)	2	1	$\frac{1}{2}$	$2 - \frac{1}{4} = 1\frac{3}{4} > 0$	ellipse
(b)	1	1	1	$1 - 1 = 0$	parabola
(c)	1	2	$\frac{3}{2}$	$2 - \frac{9}{4} = -\frac{1}{4} < 0$	hyperbola

In order to graph a conic whose equation contains an xy term we first eliminate the xy term so that the equation may be written in standard form. Once the equation is in standard form the image curve can be graphed. We shall see that the xy term can be eliminated by selecting a suitable rotation about $(0, 0)$. Hence the graph of the original curve can then be obtained from the image curve by a rotation about the origin. In some cases a translation will also be needed. We shall discuss situations where both a translation and a rotation are needed in Section 7.5.

Example 2

Given the curve $17x^2 + 16xy + 17y^2 - 225 = 0$.

(a) Name the type of conic.

(b) Find a rotation that eliminates the xy term from the given equation.

(c) Find an equation of the image curve under the rotation in (b).

(d) Graph the given curve.

Solution

(a) Here $a = 17$, $b = 17$, $h = 8$, $ab - h^2 = 289 - 64 > 0$. The conic is an ellipse.

(b) Let $P(x, y)$ on the original curve $17x^2 + 16xy + 17y^2 - 225 = 0$ map onto $P'(u, v)$ under a rotation θ about $(0, 0)$.
Thus, $P'(u, v) \rightarrow P(x, y)$ under the inverse rotation $-\theta$ about $(0, 0)$.

$$\therefore \quad \left. \begin{array}{l} x = u \cos (-\theta) - v \sin (-\theta) \\ y = u \sin (-\theta) + v \cos (-\theta) \end{array} \right\}$$

$$\Rightarrow \begin{cases} x = u \cos \theta + v \sin \theta \\ y = -u \sin \theta + v \cos \theta \end{cases} \quad \left[\begin{array}{l} \because \cos (-\theta) = \cos \theta \\ \sin (-\theta) = -\sin \theta \end{array} \right]$$

For any point on the given curve
$17x^2 + 16xy + 17y^2 - 225 = 0$
$17(u \cos \theta + v \sin \theta)^2$
$\qquad + 16(u \cos \theta + v \sin \theta)(-u \sin \theta + v \cos \theta)$
$\qquad \qquad + 17(-u \sin \theta + v \cos \theta)^2 - 225 = 0$.
$\therefore \quad 17(u^2\cos^2\theta + 2 \cos \theta \sin \theta \ uv + v^2\sin^2\theta)$
$+ 16(-u^2\cos \theta \sin \theta + uv \cos^2\theta - uv \sin^2\theta + v^2\sin \theta \cos \theta)$
$+ 17(u^2\sin^2\theta - 2 \sin \theta \cos \theta \ uv + v^2\cos^2\theta)$
$- 225$
$= 0$.

Removing brackets and grouping terms with u^2, v^2 and uv we have
$u^2(17 \cos^2\theta - 16 \cos \theta \sin \theta + 17 \sin^2\theta)$
$+ uv(34 \cos \theta \sin \theta + 16 \cos^2\theta - 16 \sin^2\theta - 34 \sin \theta \cos \theta)$
$+ v^2(17 \sin^2\theta + 16 \sin \theta \cos \theta + 17 \cos^2\theta)$
$- 225$
$= 0 \qquad (1)$

The uv term will be eliminated if its coefficient is zero. Thus we must select θ so that
$34 \cos \theta \sin \theta + 16 \cos^2\theta - 16 \sin^2\theta - 34 \sin \theta \cos \theta = 0$
$\therefore \qquad\qquad\qquad\qquad\qquad\qquad 16(\cos^2\theta - \sin^2\theta) = 0$
$\because \cos^2\theta - \sin^2\theta = \cos 2\theta$, we have $\qquad\qquad 16 \cos 2\theta = 0$
Thus any angle for which $\cos 2\theta = 0$ will be a suitable rotation.
The smallest positive angle will be $2\theta = \dfrac{\pi}{2}$

$$\text{or } \theta = \frac{\pi}{4}$$

Thus an angle of $\dfrac{\pi}{4}$ rad will eliminate the xy term in the given expression.

(c) The image equation (1) can be simplified by using the fact that $\theta = 45°$. Equation (1) becomes

$$u^2\left(17\left(\frac{1}{\sqrt{2}}\right)^2 - 16\left(\frac{1}{\sqrt{2}}\right)\left(\frac{1}{\sqrt{2}}\right) + 17\left(\frac{1}{\sqrt{2}}\right)^2\right)$$

$$+ uv\cdot 0$$

$$+ v^2\left(17\left(\frac{1}{\sqrt{2}}\right)^2 + 16\left(\frac{1}{\sqrt{2}}\right)\left(\frac{1}{\sqrt{2}}\right) + 17\left(\frac{1}{\sqrt{2}}\right)^2\right)$$

$$- 225 = 0$$

$$\therefore\ u^2\left(\frac{17}{2} - \frac{16}{2} + \frac{17}{2}\right) + v^2\left(\frac{17}{2} + \frac{16}{2} + \frac{17}{2}\right) - 225 = 0$$

reduces to $9u^2 + 25v^2 = 225$ which may be written
$$9x^2 + 25y^2 = 225.$$

(d) To graph the given curve we must first graph the image curve. The image curve is an ellipse $9x^2 + 25y^2 = 225$ having centre at $(0, 0)$ with x-intercepts 5, -5 and y-intercepts 3, -3. After graphing this ellipse, the graph is rotated through $-45°$ about the origin to obtain the graph of the original equation

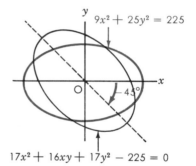

$$17x^2 + 16xy + 17y^2 - 225 = 0.$$

We shall now apply the same method as in Example 1 to determine the rotation angle about $(0, 0)$ through the angle θ that will eliminate the xy term from

$$ax^2 + 2hxy + by^2 + 2gx + 2fy + c = 0.$$

Example 3

Find a rotation about the origin that eliminates the xy term from the equation

$$ax^2 + 2hxy + by^2 + 2gx + 2fy + c = 0, h \neq 0.$$

Solution

If $P(x, y) \rightarrow P'(u, v)$ under a rotation of θ about $(0, 0)$ then $P'(u, v) \rightarrow P(x, y)$ under the *inverse rotation* of $-\theta$ about $(0, 0)$.

$$\therefore \ \left. \begin{aligned} x &= u \cos(-\theta) - v \sin(-\theta) \\ y &= u \sin(-\theta) + v \cos(-\theta) \end{aligned} \right\} \Rightarrow \begin{cases} x = u \cos\theta + v \sin\theta \\ y = -u \sin\theta + v \cos\theta \end{cases}$$

For any point on the given curve

$$ax^2 + 2hxy + by^2 + 2gx + 2fy + c = 0 \text{ we have}$$

$a(u \cos\theta + v \sin\theta)^2 + 2h(u \cos\theta + v \sin\theta)(-u \sin\theta + v \cos\theta)$
$+ b(-u \sin\theta + v \cos\theta)^2 + 2g(u \cos\theta + v \sin\theta)$
$+ 2f(-u \sin\theta + v \cos\theta) + c = 0$

$\therefore \ a(u^2\cos^2\theta + 2 \cos\theta \sin\theta \ uv + v^2\sin^2\theta)$
$+ 2h(-u^2\cos\theta \sin\theta + uv \cos^2\theta - uv \sin^2\theta + v^2\cos\theta \sin\theta)$
$+ b(u^2\sin^2\theta - 2 \sin\theta \cos\theta \ uv + v^2\cos^2\theta)$
$+ 2g(u \cos\theta + v \sin\theta) + 2f(-u \sin\theta + v \cos\theta) + c = 0$

Collecting terms in u^2, v^2, uv,
$u^2(a \cos^2\theta - 2h \cos\theta \sin\theta + b \sin^2\theta)$
$+ uv[2a \cos\theta \sin\theta + 2h(\cos^2\theta - \sin^2\theta) - 2b \sin\theta \cos\theta]$
$+ v^2(a \sin^2\theta + 2h \cos\theta \sin\theta + b \cos^2\theta)$
$+ 2g(u \cos\theta + v \sin\theta) + 2f(-u \sin\theta + v \cos\theta) + c$
$= 0$

To eliminate the uv term we shall select θ so that the coefficient of uv equals zero.

$\therefore \ 2a \cos\theta \sin\theta + 2h(\cos^2\theta - \sin^2\theta) - 2b \sin\theta \cos\theta = 0 \qquad (1)$

but $2 \cos\theta \sin\theta = \sin 2\theta$ and $\cos^2\theta - \sin^2\theta = \cos 2\theta$

Thus (1) becomes $a \sin 2\theta + 2h \cos 2\theta - b \sin 2\theta = 0$

or $\qquad\qquad\qquad 2h \cos 2\theta = (b - a) \sin 2\theta$

If $b - a \neq 0$	If $b - a = 0$
$\dfrac{2h}{b - a} = \dfrac{\sin 2\theta}{\cos 2\theta}$	$\cos 2\theta = 0$, since $h \neq 0$
$\tan 2\theta = \dfrac{2h}{b - a}$	$2\theta = \dfrac{\pi}{2}$ or $2\theta = \dfrac{3\pi}{2}$
	$\theta = \dfrac{\pi}{4}$ or $\theta = \dfrac{3\pi}{4}$

Therefore, if $b \neq a$ the angle of rotation is half an angle whose tangent is equal to $\dfrac{2h}{b - a}$. When $b = a$ the rotation angle is either $\dfrac{\pi}{4}$ or $\dfrac{3\pi}{4}$.

The xy term will be removed if the major axis of the conic is rotated either to the x axis or to the y axis. Thus, there are two possible values for the rotation angle θ, which differ by a right angle. Note that the two corresponding values of 2θ differ by π, so that if $b \neq a$, the tangents of these two double angles have the same value $\dfrac{2h}{b - a}$.

To eliminate the xy term from
$$ax^2 + 2hxy + by^2 + 2gx + 2fy + c = 0$$
apply a rotation of angle θ about $(0, 0)$, where

if $b \neq a$	if $b = a$
$\tan 2\theta = \dfrac{2h}{b - a}$	$\theta = \dfrac{\pi}{4}$ or $\dfrac{3\pi}{4}$

Example 4

Given the conic $x^2 + 2\sqrt{3}xy - y^2 = 1$.

(a) Name the type of conic.
(b) Find a rotation that eliminates the xy term from the given equation.
(c) Find an equation of the image curve.
(d) Graph the given curve.

Solution

(a) Here $a = 1$, $b = -1$, $h = \sqrt{3}$, $\therefore$ $ab - h^2 = -1 - 3 = -4$
$\because$ $ab - h^2 < 0$, $\therefore$ the conic is a hyperbola.

(b) $\because$ $b \neq a$, the angle of rotation θ about $(0, 0)$ that will eliminate the xy term is given by the following.
$$\tan 2\theta = \frac{2h}{b - a}$$
$$= \frac{2\sqrt{3}}{-1 - 1}$$
$$= -\sqrt{3}$$
The smallest positive angle satisfying this condition is given by $2\theta = \dfrac{2\pi}{3}$
$$\therefore \quad \theta = \frac{\pi}{3}$$
Thus a rotation of $\dfrac{\pi}{3}$ rad about the origin will eliminate the xy term.

(c) If $P(x, y) \rightarrow P'(u, v)$ under a rotation of $\dfrac{\pi}{3}$ about $(0, 0)$ then $P'(u, v) \rightarrow P(x, y)$ under the inverse rotation $-\dfrac{\pi}{3}$ about $(0, 0)$.

$$\therefore \quad x = u \cos\left(-\frac{\pi}{3}\right) - v \sin\left(-\frac{\pi}{3}\right)$$
$$y = u \sin\left(-\frac{\pi}{3}\right) + v \cos\left(-\frac{\pi}{3}\right) \quad \Rightarrow$$

$$\begin{cases} x = u\left(\dfrac{1}{2}\right) - v\left(-\dfrac{\sqrt{3}}{2}\right) = \dfrac{u + v\sqrt{3}}{2} \\ y = u\left(-\dfrac{\sqrt{3}}{2}\right) + v\left(\dfrac{1}{2}\right) = \dfrac{-u\sqrt{3} + v}{2} \end{cases}$$

Substituting for x and y in the equation of the original curve, $x^2 + 2\sqrt{3}\,xy - y^2 = 1$, we obtain

$$\left(\frac{u + v\sqrt{3}}{2}\right)^2 + 2\sqrt{3}\left(\frac{u + v\sqrt{3}}{2}\right)\left(\frac{-u\sqrt{3} + v}{2}\right)$$
$$- \left(\frac{-u\sqrt{3} + v}{2}\right)^2 = 1$$

$$\frac{u^2 + 2\sqrt{3}uv + 3v^2}{4} + 2\sqrt{3}\left(\frac{-\sqrt{3}u^2 + uv - 3uv + \sqrt{3}v^2}{4}\right)$$
$$- \left(\frac{3u^2 - 2\sqrt{3}uv + v^2}{4}\right) = 1$$

Multiplying by 4 and collecting like terms gives
$(1 - 6 - 3)u^2 + 0 \cdot uv + (3 + 6 - 1)v^2 = 4$
or $2u^2 - 2v^2 = -1$ which may be written
$2x^2 - 2y^2 = -1$

(d) To graph the original curve we must first graph the image curve $2x^2 - 2y^2 = -1$. The image curve is a hyperbola with centre $(0, 0)$ intersecting the y axis at $\left(0, \dfrac{1}{\sqrt{2}}\right), \left(0, -\dfrac{1}{\sqrt{2}}\right)$.

But $x^2 + 2\sqrt{3}xy - y^2 = 1$ maps onto $2x^2 - 2y^2 = -1$ under a rotation of $\dfrac{\pi}{3}$ about $(0, 0)$.

Thus $2x^2 - 2y^2 = -1$ maps back onto $x^2 + 2\sqrt{3}xy - y^2 = 1$ under the inverse rotation of $-\dfrac{\pi}{3}$ about $(0, 0)$. Thus the graph of $x^2 + 2\sqrt{3}xy - y^2 = 1$ is obtained by rotating the graph of $2x^2 - 2y^2 = -1$ through $-\dfrac{\pi}{3}$ about $(0, 0)$.

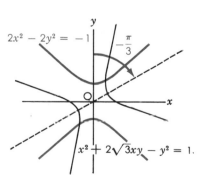

Exercise 7.4

B

1. From first principles, as in Examples 2 and 3, determine, to the nearest degree, an angle of rotation required to eliminate the xy term from the equation $x^2 + 2xy + 2y^2 - 4 = 0$

2. In each of the following use the $ab - h^2$ criterion to find the type of the curve, and find an angle of rotation about the origin required to place the image curve in standard position.

   (a) $xy = -4$
   (b) $x^2 - xy = 1$
   (c) $-x^2 + 2\sqrt{3}xy + y^2 = 2$
   (d) $(x + y)^2 = 2x$
   (e) $xy - \sqrt{3}y^2 + 2x - 3y = 1$
   (f) $2x^2 + xy + y^2 = 4$

3. For each of the following conics:

   (*i*) Name the type of conic.
   (*ii*) Find an angle of rotation about the origin that will eliminate the xy term.
   (*iii*) Find an equation of the image curve.
   (*iv*) Graph the given curve.

   (a) $13x^2 + 10xy + 13y^2 = 8$
   (b) $x^2 - 2\sqrt{3}xy - y^2 = 2$
   (c) $xy = -4$
   (d) $x^2 + 2xy + y^2 - 2\sqrt{2}x + 2\sqrt{2}y = 0$
   (e) $5x^2 + 2\sqrt{3}xy + 3y^2 = 36$
   (f) $3x^2 + 2\sqrt{3}xy + y^2 - 4x + 4\sqrt{3}y = 0$

4. (a) Eliminate the xy term from $x^2 + 2xy + y^2 - 1 = 0$ by a suitable rotation.
   (b) Describe the given curve.
   (c) Calculate $ab - h^2$ for the equation of part (a).
   (d) Obtain the result of part (b) by factoring the left side of the given equation.

5. Explain why an xy term will not be introduced into the equation of a circle if the circle is rotated about the origin.

C

6. (a) What rotations about the origin will carry the curve

$$ax^2 + 2hxy + ay^2 + c = 0, \qquad a, h \in R,$$

   into standard position?

248   *7.4/Graphing Second Degree Equations Using Rotations*

(b) Perform a rotation of $\frac{\pi}{4}$ rad about the origin for the equation of part (a) and hence state the lengths of the semi axes of the curve.

(c) Find the condition that this curve in part (a) is

   (i) an ellipse
   (ii) a hyperbola
   (iii) a pair of parallel straight lines

7. Show that the graph of $ax^2 + 2hxy + by^2 + c = 0$ is a hyperbola if $ab - h^2 < 0$ and $c \neq 0$. What is the nature of the locus if $ab - h^2 < 0$ and $c = 0$?

8. Given that a rotation about the origin through the angle θ takes the conic $ax^2 + 2hxy + by^2 + c = 0$ into the conic

$$Ax^2 + 2Hxy + By^2 + C = 0.$$

(a) Show that

$$A = \frac{a+b}{2} + \frac{a-b}{2} \cos 2\theta - h \sin 2\theta$$

$$B = \frac{a+b}{2} - \frac{a-b}{2} \cos 2\theta + h \sin 2\theta$$

$$H = h \cos 2\theta + \frac{a-b}{2} \sin 2\theta$$

(Hint: Example 3 and the double angle formulas of Section 3.4)

(b) Deduce that $A + B = a + b$ and $AB - H^2 = ab - h^2$.

7.5 Graphing Using both Rotations and Translations

In Section 7.2 we graphed equations of the form $ax^2 + 2hxy + by^2 + 2gx + 2fy + c = 0$, where $h = 0$, using translations. In Section 7.4 we graphed equations of the form $ax^2 + 2hxy + by^2 + 2gx + 2fy + c = 0$ where, for the most part, $g = f = 0$, using rotations. In general, if there are no restrictions on the coefficients of the equation $ax^2 + 2hxy + by^2 + 2gx + 2fy + c = 0$ both rotations and translations will be needed to assist in the graphing of the equation.

Example 1

Given the conic with equation

$$13x^2 + 10xy + 13y^2 + 34\sqrt{2}x + 2\sqrt{2}y = 0.$$

(a) Name the type of conic.
(b) Use transformations to reduce the given equation to standard form.
(c) Graph the conic.
(d) Find the coordinates of the centre and vertices of the conic.

Solution

(a) Here $a = 13$, $b = 13$, $h = 5$, $\therefore ab - h^2 = 169 - 25 > 0$.
$\therefore$ the conic is an ellipse.

(b) To reduce the equation of the conic to standard form we must first eliminate the xy term.
$\because a = b$, a rotation of $45°$ about the origin will eliminate the xy term.
If $P(x, y) \to P'(u, v)$ under a rotation of $45°$ about $(0, 0)$, then $P'(u, v) \to P(x, y)$ under the *inverse rotation* of $-45°$ about $(0, 0)$.

$$\therefore \left. \begin{array}{l} x = u \cos(-45°) - v \sin(-45°) \\ y = u \sin(-45°) + v \cos(-45°) \end{array} \right\}$$

$$\Rightarrow \begin{cases} x = u\left(\dfrac{1}{\sqrt{2}}\right) - v\left(-\dfrac{1}{\sqrt{2}}\right) = \dfrac{u + v}{\sqrt{2}} \\ y = u\left(-\dfrac{1}{\sqrt{2}}\right) + v\left(\dfrac{1}{\sqrt{2}}\right) = \dfrac{-u + v}{\sqrt{2}} \end{cases}$$

For any point $P(x, y)$ on the original curve

$$13x^2 + 10xy + 13y^2 + 34\sqrt{2}x + 2\sqrt{2}y = 0$$

we have $13\left(\dfrac{u + v}{\sqrt{2}}\right)^2 + 10\left(\dfrac{u + v}{\sqrt{2}}\right)\left(\dfrac{-u + v}{\sqrt{2}}\right)$

$$+ 13\left(\dfrac{-u + v}{\sqrt{2}}\right)^2 + 34\sqrt{2}\left(\dfrac{u + v}{\sqrt{2}}\right) + 2\sqrt{2}\left(\dfrac{-u + v}{\sqrt{2}}\right) = 0$$

$$\therefore 13\left(\dfrac{u^2 + 2uv + v^2}{2}\right) + 10\left(\dfrac{-u^2 + uv - uv + v^2}{2}\right)$$

$$+ 13\left(\dfrac{u^2 - 2uv + v^2}{2}\right) + 34u + 34v - 2u + 2v = 0$$

7.5/Graphing Using both Rotations and Translations

$$\therefore \ u^2\left(\frac{13}{2} - \frac{10}{2} + \frac{13}{2}\right) + 0 \cdot uv + v^2\left(\frac{13}{2} + \frac{10}{2} + \frac{13}{2}\right)$$
$$+ 32u + 36v = 0$$
$$\therefore \ 8u^2 + 18v^2 + 32u + 36v = 0$$
$$\therefore \ 4u^2 + 9v^2 + 16u + 18v = 0 \qquad (1)$$

To reduce equation to standard form (no u term or v term) a translation is needed. To determine the translation, we shall complete the squares.

(1) becomes
$$4(u^2 + 4u) + 9(v^2 + 2v) = 0$$
$$4(u^2 + 4u + 4) + 9(v^2 + 2v + 1) = 16 + 9$$
$$4(u + 2)^2 + 9(v + 1)^2 = 25$$
$$\text{Let } u + 2 = s \text{ and } v + 1 = t$$
$$\therefore \ 4s^2 + 9t^2 = 25$$

Thus under the $(2, 1)$ translation $(u, v) \rightarrow (s, t) = (u + 2, v + 1)$ the curve $4u^2 + 9v^2 + 16u + 18v = 0$ maps onto the curve $4s^2 + 9t^2 = 25$.

(c) To graph the given curve we must first graph the final image $4s^2 + 9t^2 = 25$. The graph of $4s^2 + 9t^2 = 25$ is an ellipse with centre $(0, 0)$, x-intercepts $\frac{5}{2}, -\frac{5}{2}$ and y-intercepts $\frac{5}{3}, -\frac{5}{3}$. Since $4s^2 + 9t^2 = 25$ maps onto $4u^2 + 9v^2 + 16u + 18v = 0$ under the inverse translation $(-2, -1)$, translating the graph of $4s^2 + 9t^2 = 25$, 2 units left and 1 unit down gives the graph of $4u^2 + 9v^2 + 16u + 18v = 0$.

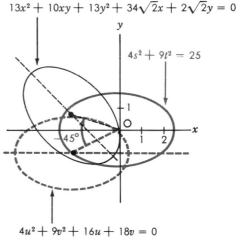

$13x^2 + 10xy + 13y^2 + 34\sqrt{2}x + 2\sqrt{2}y = 0$

$4s^2 + 9t^2 = 25$

$4u^2 + 9v^2 + 16u + 18v = 0$

But $4u^2 + 9v^2 + 16u + 18v = 0$ maps onto $13x^2 + 10xy + 13y^2 + 34\sqrt{2}x + 2\sqrt{2}y = 0$ under the inverse rotation of $-45°$ about $(0, 0)$. Thus, rotating the graph of $4u^2 + 9v^2 + 16u + 18v = 0$ about $(0, 0)$ through $-45°$ gives the graph of $13x^2 + 10xy + 13y^2 + 34\sqrt{2}x + 2\sqrt{2}y = 0$.

Note: The rotation of $4u^2 + 9v^2 + 16u + 18v = 0$ through $-45°$ is most easily obtained by using tracing paper.

(d) For the conic $4s^2 + 9t^2 = 25$, the centre is $(0, 0)$ and the vertices are $\left(2\frac{1}{2}, 0\right)$ and $\left(-2\frac{1}{2}, 0\right)$.

Under the inverse translation $(-2, -1)$
$$(s, t) \to (s - 2, t - 1) = (u, v)$$
$\therefore$ centre $(0, 0) \to (-2, -1)$

vertex $\left(2\frac{1}{2}, 0\right) \to \left(\frac{1}{2}, -1\right)$

vertex $\left(-2\frac{1}{2}, 0\right) \to \left(-4\frac{1}{2}, -1\right)$

Under the rotation of $-45°$
$$(u, v) \to (x, y) = \left(\frac{u + v}{\sqrt{2}}, \frac{-u + v}{\sqrt{2}}\right)$$
$\therefore$ centre $(-2, -1) \to \left(\dfrac{-2 + (-1)}{\sqrt{2}}, \dfrac{-(-2) + (-1)}{\sqrt{2}}\right)$
$$= \left(\frac{-3}{\sqrt{2}}, \frac{1}{\sqrt{2}}\right)$$

vertex $\left(\frac{1}{2}, -1\right) \to \left(\dfrac{\frac{1}{2} + (-1)}{\sqrt{2}}, \dfrac{-\frac{1}{2} + (-1)}{\sqrt{2}}\right) = \left(\frac{-1}{2\sqrt{2}}, \frac{-3}{2\sqrt{2}}\right)$

vertex $\left(-4\frac{1}{2}, -1\right) \to \left(\dfrac{-4\frac{1}{2} + (-1)}{\sqrt{2}}, \dfrac{-\left(-4\frac{1}{2}\right) + (-1)}{\sqrt{2}}\right)$
$$= \left(\frac{-11}{2\sqrt{2}}, \frac{7}{2\sqrt{2}}\right)$$

Thus the conic $13x^2 + 10xy + 13y^2 + 34\sqrt{2}x + 2\sqrt{2}y = 0$ has centre at $\left(-\dfrac{3}{\sqrt{2}}, \dfrac{1}{\sqrt{2}}\right)$ and vertices at $\left(-\dfrac{1}{2\sqrt{2}}, -\dfrac{3}{2\sqrt{2}}\right)$ and $\left(-\dfrac{11}{2\sqrt{2}}, \dfrac{7}{2\sqrt{2}}\right)$.

The following summarizes the method used in Example 1.

Method of graphing $ax^2 + 2hxy + by^2 + 2gx + 2fy + c = 0$

(1) Determine the type of conic using $ab - h^2$.

(2) Determine the rotation about $(0, 0)$ that eliminates the xy term.

(3) Find an equation of the image of

$$ax^2 + 2hxy + by^2 + 2gx + 2fy + c = 0$$

under the rotation of (2).

(4) (a) If the image equation of (3) is *not* in standard form, then apply a translation (by completing the square(s)) to obtain an equation in standard form.

(b) If the image equation of (3) *is* in standard form, graph this equation and proceed to (6).

(5) Graph the equation of 4(a) and apply the inverse translation to this graph to obtain a new graph.

(6) Apply the inverse rotation about $(0, 0)$ to the rotation in (2) to this last graph to obtain the graph of

$$ax^2 + 2hxy + by^2 + 2gx + 2fy + c = 0.$$

Exercise 7.5

B 1. Determine a rotation angle θ for which the xy term is eliminated from each of the given equations.

(a) $x^2 - xy + y^2 + x - y + 3 = 0$
(b) $x^2 + 6xy - y^2 - 2x + 4y + 7 = 0$
(c) $x^2 - 4xy + 4y^2 + 6x = 0$
(d) $2x^2 - 2xy + y^2 + 8y + 6 = 0$

2. For each of the following conics,
   (i) name the type of conic, and
   (ii) graph the conic.

(a) $xy + 5\sqrt{2}x - \sqrt{2}y - 6 = 0$
(b) $7x^2 + 6\sqrt{3}xy + 13y^2 + 8(\sqrt{3} - 2)x - 8(1 + 2\sqrt{3})y + 16 = 0$
(c) $x^2 + 4xy + y^2 - 4x + 4y + 3 = 0$
(d) $3x^2 + 2\sqrt{3}xy + y^2 - 8x + 8\sqrt{3}y + 4 = 0$
(e) $5x^2 - 6xy + 5y^2 + 4\sqrt{2}x - 12\sqrt{2}y + 8 = 0$
(f) $x^2 - xy + y^2 + x - y - 3 = 0$

3. For each of the ellipses and hyperbolas in Question 2 find the coordinates of the centre, vertices and foci.

4. For each of the parabolas in Question 2 find the coordinates of the vertex and the focus and an equation of the axis of symmetry.

C 5. Graph the conic $x^2 - xy + 2x - 6y = 0$. Determine the coordinates of its centre.

7.5/Graphing Using both Rotations and Translations 253

6. Given the curve $41x^2 - 24xy + 34y^2 - 100 = 0$.

   (a) If a rotation of angle θ about $(0, 0)$ will eliminate the xy term show that $\tan 2\theta = \dfrac{24}{7}$.

   (b) If $0 \le 2\theta \le \dfrac{\pi}{2}$ show that $\cos 2\theta = \dfrac{7}{25}$.

   (c) Use the formulas for $\cos 2\theta$ in terms of $\sin \theta$ and $\cos \theta$ to determine $\cos \theta$ and $\sin \theta$.

   (d) If $P(x, y)$ on the given curve maps onto $P'(u, v)$ under the rotation of (a) show that
   $$x = \frac{4u + 3v}{5} \text{ and } y = \frac{-3u + 4v}{5}$$

   (e) Use the results of part (d) to find an equation for the image of the given curve under the rotation of (a).

7. Graph the following conics. [Hint: Use the method of Question 6 to determine the rotation image.]

   (a) $8x^2 - 12xy - 8y^2 + 6\sqrt{10}x - 2\sqrt{10}y - 30 = 0$
   (b) $x^2 + 4xy + 4y^2 + 12x - 6y - 6\sqrt{5} = 0$

8. (a) Find an equation of the second degree curve containing the points of the locus $\sqrt{x} + \sqrt{y} = 1$.

   (b) Graph this second degree curve and find the coordinates of its vertex.

   (c) Which points of the second degree curve belong to the given locus?

Review Exercise 7.6

B 1. Find equations of the images of the given curves under the translation $(x, y) \rightarrow (x + 3, y + 2)$.

   (a) $x^2 = 2y$
   (b) $x^2 + y^2 = 2x$
   (c) $2x^2 - y^2 = 3$
   (d) $x^2 + 3y^2 + 4x - 6y - 2 = 0$
   (e) $4x^2 + 9y^2 = 36$
   (f) $y^2 = 4x + 4$

2. (a) Find an equation of the image under the translation $(x, y) \rightarrow (x - 5, y + 4)$ of the circle $x^2 + y^2 + 10x + 6y + 18 = 0$.

   (b) Find the centre and radius of the image circle.

   (c) Graph the given circle and its image.

3. (a) Find an equation of the image under the translation $(x, y) \rightarrow (x + 3, y - 2)$ of the hyperbola $144x^2 - 25y^2 + 3600 = 0$

   (b) Find the vertices, centre, foci and axes of the image hyperbola.

   (c) Graph the hyperbola and its image.

4. By means of a translation find the equation of the ellipse with foci $(5, -4)$ and $(-1, -4)$, and semi major axis of length 5.

5. Given the curve $4x^2 + y^2 - 8x + 6y - 3 = 0$.

   (a) Find the translation that transforms the given curve into standard form.

   (b) From the results of (a), describe the graph of the given equation.

6. Given the parabola $y^2 - 4x - 2y - 7 = 0$.

   (a) Find the translation that transforms the given parabola into standard form.

   (b) From the results of (a), describe the graph of the given parabola, and state the coordinates of its focus and equation of its directrix.

7. Graph each of the following ellipses and find the centre of each.

   (a) $2x^2 + y^2 - 8x + 4y - 4 = 0$
   (b) $x^2 + 9y^2 - 6x + 18y \quad 7 = 0$
   (c) $4x^2 + 9y^2 - 4x + 36y + 1 = 0$
   (d) $\frac{1}{2}x^2 + y^2 + 2x + 6y - 5 = 0$

8. State whether each of the given curves is an ellipse, a parabola, or a hyperbola.

   (a) $x^2 + 2y = 0$
   (b) $y^2 - 6x + 4y = 2$
   (c) $x^2 + y^2 + 6x = 0$
   (d) $x^2 + 4y^2 + 2x - 8y - 10 = 0$
   (e) $y^2 - x^2 + 2y = 7$
   (f) $x^2 - 4y^2 + 10x = 0$

9. For each of the following name the type of conic and draw its graph.

   (a) $x^2 - 4y^2 + 4x + 4y - 1 = 0$
   (b) $16x^2 + 9y^2 - 32x + 18y = 119$
   (c) $y^2 + 4x + 8y + 20 = 0$
   (d) $9x^2 - 4y^2 - 36x - 24y = 36$

10. Find equations of the curves obtained by rotating each given curve through an angle of $\frac{\pi}{4}$ rad about the origin. Graph each curve and its image.

(a) $x^2 + 3y^2 = 4$ (c) $y^2 = 4x$
(b) $xy = -2$ (d) $4x^2 - 9y^2 = 1$

11. Find equations of the curves obtained by rotating each given curve through an angle of $\frac{\pi}{3}$ rad about the origin. Graph each curve and its image.

(a) $2x^2 + y^2 = 6$ (c) $x^2 = y$
(b) $x^2 - 6y^2 = 12$ (d) $x^2 - y^2 = 1$

12. Determine the rotation about the origin that eliminates the xy term from each of the following equations.

(a) $xy = 2$ (c) $-x^2 + 2xy + y^2 = 6$
(b) $x^2 + xy - 2y^2 = 4$ (d) $x^2 + \sqrt{3}xy = 1$

13. For each of the following name the type of conic and draw its graph.

(a) $xy = 2$ (c) $3x^2 + 2\sqrt{3}xy + 5y^2 = 36$
(b) $x^2 + \sqrt{3}xy = 1$ (d) $3x^2 + 2\sqrt{3}xy + y^2 = 3$

14. Find the inclination of the axes of the curve $3x^2 + 2\sqrt{3}xy + y^2 = 3$ to the coordinate axes. Sketch the graph of the curve.

15. State whether each of the given curves is an ellipse, parabola, or hyperbola.

(a) $x^2 + xy + 2y^2 = 1$ (c) $x^2 + 2xy + 2y^2 = 4x$
(b) $x^2 + 3xy + 2y^2 = 5$ (d) $x^2 + 2xy + y^2 = 4x$

16. For each of the given curves, determine its type and sketch its graph.

(a) $xy - 2x + 4y = 0$
(b) $x^2 + xy + y^2 + x - y - 3 = 0$
(c) $x^2 - 2xy + y^2 - 12x - 12y = 0$
(d) $x^2 + 2\sqrt{3}xy + 3y^2 + 4\sqrt{3}x + 4y = 0$
(e) $5x^2 - 6xy + 5y^2 - 12\sqrt{2}x + 4\sqrt{2}y + 8 = 0$
(f) $x^2 + 2\sqrt{3}xy + 3y^2 + 8\sqrt{3}x - 8y + 4 = 0$

17. Determine the coordinates of the centre, vertices and foci, and find the length of the semi axes for each of the ellipses and hyperbolas in Question 16.

$8/$ Permutations and Combinations

For many problems involving choice and chance we need to know the number of ways of arranging objects. How many different combinations can we have for opening a wall safe? In how many ways can a person take a walk of 7 blocks, if he walks 4 blocks east and 3 blocks north? Such questions often appear in puzzles and problems and are helpful in answering questions in the study of probability.

8.1 Permutations

In how many different ways can Albert, Bob and Charles be arranged in a line? By trial we can find exactly 6 different arrangements.

ABC, ACB, BCA, BAC, CAB, CBA.

Notice that there are 3 possible letters that can occupy the first place. Once this place has been filled there are two letters remaining for the second place. Having filled the first two places the third letter is used for the last place.

$$\boxed{3} \quad \boxed{2} \quad \boxed{1}$$

The total number of different ways is the product

$$3 \times 2 \times 1$$

A *tree diagram* shows the same result.

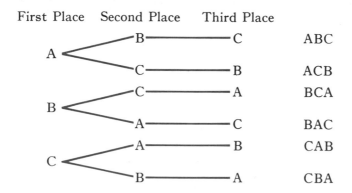

First Place   Second Place   Third Place

A	B	C	ABC
	C	B	ACB
B	C	A	BCA
	A	C	BAC
C	A	B	CAB
	B	A	CBA

If we had used 4 boys and arranged them in line, the same pattern would occur.

4	4 ways to fill the first place.
3	Having filled the first place there are 3 ways of filling the second place.
2	Having filled the first and second places there are 2 ways of filling the third place.
1	Having filled the first, second, and third places there is only 1 way to fill the last place.

The total number of arrangements of four boys in a line is

$$4 \times 3 \times 2 \times 1 = 24$$

Each arrangement in the preceding examples is called a *permutation*. In the arrangement of 4 boys we say that there are 24 permutations of the 4 boys taken 4 at a time, or all together.

The same method of reasoning suggested by the tree diagram and the "boxes" can be extended to give a general method for solving permutation problems. If an operation can be performed in n_1 ways and, after it is performed in one of these ways, a second operation can be performed in n_2 ways, and so on for k operations, then the k operations can be performed in

$$n_1 \times n_2 \times n_3 \times \cdots \times n_k \text{ ways.}$$

Example 1

How many license plates can be made using 2 letters followed by a 3-digit number?

Solution

There are 5 spaces to fill.

The 1st place can be filled in 26 ways. (Any one of the 26 letters of the alphabet.)

| 26 | | | | |

The 2nd place can be filled in 26 ways. (Any one of the 26 letters of the alphabet.)

| 26 | 26 | | | |

The 3rd place can be filled in 9 ways. (Zero will not give a 3-digit number.)

| 26 | 26 | 9 | | |

The 4th place can be filled in 10 ways (Any one of the 10 digits.)

| 26 | 26 | 9 | 10 | |

The 5th place can be filled in 10 ways.

| 26 | 26 | 9 | 10 | 10 |

The number of license plates that can be made is

$$26 \times 26 \times 9 \times 10 \times 10 = 608\ 400$$

Example 2

Given the ten digits 0, 1, 2, $\cdots$, 9, find how many 4-digit numbers can be made from them with each of the following restrictions.

(a) No digit may be repeated.
(b) Repetitions are allowed.
(c) No digit is repeated and the number is odd.

Solution

(a)

| 9 | | | |

Zero not allowed in 1st place. (Why?)

| 9 | 9 | | |

9 digits left. Select 1.

| 9 | 9 | 8 | |

8 digits left. Select 1.

| 9 | 9 | 9 | 7 |

7 digits left. Select 1.

The number of 4-digit numbers is $9 \times 9 \times 8 \times 7 = 4536$.

(b) | 9 | | | | Zero not allowed in 1st place.

| 9 | 10 | 10 | 10 | Any one of the 10 digits can be used in the last 3 places.

The number of 4-digit numbers is $9 \times 10 \times 10 \times 10 = 9000$.

(c) | | | | 5 | Use 1 of 5 odd digits in last place.

| 8 | | | | Exclude zero for 1st place; 8 digits available. Select one.

| 8 | 8 | | 5 | 8 digits available for 2nd place. Select one.

| 8 | 8 | 7 | 5 | 7 digits available for 3rd place. Select one.

Number of 4-digit numbers is $8 \times 8 \times 7 \times 5 = 2240$.

Notice that in Example 2 some places *had to be filled first*. Restrictions may make it necessary to fill some boxes before others.

Example 3

Given 5 flags of different colors. How many different signals can be made if at least 3 flags must be used for each signal?

Solution

There are 3 cases to consider.

(1) Five flags in each signal. | 5 | 4 | 3 | 2 | 1 |
Number of signals is $5 \times 4 \times 3 \times 2 \times 1 = 120$

(2) Four flags in each signal. | 5 | 4 | 3 | 2 |
Number of signals is $5 \times 4 \times 3 \times 2 = 120$

(3) Three flags in each signal. | 5 | 4 | 3 |
Number of signals is $5 \times 4 \times 3 = 60$.

Total number of signals is $120 + 120 + 60 = 300$.

Notice that in Example 3 two signals cannot be given at the same time so that each case is *mutually exclusive* of the other. Thus, if two operations are mutually exclusive and one can be done in p ways and the other in q ways, then one operation *or* the other can be done in $p + q$ ways.

Exercise 8.1

A 1. In how many ways can 6 people line up at a theatre box office?

2. Given 7 flags of different colors. How many signals can be made by arranging two flags one above the other on a vertical mast?

3. How many tunes of 5 notes can you compose using each of the 6 different strings on a guitar once and only once?

4. Tony's Pizza Parlor makes 3 sizes of pizza and a choice of 5 toppings is given. How many different pizzas can be ordered with 1 topping only?

5. In how many ways can a pilot and co-pilot be selected from 6 pilots?

B 6. In how many ways can first-, second-, and third-place medals be awarded among 12 runners?

7. A combination lock has 20 numbers on it. If a combination consists of 3 different numbers, how many combinations are possible?

8. (a) How many 5-digit numbers can be formed from the integers 1, 2, 4, 6, 7, 8, if no repetitions are allowed?
    (b) How many of the numbers formed in (a) are odd? How many are even?

9. If the call letters of Canadian Broadcasting stations must begin with the letter C, how many different names can be made for a station using 3 call letters where repetitions are allowed?

10. From nine players a pitcher and a catcher are to be chosen. In how many ways can this be done?

11. In how many ways can 3 prizes be distributed among 20 students in the following situations?

    (a) No student can receive more than one prize.
    (b) There are no restrictions.

12. In how many ways can 6 books be arranged on a shelf?

13. There are 6 seats in a car. In how many ways can 6 people be seated in a car if only 3 of them are able to drive?

14. In how many ways can 3 adjacent doors be painted if there are 6 different colors of paint available?

15. In how many ways can 5 students be seated in a seminar room with 12 seating positions randomly situated?

16. In how many ways can 5 boys and 5 girls be seated alternately in a row of 10 chairs, if a boy always occupies the first chair?

17. A 10-volume encyclopedia sits on a shelf. In how many ways can the 10 volumes be arranged on the shelf so that some or all of the volumes are out of order?

18. How many different licence plate designations can be made using 3 letters followed by a 3-digit number?

19. From 4 married couples in how many ways can a pair of bridge partners be formed consisting of a woman and a man if husband and wife are not to play together?

20. Seven students pose for a photograph.
    (a) In how many ways can they be placed in a line?
    (b) In how many ways can they be placed 4 in the front and 3 behind?

21. In how many ways can 5 boys and 5 girls stand in a row if no two boys are to be together?

22. At an examination there are 7 papers to be written, 3 of which are mathematics. How many possible timetables can be made if the first and last papers must be mathematics papers?

23. (a) How many 5-digit numbers are there?
    (b) How many 5-digit numbers begin with 3 and end with 7?
    (c) How many 5-digit numbers do not contain the digit 3?
    (d) How many 5-digit numbers are divisible by 5?

24. Find the sum of all the five-digit numbers that can be formed using the digits 1, 2, 3, 4, 5 without repeating any digit.

25. How many different signals can be made by arranging signal flags on a vertical mast if there are 5 flags available each of a different color?

26. How many whole numbers less than 500 can be formed using the digits 1, 2, 3, 4, 5 and 6 in each of the following cases?
    (a) No repetition is allowed.
    (b) Repetitions are allowed.
    (c) Any digit can be used at most twice.

262

8.2 Permutation Formulas

The answer to a permutation problem is often expressed as a sequence of factors. For example,

(1) 8 people can be arranged in a row in

$$8 \times 7 \times 6 \times 5 \times 4 \times 3 \times 2 \times 1 \text{ ways.}$$

(2) 19 books can be arranged on a shelf in

$$19 \times 18 \times 17 \times \cdots \times 3 \times 2 \times 1 \text{ ways.}$$

We abbreviate $8 \times 7 \times 6 \times 5 \times 4 \times 3 \times 2 \times 1$ to 8! which is read "8 factorial".

Thus, $19 \times 18 \times 17 \times \cdots \times 3 \times 2 \times 1 = 19!$

$$n(n - 1) (n - 2) \cdots 3 \times 2 \times 1 = n!, n \in N$$

Notice the pattern in the following factorials.

$$1! = 1$$
$$2! = 2 \times 1 \qquad\qquad = 2 \times 1! = 2$$
$$3! = 3 \times 2 \times 1 \qquad\quad = 3 \times 2! = 6$$
$$4! = 4 \times 3 \times 2 \times 1 \quad\;\; = 4 \times 3! = 24$$
$$5! = 5 \times 4 \times 3 \times 2 \times 1 = 5 \times 4! = 120$$
$$6! \qquad\qquad\qquad\qquad = 6 \times 5! = 720$$
$$7! \qquad\qquad\qquad\qquad = 7 \times 6! = 5040$$

In general, $n! = n \times (n - 1)!$

The number of arrangements of n different objects, taken n at a time, is denoted by $P(n, n)$

$$P(n, n) = n!$$

The number of arrangements of n different objects, taken r at a time is denoted by $P(n, r)$.

Example 1

Find the number of permutations of 7 different things taken 3 at a time.

Solution

The number of permutations of 7 different things taken 3 at a time is denoted by $P(7, 3)$.

$$P(7, 3) = 7 \times 6 \times 5 = 210$$

Factorials can be used to express the product $7 \times 6 \times 5$ as follows.

$$7 \times 6 \times 5 = \frac{7 \times 6 \times 5 \times 4 \times 3 \times 2 \times 1}{4 \times 3 \times 2 \times 1}$$

$$= \frac{7!}{4!}$$

Thus, $P(7, 3) = \dfrac{7!}{4!}$

In general, the number of permutations of n different things taken r at a time is given by the following.

$$P(n, r) = \frac{n!}{(n - r)!}, \; r \leq n \text{ and } r, n \in N$$

To prove this formula, set out r boxes.

☐ ☐ ☐ . . . . ☐

The factor in the 1st box is n
The factor in the 2nd box is $n - 1$
The factor in the 3rd box is $n - 2$

The factor in the 7th box is $n - 6$

The factor in the rth box is $n - (r - 1) = n - r + 1$

$$P(n, r) = n(n - 1)(n - 2) \cdots (n - r + 1)$$
$$= \frac{n(n - 1) \cdots (n - r + 1)(n - r) \cdots \times 3 \times 2 \times 1}{(n - r) \cdots \times 3 \times 2 \times 1}$$
$$= \frac{n!}{(n - r)!}$$

Applying the formula for $r = n$.

$$P(n, n) = \frac{n!}{(n - n)!}$$
$$= \frac{n!}{0!}$$

But $P(n, n) = n!$
Thus,
$0! = 1$ if our formula is to remain valid for $r = n$.

8.2/*Permutation Formulas*

Example 2

How many 5-letter "words" can be formed from the letters of the word *hexagon*? A "word" means an arrangement of letters.

Solution

There are 7 different letters in *hexagon*.

Number of words is $P(7, 5) = \dfrac{7!}{2!}$

$$= \dfrac{5040}{2}$$

$$= 2520$$

Example 3

In how many ways can 12 men stand in a row if two specified men must always be together?

Solution

For the sake of arrangements consider the two specified men A and B as one unit giving 11 units altogether. Thus, we are arranging 11 things which can be done in 11! ways.

However, in each of these arrangements the men may line up either as AB or BA. Thus, each of the 11! ways gives rise to two more arrangements.

$\therefore$ Total number of arrangements is $2 \times 11! = 79\,833\,600$.

Example 4

Evaluate or simplify.

(a) $\dfrac{8!}{4!}$ 　　　　(b) $\dfrac{n!}{(n-2)!}$ 　　　　(c) $\dfrac{(n-r+1)!}{(n-r)!}$

Solution

(a) $\dfrac{8!}{4!} = \dfrac{8 \times 7 \times 6 \times 5 \times 4!}{4!} = 1680$

(b) $\dfrac{n!}{(n-2)!} = \dfrac{n(n-1) \times (n-2)!}{(n-2)!} = n(n-1)$

(c) $\dfrac{(n-r+1)!}{(n-r)!} = \dfrac{(n-r+1) \times (n-r)!}{(n-r)!} = (n-r+1)$

Exercise 8.2

B 1. Evaluate each of the following.

(a) $P(12, 3)$ (e) $P(9, 3)$

(b) $P(7, 2)$ (f) $P(12, 5)$

(c) $P(9, 1)$ (g) $P(101, 2)$

(d) $P(5, 5)$ (h) $P(8, 5)$

2. Evaluate or simplify.

(a) $\dfrac{12!}{7!}$ (d) $\dfrac{(n+1)!}{n!}$ (g) $\dfrac{(n-r)!}{(n-r-1)!}$

(b) $\dfrac{15!}{13!}$ (e) $\dfrac{(2n)!}{(2n-2)!}$ (h) $\dfrac{(n-r+1)!}{(n-r-1)!}$

(c) $\dfrac{20!}{18!\,2!}$ (f) $\dfrac{r!}{(r-1)!}$ (i) $\dfrac{(n-r)!}{(n-r+1)!}$

3. (a) If $P(n, 2) = 42$, find the value of n.

    (b) If $P(n, 2) = 56$, find n.

4. How many 4-letter words can be formed using the letters of the word *number?*

5. How many words may be formed from the letters of the word *hyperbola?*

(a) taking all the letters at a time

(b) taking 8 letters at a time

(c) taking 4 letters at a time

6. A student has 6 examinations to write and there are 10 examination periods available. How many different examination time-tables can he get?

7. Show that the number of 3-letter words that can be formed using the letters of the word *background* is the same as the number of words obtained by rearranging the letters in the word *ground.*

8. A student has 4 mathematics books, 5 history books and 7 English books. In how many ways can he arrange his books on a shelf if books of the same subject are to be kept together?

9. How many arrangements of all the letters of the word *pentagon* can be formed if the word begins as follows?

(a) with a *p*   (b) with *pe*   (c) with a vowel

10. How many words of 3 letters, beginning and ending with different consonants, and with the middle letter a vowel, can be formed from the letters of the word *beacon?*

11. Find the number of arrangements of the letters of the word *algebra* in which the two *a*'s are together.

12. In how many ways can 8 books be arranged on a shelf under the following restrictions?
    (*a*) Two specified books must be side by side.
    (*b*) Two specified books must *not* be side by side.

13. The letters *L, O, C, U, S,* are placed on cards and a monkey arranges them to make a 5 letter word. How many mistakes can he make if he is trying to form the word *LOCUS?*

14. If the letters of the word *special* are written in every possible way, how many of them will not begin with *sp?*

15. In geometry, figures are commonly labelled by naming their vertices.
    (*a*) How many ways are there of naming a triangle?
    (*b*) How many ways are there of naming a pentagon?

16. How many 5-digit odd numbers can be formed from the digits of the number 5 390 864?

17. Show that the number of ways of arranging *n* people in a row so that 2 particular people must not be together is
$$(n-2) \times (n-1)!.$$

18. Find the number of words that can be formed using the letters of the word *Washington* if the two *n*'s are always together.

19. A round table has a special chair at its head. In how many ways can 6 people arrange themselves at it?

C 20. In how many ways might 7 persons be seated at a round table in each of the following cases?
    (*a*) The seats are distinguishable.
    (*b*) Only relative position is considered.

21. Seven beads of different colors are strung on a string to make a bracelet. How many different arrangements are there?

22. Show that $P(n, r) - P(n, r-1) = (n-r) \times P(n, r-1)$.

23. Solve for *n*. $P(n, r) = 7 \times P(n-1, r-1)$.

8.3 Combinations

How many hands of five cards can be selected from a standard deck of 52 cards? The order in which the cards are obtained does not affect the hand.

Thus, our selections are not affected by order, whereas order was important in permutations. Each hand above gives 5! different permutations of cards.

A selection in which order does not count is called a *combination*. In our card problem, we seek the number of combinations of 52 cards taken 5 at a time which is denoted by $C(52, 5)$. To evaluate $C(52, 5)$ we proceed as follows.

Each combination, or hand, can be made into 5! permutations by allowing order to change. Thus, $C(52, 5) \times 5!$ will be the number of 5 card hands where order counts. But, this number is represented by $P(52, 5)$.

$$\therefore \ C(52, 5) \times 5! = P(52, 5)$$
$$= \frac{52!}{47!}$$
$$\therefore \ C(52, 5) = \frac{52!}{47! \ 5!}$$
$$= \frac{52 \cdot 51 \cdot 50 \cdot 49 \cdot 48 \cdot 47!}{47! \ 5!}$$
$$= 2 \ 598 \ 960$$

The language of sets can be used in the discussion of combinations because the order in which the elements of a set are listed does not count. For example $\{A, B, C\}$ and $\{C, A, B\}$ are the same set. Thus, $C(52, 5)$ may be described as the number of subsets of 5 elements from a set of 52 elements. More briefly, $C(52, 5)$ is the number of 5-subsets in a 52-set.

In general, the number of combinations of n things taken r at a time is denoted by $C(n, r)$. Each combination can be arranged in $r!$ ways to give $r!$ permutations. $C(n, r) \times r!$ is the total number of permutations of n things taken r at a time.

$$C(n, r) \times r! = P(n, r)$$
$$= \frac{n!}{(n - r)!}$$

$$\therefore\ C(n, r) = \frac{n!}{r!\,(n - r)!}$$

In particular $C(n, 1) = \dfrac{n!}{1!(n - 1)!} = n$

and $\qquad C(n, n) = \dfrac{n!}{n!\,0!} = 1$

Example 1

There are 5 boys and 8 girls playing tennis. In how many ways can a game be arranged where 2 boys play against 2 girls?

Solution

Number of ways of selecting the boys is $C(5, 2) = \dfrac{5!}{3!\,2!} = 10$.

Number of ways of selecting the girls is $C(8, 2) = \dfrac{8!}{6!\,2!} = 28$.

Number of ways of playing the match is $10 \times 28 = 280$ ways.

Example 2

Prove $C(n, r) = C(n, n - r)$

Solution

$$C(n, r) = \frac{n!}{r!(n - r)!}$$
$$C(n, n - r) = \frac{n!}{(n - r)!\,[n - (n - r)]!} = \frac{n!}{(n - r)!\,r!}$$
$$C(n, r) = C(n, n - r)$$

The result of Example 2 is apparent if you consider that whenever r objects are selected, then $(n - r)$ objects have been rejected. For example, in selecting 5 boys from 9 for a basketball game you can either select 5 or reject 4.

Thus, $C(9, 5) = C(9, 4)$.

Example 3

In how many ways can a committee of 3 be chosen from 4 married couples for each of the following?

    (*a*) All are equally eligible.

    (*b*) The committee must consist of 2 men and 1 woman.

    (*c*) Husband and wife cannot serve on the same committee.

Solution

    (*a*) From 8 people select 3.

$$C(8, 3) = \frac{8!}{3!\,5!} = \frac{8 \times 7 \times 6}{3 \times 2 \times 1} = 56$$

There are 56 ways.

    (*b*) Select the 2 men first in $C(4, 2)$ ways.
Select the woman next in $C(4, 1)$ ways.
Total number of ways is $C(4, 2) \times C(4, 1) = 24$ ways.

    (*c*) If husband and wife cannot both serve, then 3 couples must be represented. Three couples can be selected in $C(4, 3) = 4$ ways. After 3 couples have been selected, there are two choices of selecting one person from the first couple, two from the second and two from the third.
Total number of committees is $4 \times 2 \times 2 \times 2 = 32$.

Example 4

Find the number of combinations of n things taken any number at a time.

Solution (1)

Number of ways of selecting 0 things is	$C(n, 0)$
Number of ways of selecting 1 thing is	$C(n, 1)$
Number of ways of selecting 2 things is	$C(n, 2)$

.

.

.

Number of ways of selecting n things is	$C(n, n)$

Total number of ways is
$C(n, 0) + C(n, 1) + C(n, 2) + \cdots + C(n, n)$.

Solution (2)

Draw n boxes to represent each thing.

□ □ □ · · · □

                                               8.3/Combinations

There are 2 ways of considering the first thing — take it or leave it. If we take it we write a "1" in the box; if we leave it we write "0".

All selections can be recorded using a set of n boxes containing a zero or a one.

For example, $01011\cdots1$

The first place can be filled in 2 ways.

The second place can be filled in 2 ways.

The nth place can be filled in 2 ways.

Altogether the n places can be filled in

$2 \times 2 \times 2 \cdots \times 2 = 2^n$ ways.

Solution 1 and Solution 2 illustrate an important relationship.

$$C(n, 0) + C(n, 1) + C(n, 2) + \cdots + C(n, n) = 2^n$$

Example 5

In how many ways can a selection of fruit be made from 6 plums, 5 apples and 8 oranges?

Solution

You may select 0, 1, 2, 3, 4, 5, or 6 plums.

∴ the plums can be considered in 7 ways. Similarly the apples can be considered in 6 ways and the oranges in 9 ways. Altogether we have $6 \times 7 \times 9 = 378$ ways. This total includes the case where none is taken.

∴ the number of selections is $378 - 1 = 377$.

Exercise 8.3

B

1. Evaluate the following.

   (a) $C(9, 3)$
   (b) $C(9, 6)$
   (c) $C(12, 2)$
   (d) $C(20, 18)$

2. Solve for n.

   (a) $C(n, 2) = 45$
   (b) $C(n, 3) = C(n, 4)$
   (c) $P(n, 4) = 60C(n - 1, 3)$
   (d) $5P(n + 1, 3) = 36C(n, 4)$

3. Find the number of combinations of each of the following.

   (a) 3-subsets from a 5-set.
   (b) 6-subsets from an 8-set.
   (c) 4-subsets from a 20-set.

4. In how many ways can a student select 2 different pens from 6 different kinds of pens?

5. If 8 points, no three of which are in a straight line, are joined in pairs in all possible ways, how many lines are formed?

6. If a polygon has 8 sides, how many diagonals has it?

7. How many diagonals has a polygon of n sides.

8. If a polygon has 44 diagonals, how many sides has it?

9. In how many ways can a student committee of 5 boys and 5 girls be selected from 9 boys and 11 girls?

10. Given a set of 12 points, no 3 of which are on a straight line, find the number of triangles whose vertices belong to the given set.

11. There are 20 points all in one straight line and 15 others in a parallel line. How many possible triangles having these points as vertices can be formed?

12. Given 11 lines in a plane. If no two of these lines are parallel and no three of them pass through the same point, in how many points do they intersect?

13. (a) In how many ways can a selection of 6 books be made from 10 books?

   (b) If a certain book must be selected, in how many ways can the selection in (a) be made?

   (c) If a certain book must be left out, in how many ways can the selection in (a) be made?

   (d) Prove $C(10, 6) = C(9, 6) + C(9, 5)$.

14. Prove that $C(n + 1, r) = C(n, r) + C(n, r - 1)$.

15. How many selections of 1 or more letters can be made from 3 A's, 7 B's and 11 C's?

16. How many different sums of money can be obtained from a penny, a nickel, a dime, a quarter and a fifty-cent piece?

17. Find the number of whole-number factors of 3960.

18. What is the maximum number of points of intersection of 6 circles each circle having a different centre?

19. What is the maximum number of points of intersection of 5 circles and 4 straight lines?

8.3/Combinations

20. In how many ways can a deck of 52 cards be dealt to 4 players so that each receives 13 cards? Express your answer in factorial form.

21. In how many ways can a deck of 52 cards be dealt into 4 equal piles of cards? Express your answer in factorial form.

8.4 The Binomial Theorem

The rule for expanding $(a + x)^n$ is called the binomial theorem. In 1556 Tartaglia showed how to obtain the coefficients in the expansion of $(1 + x)^n$ if he knew those of $(1 + x)^{n-1}$. The theorem was generalized by Newton who showed how to expand $(1 + x)^n$ when $n \in Q$. Abel proved the theorem true when x and n are complex numbers.

We shall show Tartaglia's method.

$$(a + x)^1 = a + x$$
$$(a + x)^2 = a^2 + 2ax + x^2$$
$$(a + x)^3 = a^3 + 3a^2x + 3ax^2 + x^3$$
$$(a + x)^4 = a^4 + 4a^3x + 6a^2x^2 + 4ax^3 + x^4$$

Notice the triangle pattern formed by the coefficients.

$$\begin{array}{ccccccc} & & & 1 & & 1 & & \\ & & 1 & & 2 & & 1 & \\ & 1 & & 3 & & 3 & & 1 \\ 1 & & 4 & & 6 & & 4 & & 1 \end{array}$$

If the pattern continues the next row should be

$$\begin{array}{ccccccccccc} 1 & & 4 & & 6 & & 4 & & 1 \\ & 1 & & 5 & & 10 & & 10 & & 5 & & 1 \end{array}$$

and $(a + x)^5$ should be $a^5 + 5a^4x + 10a^3x^2 + 10a^2x^3 + 5ax^4 + x^5$ which can be verified by multiplication.

For brevity, let us write $C(n, r) = \binom{n}{r}$

Note that $\binom{1}{0} = 1$ and $\binom{1}{1} = 1$

$$\binom{2}{0} = 1, \quad \binom{2}{1} = 2, \quad \binom{2}{2} = 1$$

and $\binom{3}{0} = 1, \quad \binom{3}{1} = 3, \quad \binom{3}{2} = 3, \quad \binom{3}{3} = 1$

The triangle pattern becomes

$$\binom{1}{0} \quad \binom{1}{1}$$

$$\binom{2}{0} \quad \binom{2}{1} \quad \binom{2}{2}$$

$$\binom{3}{0} \quad \binom{3}{1} \quad \binom{3}{2} \quad \binom{3}{3}$$

$$\binom{4}{0} \quad \binom{4}{1} \quad \binom{4}{2} \quad \binom{4}{3} \quad \binom{4}{4}$$

$$\binom{5}{0} \quad \binom{5}{1} \quad \binom{5}{2} \quad \binom{5}{3} \quad \binom{5}{4} \quad \binom{5}{5}$$

This triangle pattern is called *Pascal's triangle.*

Notice the pattern again.

$$\binom{3}{1} \qquad \binom{3}{2}$$
$$\binom{4}{2} \qquad\qquad \binom{3}{1} + \binom{3}{2} = \binom{4}{2}$$

In general,

$$\binom{n}{r-1} \qquad \binom{n}{r}$$
$$\binom{n+1}{r} \qquad\qquad \binom{n+1}{r} = \binom{n}{r-1} + \binom{n}{r}$$

which you proved in Question 14, Exercise 8.3.
Thus, Tartaglia was able to show that

$$(a+x)^6 = \binom{6}{0}a^6 + \binom{6}{1}a^5x + \binom{6}{2}a^4x^2 + \binom{6}{3}a^3x^3 + \binom{6}{4}a^2x^4$$
$$+ \binom{6}{5}ax^5 + \binom{6}{6}x^6$$

The generalization of $(a + x)^n$ for any positive integer, n, is called the *Binomial Theorem.*

$$(a+x)^n = \binom{n}{0}a^n + \binom{n}{1}a^{n-1}x + \binom{n}{2}a^{n-2}x^2 + \cdots + \binom{n}{n}x^n.$$

Before proving the theorem we make several observations. In $(a + x)^5$, the terms without their coefficients are

$$a^5, \ a^4x, \ a^3x^2, \ a^2x^3, \ ax^4, \ x^5.$$

8.4/The Binomial Theorem

There are 6 terms [i.e. $(5 + 1)$] each of degree 5. In each term, the total number of a and x factors is 5. Thus, the degree of each term is 5. To decide on the coefficients we examine the multiplication process. $(a_1 + x_1)(a_2 + x_2)(a_3 + x_3)$

$$= a_1a_2a_3 + \boxed{a_1a_2x_3} + \boxed{a_1x_2a_3} + \boxed{x_1a_2a_3} + a_1x_2x_3 + x_1a_2x_3$$
$$+ x_1x_2a_3 + x_1x_2x_3$$

Notice the following properties.

(a) The degree of each term is 3, the number of factors multiplied.

(b) The terms are formed by selecting exactly one letter from each of the factors.

(c) The expansion consists of the sum of all possible terms formed in (b).

Let us apply these three properties to $(a + x)^5$.

(a) The terms are of degree 5 and without coefficients are a^5, a^4x, a^3x^2, a^2x^3, ax^4, x^5.

(b) Each term is obtained by selecting one letter from each of the 5 factors.

For a^5 we select no x's and five a's from the 5 factors. This can be done in $\binom{5}{0}$ or 1 way.

Thus, a^5 occurs only once in the expansion.

For a^4x we select an x from one of the factors and an a from each of the remaining four factors. This can be done in $\binom{5}{1}$ or 5 ways.

Thus, a^4x occurs 5 times and has coefficient 5.

For a^3x^2 we select an x from each of two factors and an a from each of the remaining three factors. This can be done in $\binom{5}{2}$ or 10 ways. Thus the coefficient of a^3x^2 is 10.

Repeat the procedure for each term.

(c) The expansion is

$$(a + x)^5 = \binom{5}{0}a^5 + \binom{5}{1}a^4x + \binom{5}{2}a^3x^2 + \binom{5}{3}a^2x^3$$
$$+ \binom{5}{4}ax^4 + \binom{5}{5}x^5$$

To prove that

$$(a + x)^n = \binom{n}{0}a^n + \binom{n}{1}a^{n-1}x + \binom{n}{2}a^{n-2}x^2 + \cdots + \binom{n}{n}x^n$$

we proceed as before.

(a) Each term in the expansion is of degree n in the variables a and x. Without coefficients the terms are

$$a^n, a^{n-1}x, a^{n-2}x^2, \cdots, a^{n-r}x^r, \cdots, x^n$$

Each term is of the form

$$a^{n-r}x^r, \text{ where } r = 0, 1, 2, \cdots, n$$

(b) For a^n we select an a from each of the n factors. This selection can be done in 1 way. Therefore the coefficient of a^n is 1.

For $a^{n-1}x$ we select an x from one factor and an a from each of the remaining $(n-1)$ factors. This selection can be made in $\binom{n}{1}$ ways. Therefore the coefficient of a^{n-1} is $\binom{n}{1}$.

(c) For $a^{n-r}x^r$ we select an x from each of r factors and an a from each of the remaining $(n-r)$ factors. This selection can be made in $\binom{n}{r}$ ways.

Thus, the terms in the expansion have the form

$$\binom{n}{r}a^{n-r}x^r \text{ where } r = 0, 1, 2, 3, \cdots, n$$

(d) Write the sum of all such terms by giving r its successive values and adding.

$$(a + x)^n = \binom{n}{0}a^n + \binom{n}{1}a^{n-1}x + \binom{n}{2}a^{n-2}x^2 + \cdots$$
$$+ \binom{n}{r}a^{n-r}x^r + \cdots + \binom{n}{n}x^n$$

Noting that $\binom{n}{0} = 1$, $\binom{n}{1} = n$, $\binom{n}{2} = \dfrac{n(n-1)}{2!}$,

$$\binom{n}{3} = \frac{n(n-1)(n-2)}{3!}, \text{ etc.,}$$

the binomial expansion can be written as

$$(a + x)^n = a^n + na^{n-1}x + \frac{n(n-1)}{2!}a^{n-2}x^2 + \cdots + x^n$$

The term $\binom{n}{r}a^{n-r}x^r$ is frequently called the *general term*. In the expansion it is the $(r+1)$th term.

$$T_{r+1} = \binom{n}{r}a^{n-r}x^r$$

Example

Expand $(3x - 2y)^4$.

Solution

$(a + b)^n$ becomes $(3x - 2y)^4$ if $a = 3x$, $b = -2y$, $n = 4$.

$$(3x - 2y)^4 = (3x)^4 + 4(3x)^3(-2y) + \frac{4(4 - 1)}{2!}(3x)^2(-2y)^2$$
$$+ \frac{4(4 - 1)(4 - 2)}{3!}(3x)(-2y)^3$$
$$+ \frac{4(4 - 1)(4 - 2)(4 - 3)}{4!}(-2y)^4$$
$$= 81x^4 - 216x^3y + 216x^2y^2 - 96xy^3 + 16y^4$$

Exercise 8.4

A

1. State the expansion of each of the following in unsimplified form.
   - (a) $(a + x)^6$
   - (b) $(p + q)^5$
   - (c) $(1 + x)^3$
   - (d) $(2 + y)^4$
   - (e) $(1 - x)^4$
   - (f) $(1 - 2x)^5$

2. In the expansion of $(a + b)^{20}$ state the coefficient of each of the following.
   - (a) a^{20}
   - (b) $a^{17}b^3$
   - (c) $a^{15}b^5$
   - (d) $a^{10}b^{10}$
   - (e) a^6b^{14}
   - (f) ab^{19}

3. State the 3rd, 7th and $(r + 1)$th term in the expansion of $(a + b)^{30}$.

B

4. Expand each of the following.
   - (a) $(a + 2b)^4$
   - (b) $(x - y)^5$
   - (c) $(3 - 6c)^3$
   - (d) $(p - 2q)^6$

5. Expand.
   - (a) $\left(x + \dfrac{2}{x}\right)^5$
   - (b) $(1 - x^2)^4$
   - (c) $\left(x - \dfrac{1}{x}\right)^3$
   - (d) $(1 - x^3)^5$

6. Find the first 3 terms in each of the following expansions.
   - (a) $(a + x)^{50}$
   - (b) $(x - y)^{100}$
   - (c) $(x^2 - 1)^{40}$
   - (d) $\left(\dfrac{a}{2} + 4b^2\right)^{12}$

7. Noting that $(a + x)^n = 2^n$ when $a = x = 1$, prove the following.

(a) $\dbinom{n}{0} + \dbinom{n}{1} + \dbinom{n}{2} + \cdots + \dbinom{n}{n} = 2^n$

(b) $1 + n + \dfrac{n(n-1)}{2!} + \dfrac{n(n-1)(n-2)}{3!} + \cdots + 1 = 2^n$

Review Exercise 8.5

B

1. Evaluate each of the following.

   (a) $P(6, 4)$ (c) $C(12, 0)$

   (b) $C(6, 4)$ (d) $P(9, 9)$

   (e) $\dfrac{88!}{11 \times 87!}$

   (f) $\dfrac{12!}{6!6!}$

2. There are 10 teams in the basketball house league. If each team plays each of the other teams once, how many games must be scheduled?

3. A baseball catcher can signal the pitcher with hand motions. If he has 4 hand motions available, how many signals can he give using two hand motions?

4. How many numbers greater than 5 000 000 can be formed using the digits 0, 1, 2, 3, 4, 5, 6 where no repetitions are allowed?

5. A keymaker has 15 blanks. Each blank has 5 positions for notches and the notches can be cut to 3 different depths. How many different keys can he make, using one notch only?

6. The Greek alphabet contains 24 letters. How many fraternity names can be formed using 3 different letters?

7. In how many ways can 10 books be arranged on a shelf for each of the following cases?
   (a) 3 particular books are kept together in a given order
   (b) 3 particular books are kept together

8. Solve the following equations for n.
   (a) $C(n, 2) = 45$ (c) $C(n, 8) = C(n, 12)$
   (b) $\dfrac{P(n, 4)}{C(n-1, 3)} = 60$

9. A deck of cards consists of 52 different cards. If a hand is made up of 13 cards, use the factorial notation to express the number of possible hands.

10. How many different hands can be dealt each containing 5 spades, 4 hearts, 2 diamonds and 2 clubs? (Use factorials.)

11. On the circumference of a circle 12 points are located and joined in all possible ways.

    (a) How many chords are formed?
    (b) How many triangles with chords as sides are formed?

12. Given 5 points in space, no four of which lie in the same plane, how many planes can be named using these points? (Three points name a plane.)

13. How many diagonals has a 14-sided polygon?

14. In how many numbers of four digits does the digit 3 appear?

15. Ten boys wish to divide themselves into two opposing teams for a basketball game. If two boys are brothers, in how many ways can the two teams be made up so that the two brothers will not play on the same side?

16. Find the number of ways in which 16 different objects can be divided into 3 parcels containing 4, 5 and 7 objects.

17. (a) How many 4-letter words can be made from the letters of the word "second"?
    (b) How many of these words will not contain the letter s?
    (c) How many of these words will contain the letter s?
    (d) How many will begin with s and end with d?

18. The Greek alphabet contains 24 letters. How many Greek-letter fraternity names can be formed each containing 2 or 3 letters? Repetitions are allowed.

19. How many different characters can be transmitted by Morse code if each character is represented by not more than 5 dots and/or dashes?

20. If $P(n, 5) = 42P(n, 3)$ solve for n.

21. Expand each of the following.

    (a) $(1 - b)^5$ (b) $(1 + x^2)^6$ (c) $(2a - 5x)^4$ (d) $(1 - x^3)^6$

C 22. (a) Expand $(q + p)^4$.

    (b) If $p = \dfrac{2}{3}$ and $q = \dfrac{1}{3}$ find the value of each term.

23. Show that $C(2n, n) = \dfrac{1 \cdot 3 \cdot 5 \cdot \ldots \cdot (2n - 1)}{n!} \cdot 2^n$.

24. If n is even, show that

$$\binom{n}{0} + \binom{n}{2} + \binom{n}{4} + \cdots + \binom{n}{n} = \binom{n}{1} + \binom{n}{3} + \cdots + \binom{n}{n-1}$$

9 / Probability

Jerome Cardan, 1501-1576, was the real pioneer in the field of probability. Cardan was quick-tempered and found it hard to control his outbursts. His genius bordered on insanity and he got involved in the weirdest arguments. He was once put into prison for publishing a horoscope of Christ. Cardan wrote a book entitled "Book on Games of Chance" which was really a gambler's manual. The book tells how to calculate probabilities, describes gambling games and includes tips on how to cheat. Cardan predicted the day of his death. When the day arrived, he was so determined to preserve his reputation, he committed suicide.

9.1 Sets and Subsets

A set is a well defined collection of objects. It should be possible to tell whether an object belongs to the set or not.

An *element* or a *member* of a set is a thing that belongs to the set. Sets may be described in many ways. For example,

listing: $\{1, 2, 3, 5, 7, 9\}$
description: The set of all Canadians.
set builder: $\{x \in R \mid -2 < x < 5\}$

The set that has *no* elements is called the *null set* or *empty set*.

$\phi = \{\ \}$ is a set with no elements

280

Consider two sets $A = \{0, 2, 4, 6, 8\}$ and $B = \{2, 6, 8\}$. Notice that each member of B is also a member of A. We call B a *subset* of A. By definition, every set is a subset of itself. The empty set is a subset of every set.

There are two set operations that we will encounter. The *intersection* $A \cap B$, of two sets A and B is the set of all elements common to A and B. The *union* of two sets, $A \cup B$, is the set of elements that belong to A or to B or to both A and B.

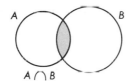

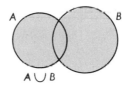

Given a set A and a subset B of A, the *complement* of B in A is the set of elements in A that do not belong to B. (Call the set $\bar{B}$.)

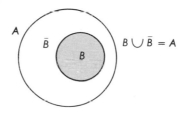

Exercise 9.1

B

1. List the elements of each of the following sets.

   (a) The set of integers between -2 and 5 (inclusive).
   (b) $\{x \in I \mid -4 \leq x \leq 0\}$.
   (c) The set of even prime numbers.
   (d) The set of students 3 m tall in your class.

2. List the 8 subsets of $\{1, 2, 3\}$.

3. Find the number of subsets in the following table.

Set	Number of Subsets
$\{\}$	
$\{a\}$	
$\{a, b\}$	
$\{a, b, c\}$	8
$\{a, b, c, d\}$	

9.1/Sets and Subsets

281

4. Find a formula for the number of subsets of a set of n elements.

5. Given $A = \{1, 2, 3, 4, 5, 6\}$ and $B = \{0, 2, 4, 6\}$ list the following sets.

    (a) $A \cap B$
    (b) $A \cup B$

6. Given $A = \{1, 2, 3, 4, 5, 6, 7, 8\}$. Find $\bar{B}$ where B is a subset of A and is given as follows.

    (a) $B = \{1, 3, 5, 7\}$
    (b) $B = \{2, 3, 4, 5, 6\}$
    (c) $B = A$
    (d) $B = \phi$

9.2 Sample Spaces and Events

An important kind of set in probability is the set of all possible outcomes of an experiment. This set is called a *sample space.*

Example 1

List a sample space for the experiment of tossing a penny and a dime simultaneously.

Solution

Each coin may fall heads (H) or tails (T). The possible outcomes of the two tosses are shown in the *tree diagram*. The sample space is

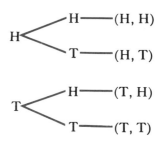

$\{(H, H)\ (H, T),\ (T, H),\ (T, T)\}$

If a single "fair" coin is tossed, we expect the outcomes, Heads or Tails, to be *equally likely*. That is, there is an equal chance of getting a head or of getting a tail.

If a thumb tack is dropped on the floor the outcomes are "point up" or "point down." Is each outcome equally likely? To answer questions like this we perform experiments. Drop ten thumb tacks on a flat surface and record the number with "point up" and the number with "point down." Repeat the experiment ten times and make a table.

Trial Number	Point up	Point down
1		
2		
3		
.		
.		
.		
10		
Total		

Are the outcomes equally likely? Would you expect different results if the head of the tack was smaller? larger?

Consider the outcomes of the toss of a penny, a nickel and a dime. Each outcome depends on how each coin turns up. We can find all of these outcomes by making a *tree diagram*.

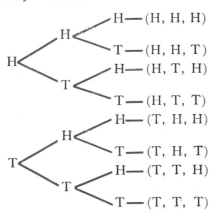

Penny   Nickel   Dime

This set of ordered triples is the sample space of tossing the three coins.

Suppose we are interested in an outcome of two heads and a tail in our 3 coin tossing experiment. This outcome may occur in three ways

$$(H, H, T), (H, T, H), (T, H, H)$$

The set of these special outcomes is called an *event*. Here

$$E = \{(H, H, T), (H, T, H), (T, H, H)\}$$

and E is a subset of our sample space.

In an experiment, an event, E, *occurs* if an outcome of the experiment is an element of E.

Exercise 9.2

B

1. A pair of dice is tossed.
   (a) List the sample space by making a tree diagram.
   (b) List the event for which the number on one die is 1.
   (c) List the event for which the sum of the numbers showing on both dice is 7.
   (d) List the event for which the sum is greater than 8.

2. Three coins are tossed. List the following events.
   (a) three heads
   (b) two heads
   (c) one head
   (d) no heads

3. A coin and a die are tossed.
   (a) List the sample space.
   (b) List the event: "a head on the coin and an odd number on the die."
   (c) List the event: "a tail on the coin and a number less than 3 on the die."

4. A card is selected from an ordinary deck of 52 playing cards. Find the number of elements in each of the following events.
   (a) The card selected is a diamond.
   (b) The card selected is an Ace.
   (c) The card selected is a Queen of Hearts.

5. A card is selected from a deck of playing cards. In each of the following state if the outcomes are equally likely or if one is more likely than the other. In the latter case indicate which outcome is more likely.
   (a) Picking an Ace, picking a Queen.
   (b) Picking a heart, picking a spade.
   (c) Picking a heart, picking an 8.
   (d) Picking a face card, picking a 7.
   (e) Picking a face card, picking a 5 or 6.

6. A jar contains 10 marbles, some white, some red. Suggest a number for each color that would make the following possible.
   (a) Drawing a red marble is as equally likely as drawing a white marble.
   (b) Drawing a red marble is more likely than drawing a white marble.

7. Two dice are thrown.
    (a) List the event E: "A 3 showing on at least one die."
    (b) List the elements of $\bar{E}$.
    (c) List the event S: "The same number on each die."
    (d) List $\bar{S}$.

8. Five cards consisting of two Aces and three Kings are taken from a deck of cards. Two cards are dealt from the 5 cards.
    (a) List the sample space.
    (b) List the elements of the event E: "two Aces."
    (c) List the elements of the event F: "an Ace and a King."
    (d) List $\bar{E}$.
    (e) List $\bar{F}$.

9.3 Probability

If we toss a coin we expect one of two possible outcomes, a head or a tail. Each outcome is equally likely for a "fair" coin. There is one chance in two that the coin will turn up a head. We express this fact, using the symbol

$$P(\text{H}) = \frac{1}{2}$$

and is read "The probability of heads is $\frac{1}{2}$."

Suppose we throw a die. What is the probability of rolling a 6? We know that the face with six dots on it is one of six equally likely ways a die may turn up. Thus, the probability that a 6 will turn up is $\frac{1}{6}$. We write

$$P(6) = \frac{1}{6}$$

What is the probability of a 4 turning up?

In an experiment of n outcomes *each of which is equally likely*, the probability of an event E of the sample space S is given by

$$P(E) = \frac{\text{number of elements in } E}{\text{number of elements in } S}$$

$$= \frac{\text{number of elements in } E}{n}$$

B
1. Two dice are tossed. What is the probability of each of the following events?

(a) rolling a sum of 12
(b) rolling a sum of 7
(c) rolling a sum of 10
(d) rolling a double (same number on each die)
(e) rolling a sum greater than 5

2. Two coins are tossed. What is the probability of each of the following events?

(a) two tails
(b) two heads
(c) one head and one tail

3. Three coins are tossed. What is the probability of each of the following events?

(a) three tails   (d) exactly one head
(b) at least one head   (e) no head
(c) exactly two heads

4. Draw a card from a deck of 52 playing cards. What is the probability of each of the following events?

(a) drawing a spade   (c) drawing the Ace of Spades
(b) drawing an Ace   (d) drawing a face card

5. Four faces of a six-sided cube are painted blue, and the other two are painted white. The cube is rolled once. Find the probability of each of the following events.

(a) the top face is blue
(b) the top face is white

6. From a class of 30 students with 20 girls, one student is selected at random. What is the probability that a boy is chosen?

7. To determine the probability that the next baby born in Canada will be from Ontario, a student reasons as follows. There are ten provinces, therefore the probability is $\frac{1}{10}$. Is his reasoning correct? Suggest a procedure to find this probability.

8. A letter is chosen at random from a sign reading MISSISSIPPI. What is the probability of each of the following events?

(a) picking an S
(b) picking an M

9. There are 2 red, 3 white and 5 black jelly beans in a bag. One jelly bean is drawn at random. What is the probability of drawing each of the following?

    (a) a red jelly bean   (c) a black jelly bean

    (b) a white jelly bean   (d) a yellow jelly bean

10. Mr. Ford bought 6 chances on a car to be raffled. If 1000 tickets are sold, what is the probability that Mr. Ford will win the car?

11. A family consists of 3 children of different ages. Find the probability of each of the following.

    (a) the oldest is a boy   (c) the youngest is a girl

    (b) there are three girls   (d) the oldest and youngest are boys

C 12. Twelve balls numbered 1 to 12 are placed in a bag and two balls are drawn at random. What is the probability that the balls numbered 7 and 11 are drawn?

13. Five cards numbered 1, 2, 3, 4 and 5 are shuffled. What is the probability that when turned face up the cards are in the order 1, 2, 3, 4, 5?

14. If 5% of all males and 1% of all females are color blind and 50% of all Canadians are male, what is the probability of each of the following?

    (a) the next baby born in Canada is a color blind male.

    (b) the next baby born in Canada is a female, *not* color blind.

9.4 Compound Events

Suppose we have a jar containing 3 red marbles and 4 black marbles and we select one marble at random. The sample space might be listed as

$$\{R_1, R_2, R_3, B_1, B_2, B_3, B_4\}$$

where we use subscripts to identify the individual marbles.

Let R be the event of selecting a red marble.

We have $P(R) = \dfrac{3}{7}$. What is $P(\bar{R})$?

$\bar{R}$ means the complement of R and is the event of selecting a black marble.

$$P(\bar{R}) = \frac{4}{7}$$

In general, we have for a sample space S of n elements and an event E of k elements.

$$P(E) = \frac{k}{n} \text{ and } P(\bar{E}) = \frac{n-k}{n}$$

$$P(\bar{E}) = \frac{n-k}{n}$$

$$= \frac{n}{n} - \frac{k}{n}$$

$$= 1 - \frac{k}{n}$$

$$= 1 - P(E)$$

For complementary events E and $\bar{E}$

$$P(E) + P(\bar{E}) = 1$$

We shall now consider the probability of two events E *and* F.

Example 1

Roll two dice. What is the probability of obtaining a sum of 7 *and* a 3 on one die?

Solution

E (obtaining a 7) $= \{(1, 6), (2, 5), (3, 4), (4, 3), (5, 2), (6, 1)\}$
F (a 3 on one die) $= \{(1, 3), (2, 3), (3, 3), (4, 3), (5, 3), (6, 3),$
$\qquad\qquad\qquad\quad (3, 1), (3, 2), (3, 4), (3, 5), (3, 6)\}$

Outcomes that belong to E *and* F belong to $E \cap F$.

$$E \cap F = \{(4, 3), (3, 4)\}$$

$$P(E \cap F) = \frac{\text{number of elements in } E \cap F}{\text{number of elements in the sample space}}$$

$$= \frac{2}{36}$$

$$= \frac{1}{18}$$

What is the probability of rolling a 7 and an 11 with one throw of two dice? In this case, $E \cap F = \phi$

$$\text{and } P(E \cap F) = \frac{\text{number of elements in } E \cap F}{36}$$

$$= \frac{0}{36} = 0$$

Two events that have no elements in common are said to be *mutually exclusive events*.

> Thus, if two events E and F are mutually exclusive,
> $$P(E \cap F) = 0$$

Example 2

What is the probability of obtaining a sum of 6 or a sum of 10 with a roll of two dice?

Solution

E (sum of 6) $= \{(1, 5), (2, 4), (3, 3), (4, 2), (5, 1)\}$
F (sum of 10) $= \{(4, 6), (5, 5), (6, 4)\}$
Outcomes that belong to E *or* F belong to $E \cup F$.

$$E \cup F = \{(1, 5), (2, 4), (3, 3), (4, 2), (5, 1), (4, 6), (5, 5), (6, 4)\}$$

$$P(E \cup F) = \frac{\text{number of elements in } E \cup F}{36}$$

$$= \frac{8}{36}$$

$$= \frac{2}{9}$$

Notice in the above example that E and F are mutually exclusive events and

$$P(E \cup F) = \frac{8}{36}$$

$$= \frac{5}{36} + \frac{3}{36}$$

$$= P(E) + P(F)$$

> For two mutually exclusive events E and F
> $$P(E \cup F) = P(E) + P(F)$$

What is the formula for $P(E \cup F)$ if $E \cup F \neq 0$?

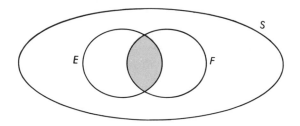

Let the number of elements in S be n,
the number in E be k,
the number in F be p,
and the number of elements in $E \cap F$ be t.
Clearly the number of elements in $E \cup F$ is $k + p - t$.

$$\therefore \quad P(E \cup F) = \frac{k + p - t}{n}$$

$$= \frac{k}{n} + \frac{p}{n} - \frac{t}{n}$$

$$= P(E) + P(F) - P(E \cap F)$$

If two events E and F are not mutually exclusive
$$P(E \cup F) = P(E) + P(F) - P(E \cap F)$$

Example 3

Balls numbered 1, 2, 3, $\cdots$, 18 are placed in a bag. One ball is selected at random. What is the probability that the number drawn is a prime number *or* is divisible by 3?

Solution

$S = \{1, 2, 3, \cdots, 18\}$
E (prime number) $= \{2, 3, 5, 7, 11, 13, 17\}$
F (divisible by 3) $= \{3, 6, 9, 12, 15, 18\}$
$P(E \cup F) = P(E) + P(F) - P(E \cap F)$

$$= \frac{7}{18} + \frac{6}{18} - \frac{1}{18}$$

$$= \frac{12}{18}$$

$$= \frac{2}{3}$$

290

Exercise 9.4

A

1. A die is rolled. Let E be the event "die turns up 3"
   F be the event "die turns up odd."

   (*a*) Are the events E and F mutually exclusive? Explain.
   (*b*) List $E \cap F$ and $E \cup F$.

2. A die is rolled. Let E be the event "die turns up even"
   F be the event "die turns up odd."

   (*a*) Are the events E and F mutually exclusive? Explain.
   (*b*) Are the events E and F complementary?
   (*c*) List $E \cap F$ and $E \cup F$.

3. (*a*) What is the probability of an event that is certain to occur?
   (*b*) What is the probability of an event that cannot occur?

4. The probability of rain tomorrow is 0.6. What is the probability of no rain tomorrow?

B

5. Two dice are rolled. What is the probability of each of the following?

   (*a*) A sum of 7 turns up.
   (*b*) The sum is not 11.
   (*c*) A 3 turns up on one die.
   (*d*) A 3 appears on one die or a sum of 7.
   (*e*) Neither 3 nor 4 appears.
   (*f*) Each die shows a 3 or more.
   (*g*) At least one die shows less than a 3.
   (*h*) Both dice show less than a 3.
   (*i*) Only one die shows less than 3.

6. In a bag there are 4 red, 3 white and 2 black jelly beans. One jelly bean is picked at random. What is the probability of each of the following?

   (*a*) picking a red jelly bean
   (*b*) picking a red or white jelly bean
   (*c*) picking neither a red nor a white jelly bean
   (*d*) picking a red *and* a black jelly bean

7. From the numbers 3, 4, 5, $\cdots$, 15, two numbers are chosen at random. Find the probability of each of the following events.

   (*a*) One number is a factor of the other.
   (*b*) The sum of the numbers is 18.
   (*c*) One integer is a factor of the other *and* their sum is 18.
   (*d*) One integer is a factor of the other *or* their sum is 18.

8. At the Fair, Pat, Mike and Jerry try the dart game. Their respective probabilities of winning are $\frac{1}{5}$, $\frac{1}{4}$, $\frac{1}{3}$. What is the probability that at least one of them wins?

9.5 Independent Events

Example 1

Given a box containing 3 beads: 1 red, 1 green and 1 yellow. Draw a bead, record its colour and put it back. Draw another bead and record its colour. What is the probability of drawing a red bead and then a green bead?

Two or more events are said to be *independent* if the outcome of one is not influenced by the outcome of the other. That is, two events are independent if they "have nothing to do with each other." For example, a rise on the stock market and your success on the next test paper are independent events — unless you are playing the market.

Solution

The sample space $S = \{(R, R), (R, G), (R, Y), (G, R), (G, G),$
$$(G, Y), (Y, R), (Y, G), (Y, Y)\}$$

$$P(R, G) = \frac{1}{9}$$

In Example 1 we ask for two conditions to be solved simultaneously.
(1) Those pairs for which the first member is R.
(2) Those pairs for which the second member is G.
If $E = \{(R, R), (R, G), (R, Y)\}$
and $F = \{(R, G), (G, G), (Y, G)\}$
then we want the members that are common to E and F, that is, $E \cap F$.

$$\therefore P(E \cap F) = \frac{1}{9}$$

We notice that $P(E) = \frac{3}{9} = \frac{1}{3}$ and $P(F) = \frac{3}{9} = \frac{1}{3}$

and that $P(E \cap F) = \frac{1}{9}$

$$= \frac{1}{3} \times \frac{1}{3}$$
$$= P(E) \cdot P(F)$$

292

Example 2

A red and a white die are rolled. What is the probability of the number on the red die being less than 4 and the number on the white die being greater than 4?

Solution

The sample space of outcomes of rolling two dice has 36 elements of the form (x, y).

red die   white die

We want those pairs (x, y) for which the first number is 1, 2, or 3 *and* the second number is 5 or 6.

Red   White

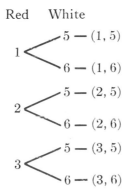

$$5 - (1, 5)$$
$$6 - (1, 6)$$
$$5 - (2, 5)$$
$$6 - (2, 6)$$
$$5 - (3, 5)$$
$$6 - (3, 6)$$

Only 6 pairs satisfy these conditions.

∴ the probability is $\dfrac{6}{36} = \dfrac{1}{6}$.

In Example 2, if A is the set of number pairs for which the first number is 1, 2 or 3, then

$$P(A) = \frac{18}{36} = \frac{1}{2}.$$

If B is the set of number pairs for which the second number is 5 or 6,

$$\text{then } P(B) = \frac{12}{36} = \frac{1}{3}.$$

We were looking for those number pairs in $A \cap B$.

$$\therefore P(A \cap B) = \frac{1}{6}$$
$$= \frac{1}{2} \times \frac{1}{3}$$
$$= P(A) \cdot P(B)$$

It appears that the following is true for independent events.

If A and B are independent events
$$P(A \cap B) = P(A) \cdot P(B)$$

Exercise 9.5

A

1. Which of the following pairs of events are independent?
   (a) A 4 on a first toss of a die, a 5 on the second toss.
   (b) Heads on a first toss of a coin, tails on the second toss.
   (c) From a deck of cards, drawing a diamond and then drawing a club.
   (d) From a box containing 5 red beads and 6 black beads, drawing two beads — a red bead and then a black bead.

2. When a child is born, the probability of a girl is $\frac{1}{2}$. The Browns have two children. What is the probability of each of the following?
   (a) the older is a boy and the younger a girl
   (b) two boys
   (c) two girls

3. What is the probability of drawing a diamond from a deck of cards, replacing the card, then drawing a club?

B

4. The probability that it rains tomorrow is 0.3 and the probability that the Expos win their baseball game is 0.4. What is the probability of each of the following?
   (a) It does not rain and the Expos win.
   (b) It does not rain and the Expos lose.

5. An insurance company estimates that the probability of a car having an accident during a year in Toronto is 0.003 and the probability of a home having a fire during a year is 0.001. What is the probability that Mr. Jones will have a car accident and a fire in his home?

6. What is the probability of throwing 2 sevens in a row with a pair of dice?

C 7. Given 3 boxes each with white and black beads.

If one bead is drawn from each box, what is the probability that exactly two black beads are drawn?

8. Joe buys tickets to two raffles. The probability of winning in one is 0.15 and in the other 0.2. What is the probability that he will win at least one prize?

9. A prisoner was given a chance of winning his freedom. He was given two containers and 10 black marbles and 10 white marbles. He was given permission to mix the marbles any way he wished. After he was blindfolded, he was to choose a container and select a marble. If he drew a white marble he would go free, otherwise he would remain in prison.

 (a) How should he arrange the marbles to obtain the best chance of going free?
 (b) What is his probability of going free after this best arrangement?

10. Assume that a year has 365 days.

 (a) What is the probability that two people do not have the same birthday?
 (b) What is the probability that of three people no two have the same birthday?
 (c) What is the probability that of three people, at least two have the same birthday?

11. If you have a calculator, verify the probabilities in the following table.

Number of people	Probability that at least 2 persons have the same birthday
5	0.027
10	0.117
15	0.252
20	0.411
25	0.569
30	0.706
40	0.891
60	0.994

9.5/Independent Events

9.6 Statistical Probability

What is the probability that the first grade 12 student you meet is between 168 cm and 172 cm tall? What is the probability that you will live another forty years? What is the probability that your friend Joe wears a size 9 shoe?

If adequate records, called *statistical records*, are kept on situations like those above, business and industry can plan and make reasonable predictions about sales and production runs. For example, if you were ordering 1000 sets of golf clubs for your business, how many left-handed sets would you order? Probability determined from records or the collection of data is called *statistical probability*.

The National Safety Council reported that for 100 000 accidents occurring in one year 12 300 were caused by falls. The probability that the next accident that occurs will be a fall is

$$P(\text{fall}) = \frac{12\ 300}{100\ 000}$$
$$= \frac{123}{1000}$$
$$\doteq \frac{1}{8}$$

The Council will probably tell people that one in eight accidents is caused by a fall.

Notice that the number of cases recorded is large. The larger the number of cases, the more *dependable* is the probability. If Herbert "sinks" 10 out of 25 foul shots in basketball, what is the probability that he will score on his next free throw?

$$P(\text{basket}) = \frac{10}{25}$$
$$= \frac{2}{5}$$

This probability figure, $\frac{2}{5}$, is not very dependable because the number of cases recorded is small.

Canadian Population Mortality Tables are prepared by Statistics Canada from census results and observed deaths. Starting with a large number of male and female babies, deaths are calculated for each sex, using rates of mortality derived from the observed statistics.

The tables on page 420 show the number that die each year. For example,

296

Male Mortality Table

Age	Number Living	Number Dying
18	96 198	135

The table indicates that for age 18, the number of males living at the end of the eighteenth year is 96 198 and the number who are expected to die during the nineteenth year is 135. Thus, the probability that an eighteen year old male will live for one year is

$$\frac{96\ 198 - 135}{96\ 198} \doteq 0.9986$$

Example

What is the probability that a male age 20 will be alive at age 60?

Solution

The number of males living at age 20 is 95 915. The number of males living at age 60 is 77 861. ∴ The probability that a male age 20 will be alive at age 60 is

$$\frac{77\ 861}{95\ 915} \doteq 0.8118$$

Exercise 9.6

B

1. Mary hit the bull's-eye 18 times out of 120 throws in a dart game. What is the probability that Mary will hit the bull's-eye on her next throw?

2. Discuss how an insurance company might use the mortality table for males to help calculate the yearly premium that a man age 20 must pay for a policy that has benefits as given in each of the following.
   (a) $5000 paid to his beneficiary if he dies within the next year.
   (b) $5000 paid to his beneficiary if he dies before 60.

3. Of 100 000 accidents, 1000 were the results of drowning.
   (a) What is the probability that the next accident is a drowning?
   (b) On a holiday weekend the predicted number of accidents is 600 across the nation. How many of these accidents will probably be drownings?

4. Use the mortality table for males, page 420, to answer the following.

   (a) How many eighteen year old males are alive out of the original group?

   (b) How many men will die as the group increases in age from 18 to 38?

   (c) What is the probability that a male age 18 will die within twenty years?

   (d) What is the probability that a male age 18 will live to be 38?

5. Repeat Question 4 for females. See table, page 420.

6. (a) What is the probability that a male age 15 will live to be 65?

   (b) What is the probability that a female age 15 will live to be 65?

7. (a) What is the probability that a male age 40 will live to be 60?

   (b) What is the probability that a female age 40 will live to be 60?

C 8. Survey 100 male students in your school and record the following information.   (i) height   (ii) shoe size

   (a) What is the probability that the first male student you meet in the corridor is between 168 cm and 172 cm tall?

   (b) What is the probability that your best male friend wears a size 9 shoe?

   (c) If you were buying 1000 pairs of shoes for a store selling mostly to secondary school students, how many size 9 shoes would you buy?

9. Repeat Question 8 for 100 female students in your school.

10. The average future life time of a man aged 20 is calculated by (i) adding the number of men living after age 20, and (ii) dividing this sum by the number living at age 20.

   (a) What is the average future life time of a man age 20?

   (b) What is the average future life time of a man age 40?

Recommended Reading

The Science of Chance, Horace C. Levinson, Holt Rinehart Winston
Pathways to Probability, Amy C. King and Cecil Read, Holt Rinehart Winston

Review Exercise 9.7

1. Two dice are tossed. What is the probability of each of the following events?
    (a) rolling a sum of 6
    (b) rolling a sum of 11
    (c) rolling a sum of 6 or 11
    (d) rolling a sum greater than 7

2. Two dice are tossed. What is the probability of each of the following?
    (a) At least one die shows a 5.
    (b) At least one die shows an odd number.
    (c) Both dice show the same number.

3. One die is tossed. What is the probability of each the following?
    (a) An odd number appears on the up face.
    (b) A prime number appears on the up face.
    (c) Either an odd number or a prime number appears on the up face.

4. A game is played in which two dice are tossed. You win if a sum of 5 or 9 occurs. You lose if a sum of 3 or 7 occurs. Find the following.
    (a) the probability that you win.
    (b) the probability that you lose
    (c) Is this a fair game? Explain.

5. You are given two dice. One die has 2 faces colored red, 3 colored green, and one colored white. The other die has 4 faces colored black, one face colored blue, and one face colored red. The two dice are tossed. Find the probability that the following colors will occur on an up face.
    (a) green   (d) green or black
    (b) black   (e) red
    (c) green and black   (f) green or red

6. A bag contains 2 red, 4 white and 6 black jelly beans.

   (*a*) One jelly bean is drawn at random. What is the probability of drawing a red jelly bean?

   (*b*) One jelly bean is drawn and then replaced. A second jelly bean is drawn. What is the probability of drawing a red jelly bean and then a black one?

   (*c*) One jelly bean is drawn but not replaced. Then a second jelly bean is drawn. What is the probability of drawing a red jelly bean and then a black one?

7. (*a*) In Question 6 (*b*) what is the probability that both beans drawn are black?

   (*b*) In Question 6 (*c*) what is the probability that both beans drawn are black?

8. A coin is tossed 7 times in a row. What is the probability of getting 7 heads?

9. A coin is tossed at the same time that a die is rolled. Find the probability of each of the following occurring.

   (*a*) a head on the coin and 3 on the die

   (*b*) a head on the coin or 3 on the die

   (*c*) neither a head on the coin nor a 3 on the die

10. What is the probability of drawing two Jacks successively from a deck of 52 playing cards? Assume replacement is not made after the first draw.

11. (*a*) What is the probability of throwing a sum of 7 with three dice?

    (*b*) What is the probability of throwing a sum of 7 or less with three dice?

12. From the integers 3 to 12 inclusive, two integers are chosen at random. Find the probability of each of the following.

    (*a*) One integer is a factor of the other.

    (*b*) The sum of the two integers is 15.

    (*c*) One integer is a factor of the other or their sum is 15.

13. In a game using two dice a player rolls a sum of 4. What is the probability that the player rolls a sum of 4 before a sum of 7 in subsequent rolls?

14. What is the probability of throwing a sum of at least one of 7, 10 or 12 with two dice?

15. A regular tetrahedron has one of the numerals 1, 2, 3, 4, on each of its four faces. Another regular tetrahedron has the numeral 3 on one face, 4 on another face, and 5 on its other two faces. If these two tetrahedrons are tossed, what is the probability of each of the following events?

   (a) The sum of the down face is 6.
   (b) The down face on the second tetrahedron is greater than the down face on the first tetrahedron.
   (c) The three up faces of the first tetrahedron have a sum greater than five.

16. A box contains three white discs, two red discs, and four green discs. Find the probability of each of the following.

   (a) One disc is drawn and the disc is white.
   (b) One disc is drawn and the disc is green.
   (c) Three discs are drawn simultaneously and one disc of each color appears.

17. Five students check their coats at a school dance. In the confusion at the end of the dance, the attendant, in despair, hands the coats back at random. What is the probability that all the students get their own coats?

18. In testing the claims of a telepathist, a test is made with five cards, each having a different symbol on it. The "sender" concentrates on two of these cards. What is the probability that the telepathist names the two symbols correctly by just guessing?

19. On the average a certain baseball player hits safely three out of ten times at bat. Find the probability that in his next two times at bat he does not get a hit.

20. Three marksmen fire at a target, the respective probabilities of their hitting being 0.1, 0.2 and 0.3. Find the probability of each of the following.

   (a) No shot hits the target.
   (b) Only one shot hits the target.
   (c) Only two shots hit the target.
   (d) All three shots hit the target.

21. (a) What is the probability that a male age 18 will live to be 70?
   (b) What is the probability that a female age 16 will not be living at age 80?

$10/$ Statistics

Statistics is a science that deals with problems capable of being answered by numerical information obtained by counting and measuring. The study of statistics involves the *collection of data, analyzing data*, and *making inferences from data*.

Statistics as a science in its broader sense is not only a means of guiding our daily decisions of life, but also is a device or tool for discovering new truths. Statistics is one of the most powerful engines for research. The meaning of hitherto unknown biological, psychological, physical, economical, social and technical relationships is revealed or clarified by statistics. Those doing effective research today have been well trained in its theory and methods. We can only hope to give you a brief glimpse of statistics in the ensuing work of this chapter.

10.1 Frequency Distribution

A quality control engineer in a tire manufacturing company took 25 steel cord radial tires at random from a week's production in the plant. To determine their wearing characteristics, he put them on a machine that in 1 h simulated the wear under normal conditions of 60 km of driving. He ran them till they were worn smooth and hoped to make a decision about the quality of the whole production from an examination of the sample. His problem was to decide from the properties of the sample how to adjust the manufacturing process to maintain or improve the quality of future production runs.

The tires may be regarded as a *sample* of 25 tires taken at random from a *population* (a week's production). The following table gives the life measurements in hours, each life being measured to the nearest 10 h.

Hours of wear for 25 tires				
610	810	710	770	990
700	690	580	480	850
850	730	730	970	1010
930	870	880	1080	780
750	760	830	560	660

A pictorial representation of this data can be obtained from a *dot frequency* diagram, Figure 10.1, where each dot represents a tire.

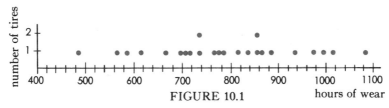

FIGURE 10.1

Notice that the measurements are all contained between 400 and 1100 and there is a clustering of dots around 750.

A more useful graph of tire life measurements is the *cumulative graph*. A point (x, y) on this graph is determined as follows.

x is the number of hours elapsed.

y is the *total* number of worn tires in x h.

$$\text{Thus for } \quad 0 \le x < 480, y = 0$$
$$\text{for } 480 \le x < 560, y = 1$$
$$\text{for } 560 \le x < 580, y = 2$$
$$\vdots$$

It is often convenient to scale the vertical axis using percent, where 100% gives the whole sample of 25 tires.

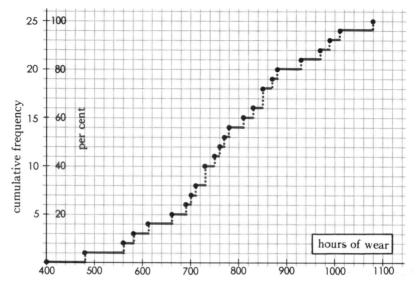

It is obvious that the cumulative graph consists of a number of discrete points. There are certain values of percent, p, that do not correspond to values of x. For example, $p = 50$ has no corresponding x value. In practice it is useful to assign a value of x to $p = 50$. We make an arbitrary rule for obtaining such values.

(a) Draw a horizontal line at $p = 50$ to meet the "vertical jump."

(b) Draw a vertical line through the point of intersection to meet the x axis. (The point is 770.)

Thus, to $p = 50$ we associate the value 770. That is, 50% of the tires are worn out in 770 h. This number, 770, is the 50th *percentile* and is also the *median* of the measurements.

The 25th percentile is called the *lower quartile* and is the x value for $p = 25$. The x value for $p = 75$, that is, the 75th percentile is called the *upper quartile*. The *range* of the sample is the difference between the largest and smallest measurement. The range in hours is $1080 - 480 = 600$.

The *median* of a set of n numbers arranged in order of magnitude is the middle number of the set if n is odd, and the average of the two middle numbers if n is even. For example, the median of

3, 4, 10 is 4

and of

2, 4, 6, 10 is $\dfrac{4 + 6}{2} = 5$.

10.1/Frequency Distribution

Exercise 10.1

B 1. Pierre Slalom, the famous skier, had the following times, in seconds, for his practice ski runs.

77, 84, 81, 78, 74, 86, 85, 81, 70, 82, 88, 83, 78, 85, 84

(a) Make a dot frequency diagram and a cumulative graph.
(b) Find the median.
(c) Find the upper and lower quartile.
(d) Find the range.

2. The masses of 32 members of the track team are listed.

74.0	80.5	73.0	79.0
80.0	73.5	78.0	78.0
80.5	91.5	82.0	81.0
85.5	86.5	79.0	75.0
73.0	75.0	70.5	77.0
72.5	74.0	76.0	75.0
77.0	80.5	89.0	77.0
81.5	71.5	80.5	76.0

(a) Construct a dot frequency diagram and a cumulative graph.
(b) Determine the median and the two quartiles.

3. Joe Scout surveyed members of his cub pack and recorded their heights in centimetres. Here is his chart.

Height	Number	Height	Number	Height	Number
159	/	166	//////	173	///
160	///	167	/////	174	/
161	//	168	///////	175	/
162	///	169	//////////	176	
163	/////	170	//////	177	
164	////	171	/////	178	
165	//////	172	//	179	

(a) Construct a dot frequency diagram and a cumulative graph.
(b) Find the median and the two quartiles.

4. Place 10 pennies in a box. Shake well, open the box and record the total number of heads. Repeat this experiment 15 times in all.

(a) Guess the 50th, 25th and 75th percentile.
(b) Construct a dot frequency diagram and a cumulative graph.
(c) Determine the median and the two quartiles and compare with your guess.

10.1/Frequency Distribution

5. Throw 4 dice 25 times and record the total each time.
   (a) Guess the median and upper and lower quartiles.
   (b) Construct a dot frequency diagram and a cumulative graph.
   (c) Determine the median and the two quartiles and compare with your guess.

10.2 Histograms

Dot frequency diagrams are adequate for a small number of samples, but the procedure is tedious for a large number of measurements. We can shorten the work and still represent the main features of the samples by grouping the measurements in intervals and constructing a *frequency histogram* and a *cumulative polygon*.

We first construct a *frequency table* using some data such as the tire life that was used in Section 10.1. The range of values is divided into a number of equal intervals or *classes*. A convenient number of classes is between 10 and 25. The number is chosen so that the classes have relatively simple midpoints.

Figure 10.2 shows that our range is from 480 to 1080. Select classes of 50 h with midpoints at 500, 550, 600, $\cdots$, 1100 along the x axis. The actual intervals will be 475 to 525, 525 to 575, $\cdots$, 1075 to 1125. The following chart, obtained from Figure 10.1 for tire life, will assist us in drawing our frequency histogram and cumulative polygon.

Interval		Frequency	Cumulative Frequency
475- 525	/	1	1
525- 575	/	1	2
575- 625	//	2	4
625- 675	/	1	5
675- 725	///	3	8
725- 775	##/	5	13
775- 825	//	2	15
825- 875	////	4	19
875- 925	/	1	20
925- 975	//	2	22
975-1025	//	2	24
1025-1075		0	24
1075-1125	/	1	25

Frequency table for tire life

FIGURE 10.2

Various procedures can be used for a number falling on a class boundary. We shall adopt the method of always tabulating such a number in the higher class. Thus, 675 is placed in the class 675-725. In general, we place a measurement, x, in the interval a to b if $a \leq x < b$.

Often, especially for discrete data, noncontiguous boundaries are used. For example, in a set of examination marks based on a total of 100, the class boundaries might be $\cdots$, 40-49, 50-59, 60-69, $\cdots$. Clearly a mark of 60 appears in the class 60-69.

The frequency table for tire life can now be used in drawing a *frequency histogram* or a *cumulative polygon*. A *histogram*, for frequency distributions with contiguous boundaries, is a vertical bar graph with no spaces between the bars. The class boundaries are points on the horizontal axis and frequencies are points on the vertical axis.

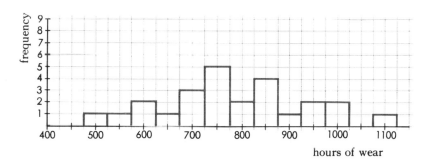

Frequency histogram of tire life

Both the dot frequency diagram and the frequency histogram show information about the distribution of the measurements. We lose information in the frequency histogram because we record intervals rather than exact values. We gain when the number of measurements is large and we are interested only in "trends."

Another way of representing data is using a *cumulative polygon* with vertices found in the following way.

(a) The x coordinate of a vertex is the upper boundary of the class.

(b) The y coordinate of the vertex is the cumulative frequency up to that class.

Thus for the tire life the vertices of the cumulative polygon are $(525, 1)$, $(575, 2)$, $(625, 4)$, $\cdots$, $(1125, 25)$. Note that $(475, 0)$ is also included as a vertex of the polygon.

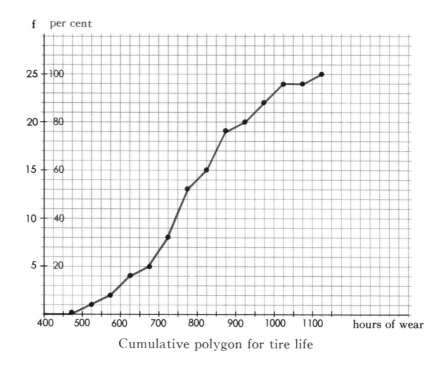

f   per cent

25 ┼ 100

20 ┼ 80

15 ┼ 60

10 ┼ 40

5 ┼ 20

400   500   600   700   800   900   1000   1100   hours of wear

Cumulative polygon for tire life

If the vertical axis is also labelled in per cent, then the cumulative polygon provides an easy way of approximating percentiles of the distribution of measurements. For example, the 50th percentile or median obtained using the colored segment is about **770**.

Exercise 10.2

A 1. Marks in a mathematics exam range from 22 to 97. Suggest interval midpoints and interval boundaries for a frequency table.

B 2. The following is the frequency distribution of the mass of 100 eighteen-year-old school boys.

Mass (kg)	Frequency		Mass (kg)	Frequency	
50-55	1	1	80- 85	17	77
55-60	2	3	85- 90	10	87
60-65	5	8	90- 95	6	93
65-70	11	19	95-100	4	97
70-75	21	40	100-105	2	99
75-80	20	60	105-110	1	100

308

(a) Make a frequency table.

(b) Draw a histogram and a cumulative polygon from the measurements.

(c) Find the median and two quartiles on the cumulative polygon.

3. The following is a record of a set of marks obtained by all senior classes in an examination.

(a) Make a frequency table.

(b) Draw a histogram and a cumulative polygon from the marks.

(c) Find the median and the two quartiles on the cumulative polygon.

4. (a) Select a novel of your choice and record the number of words per sentence in the first hundred sentences.

(b) Draw a histogram and a cumulative polygon from the data.

(c) Find the median.

5. In a deck of cards let Ace, 2, 3, $\cdots$, 10 have values of 1, 2, 3, $\cdots$, 10 respectively, and let J, Q, K have values 11, 12, 13 respectively.

(a) Draw 3 cards and record the sum of the values. Replace the cards, shuffle and repeat 50 times in all. Record the data.

(b) Choose intervals of length 4 and make a frequency distribution table for grouped sums.

(c) Draw a frequency histogram and a cumulative polygon.

(d) Find the median and the upper and lower quartiles.

6. Roll three dice and add the numbers turned up.

(a) Roll 100 times and record the totals.

(b) Predict the median total.

(c) Find the median from a cumulative polygon.

10.3 Measures of Central Tendency

To reduce a mass of data to an understandable form we have constructed a frequency table for the data and drawn the corresponding histogram or frequency polygon. Statisticians have found it useful to describe the distribution further by indicating the centre of distribution or the *measure* of *central tendency.*

The first measure of central tendency is the *arithmetic mean* or *mean.* For a set of numbers $x_1, x_2, x_3, \cdots, x_n$ the mean is defined as

$$\overline{X} = \frac{x_1 + x_2 + x_3 + \cdots + x_n}{n}$$

$$= \frac{\sum_{i=1}^{n} x_i}{n}$$

Example 1

Find to two decimal places the mean of 12, 15, 18, 21, 17, 11.

Solution

$$\overline{X} = \frac{12 + 15 + 18 + 21 + 17 + 11}{6}$$

$$= 15.67$$

Notice that since $\overline{X} = \dfrac{\sum_{i=1}^{n} x_i}{n}$

$$n\overline{X} = \sum_{i=1}^{n} x_i$$

Thus, if the mean of a number of the measurements is known, the sum of these measurements can easily be obtained. For example, if the mean salary of 250 plant employees is $193.20, then the total payroll is

$$\$193.20 \times 250 \text{ or } \$48\ 300.$$

Another property of the arithmetic mean, $\overline{X}$, is the relationship among the *deviations* of the measurements from the mean. For example, for the measurements 1, 3, 11, $\overline{X} = 5$, and the deviations are

$$1 - 5 = -4$$
$$3 - 5 = -2$$
$$11 - 5 = \underline{6}$$

Sum of the deviations = 0

In general, if $\overline{X}$ is the mean of a set of measurements x_i, $i = 1$, 2, 3, $\cdots$, n, then the deviation of x_i is $x_i - \overline{X}$ and the sum of the deviations is given by the following.

$$\sum_{i=1}^{n} (x_i - \overline{X}) = (x_1 - \overline{X}) + (x_2 - \overline{X}) + \cdots + (x_n - \overline{X})$$
$$= (x_1 + x_2 + \cdots + x_n) - n\overline{X}$$
$$= \sum_{i=1}^{n} x_i - \sum_{i=1}^{n} x_i$$
$$= 0$$

Example 2

Given the measurements 1, 3, 11. Show that $\overline{X}$ is the value of x that makes $(1 - x)^2 + (3 - x)^2 + (11 - x)^2$ minimum.

Solution

$$\overline{X} = \frac{1 + 3 + 11}{3} = 5$$
$$(1 - x)^2 + (3 - x)^2 + (11 - x)^2 = 3x^2 - 30x + 131$$

But
$$3x^2 - 30x + 131 = 3(x^2 - 10x) + 131$$
$$= 3(x^2 - 10x + 25) + 131 - 75$$
$$= 3(x - 5)^2 + 56$$

$\because 3(x - 5)^2 \geq 0$, the expression $3x^2 - 30x + 131$ has a minimum value of 56 when $x = 5$. Thus, the minimum value occurs when $x = \overline{X}$.

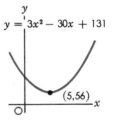

In a frequency table with h classes with midpoints x_1, x_2, x_3, $\cdots$, x_h and respective frequencies f_1, f_2, f_3, $\cdots$, f_h, the mean is defined as

$$\overline{X} = \frac{x_1 f_1 + x_2 f_2 + x_3 f_3 + \cdots + x_h f_h}{f_1 + f_2 + f_3 + \cdots + f_h}$$
$$= \frac{\displaystyle\sum_{i=1}^{h} x_i f_i}{\displaystyle\sum_{i=1}^{h} f_i}$$

Note that if the total number of measurements is n, then

$$f_1 + f_2 + \cdots + f_h = n \quad \text{and} \quad \overline{X} = \frac{\displaystyle\sum_{i=1}^{h} x_i f_i}{n}$$

Example 3

Find the mean of the data given in Figure 10.2.

Solution

Class boundary	x_i	f_i	x_if_i
475- 525	500	1	500
525- 575	550	1	550
575- 625	600	2	1200
625- 675	650	1	650
675- 725	700	3	2100
725- 775	750	5	3750
775- 825	800	2	1600
825- 875	850	4	3400
875- 925	900	1	900
925- 975	950	2	1900
975-1025	1000	2	2000
1025-1075	1050	0	—
1075-1125	1100	1	1100
		25	19 650

$$\overline{X} = \frac{\sum x_if_i}{n}$$

$$\overline{X} = \frac{19\ 650}{25} = 786$$

When h, the number of classes, is large the method used in Example 3 to calculate X may be lengthy. A faster method consists of *assuming a mean* and determining the difference between the *assumed mean* and the actual mean. The assumed mean is usually selected to be a class midpoint. Thus, if

A is any class midpoint (the assumed mean),

C is the difference between two consecutive class midpoints,

x_i is a class midpoint,

we define $$d_i = \frac{x_i - A}{C},$$

that is, d_i is the number of classes that x_i is away from A.

$\therefore$ $$\overline{X} = A + \frac{C\sum_{i=1}^{h} d_if_i}{n}$$

10.3/Measures of Central Tendency

Example 4

Find $\overline{X}$ in Figure 10.2 using an assumed mean.

Solution

Here $C = 50$
Let the assumed mean be $A = 800$.
For the first class 475-525,

$$x_1 = 500$$
$$f_1 = 1$$
$$d = \frac{x_1 - A}{C} = \frac{-300}{50}$$
$$= -6$$

The following table shows the completed results.

Class	x	f	d	df
475-525	500	1	-6	-6
525-575	550	1	-5	-5
575-625	600	2	-4	-8
625-675	650	1	-3	-3
675-725	700	3	-2	-6
725-775	750	5	-1	-5
775-825	800	2	0	0
825-875	850	4	1	4
875-925	900	1	2	2
925-975	950	2	3	6
975-1025	1000	2	4	8
1025-1075	1050	0	5	0
1075-1125	1100	1	6	6
		$\overline{25}$		$\overline{-7}$

Since
$$A = 800, \sum_{i=1}^{h} d_i f_i = -7, n = 25, C = 50$$

∵
$$\overline{X} = A + \frac{C \sum_{i=1}^{h} d_i f_i}{n}$$

∴
$$\overline{X} = 800 + \frac{50(-7)}{25}$$
$$= 800 - 14$$
$$= 786$$

Another measure of central tendency, the *median*, was defined in Section 10.1.

Example 5

Find the median for each of the following.

(a) 3, 7, 12, 16, 8, 9, 11
(b) 9, 6, 7, 16, 20, 12

Solution

List the data in ascending order of magnitude.

(a) 3, 7, 8, 9, 11, 12, 16

∵ the number of data is odd, that is, 7 and $\dfrac{7+1}{2} = 4$,

the fourth number is the median.

∴ $M = 9$.

(b) 6, 7, 9, 12, 16, 20

∵ the number of data is even, that is, 6 and $\dfrac{6}{2} = 3$, the arith-

metic mean of the *third* and *fourth* numbers is the median.

∴ $M = \dfrac{9+12}{2} = 10.5$

To obtain a formula for calculating the median from a frequency distribution with h classes we introduce the following notation:

M = median
L_M = lower limit of the class containing M
f_L = number of observations up to L_M
f_M = number of observations in the class containing M
i = width of the class

If we assume that the data in the median class is distributed uniformly throughout the class we may draw the following diagram.

$$\therefore \ \frac{M - L_M}{i} = \frac{\dfrac{n}{2} - f_L}{f_M}$$

$$\therefore \ M = L_M + \left(\frac{\dfrac{n}{2} - f_L}{f_M}\right) i$$

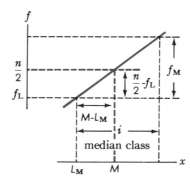

Other central tendencies are the *mode, geometric mean,* and *harmonic mean.* They are not studied in this book, but the topics merit further reading for those interested in the subject.

10.3/Measures of Central Tendency

B

1. The temperatures, in °C, on five successive days were 21, 24, 26, 29 and 33. Find the mean temperature for the five days and compare it with the median temperature.

2. For a senior class a frequency chart of mathematics test results is given.

Mark	Frequency
0	/
1	//
2	////
3	/////
4	///
5	////
6	////////
7	///////
8	////
9	///
10	//

   (a) Find the mean test mark for the class.
   (b) Find the mean using an assumed mean.
   (c) Find the median using a formula.

3. Use the formula for a median to show that the median tire life for our steel cord radial tires is 770 h. (Figure 10.2)

4. Ted was selling T-shirts at the Annual Fair. His average sales were 96 shirts a day for six days. If he made 12¢ a shirt, how much did he earn in the six days?

5. (a) Compare the mean of 1, 3, and 11 with the mean of $1 + 8$, $3 + 8$, and $11 + 8$.
   (b) Compare the mean of 1, 3, and 11 with the mean of 1×7, 3×7, and 11×7.

6. (a) Compare the mean of $x_1, x_2, \cdots, x_n$ with the mean of $x_1 + c, x_2 + c, \cdots, x_n + c$.
   (b) Compare the mean of $x_1, x_2, \cdots, x_n$ with the mean of $cx_1, cx_2, \cdots, cx_n$.

7. If the mean of 75 items is 72.4 L and the mean of 25 items is 58.2 L, find the mean of the 100 items.

8. The mean height of 500 grade 9 students is 166.8 cm. In this grade there are 150 girls whose mean height is 161.0 cm. What is the mean height of the boys?

9. The average mass of the Delta Collegiate football team is 93.1 kg. The 16 backfielders average 86.2 kg. How much do the 22 linemen average in mass?

10. The mean $\overline{X}$ of one set of measurements is 9, the mean $\overline{Y}$ of another set of measurements is 15. There are twice as many measurements in the first set as in the second. Find the arithmetic mean of all the measurements (the *grand mean*).

11. A list of heights in centimetres of 1000 students is given.

Interval	x_i	f_i
155-157	156	4
158-160	159	8
161-163	162	26
164-166	165	53
167-169	168	89
170-172	171	146
173-175	174	188
176-178	177	181
179-181	180	125
182-184	183	92
185-187	186	60
188-190	189	22
191-193	192	4
194-196	195	1
197-199	198	1
Total		1000

(a) Find the mean using $\overline{X} = \dfrac{\sum\limits_{i=1}^{h} x_i f_i}{n}$

(b) Find the mean using an assumed mean.

(c) Find the median M using $M = L_M + \left(\dfrac{\dfrac{n}{2} - f_L}{f_M}\right) i$

10.3/Measures of Central Tendency

C 12. For three numbers a, b, and c show that the minimum value of

$$(a - x)^2 + (b - x)^2 + (c - x)^2$$

occurs when $x = \dfrac{a + b + c}{3}$

13. Show that, for n measurements x_1, x_2, $\cdots$, x_n the mean $\overline{X}$, minimizes

$$S = \sum_{i=1}^{n} (x_i - x)^2$$

14. Prove the formula for $\overline{X}$ using the assumed mean as follows.

(a) Show that $x_i = A + Cd_i$ and $n = \sum_{i=1}^{h} f_i$

(b) Show that $\displaystyle\sum_{i=1}^{h} \frac{x_i f_i}{n} = \sum_{i=1}^{h} \frac{A f_i}{n} + \sum_{i=1}^{h} \frac{C d_i f_i}{n}$

$$- A + C \sum_{i=1}^{h} \frac{d_i f_i}{n}$$

10.4 Measures of Dispersion

Although the arithmetic mean, $\overline{X}$, is a satisfactory measure of central tendency, it does not give a clear picture of a set of measurements or their distribution or scatter. In Figure 10.3 we show very different frequency distributions having the identical mean. The mean, 10, does not describe the sets of measurements equally well. We need some measure of "spread" or dispersion of a set of measurements about their mean.

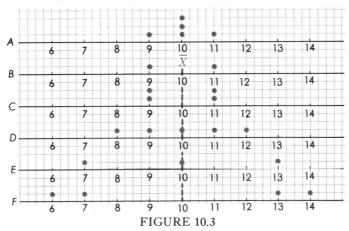

FIGURE 10.3

Intuitively we might reason as follows.

> *A* has the least spread of all the examples.
> *B* and *C* are about the same.
> *C* and *D* are hard to compare.
> *D* is spread less than *E*.
> *F* has the most spread of all the examples.

Would the range be a good measure of dispersion or scatter? Notice that *A* and *B* have the same range and *A* has less spread than *B*. Thus, range by itself will not do.

Consider (range $\div n$). In this case *C* has less spread than *B*. But we thought that they should be the same. This measure of spread is not suitable.

One might suggest the mean of the deviations of measurements from $\overline{X}$. But, from Section 10.3, we know that

$$\sum_{i=1}^{n} (x_i - \overline{X}) = 0$$

Thus, the mean of the deviations of measurements from $\overline{X}$ is of no value in measuring dispersions.

In describing dispersions it is immaterial whether a measurement is greater than or less than the mean. The important measure is the *distance* from the mean. Thus, the sign of the deviation can be ignored. The average of the deviations, all taken positive, therefore measures the dispersion of data about the mean and is called the *mean deviation* and is denoted by $\overline{M}$. Thus,

$$\overline{M} = \frac{1}{n}\left[|x_1 - \overline{X}| + |x_2 - \overline{X}| + \cdots + |x_n - \overline{X}| \right]$$

$$= \frac{1}{n} \sum_{i=1}^{n} |x_i - \overline{X}|$$

Another method of converting positive and negative numbers to positive numbers is the process of squaring. Recall that $\sqrt{x^2} = |x|$. In more advanced mathematical treatments of dispersion, it is more useful to use a measure of dispersion called *standard deviation*, denoted by the Greek letter σ. We define σ as follows.

$$\sigma = \sqrt{\frac{1}{n}[(x_1 - \overline{X})^2 + (x_2 - \overline{X})^2 + \cdots + (x_n - \overline{X})^2]}$$

$$= \sqrt{\frac{1}{n} \sum_{i=1}^{n} (x_i - \overline{X})^2}$$

10.4/ Measures of Dispersion

If in a frequency table the class midpoints are $x_1, x_2, \cdots, x_h$ and the respective frequencies are $f_1, f_2, \cdots, f_h$, then the mean deviation is defined as

$$\overline{M} = \frac{1}{n}\left[\,|\,x_1 - \overline{X}\,|f_1 + |\,x_2 - \overline{X}\,|f_2 + \cdots + |\,x_h - \overline{X}\,|f_h\right]$$

$$= \frac{1}{n}\sum_{i=1}^{h}|\,x_i - \overline{X}\,|f_i$$

$$\text{and } \sigma = \sqrt{\frac{(x_1 - \overline{X})^2 f_1 + (x_2 - \overline{X})^2 f_2 + \cdots + (x_h - \overline{X})^2 f_h}{n}}$$

$$= \sqrt{\frac{\sum\limits_{i=1}^{h}(x_i - \overline{X})^2 f_i}{n}}$$

The following chart shows the measures of dispersion or scatter about the mean $\overline{X} = 10$ for our examples in Figure 10.3.

Set of Measurements	Range	$\dfrac{\text{Range}}{n}$	Sum of Absolute Deviations	$\overline{M}$	σ
A	2	0.4	2	0.4	0.632
B	2	1	2	1.0	1.0
C	2	0.5	4	1.0	1.0
D	4	0.8	6	1.2	1.414
E	6	2	6	2.0	2.45
F	8	2	14	3.5	3.54

Notice that both $\overline{M}$ and σ order the sets as we intuitively felt they should be. Statisticians prefer to work with standard deviation because they find the measure has properties that prove to be very useful.

For faster calculations where an assumed mean is used for finding $\overline{X}$, the value of σ can be obtained by the following formula which is given without proof.

$$\sigma = C\sqrt{\frac{\sum\limits_{i=1}^{h} d_i^2 f_i - \dfrac{\left(\sum\limits_{i=1}^{h} d_i f_i\right)^2}{n}}{n}}$$

$$= \frac{C}{n}\sqrt{n\sum_{i=1}^{h} d_i^2 f_i - \left(\sum_{i=1}^{h} d_i f_i\right)^2}$$

Exercise 10.4

B 1. Verify the values recorded in the preceding table for $\overline{M}$ and σ.

2. For the set of numbers 76, 70, 81, 72, 76 calculate the following.

   (a) the mean   (c) the mean deviation
   (b) the median   (d) the standard deviation

3. Calculate the mean deviation and the standard deviation for the measurements 47, 41, 50, 39, 45, 48, 42, 32, 60, 20.

4. A large coffee company uses machines to automatically pack 1 kg tins of coffee. As the tins emerge in a continuous stream an inspector periodically selects a sample at random and finds its mass accurately to the nearest gram. The results of two machines follow.

Machine A	Machine B
1017	995
1051	1009
1078	1028
996	1036
1059	1000
1082	1019
1014	1027
1040	1045
1072	1008
998	1018
1033	1039

   (a) Find the mean for the measurements from each machine.
   (b) Find the standard deviation for each.
   (c) Which machine do you think is functioning more accurately? Explain.

5. With the frequency distribution given, calculate the following to two decimal places.

   (a) the mean
   (b) the median
   (c) the mean deviation
   (d) the standard deviation

Class boundaries	Frequencies
10- 30	5
30- 50	8
50- 70	12
70- 90	18
90-110	3
110-130	2

6. Given the measurements 7, 9, 23.

   (a) Calculate the standard deviation.
   (b) Add 5 to each measurement and calculate the standard deviation.
   (c) Subtract 6 from each measurement and calculate the standard deviation.
   (d) Conjecture a rule about standard deviation when the same constant is added to or subtracted from each measurement.

7. Calculate the standard deviation of the measurements 7999, 7997 and 8001.

8. Design an example to illustrate the following rule. If σ is the standard deviation of x_1, x_2, $\cdots$, x_n then $c\sigma$ is the standard deviation of cx_1, cx_2, $\cdots$, cx_n.

C

9. Given that $\sigma^2 = \dfrac{1}{n}\left[(x_1 - \overline{X})^2 + (x_2 - \overline{X})^2 + \cdots + (x_n - \overline{X})^2\right]$

   and $n\overline{X} = x_1 + x_2 + \cdots + x_n$

   Prove that $\sigma^2 = \dfrac{1}{n}\left[x_1^2 + x_2^2 + \cdots + x_n^2\right] - \overline{X}^2$

   (Hint: Expand the expression for σ^2.)

10. Chebyshev, a 19th century Russian mathematician, proved the following theorem.

    "For any set of numbers, *at least* the fraction $\left(1 - \dfrac{1}{h^2}\right)$ of the numbers lie between h standard deviations of the mean."

    Use Chebyshev's theorem for each of the following.

    (a) Calculate the percentage of a set of numbers that lie between $\overline{X} + \sigma$ and $\overline{X} - \sigma$.
    (b) Calculate the percentage of a set of numbers that lie between $\overline{X} + 2\sigma$ and $\overline{X} - 2\sigma$.

11. Six playing cards are thrown in the air and land on the floor. The number of cards falling face up and the corresponding frequency is given in the chart.

Number face up	0	1	2	3	4	5	6
Frequency	2	10	24	35	22	6	1

    (a) Calculate the mean for this distribution.
    (b) Calculate the standard deviation.

10.4/ Measures of Dispersion   321

12. The following frequency distribution of a set of marks is given.

Interval	Frequency
40-50	4
50-60	11
60-70	19
70-80	14
80-90	0
90-100	2

(a) Calculate the mean.
(b) Calculate the standard deviation.
(Hint: Use the midpoint of the interval.)

13. Use $\sigma = \sqrt{\dfrac{\sum\limits_{i=1}^{h}(x_i - \overline{X})^2 f_i}{n}}$ and $\overline{X} = \dfrac{\sum\limits_{i=1}^{h} x_i f_i}{n}$ to show that

$$\sigma = \sqrt{\dfrac{\sum\limits_{i=1}^{h} x_i^2 f_i - \dfrac{\left(\sum\limits_{i=1}^{h} x_i f_i\right)^2}{n}}{n}}$$

14. Use the new formula for σ in Question 13 and $x_i = A + Cd_i$ to prove the formula for σ when an assumed mean is employed.

$$\sigma = \dfrac{C}{n}\sqrt{n \sum\limits_{i=1}^{h} d_i^2 f_i - \left(\sum\limits_{i=1}^{h} d_i f_i\right)^2}$$

10.5 The Binomial Distribution

The idea of a frequency distribution leads naturally to the idea of a *probability distribution*. Where a frequency distribution represents observations from actual measurements or experiments, a probability distribution represents a theoretical or hypothetical distribution. Thus, a probability distribution tells us what we should expect to observe in a frequency distribution.

What is the probability of getting 5 heads when 9 coins are tossed? Of getting 3 aces when 6 dice are thrown? We answered questions like this in the Probability chapter by counting in a sample space. However, the binomial theorem can also be employed to get results of this kind.

Example 1

Three thumbtacks, 1 red, 1 white and 1 blue (exactly alike except for color) are dropped on the floor.

   (a) List the sample space.
   (b) If $P(U) = p$ and $P(D) = q$,
       find the probability of each
       outcome.

Solution

   (a) The sample space is
          $\{DDD, DDU, DUD, UDD, DUU, UDU, UUD, UUU\}$
   (b) Since U and D occur independently for the three tacks, the probability of any outcome is the product of three probabilities. For example, $P(DUD) = P(D) \cdot P(U) \cdot P(D)$
$$= q \cdot p \cdot q$$
$$= q^2 p$$

$$P(DDD) = q \cdot q \cdot q = q^3$$
$$P(DDU) = q \cdot q \cdot p = q^2 p$$
$$P(DUD) = q \cdot p \cdot q = q^2 p$$
$$P(UDD) = p \cdot q \cdot q = q^2 p$$
$$P(DUU) = q \cdot p \cdot p = q p^2$$
$$P(UDU) = p \cdot q \cdot p = p^2 q$$
$$P(UUD) = p \cdot p \cdot q = p^2 q$$
$$P(UUU) = p \cdot p \cdot p = p^3$$

From Example 1 we can obtain the probabilities of getting the following.

    0 U is $P(DDD) = q^3$
    1 U is $P(DDU) + P(DUD) + P(UDD) = 3q^2 p$
    2 U is $P(DUU) + P(UDU) + P(UUD) = 3q p^2$
    3 U is $P(UUU) = p^3$

The sum of these probabilities is $q^3 + 3q^2 p + 3q p^2 + p^3$ which is the binomial expansion of $(q + p)^3$.

Example 2

What is the probability of rolling one ace with a roll of 6 dice?

Solution

The probability that 5 of the dice are not aces and that the other is an ace is $\left(\dfrac{5}{6}\right)^5 \left(\dfrac{1}{6}\right)$.

There are $C(6, 1)$ ways of selecting the die that is an ace.

$\therefore$ Probability of one ace is $C(6, 1) \left(\dfrac{5}{6}\right)^5 \left(\dfrac{1}{6}\right)$.

The method of Example 2 enables us to make the following table.

Number of Aces	Probability
0	$C(6, 0) \left(\dfrac{5}{6}\right)^6 \left(\dfrac{1}{6}\right)^0 = 0.334\ 90$
1	$C(6, 1) \left(\dfrac{5}{6}\right)^5 \left(\dfrac{1}{6}\right) = 0.401\ 88$
2	$C(6, 2) \left(\dfrac{5}{6}\right)^4 \left(\dfrac{1}{6}\right)^2 = 0.200\ 94$
3	$C(6, 3) \left(\dfrac{5}{6}\right)^3 \left(\dfrac{1}{6}\right)^3 = 0.053\ 58$
4	$C(6, 4) \left(\dfrac{5}{6}\right)^2 \left(\dfrac{1}{6}\right)^4 = 0.008\ 04$
5	$C(6, 5) \left(\dfrac{5}{6}\right) \left(\dfrac{1}{6}\right)^5 = 0.000\ 64$
6	$C(6, 6) \left(\dfrac{5}{6}\right)^0 \left(\dfrac{1}{6}\right)^6 = 0.000\ 02$

We can easily see that the probabilities above can be obtained from the expansion of $(q + p)^6$ where $q = \dfrac{5}{6}$ and $p = \dfrac{1}{6}$

In general, the term $C(n, x)\ q^{n-x}\ p^x$ of the binomial expansion of $(q + p)^n$ gives the probability of $(n - x)$ failures and x successes where the probability of success is p and of failure q.

Example 2 illustrates that the binomial theorem can be employed to construct a "theoretical frequency table." If a frequency distribution is obtained through the binomial expansion, the distribution is called a *binomial distribution*. Elaborate tables are available to statisticians for calculations involving a binomial distribution. The study of such tables and related problems are beyond the scope of this book.

10.5/The Binomial Distribution

Exercise 10.5

B

1. Show that the probability of getting exactly 2 heads when 5 coins are tossed is $\frac{5}{16}$.

2. Show that the probability of getting more than 1 head when 5 coins are tossed is $\frac{13}{16}$.

3. The probability of a batter getting a hit is $\frac{1}{3}$. What is the probability of getting a hit if he bats three times?
   (Hint: The probability of at least one hit is required.)

4. A player's batting average is 0.300. What is the probability that he gets two hits in four times at bat?

5. Use the results of Example 2 to find how many times in 1000 experiments you might expect 0, 1, 2, 3, 4, 5, or 6 aces to turn up when six dice are rolled.

6. In an experiment of throwing 5 thumbtacks on a table the probability of point up, $P(U)$, is $\frac{1}{4}$.

   (a) Write the binomial whose expansion gives the probabilities of the different outcomes.
   (b) What is the probability of exactly 3 thumbtacks having point up?
   (c) If the experiment is tried 1024 times, how many times would you expect exactly three points up?

C

7. In Toronto, between 11:00 and 13:00, two out of three telephone calls on the average are answered. If 4 telephone calls are made at random, what is the probability that 4 calls will be answered? That 2 calls will be answered?

8. The probability of x successes in n trials where the probability of success is p is denoted by $b(x; n, p)$.

   (a) Show that $b(x; n, p) = C(n, x)\ p^x q^{n-x}$.
   (b) Evaluate $b(10; 10, 0.90)$.

9. A table showing particular values of $b(x; n, p)$, defined as in Question 8, for $n = 5$, is given on the following page. Draw a graph of $x \to b(x)$ for each value of p.

10.5/The Binomial Distribution   325

$n = 5$			p			
x	0.05	0.20	0.40	0.50	0.60	0.80
0	0.774	0.328	0.078	0.031	0.010	0.000
1	0.204	0.410	0.259	0.156	0.007	0.006
2	0.021	0.205	0.346	0.312	0.230	0.051
3	0.001	0.051	0.230	0.312	0.346	0.205
4	0.000	0.006	0.077	0.156	0.259	0.410
5	0.000	0.000	0.010	0.031	0.078	0.328

10.6 The Normal Distribution

Tedious calculations hinder the calculation of frequencies in a binomial distribution. Since many practical problems involve large numbers, n, a more rapid method of calculation is required. For large n, a good approximation of the binomial distribution is the *normal distribution*. The normal distribution is the most important continuous probability distribution and one on which much statistical theory is based. We give only a brief description of the normal distribution in this section.

Consider the shape of the tops of rectangles of the histograms for expected frequencies of heads in tossing 1 to 6 coins 64 times.

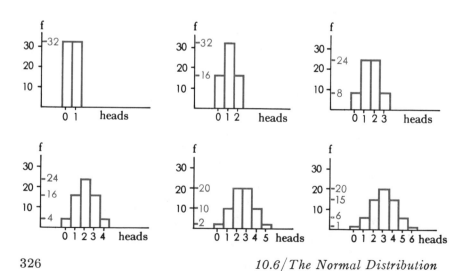

The limiting frequency curve obtained as the number of coins tossed becomes larger and larger is called the *normal frequency curve*. For N experiments or samples, this curve has equation

$$y = \frac{N}{\sigma\sqrt{2\pi}} e^{\frac{-(x-\overline{X})^2}{2\sigma^2}}$$

where e is an irrational number ($e \doteq 2.718\ 28$).

We illustrate by showing the histogram for the expected frequencies of heads in tossing 9 coins 512 times. The histogram is approximated by the normal curve shown in color. The agreement between normal curve and histogram is good even though the number of coins used (9) is not large.

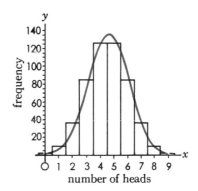

If X is placed along the vertical axis and the scale of the horizontal axis is $\sigma = 1$, then the curve's equation is

$$y = \frac{1}{\sqrt{2\pi}} e^{\frac{-x^2}{2}}$$

Table 1 gives the coordinates of points on this curve. The y coordinates give the relative frequencies or probabilities.

$$y = \frac{1}{\sqrt{2\pi}} e^{\frac{-x^2}{2}}$$

Table 1

x	y	x	y	x	y
0	0.3989	1.0	0.2420	2.0	0.0540
0.1	0.3969	1.1	0.2178	2.1	0.0440
0.2	0.3910	1.2	0.1942	2.2	0.0355
0.3	0.3814	1.3	0.1714	2.3	0.0283
0.4	0.3683	1.4	0.1497	2.4	0.0224
0.5	0.3521	1.5	0.1295	2.5	0.0175
0.6	0.3332	1.6	0.1109	2.6	0.0136
0.7	0.3122	1.7	0.0904	2.7	0.0104
0.8	0.2897	1.8	0.0789	2.8	0.0079
0.9	0.2661	1.9	0.0656	2.9	0.0059

Table 2

Area under the normal probability curve.

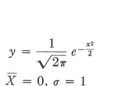

$$y = \frac{1}{\sqrt{2\pi}} e^{-\frac{x^2}{2}}$$

$\overline{X} = 0, \sigma = 1$

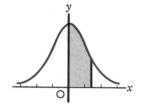

x	A	x	A	x	A
0	0	1.1	0.3643	2.1	0.4821
0.1	0.0398	1.2	0.3849	2.2	0.4861
0.2	0.0793	1.3	0.4032	2.3	0.4893
0.3	0.1179	1.4	0.4192	2.4	0.4918
0.4	0.1554	1.5	0.4332	2.5	0.4938
0.5	0.1915	1.6	0.4452	2.6	0.4953
0.6	0.2258	1.7	0.4554	2.7	0.4965
0.7	0.2580	1.8	0.4641	2.8	0.4974
0.8	0.2881	1.9	0.4713	2.9	0.4981
0.9	0.3159	2.0	0.4772	3.0	0.4987
1.0	0.3413				

The area under the normal curve is used in many applications. Table 2 gives the area A under the normal curve, above the x axis, and between the vertical lines through 0 and some number x. Using this table, it is simple to compute the area under the normal curve for any interval on the x axis. For example,
the area between $x = 0.4$ and $x = 0.9$ is
Area (between $x = 0$ and $x = 0.9$) − Area (between $x = 0$ and $x = 0.4$)
= 0.3159 − 0.1554
= 0.1605

Thus the area under the normal curve between $x = 0.4$ and $x = 0.9$ is 0.1605.

Since the normal curve is symmetric about the y axis, areas for negative values of x are the same as for corresponding positive values. Thus the area between $x = 0$ and $x = -0.4$ is 0.1554.

To find the area between a positive number and a negative number, we add areas. Thus the area between $x = -0.4$ and $x = 0.9$ is 0.1554 + 0.3154 = 0.4708.

Since the y axis is placed at the mean $\overline{X}$ and the scale on the x axis is $\sigma = 1$, the preceding results can be stated as follows.

The area under the normal curve between $\overline{X} + 0.4\sigma$ and $\overline{X} + 0.9\sigma$ is 16.05% of the total area under the curve.

The area under the normal curve between $\overline{X} - 0.4\sigma$ and $\overline{X} + 0.9\sigma$ is 47.08% of the total.

For measurements that follow a normal distribution, statisticians have shown that the total area under the normal curve represents the total number of measurements being considered. Since $\overline{X}$ corresponds to the 50th percentile, the following is true about such a set of measurements.

1. 50% of the measurements have a value less than $\overline{X}$.

2. 68.26% of the measurements have a value between $\overline{X} + \sigma$ and $\overline{X} - \sigma$.

3. 95.46% of the measurements have a value between $\overline{X} - 2\sigma$ and $\overline{X} + 2\sigma$.

4. The probability of a particular measurement of a set of measurements falling between $\overline{X} - 2\sigma$ and $\overline{X} + 2\sigma$ is 0.9544.

Knowledge of this kind makes possible the control of production lines in industry through *statistical quality control.*

Example 1

The Light-M Electric Company advertises bulbs to burn at least 1000 h. A sample of bulbs follows a normal distribution and has a mean life of 1060 h and a standard deviation of 30 h.

(a) What percent of bulbs will last more than 1000 h?
(b) What percent of bulbs will last more than 1105 h?

Solution

Here $\overline{X} = 1060$, $\sigma = 30$
(a) $1000 = 1060 - 60 = \overline{X} - 2\sigma$
From Table 2, the area to the right of $\overline{X} - 2\sigma = 0.4773 + 0.5$
$$= 0.9773$$
Thus, 97.73% of the bulbs last more than 1000 h.

(b) $1105 = 1060 + 45 = \overline{X} + 1.5\sigma$
But the area to the right of $\overline{X} + 1.5\sigma$ equals the total area
to the right of the y axis minus the area between the y axis
and $x = 1.5$
$= 0.5 - 0.4332$
$= 0.0668$
Thus 6.68% of the bulbs last more than 1105 h.

Example 2

On a Canadian Scholastic Aptitude Test (CSAT) the mean is 500
and the standard deviation is 100. Ms. I. M. Smart obtains a mark
of 650 on a CSAT test. What percent of students who wrote the test
received a lower mark than Ms. Smart?

Solution

Here $\overline{X} = 500, \sigma = 100$
$650 = 500 + 150 = \overline{X} + 1.5\sigma$
From Table 2, the area to the left of $\overline{X} + 1.5\sigma = 0.5 + 0.4332$
$= 0.9332$
Thus, 93.32% of the students received a lower mark than Ms.
Smart.

Exercise 10.6

1. What is the area under the normal curve between the following
   intervals?

   (a) 0 to 0.6   (d) 1.5 to 2.5
   (b) 0 to 2.1   (e) −1.2 to 1.2
   (c) 0 to −1.6   (f) −0.5 to 2.5

2. If $\overline{X} = 63.7$ and $\sigma = 5.4$ for a normal distribution, find the
   number of σ each of the following is from $\overline{X}$.

   (a) 39.4   (b) 79.3   (c) 51.2   (d) 72.8

3. For a set of data that fits the normal curve, $\overline{X} = 9.2$ and $\sigma = 1.4$.

   (a) Find how many σ a measurement of 6.4 is from $\overline{X}$.
   (b) Find how many σ a measurement of 11.3 is from $\overline{X}$.
   (c) Find the area under a normal curve with $\overline{X} = 9.2$, $\sigma = 1.4$
        between $x = 6.4$ and $x = 11.3$.
   (d) What percent of measurements lie between 6.4 and 11.3?

4. Find the area under the normal curve between 29.1 and 33.6 for a normal distribution with mean 30.6 and standard deviation 1.5.

5. Find the area under the normal curve between 550 and 610 for a normal distribution with mean 500 and standard deviation 100.

6. On College Entrance Examination Board (CEEB) tests, the mean is 510 and the standard deviation is 100.

    (a) If you score 610, in what percentile are you?

    (b) If you score 450, in what percentile are you?

7. On an IQ test, the mean is 100 and the standard deviation is 20.

    (a) How do you rate if your IQ is 130?

    (b) How does the other fellow rate with an IQ of 90?

8. The Tays-Tee Candy Company makes boxes of jelly beans advertised to contain at least 40 jelly beans. The company knows that the number of jelly beans in its boxes follows a normal distribution with a mean of 44 jelly beans to a box and a standard deviation of 2 jelly beans.

    (a) What percent of the boxes made will contain less than 40 jelly beans?

    (b) If 20 000 boxes are made each day, how many boxes per day will contain less than 40 jelly beans?

    (c) How many boxes per day will contain more than 47 jelly beans?

9. The Lightlong Battery Company manufactures batteries for hand calculators whose life follows a normal distribution. The batteries have an average life of 90 h with a standard deviation of 3 h.

    (a) What percent of the batteries will have a life less than 87 h?

    (b) What percent of the batteries will have a life greater than 99 h?

    (c) What percent of the batteries will have a life greater than 87 h but less than 99 h?

10. A random sample of 100 people in Ailliro, a city of 40 000, was asked the time they went to bed. The mean time of going to bed was 23:00 with a standard deviation of 40 min. (Assume a normal distribution.)
   (a) What percent of people go to bed before 22:00?
   (b) What percent of people go to bed after midnight?
   (c) How many people in Ailliro should we expect to be going to bed between 22:00 and midnight?
   (d) By what time will 98.21% of the people be in bed?

11. The city of Norbeh replaces the bulbs in 4000 of its street lamps. The bulbs have a mean life of 1000 burning hours with a standard deviation of 200 h. (Assume a normal distribution.)
   (a) How many bulbs might be expected to fail in the first 860 burning hours?
   (b) How many burning hours might be expected to elapse before all but 14 bulbs have failed?

12. Dooda Mathwell received a mark of 85 on a mathematics examination in which the mean was 65 and the standard deviation was 10. On an English examination Dooda received a mark of 88 where the mean was 76 and the standard deviation was 8. On which exam was Dooda's mark relatively higher?

Review Exercise 10.7

B

1. A company that manufactures TV picture tubes conducted a test of a sample batch of 1000 tubes and recorded the number of faults in each tube. The following information was recorded.

Number of faults (x_i)	Frequency (f_i)
0	620
1	260
2	88
3	20
4	8
5	2
6	2

   (a) Tabulate $x_i, f_i, x_i \times f_i, \dfrac{f_i}{n}, \dfrac{x_i \times f_i}{n}$.
   (b) Calculate $\overline{X}$ and $\dfrac{1}{n} \sum x_i f_i$.
   (c) Calculate the standard deviation.

2. On a survey of 1000 families, the number of children per family was reported as follows.

Number of children (x_i):   0   1   2   3   4   5   6   7

Number of families (f_i):   25   306   402   200   53   8   4   2

(a) Calculate the mean (i) directly, (ii) using an assumed mean.
(b) Draw a conclusion from your calculations.

3. Consider the experiment of throwing two dice and recording the total score.

(a) Calculate the probability, as a decimal fraction, of each score from 2 to 12, and record them in a table as follows.

Score E: 2   3   4   5   6   7   8   9   10   11   12
   $P(E)$: 0.028

(b) As a group experiment (about 20 students), throw two dice 720 times. Record the score, frequency and relative frequency as in the following table:

Score x_i: 2   3   4   5   6   7   8   9   10   11   12
   f_i:
   $\dfrac{f_i}{n}$:

(c) Draw histograms for the probabilities of (a) and the relative frequencies of (b) on the same axes, and compare the two.

4. The following is the annual rainfall in millimetres, measured at Rainy Observatory, Hotspot, from 1941 to 1970 inclusive.

1251.9	1255.7	1344.2	1251.8	1240.1	1280.8
1265.7	1289.0	1284.5	1285.9	1252.7	1301.7
1257.8	1260.2	1268.3	1248.7	1305.9	1319.3
1291.2	1333.4	1224.7	1259.7	1309.2	1328.7
1280.0	1289.5	1348.1	1291.1	1251.5	1365.0

(a) Organize the data into classes
(b) Calculate the mean.
(c) Draw a histogram.
(d) Calculate the median.
(e) Calculate the standard deviation.

5. The following lists the life of 100 light bulbs, in hours.

800	892	873	831	837	754	546	914	694	862
705	798	708	828	866	921	715	691	666	816
873	952	840	985	714	796	999	897	746	955
909	861	743	742	802	652	622	810	842	777
818	841	715	811	943	940	805	745	889	768
712	975	684	713	752	956	815	773	773	639
827	917	686	571	859	798	809	574	733	698
792	844	870	958	729	794	930	856	855	918
923	1030	826	858	956	582	757	831	866	971
742	775	827	701	834	824	746	867	711	854

Repeat Question 4 for these data.

6. Find the population, to the nearest 100, of fifty Ontario towns with populations under 20 000. Form a frequency distribution table using class marks (multiples of 100) as follows.

0-24, 25-49, 50-74, 75-99, · · ·, 175-199

(a) Find the mean population in these 50 towns.
(b) Calculate the median population.
(c) Show the information by a histogram.
(d) Calculate the mean deviation.
(e) Calculate the standard deviation.
(f) Draw conclusions from your calculations.

7. The lengths of 100 leaves from a poplar tree were measured to the nearest millimetre and the following frequencies were obtained:

Length:	20-24	25-29	30-34	35-39	40-44	45-49	50-54	55-59	60-64
Frequency:	1	5	10	19	25	21	15	3	1

Repeat Question 6 for these data.

8. The Nutty-Razin Candy Company makes chocolate bars that are supposed to have a mass of 200 g. The company knows that the masses of its bars follow a normal distribution with a mean of 210 g and a standard deviation of 5 g.

(a) What percent of bars made will have a mass less than 200 g?
(b) If 30 000 bars are made each day, how many bars will have a mass of more than 215 g?
(c) What percent of bars will have a mass between 205 g and 220 g?

334   *10.7/Review Exercise*

9. During a survey of poultry farming the following data were collected. The number of poultry per farm varied from 2 to 200.

Class Marks	x_i	f_i	$f_i x_i$	$x_i - \overline{X}$	$f_i(x_i - \overline{X})^2$
1- 10	5.5	5			
11- 20	15.5	12			
21- 30		19			
31- 40		24			
41- 50		33			
51- 60		52			
61- 70		69			
71- 80		75			
81- 90		108			
91-100		120			
101-110		123			
111-120		101			
121-130		85			
131-140		79			
141-150		60			
151-100		43			
161-170		21			
171-180		9			
181-190		4			
191-200		2			
Total		1044			

(a) Complete the table.
(b) Calculate $\overline{X}$ using an assumed mean.
(c) Find σ.
(d) Comment on your calculations.

10. On an IQ test, the mean is 100 and the standard deviation is 20.

(a) Bill Bright has an IQ of 130. To what percentile does 130 correspond?
(b) Lil Wisegirl has an IQ in the 97.73 percentile. What is her IQ?

11. The life of a television tube follows a normal distribution with a mean (in years) of 3.1 and a standard deviation of 1.4. Tubes lasting less than one year are replaced free. For every 100 sets (one tube per set) sold, how many tubes can be expected to have to be replaced free?

11 / Mathematics of Investment

Most people are confronted with the problems of money investment sometime in their lives. Whether to hide money in a mattress, buy some bonds, invest in a house rather than pay rent or pay towards a professional or trade training are some of the problems that may soon confront you. In this chapter we hope to give you an insight into, and to broaden your outlook on, many of the financial and investment situations that are common today.

11.1 The Growth of Money — Compound Interest

Money hidden away in some secure spot actually decreases in value because of rises in the cost of living. Invested money grows in value because a certain per cent of this money is added to the money each year. If $100 is invested at 5%/a, then 5% of $100, or $5, is added to the $100 at the end of the year. It is as though the person with whom the money has been invested is paying a rent of $5/a to use it. The total amount of money is now $105. The 5%/a is called the *rate of interest* and $5 is called the *interest* for one year on $100. If the $105 remains invested, the interest is paid on this sum at the end of the second year to the amount of 5% of $105 or $5.25. Thus after two years the $100 has increased to $100 + $5 + $5.25 or $110.25. This process is continued so that the amount of money continues to grow as long as the money remains invested. The original $100 is called the *principal* while the final $110.25 is called the *accumulated amount* or simply the *amount after two years*.

Example 1

$500 is invested for three years at 6%/a compounded annually. Find the amount of money to which the $500 has grown.

Solution

Let the amount of money accumulated be A.
At the end of one year,
$$A = 500 + 6\% \text{ of } 500$$
$$= 500 + 500(0.06)$$
$$= 500(1.06)$$

At the end of two years, $A = 500(1.06) + 6\%$ of $500(1.06)$
$$= 500(1.06) + 500(1.06)(0.06)$$
$$= 500(1.06)(1 + 0.06)$$
$$= 500(1.06)^2$$
At the end of three years, $A = 500(1.06)^2 + 500(1.06)^2(0.06)$
$$= 500(1.06)^2(1 + 0.06)$$
$$= 500(1.06)^3$$

The numerical value of $(1.06)^3$ can be found from the table on page 409. This value is in row $n = 3$ at the column corresponding to 6% interest. Hence $(1.06)^3 \doteq 1.191\ 02$.

Thus after three years the $500 has grown to an amount of $500 \times 1.191\ 02$ or $595.51.

Interest may be taken on the money more than once a year. If interest of 2% is taken four times a year, we say the interest is $4 \times 2\%$ each year or 8%/a *compounded quarterly*. Interest of 12%/a compounded monthly is the same as 1% interest taken each month.

Example 2

Find the amount of $1000 in eight years at 6%/a compounded semi-annually.

Solution

Interest of $\frac{1}{2} \times 6$, or 3% is paid every half year.
A total of 2×8 or 16 interest payments will be made.
Let the amount of money accumulated be A.
After 1 interest payment, $A = 1000 + 1000(0.03)$
$$= 1000(1.03)$$
After 2 interest payments, $A = 1000(1.03) + 1000(1.03)(0.03)$
$$= 1000(1.03)(1 + 0.03)$$
$$= 1000(1.03)^2$$
After 3 interest payments, $A = 1000(1.03)^2 + 1000(1.03)^2(0.03)$
$$= 1000(1.03)^2(1 + 0.03)$$
$$= 1000(1.03)^3$$
After 4 interest payments, $A = 1000(1.03)^4$
Similarly after 16 interest payments, $A = 1000(1.03)^{16}$

The numerical value of $(1.03)^{16}$ is found on page 408 in the row $n = 16$ at the column corresponding to 3%. Thus $(1.03)^{16} \doteq 1.604\ 71$.

Therefore, after 16 interest payments, that is eight years, the amount of $1000 is $1000 \times 1.604\ 71$ or $1604.71.

Example 3

For a principal, P, at interest rate i, calculate the amount A after n interest payments.

Solution

After 1 interest payment, $\quad A = P + P \times i$
$$= P(1 + i)$$
After 2 interest payments, $A = P(1 + i) + P(1 + i)i$
$$= P(1 + i)(1 + i)$$
$$= P(1 + i)^2$$
After 3 interest payments, $A = P(1 + i)^2 + P(1 + i)^2 i$
$$= P(1 + i)^2 (1 + i)$$
$$= P(1 + i)^3$$
After 4 interest payments, $A = P(1 + i)^4$
Similarly, after n interest payments, $A = P(1 + i)^n$

$$A = P(1 + i)^n$$

A is the amount after n interest periods.
P is the principal invested.
i is the rate of interest each interest period.
n is the number of interest periods.

Example 4

Ima Saver deposits $50 in a bank paying interest at 6%/a compounded quarterly. She leaves the money in the bank for two and a half years. What is the amount of the $50 at the end of this time?

Solution

$A = P(1 + i)^n$ where $P = 50$, $i = \dfrac{0.06}{4} = 0.015$, $n = 2\frac{1}{2} \times 4 = 10$
$A = 50(1.015)^{10}$

$\doteq 50 \times 1.160\ 54 \quad \left(\text{from the table page 408, } n = 10, i = 1\frac{1}{2}\%\right)$

$= 58.027$

$\doteq 58.03$

$\therefore$ The amount after two and a half years is $58.03.

Exercise 11.1

A

1. Express each of the following as a decimal.

    (a) 3% (b) 6% (c) $3\frac{1}{2}\%$ (d) $5\frac{1}{4}\%$

2. Find an expression for the amount of each of the following.

    (a) $300 for four years at 5%/a compounded annually.
    (b) $600 for seven years at 4%/a compounded annually.
    (c) $100 for three years at 6%/a compounded semi-annually.
    (d) $500 for six years at 7%/a compounded semi-annually.
    (e) $1000 for five years at 8%/a compounded quarterly.
    (f) $50 for three years at 12%/a compounded monthly.

3. For each of the following amounts state:

    (i) the principal
    (i) the number of interest periods
    (iii) the interest rate per period.

    (a) $300(1.03)^6$ (b) $540(1.02)^{14}$ (c) $750(1.01)^{10}$ (d) $12(1.035)^8$

B

4. Use the tables on pages 408-9 to evaluate to five decimal places the following.

    (a) $(1.03)^{12}$ (b) $(1.07)^{20}$ (c) $(1.05)^{17}$ (d) $(1.035)^{15}$

5. Calculate the amount of each of the following.

    (a) $100 for five years at 6%/a compounded annually.
    (b) $1000 for eight years at 4%/a compounded annually.
    (c) $700 for six years at 5%/a compounded annually.
    (d) $100 for five years at 6%/a compounded semi-annually.
    (e) $400 for six years at 5%/a compounded semi-annually.
    (f) $1000 for four and a half years at 8%/a compounded semi-annually.

    Compare your answers for (a) and (d). Which is larger? Why?

6. Bouncing Bob decides to purchase a motorbike costing $500. If he invests $200 at 6%/a compounded half-yearly, what is the minimum length of time the $200 must remain invested until Bob has enough to buy the motorcycle for $500?

7. Racing Rita wishes to buy a used sports car when she graduates in a year and half. The car will cost her $3000 at that time. If Rita can invest money at 12%/a compounded monthly, what is the minimum amount of money she must invest now to have the $3000 at graduation?

11.1/The Growth of Money—Compound Interest 339

8. In how many years will $200 double itself if it is invested at 4%/a compounded semi-annually?

9. If one of your ancestors had invested $100 fifty years ago at 2%/a compounded annually, what would the amount be today? How much of this money is interest?

10. The world's population in 1970 was estimated to be 3.580 billion people.

   (a) If population increases at 1%/a, what will the approximate world's population be in the year 2000?

   (b) If population increases at 2%/a, what will the approximate world's population be in the year 2000?

   (c) Complete the following chart for projected world's population.

		1970	1980	1990	2000	2010	⋯	2070
Rate of	1%	3.580						
growth	2%	3.580						

   (d) Make a graph showing your results of (c).

C 11. The world population was estimated as 3.285 billion in 1965 and 3.580 billion in 1970. Find the approximate rate of yearly increase of population for the world.

12. At the rate of growth established in Question 11, what is the predicted world population in the year 2000 and the year 2070?

13. H. P. Morgan, a financial tycoon, gave the following advice to an upcoming executive. "It's not how much you make but how fast you make it."

   (a) Show that $1\left(1 + \dfrac{1}{t}\right)^{t}$ is the amount of 1 dollar at the end of a year if interest is 100% p.a. compounded t times a year.

   (b) Expand $\left(1 + \dfrac{1}{t}\right)^{t}$ using the binomial theorem.

   (c) Show that $\left(1 + \dfrac{1}{t}\right)^{t}$ approaches 2.7183 as t becomes very large.

   When asked by a prosperous executive how much his yacht cost to maintain, H. P. Morgan answered, "If you have to ask that question, you can't afford it!"

11.2 Growth of a Regular Investment — Annuities

Mr. Ben E. Fishery decides to invest $120 at the end of each year for the next five years at the rate of 6%/a compounded yearly. Ben's payments make up a regular investment, usually called an annuity. An *annuity* is a sequence of payments made at periodic intervals. The interval of time between two successive payments is called the *period* of the annuity. Unless the contrary is stated, we shall assume that the period is one year. Indeed, the word annuity itself suggests an annual payment.

Suppose Ben leaves all of the money invested for the whole five years. What is the amount that he has at the end of this time, that is, what is the amount of the annuity?

On a number line representing the time, we mark the date and amount of each payment. Notice that the first payment is made at the *end* of the year.

6% p.a. compounded yearly

What is the value of each payment after five years?

We shall calculate the amount of each payment beginning with the last one made, the fifth payment. The fifth payment, just made, has gained no interest so it is worth $120.

The fourth payment has gained interest for one year and is worth $120(1.06)$.

The third payment has gained interest for two years and is worth $120(1.06)^2$.

The second payment has gained interest for three years and is worth $120(1.06)^3$.

The first payment has gained interest for four years and is worth $120(1.06)^4$.

The amount of the annuity is the sum of these, and is given by the series

$$120 + 120(1.06) + 120(1.06)^2 + 120(1.06)^3 + 120(1.06)^4.$$

The five terms of this series form a *geometric series* with common ratio 1.06 and first term 120. The sum can be obtained by using the following formula for the sum of a geometric series.

For a geometric series,

$$S_n = a\frac{(r^n - 1)}{r - 1}, r \neq 1$$

where S_n is the sum of n terms,
n is the number of terms,
a is the first term,
r is the common ratio.

For Ben's annuity, $n = 5$, $a = 120$, $r = 1.06$

The sum is $S_5 = a\dfrac{(r^5 - 1)}{r - 1}$

$$= 120\frac{(1.06)^5 - 1}{1.06 - 1}$$

$$= 120\frac{(1.06)^5 - 1}{0.06}$$

$$= 2000[(1.06)^5 - 1]$$

From the table on page 409 $(1.06)^5 \doteq 1.338\ 23$

$$\therefore \quad S_5 \doteq 2000[1.338\ 23 - 1]$$
$$= 2000[0.338\ 23]$$
$$= 676.46$$

Therefore, Ben has accumulated $676.46, after the fifth payment.

The sum of the value of the payments of an annuity, accumulated at compound interest until the last payment is made, is called the *amount* of the annuity. Thus the amount of the annuity of $120 for five years at 6%/a compounded yearly is $676.46.

Example 1

Find the amount of an annuity of $500 per year for ten years when interest is 7%/a compounded yearly.

Solution

A schematic diagram of the payments and their values at the time of the final payment is as follows. Note the first payment is at the *end* of the first year.

11.2/Growth of a Regular Investment—Annuities

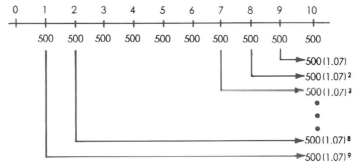

If the amount of the annuity is A, then
$$A = 500 + 500(1.07) + 500(1.07)^2 + 500(1.07)^3 + \cdots$$
$$+ 500(1.07)^8 + 500(1.07)^9$$
This is a geometric series of 10 terms where $a = 500, r = 1.07, n = 10$.

$$S_n = a\frac{(r^n - 1)}{r - 1}$$

$$\therefore \quad A = S_{10} = a\frac{(r^{10} - 1)}{r - 1}$$

$$= 500\frac{(1.07)^{10} - 1}{1.07 - 1}$$

Using the 7% amount table, $A \doteq 500 \times \dfrac{(1.96715 - 1)}{0.07}$

$$= 5000 \times \frac{0.96715}{0.7}$$

$$\doteq 6908.21$$

The amount of the annuity is approximately $6908.21.

In Example 1, the amount of the annuity of $500 for 10 payments at 7% each payment period, was $500\dfrac{(1.07)^{10} - 1}{0.07}$. Suppose each payment was R for n payments with the interest being i each payment period. Then the amount of the annuity immediately after the last payment would be $R\dfrac{(1 + i)^n - 1}{i}$. It is evident that when the periodic payment is $1, the amount of the annuity is $\dfrac{(1 + i)^n - 1}{i}$.
This quantity is called the *amount of an annuity of $1 per period*, and is denoted by $s_{\overline{n}|\,i}$ (read: s sub n at the rate i). Hence we have the following.

$$A = R \cdot s_{\overline{n}|i}$$

where A = the amount of the annuity
$\qquad R$ = the periodic payment of the annuity
$\qquad n$ = the number of payments of the annuity
$\qquad i$ = rate of interest *per payment period*
$\qquad s_{\overline{n}|i}$ = the amount of an annuity of 1 per period at rate i.

Tables for $s_{\overline{n}|i}$ are given on pages 412-413.
In Example 1, $A = 500\ s_{\overline{10}|\ 7\%} \doteq 500(13.816\ 45) \doteq 6908.23$.
Note The formula $A = R \cdot s_{\overline{n}|i}$ can only be used directly when the period between payments equals the interest period, that is, equals the time intervals between interest payments.

Example 2

Bill Fold saves \$40 each half year and deposits it in a trust company paying 6%/a compounded half-yearly. How much does Bill have in his account five years after his first deposit?

Solution

Bill's payments are indicated in the diagram. Note that interest $i = \frac{1}{2} \times 6\% = 3\%$ each half year.

3% each half year

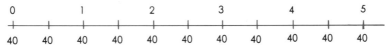

0		1		2		3		4		5
40	40	40	40	40	40	40	40	40	40	40

Since the payment period = half year = interest period, we may use the formula $A = R \cdot s_{\overline{n}|i}$
where $R = 40$, $n = 11$ (count them!), $i = 3\%$
From the table on page 412, $s_{\overline{11}|\ 3\%} \doteq 12.807\ 80$
$$\therefore \quad A \doteq 40 \times 12.807\ 80$$
$$= \$512.3120$$
Therefore Bill has \$512.31 on deposit after five years.

Example 3

Mr. B. Ready wants to have \$5000 to give to his son, Al, in four years when Al finishes college. Mr. Ready decides to make equal quarter-yearly deposits in a bank starting now and ending four years from now. If the bank pays interest at the rate of 8%/a compounded quarterly, calculate the amount of each of Mr. Ready's deposits.

Solution

Let the quarterly deposit be x dollars. The total amount of the deposits must equal $5000. The following schematic diagram shows each deposit.

2% compounded quarterly

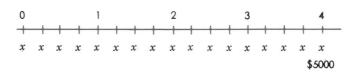

Since the payment period = one quarter year = interest period, we may use the formula $A = R \cdot s_{\overline{n}|i}$

$$\text{where} \qquad R = x$$
$$n = 17 \text{ (count them!)}$$
$$i = \tfrac{8}{4}\% = 2\%$$
$$A = 5000$$
$$\therefore \qquad 5000 = x \cdot s_{\overline{17}|\,2\%}$$

$$\therefore \qquad x - 5000\left(\frac{1}{s_{\overline{17}|\,2\%}}\right)$$

Since multiplication is usually easier to perform than division, tables are provided on pages 414-415 giving the values of $\dfrac{1}{s_{\overline{n}|i}}$

$$\therefore \ x \doteq 5000(0.049\ 97)$$
$$= 249.85$$

Mr. Ready must make 17 deposits of $249.85 each.

Exercise 11.2

B 1. Find the value of each of the following.

(a) $s_{\overline{20}|\,4\%}$ (b) $s_{\overline{15}|\,1\%}$ (c) $\dfrac{1}{s_{\overline{30}|\,5\%}}$ (d) $\dfrac{1}{s_{\overline{12}|\,1\frac{1}{2}\%}}$

2. Calculate the amount of each of the following annuities with the given rate of interest.

(a) $500/a for ten years at 3%/a compounded yearly.

(b) $750 per quarter-year for eight years at 6%/a compounded quarterly.

(c) $1000 per half-year for five years at 6%/a compounded semi-annually.

3. For the past ten years, Mr. Mydas Myser has deposited $5000 in his savings account at the end of every year. If the interest rate is 4%/a compounded annually, how much has Myser accumulated immediately after his tenth deposit?

4. Sally Fourth buys a used sports car costing $3900. She trades in her old car for $1000 and completes the purchase of the car by making a payment of $100 each month starting now, for 30 payments. If Sally could have invested the 30 payments of $100 each month at 12%/a compounded monthly, what is the total amount of money she would have had invested after her 30th payment? If the difference between this amount and the $2900 she owed on the car is considered as interest, how much interest did Sally pay?

5. Luke Ahead wishes to get married five years from now. At that time he wants to have saved $5000. He decides to deposit the same amount of money in a bank every half-year starting today and ending with a payment five years from today. If the bank pays interest at the rate of 4%/a compounded semi-annually how much money must Luke deposit each half-year?

6. A father wishes to set aside annual bank deposits to provide $10 000 at the time his daughter Lyn's twenty-first birthday. The first payment is made on the day that Lyn is born, and equal deposits are made on each birthday thereafter, up to and including the twenty-first. If the bank rate of interest is 4%/a compounded yearly, find the appropriate annual deposit a father should make.

7. It is estimated that a certain piece of machinery costing $10 000 will last fifteen years and that its scrap value then will be $1000. Find the regular semi-annual payment that must be made earning 6%/a compounded semi-annually for 30 payments, to replace the machinery when it is worn out. Such a series of deposits is called a *sinking fund*.

8. (a) Find the amount of an annuity of $100/a for five years at 6%/a compounded *semi-annually*. (Note: The formula $A = R \cdot s_{\overline{n}|\,i}$ may not be used directly. Why not?)
   (b) Show that the amount of part (a) equals
   $$100 s_{\overline{10}|\ 3\%} \cdot \frac{1}{s_{\overline{2}|3\%}}$$

C 9. If money earns 4%/a compounded *semi-annually* what sum paid *annually* for fifteen years beginning with a payment on August 1, 1975 will amount to $10 000 on August 1, 1992?

10. Al Weesaves deposits $25.00 in a bank every May 1. The first deposit is made on May 1, 1975, and the last deposit on May 1, 1990. If the bank pays interest at a rate of 2%/a compounded semi-annually, find the amount in Al's account on May 1, 1993.

11.3 Present Value

Frequently it is necessary to invest money today in order to have enough money to meet future commitments and responsibilities. For example, a grade 13 student going into dentistry may wish to invest a single sum of money now that will grow to $1000 in six years when he will need to open his dental office. This amount is calculated in Example 1.

Example 1

Find the amount that must be invested today at 3%/a compounded annually in order to have $1000 available six years from now.

Solution

Let the number of dollars invested be x.
Thus $A = P(1 + i)^n$ where $A = 1000$,
$$P = x,$$
$$i = 0.03,$$
$$n = 6.$$
$\therefore\ 1000 = x(1.03)^6$
$\therefore\qquad x = \dfrac{1000}{(1.03)^6}$
$$= 1000 \times \frac{1}{(1.03)^6}$$
The numerical value of $\dfrac{1}{(1.03)^6}$ can be found from the table, Present Value of 1, page 410. The value from row $n = 6$ of the 3% column is 0.837 48. Thus $x \doteq 1000 \times 0.837\ 48 = 837.48$.

Thus $837.48 deposited today will amount to $1000 in six years.

Example 2

Find the present value of F dollars due n periods from now if the rate of interest is i per period.

Solution

Let the present value, PV, be x dollars.

∴ $$A = F, P = x, i = i, n = n$$

Since $A = P(1 + i)^n$ where $A = F$

∴ $$F = x(1 + i)^n \qquad P = x$$

∴ $$x = \frac{F}{(1 + i)^n} \qquad i = i$$
$$n = n$$

$$PV = \frac{F}{(1 + i)^n}$$

PV is the present value
F is the future amount
i is the rate of interest per period
n is the number of interest periods

Example 3

Find the present value of \$4000 due ten years from now if the interest is 6%/a compounded semi-annually.

Solution

$$PV = \frac{F}{(1 + i)^n} \text{ where } F = 4000, i = \frac{0.06}{2} = 0.03, n = 2 \times 10 = 20$$

∴ $$PV = \frac{4000}{(1.03)^{20}}$$

$$= 4000 \times \frac{1}{(1.03)^{20}}$$

$$\doteq 4000 \times 0.553\ 68 \qquad \text{(row } n = 20, 3\% \text{ column of Present}$$
$$= 2214.72 \qquad\qquad \text{Value table, page 410)}$$

The present value of \$4000 due in ten years is \$2214.72.

Exercise 11.3

A

1. Find an expression for the present value in each of the following.

    (a) $200 due in five years at 4%/a compounded annually.

    (b) $700 due in eight years at 5%/a compounded annually.

    (c) $800 due in six years at 6%/a compounded semi-annually.

    (d) $900 due in three years at 8%/a compounded quarterly.

2. For each of the following present values determine (i) the amount due; (ii) the number of interest payments; (iii) the interest rate per period.

    (a) $\dfrac{100}{(1.06)^7}$ (b) $\dfrac{700}{(1.03)^5}$ (c) $\dfrac{800}{(1.04)^{10}}$

B

3. From the table of present values, evaluate the following.

    (a) $\dfrac{1}{(1.05)^8}$ (b) $\dfrac{1}{(1.03)^{20}}$ (c) $\dfrac{1}{(1.025)^8}$

4. Calculate the present value in each of the following.

    (a) $100 due in six years at 3%/a compounded annually.

    (b) $500 due in four years at 6%/a compounded annually.

    (c) $1000 due in five years at 4%/a compounded semi-annually.

    (d) $800 due in ten years at 6%/a compounded quarterly.

    (e) $400 due in two and a half years at 12%/a compounded monthly.

5. Anne's uncle decides to invest enough money on her sixteenth birthday to be able to give her $1000 on her twenty-first birthday. How much money should he invest at 5%/a compounded semi-annually?

6. Hi Speeder decides he will need to buy a used motorcycle in two years. He figures that he can trade his present one in at that time for $150. If Hi will want to buy a $500 motorcycle how much should he invest now at 6%/a compounded quarterly to have enough money to buy the new motorcycle?

7. The present value of $1000 due in eight years is $672.90. What is the current interest rate per annum compounded annually?

C

8. I. M. Adebtor owes $300 that is due three years from now and $500 that is due five years from now. He wishes to pay both debts by making a single payment two years from now. If the rate of interest is 8%/a compounded annually what should be the amount of I.M.'s single payment?

9. Mike and Greg have a rich uncle who has just left them $50 000 to be divided so that each receives the same sum of money on his 21st birthday. Mike and Greg are now 18 and 14 respectively. If money can be invested at 6%/a compounded annually, how much should each boy receive on his 21st birthday? What is the present value of each boy's share of the $50 000?

11.4 Present Value of an Annuity

The purchase price of an annuity is determined by the value at the present time of a sequence of payments to be made in the future. This value is called the *present value* of an annuity.

Example 1

Find the present value of an annuity of $400/a for twenty-seven years at interest of $3\frac{1}{2}\%$/a compounded yearly. The first payment is to be made one year from now.

Solution

A schematic diagram of the payments and their values at the present time is as follows.

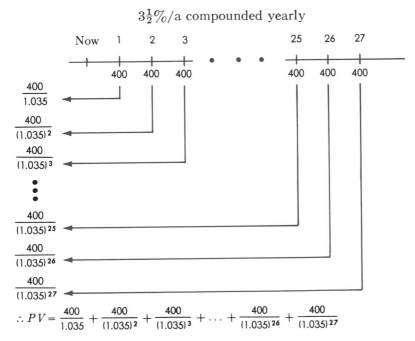

$$\therefore PV = \frac{400}{1.035} + \frac{400}{(1.035)^2} + \frac{400}{(1.035)^3} + \ldots + \frac{400}{(1.035)^{26}} + \frac{400}{(1.035)^{27}}$$

This is a geometric series of 27 terms with

$$a = \frac{400}{1.035}, \quad r = \frac{1}{1.035}, \quad n = 27$$

$\because r < 1$ we shall use $S_n = a\dfrac{1 - r^n}{1 - r}$ to keep the denominator positive.

$$\therefore PV = S_{27} = a\frac{1 - r^{27}}{1 - r}$$

$$= \frac{400}{1.035} \times \frac{1 - \left(\dfrac{1}{1.035}\right)^{27}}{1 - \dfrac{1}{1.035}}$$

$$= 400 \times \frac{1 - \dfrac{1}{(1.035)^{27}}}{1.035 - 1}$$

$$\doteq 400 \times \frac{1 - 0.395\,01}{0.035} \qquad \text{(tables, Present Value of 1, page 410)}$$

$$= \frac{400\,000}{35} \times 0.604\,99$$

$$\doteq 6914.17$$

The present value is $6914.17.

In Example 1 the present value of the annuity of $400 for 27 payments at $3\frac{1}{2}\%$ each payment period with the first payment one period from now was

$$400 \times \frac{1 - \dfrac{1}{(1.035)^{27}}}{0.035} = 400 \times \frac{1 - (1.035)^{-27}}{0.035}$$

Suppose each payment was R for n payments with the first payment *one period from now* and the interest being i each payment period. Then the present value now of the annuity would be

$$R \cdot \frac{1 - (1 + i)^{-n}}{i}.$$

It is evident that when the annuity payment is $1, the present value of the annuity is $\dfrac{1 - (1 + i)^{-n}}{i}$. This quantity is called the *present value of an annuity of 1 per period*, and is denoted by $a_{\overline{n}|i}$ (read: a sub n at the rate i). Hence we have the following.

$$P = R \cdot a_{\overline{n}|\, i}$$

where P = the present value of the annuity
R = the periodic payment of the annuity
n = the number of payments of the annuity
i = the rate of interest per payment period
$a_{\overline{n}|\, i}$ = the present value of an annuity of 1 per period at rate i.

Tables for $a_{\overline{n}|\, i}$ and $\dfrac{1}{a_{\overline{n}|\, i}}$ are given on pages 416-9.

Note the formula $P = R \cdot a_{\overline{n}|\, i}$ can only be used directly when
(1) the period between payments equals the interest period, that is, the time interval between payments equals the time interval between interest payments, and
(2) the first payment of the annuity is *one period from now.*

In Example 1, $P = 400 \cdot a_{\overline{27}|\, 3\frac{1}{2}\%}$
$\doteq 400(17.285\ 36)$ \qquad (table, page 416)
$\doteq 6914.14$

Therefore the present value is $6914.14.

Example 2

How much money must be invested now at 6%/a compounded semi-annually to provide a payment of $500 at the end of each half-year for a total of 15 payments? First payment is to be made one half year from now.

Solution

The payments are shown in the diagram.

3% per half year

Since the payment period = half year = interest period, and since the first payment is one half year from now, we may use the formula
$$P = R \cdot a_{\overline{n}|\, i} \text{ where } R = 500$$
$$n = 15$$
$$i = \tfrac{6}{2}\% = 3\%$$
$\therefore \qquad P = 500 \cdot a_{\overline{15}|\, 3\%}$
$\doteq 500(11.937\ 94)$ \qquad (table, page 416)
$= 5968.970$

Therefore, $5968.97 must be invested now at 6% compounded half-yearly to secure $500 each half-year for fifteen payments.

A *deferred annuity* is an annuity that begins at some future time. An annuity of $300 deferred for five years means that the first payment will be made at the end of the sixth year as indicated in the diagram.

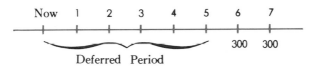

Example 3

Find the present value of a deferred annuity of $1000/a for ten years if the first payment is to be made after four years, that is, the annuity is deferred three years. The rate of interest is 5%/a compounded yearly.

Solution

The payments are indicated in diagram (1).

5% compounded yearly

Since the first payment is *not* one period from now, the formula $P = Ra_{\overline{n}|i}$ *cannot* be used directly.

Diagram (2) shows an annuity of $1000 for thirteen years beginning one year from now. Present value P_{13} of this annuity is $1000 \cdot a_{\overline{13}|5\%}$.

5% compounded yearly

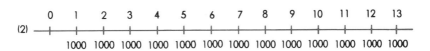

Diagram (3) shows an annuity of $1000 for three years beginning one year from now. The present value P_3 of this annuity is $1000 \cdot a_{\overline{3}|5\%}$.

5% compounded yearly

11.4/Present Value of an Annuity 353

The present value P of the given annuity deferred three years is given by $P = P_{13} - P_3$

$$= 1000 \cdot a_{\overline{13}|\ 5\%} - 1000\ a_{\overline{3}|\ 5\%}$$
$$= 1000\ (a_{\overline{13}|\ 5\%} - a_{\overline{3}|\ 5\%})$$
$$\doteq 1000\ (9 \cdot 39357 - 2 \cdot 72325) \quad \text{(table, page 417)}$$
$$= 1000\ (6 \cdot 67032)$$
$$= 6670 \cdot 32$$

Thus, the present value of the deferred annuity is $\$6670 \cdot 32$.

In general, a deferred annuity of $\$R$ per period for n payments at interest i per period, that is *deferred for k periods*, is given by

$$P = R(a_{\overline{n+k}|\ i} - a_{\overline{k}|\ i})$$

Exercise 11.4

B

1. Evaluate the following.

   (a) $a_{\overline{10}|\ 3\%}$ (b) $a_{\overline{25}|\ 2\frac{1}{2}\%}$ (c) $\dfrac{1}{a_{\overline{13}|\ 6\%}}$ (d) $\dfrac{1}{a_{\overline{7}|\ 4\%}}$

2. Calculate the present value of each of the following annuities with the given rate of interest. The first payment of each annuity is to be made one payment period from now.

   (a) $\$500$ each year for 25 years at 4%/a compounded yearly.
   (b) $\$700$ each year for ten years at 5%/a compounded yearly.
   (c) $\$1000$ each half-year for four years at 6%/a compounded semi-annually.
   (d) $\$100$ each quarter-year for seven years at 4%/a compounded quarterly.
   (e) $\$40$ each month for two and a half years at 12%/a compounded monthly.

3. Calculate the present value of the following deferred annuities with the given rate of interest. The payments of the annuities are made each year with the first payment being made *one year after* the deferred period.

   (a) $\$500$ each year for 20 payments at 4%/a compounded yearly and deferred four years.
   (b) $\$100$ each year for 10 payments at 6%/a compounded annually, and deferred eight years.

4. S. Ben Thrift has agreed to pay off a debt by making payments of $200 at the beginning of each year starting now for a total of nine payments. If money can earn interest at the rate of 8%/a compounded yearly, how much money would Ben require now to pay off the debt?

5. Serious Susie buys a sewing machine. Susie pays twelve equal monthly payments of $11.50 each with the first payment being made one month after she receives the machine. What is the present value of these payments at 12%/a compounded monthly? If this present value equals the cost price of the machine, how many dollars in interest did Susie pay?

6. Mr. Musthav A. Lot wants to provide an annuity of $100 every six months for his daughter Needa for the time she is in college. How much money should Mr. Lot invest today at 6%/a compounded half-yearly if Needa is to get her first $100 cheque in six months and her last cheque four and a half years from now?

7. Phil T. Rich decides to set aside some money for his old age. He wishes to receive an annuity of $20 000 every year for a total of fifteen years. If the first payment is to be received ten years from now, how much must Mr. Rich invest at 8%/a compounded yearly to provide the annuity?

8. The sum of $100, at interest 8%/a compounded annually, yields an annual interest payment of $8. Thus $100 is the present value of an annuity of $8/a that continues forever—in other words a perpetual annuity.
    (a) Find the value of each payment of a perpetual annuity with present value $900 at 4%/a compounded annually.
    (b) Find the present value of a perpetual annuity of $240/a at 6%/a compounded annually.

9. Ann Novitz borrows $1000 from her Aunt Hill at interest of 5%/a compounded annually. Ann agrees to wipe out her indebtedness by making the following payments to her Aunt:
    (i) twenty interest payments of $50 each at the end of years 1, 2, 3, ···, 20, and
    (ii) one principal payment of $1000 at the end of year 20.
    (a) Find the present value at 5%/a compounded annually of the twenty interest payments of (i).
    (b) Find the present value at 5%/a compounded annually of the one principal payment of (ii).

10. Mort Gage borrows \$10 000 to finance the purchase of a house. Mort must repay the loan with twenty equal annual payments, the first payment being made at the end of the first year. If interest is 6%/a compounded annually find the value of each payment.

11. Mr. N. Stalment purchased a car for \$4000. To pay for the car Mr. S. will make twenty-four equal monthly payments of which the first falls due one month after he receives the car. If interest is 12%/a compounded monthly, find the monthly payment required.

12. Find the present value of an annuity of \$100 each year for eight years at 5%/a compounded semi-annually if the first payment of the annuity is one year from now.

13. An annuity of \$$R$/a is to be paid at the end of each year until n payments are made. If the first payment is made one year from now and interest is i/a compounded yearly, prove that the dollar present value, P, of the annuity is given by

$$P = R \cdot \frac{1 - (1 + i)^{-n}}{i}$$

14. Show that the amount A and present value P of an annuity of \$$P$/a for n years at interest of i/a compounded annually satisfy

$$A = (1 + i)^n P$$

15. Show that $\dfrac{1}{a_{\overline{n}|i}} = \dfrac{1}{s_{\overline{n}|i}} + i$

    (a) by commencing with the expression on the right
    (b) by commencing with the expression on the left.

11.5 Instalment Buying and Mortgages

A recent advertisement in a newspaper offered a motorcycle for \$400 cash or \$40 down with a balance of \$456 including interest charges to be paid in monthly instalments for two years. In other words, if you want to buy the machine but do not have the ready cash, you can have the machine now by paying an extra \$96 over two years. This amounts to \$48/a or $\dfrac{48}{400} \times 100\%$ or 12%/a on the original amount.

Of course, if you had been saving money regularly, you could have had the motorcycle now and used the $96 for something else. Or if you had a job you might have been able to borrow the money from a bank or credit union that would charge about 12%/a compounded monthly on the money you still owed, that is, on the *oustanding loan*. Ordinarily it is less costly to pay interest on the outstanding loan than on the original loan. Both cases are examples of *instalment buying* because money loaned is paid back by equal payments at regular intervals.

Example 1

E. C. Rider buys a motorcycle costing $400. He decides to pay for the cycle with a down payment of $40 and to borrow the rest from a credit union at 12%/a compounded monthly. If E.C. will repay the loan by making 24 monthly equal payments with the first payment one month after receiving the loan, what will be the size of each of the instalments?

Solution

Let the value of each instalment, in dollars, be x. The present value of all of the 24 payments must equal the money borrowed, namely, $400 - $40 or $360. A schematic diagram showing each instalment follows.

1% per month

The present value of the 24 payments of x can be obtained using the formula $P = R \cdot a_{\overline{n}|i}$ where $P = 360$
$$R = x$$
$$n = 24$$
$$i = \left(\frac{12}{12}\right)\% = 1\%$$

$\therefore 360 = x \, a_{\overline{24}|1\%}$

$\therefore x = 360 \left(\dfrac{1}{a_{\overline{24}|1\%}}\right)$

$\doteq 360 \,(0.047\ 07)$ (the $\dfrac{1}{a_{\overline{n}|i}}$ tables, page 418)

$= 16.9452$

Thus 24 instalments of $16.95 must be paid.

Observe in Example 1 that 24 × $16.95 equals $406.80 so that E.C. Rider paid a total of $446.80 for his motorcycle. In this situation E.C. pays interest only on the outstanding loan. Compare this sum with the total cost $40 + $456 or $496 in the repayments considered at the beginning of this section. In this latter case, interest is always paid on the initial loan of $400 for a cost of about twice that of when interest is paid on the outstanding loan.

In the next example where interest is on the outstanding loan we shall use a table to show how the instalment payments are divided between the interest and the loan repayment. Such a table is called an *amortization table*.

Example 2

Char Git borrowed $300.00 at 8%/a compounded semi-annually. He promised to repay the loan with six equal semi-annual payments making the first instalment a half year after receiving the loan.

(a) Find the value of each instalment.
(b) Make an amortization table that shows how the instalments repay the loan, both principal and interest.

Solution

(a) Let the amount of each instalment be x dollars. Thus the present value of the six instalments is $300. A schematic diagram showing each instalment follows.

4% per half-year.

Since the payment period and interest period each equal one half year and the first payment is one half year from now we may use

$$P = R \cdot a_{\overline{n}|\,i} \text{ where } P = 300$$
$$R = x$$
$$n = 6$$
$$i = \left(\frac{8}{2}\right)\% = 4\%$$

$$\therefore\ 300 = x\, a_{\overline{6}|\,4\%}$$

$$x = 300\left(\frac{1}{a_{\overline{6}|\,4\%}}\right)$$

$$\doteq 300(0.190\ 76)$$

$$= 57.228$$

Thus, each half-yearly instalment is $57.23.

11.5/Instalment Buying and Mortgages

(b) The following amortization table indicates how the six instalments of $57.23 repay the loan.

AMORTIZATION TABLE				
Interest = 4%/0.5 a			Instalment = $57.23	
Date	Debt	Interest Due	Payment of Principal	Outstanding Debt
0	300.00			300.00
0.5	300.00	12.00	45.23	254.77
1	254.77	10.19	47.04	207.73
1.5	207.73	8.31	48.92	158.81
2	158.81	6.35	50.88	107.93
2.5	107.93	4.32	52.91	55.02
3	55.02	2.20	55.03	0

A special kind of instalment occurs when one buys a house. Ordinarily a down payment is made and the remainder is repaid by instalments at equal time intervals. For example, a house worth $60 000 might require a down payment of $15 000. The remaining $45 000 must be borrowed. In borrowing money to purchase a house, the purchaser gives a *mortgage* to the lender. A mortgage is a signed document that pledges the property—the house and land—as a guarantee that both the principal and interest will be paid when due.

Example 3

Mr. Noo Lee Wed bought a house for $60 000. To pay for the house Noo made a down payment of $15 000 and took a twenty-year mortgage on the rest at 8%/a compounded semi-annually.

(a) The mortgage will be repaid by equal semi-annual payments with the first payment six months from the date of the mortgage. What is the value of each instalment?

(b) Calculate the total amount and also the interest Mr. Wed pays over the twenty years.

Solution

(a) Let the semi-annual mortgage payment be x dollars. The present value of the payments equals the mortgage value, namely $60 000—$15 000 or $45 000. The following schematic diagram shows the mortgage payments.

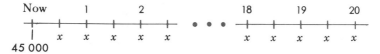

$$4\% \text{ half-yearly}$$

We may use the formula $P = Ra_{\overline{n}|i}$ where $P = 45\,000$
$$R = x$$
$$n = 40 \text{ (2 each year)}$$
$$i = \left(\frac{8}{2}\right)\% = 4\%$$

$\therefore$
$$45\,000 = xa_{\overline{40}|4\%}$$
$$x = 45\,000 \left(\frac{1}{a_{\overline{40}|4\%}}\right)$$
$$\doteq 45\,000 \,(0.050\,52)$$
$$= 2273.40$$

Thus the semi-annual mortgage payment is \$2273.40.

(b) The total amount of the forty mortgage payments is $40 \times \$2273.40$ or \$90 936. Since the down payment was \$15 000, the house costs \$105 936. But the price of the house was \$60 000. Thus, the interest paid over twenty years is \$45 936.

Exercise 11.5

B 1. Calculate the equal annual instalment that will repay a loan of \$5000 by the end of six years with the first payment being made one year from now. The interest rate is $8\%/a$ compounded yearly.

2. Make an amortization table for Question 1 showing how the instalments pay both principal and interest for the loan.

3. Calculate the equal instalment on the following monies loaned at the given interest. In each case the repayment is to continue for two and a half years from the date of borrowing the money. The first payment is made one time interval from now. Calculate the total amount of money paid out in each case.

	Amount Loaned	Type of Instalment	Interest
(a)	$1000	semi-annual	12%/a compounded half-yearly
(b)	$1000	quarterly	12%/a compounded quarterly
(c)	$1000	monthly	12%/a compounded monthly

4. Rock Session wishes to buy a new electric guitar worth $500. Rock makes a down payment of $50 and contracts to make 24 equal monthly instalments paying interest on the unpaid balance at the rate of 12%/a compounded monthly.

   (a) Calculate the amount of each instalment payment.
   (b) Rock's younger brother Jam bought the same type of $500 guitar but could not make the same financial arrangement. Jam made a down payment of $50, and then he paid twenty-four equal instalments with the total of these instalments 112% of the initial cost of the guitar. Calculate the amount of Jam's instalment. How much did Rock save over Jam by paying interest only on the unpaid loan?

5. Mr. Shar Kee lends money at the rate of 16%/a compounded semi-annually. You wish to borrow $3000 from Shar to buy a dune buggy. You decide to repay the loan in 8 semi-annual equal instalments, the first instalment being made 6 months after you receive the money.

   (a) What is the value of each instalment?
   (b) How many dollars interest will you pay over the four years it takes to repay the loan?
   (c) Make an amortization table showing how your instalment repays both principal and interest of your loan.

6. Bill Board is given $10 000 by his uncle, the lumber king. Bill wishes to buy an annuity of 15 annual payments with the first payment being made one year from now. If Bill can invest his money at 7%/a compounded yearly what is the value of each payment of his annuity?

7. (a) Calculate the size of the mortgage payment for each of the following houses. In each case, the mortgage is to last for twenty years from now with the first payment being made one time interval from now.

	Cost of House	Down Payment	Type of Mortgage Instalment	Interest Rate
i)	$20 000	$5000	yearly	10%/a compounded yearly
ii)	$20 000	$5000	semi-annual	10%/a compounded half-yearly

(b) Calculate the total interest paid over the twenty years for each of the mortgages in (a).

8. Mr. I. M. Broke borrows $1000 on March 1, 1983 from a company that charges interest at the rate of 24%/a compounded monthly. Mr. Broke agrees to repay the company in a series of equal monthly payments, the first payment to be made on July 1, 1983, and the last payment on October 1, 1985. Find the size of the monthly payments.

9. On May 1, 1974, Bill Dabigger, buys a house for $30 000. He makes a down payment of $6000, and agrees to pay the balance by means of a series of equal annual mortgage payments beginning on May 1, 1987, and ending on May 1, 2004. If the interest rate on the mortgage is 8%/a compounded annually find the size of Bill's annual payment.

C 10. U. R. Rich buys a house on August 1, 1985 for $56 800 and makes a down payment of $12 800. U.R. agrees to complete the purchase by paying $4000 on August 1, 1986 and thereafter making a series of equal quarterly mortgage payments, the first payment to be made on November 1, 1986, and the last on November 1, 1993. If money bears interest at 6%/a compounded quarterly, find the amount of the quarterly mortgage payments.

11. A house is sold for $48 000. The seller agrees to accept a down payment, a payment of $8000 at the end of one year, and thereafter a payment of $1200 at the end of each quarter for five years more. Find the down payment, if interest is computed at 6%/a compounded quarterly.

12. Will Retire has deposited $1000 in a trust fund at the end of each year for the past twenty years. 20 payments in all. Will now plans to withdraw this money in annual payments of x starting one year from his 20th deposit for a total of 30 withdrawals. If the trust fund pays 6%/a compounded annually find x.

13. Stu Dent plans to borrow $500 annually for four years and to repay the debt by making 5 equal annual payments, the first payment to be made six years after the first $500 is received. Find the amount of each annual payment if money is lent at 6%/a compounded yearly.

11.6 Bonds

Another way to invest money is by buying a *bond*. A bond is a written promise to pay a stated sum of money at a stated time. When an investor purchases a bond, he is loaning money to the issuer of the bond. The issuer of the bond promises to pay back the amount of the loan to the investor at some fixed date in the future as well as to pay interest at regular periods until this future date, called the *maturity date* of the bond. The rate of interest is called the *bond rate*. A bond is called a *coupon bond* when the interest is obtained from coupons attached to the bond. The owner of the bond detaches or "clips" the coupons and sends them to the issuer in order to receive the interest. The *face value* of the bond and the details of the agreement are stated on the bond itself. The face value of the bond is the amount the issuer promises to pay on the maturity date. The bond interest is calculated on this face value.

The *price* of a bond is the amount for which it can be sold in the bond market. If the bond sells *at par*, the price equals the face value. If the bond sells *at a premium*, the price is more than the face value. If the bond sells *at a discount*, the price is less than the face value.

Example 1

A \$1000—8%—four-year bond has half-yearly coupons. Use a schematic diagram to indicate the interest and price of the bond in each of the following cases.

(a) The bond sells at par.
(b) The bond matures at a premium of 10%.
(c) The bond matures at a discount of 10%.

Solution

In each case the interest is 4% of the face value every six months, that is, 4% of \$1000 or \$40.

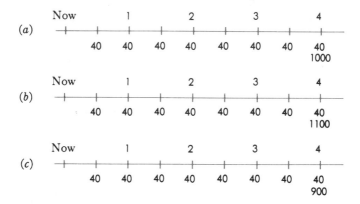

Example 2

Find the amount an investor should pay for a \$1000—8%—fifteen-year bond bearing semi-annual coupons if the investor wishes to make 10%/a compounded semi-annually on his investment.

Solution

The half-yearly interest is 4% of \$1000 or \$40 while the bond matures at \$1000. The following schematic diagram shows the present value of these monies.

10% compounded half-yearly = 5%/0.5 a

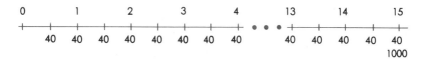

The price of the bond is the present value of an annuity of $40 for 30 payments at 5% per period plus the present value of $1000 due in 30 periods at 5% per period.

Thus the price of the bond $= 40 \; a_{\overline{30}|\,5\%} + \dfrac{1000}{(1.05)^{30}}$

$$\doteq 40(15.372\ 45) + 1000 \times \dfrac{1}{(1.05)^{30}}$$

$$\doteq 614.8980 + 231.38$$

$$= 846.2780$$

The investor should pay $846.28 for the bond.

Example 3

A $1000—eight-year bond bearing interest at 9%/a compounded semi-annually matures at a premium of 20%. What should an investor pay now for this bond if he wishes to make 12%/a compounded semi-annually on his money?

Solution

The half-yearly interest is worth $4\frac{1}{2}\%$ of $1000 or $45 while the bond matures at $1000 + 20% of $1000, that is, $1200. The following schematic diagram shows these monies.

12%/a compounded semi-annually – 6% half-yearly

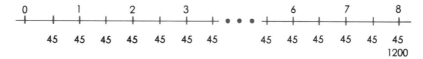

The price of the bond equals the present value of an annuity of $45 for 16 payments at 6% per period plus the present value of $1200 due 16 periods hence at 6% per period.

Thus, the price of the bond

$$= 45 \; a_{\overline{16}|\,6\%} + \dfrac{1200}{(1.06)^{16}}$$

$$\doteq 45(10.105\ 90) + 1200(0.393\ 65)$$

$$= 454.7655 + 472.380 = 927.1455$$

Thus the price of the bond is $927.15.

Exercise 11.6

B 1. (a) Find the amount an investor should pay for a $1000—6%—ten-year bond bearing yearly coupons if the investor wishes to make 8%/a compounded annually on his money.
   (b) If the bond in (a) matures at a premium of 10% how much should the investor pay for the bond?
   (c) If the bond in (a) matures at a discount of 10% how much should the investor pay for the bond?

2. A fifteen-year—$2000—7% bond bearing half-yearly coupons is bought to yield 8%/a compounded half-yearly. Find the price of this bond.

3. A six-year—$1000 bond is redeemable at a discount of 10% and bears quarterly coupons at 8%/a. Calculate the price of the bond to yield 12%/a compounded quarterly.

4. A bond for $1000 matures ten years hence and carries yearly coupons of $27.50, of which the first coupon is due one year hence. Find the present value of this bond at 5%/a compounded annually.

5. A bond for $1000 matures ten years hence and carries semi-annual coupons of $17.50, the first of which is due six months hence. Find the price of this bond if the purchaser is to receive 5%/a compounded semi-annually on his investment.

6. A $100 bond bears semi-annual coupons of $2.75 each, the first due in six months.

   (a) Assuming that the bond matures in n years, find an expression for its present value at 5%/a compounded half-yearly.
   (b) From the tables find the value of n that corresponds to a present value of $104.47.

C 7. A twenty-year bond is redeemable at a premium of 10% and bears yearly coupons at 8%/a for the first ten years, and 9%/a for the last ten years. Find the price of a $1000 bond to yield 10%/a compounded yearly.

8. (a) A bond with face value C matures in n years and bears yearly coupons at a bond rate j/a compounded yearly.

If K is the present value of C show that the price of the bond bought to yield i/a compounded yearly is given by the following

$$P = K + \frac{j}{i}(C - K)$$

(b) Use the formula of (a) to find the price of a $1000 bond due in ten years bearing yearly coupons at 8%/a if the bond is purchased to yield 10%/a compounded yearly.

Review Exercise 11.7

B

1. Calculate the amount of each of the following single payments.

   (a) $100 for three years at 2%/a compounded annually.
   (b) $400 for ten years at 5%/a compounded annually.
   (c) $1000 for fifteen years at 6%/a compounded semi-annually.
   (d) $600 for eight years at 6%/a compounded quarterly.
   (e) $250 for two years at 12%/a compounded monthly.

2. Calculate the present value of each of the following single payments.

   (a) $100 due in eight years at 5%/a compounded annually.
   (b) $300 due in five years at 6%/a compounded annually.
   (c) $1000 due in twenty years at 8%/a compounded semi-annually.
   (d) $500 due in three years at 10%/a compounded quarterly.
   (e) $200 due in three years at 18%/a compounded monthly.

3. In how many years will $200 double itself if money is worth 6%/a compounded annually?

4. Calculate the amount of each of the following annuities with the given rate of interest. In each case the first payment is one interest period from now.

   (a) $100 per annum for ten years at 4%/a compounded yearly.
   (b) $400 per half-year for eight years at 6%/a compounded half-yearly.
   (c) $500 each quarter for three years at 8%/a compounded quarterly.
   (d) $100 per month for three years at 12%/a compounded monthly.

5. Calculate the present value of each of the following annuities with the given rate of interest. The first payment is to be made one interest period from now.

   (a) $100 per annum for twelve years at 4%/a compounded annually.
   (b) $500 per half-year for eight years at 5%/a compounded half-yearly.
   (c) $1000 per quarter-year for ten years at 8%/a compounded quarterly.
   (d) $10 per month for two years at 12%/a compounded monthly.

6. Calculate the present value of the following deferred annuities with the given rate of interest. The payments of each annuity are made yearly with the first payment being made one year after the deferred period.

   (a) $100/a for 10 payments at 5%/a compounded annually and deferred three years.
   (b) $300/a for 8 payments at 6%/a compounded annually and deferred four years.

7. Jan. U. Ary saves $100 every January 2 by depositing it in a credit union paying 8%/a compounded annually. How much does Jan have in her account five years after making her first deposit?

8. Val N. Teeno wishes to buy his girl Bea U. Tee a present for her birthday in 10 months. He decides to deposit $2 in a bank at the beginning of each month starting now. If the bank pays interest at 12%/a compounded monthly, how much will Val have in the bank to spend on Bea, immediately after he has made his tenth deposit?

9. Find the annual payment to a bank account, so that after twenty annual payments the account will have risen to an amount of $10 000. The interest rate is 6%/a compounded annually.

10. Rec Reate wishes to buy a color TV set costing $600. He makes a down payment of $50 and borrows the rest from a loan company at 18%/a compounded monthly. Rec repays the loan by making 24 equal monthly payments with the first payment one month after receiving the loan. What is the size of each of these instalments?

11. Bud Jet borrows $1000 at 10%/a compounded semi-annually. He promises to repay the loan by making eight equal semi-annual payments. The first payment is paid a half year after the loan is obtained.

    (a) Find the size of each of Bud's instalments.

    (b) Make an amortization table that shows how the instalments repay the loan, both principal and interest.

12. A debt of $12 500, with interest at 6%/a, payable semi-annually, will be discharged, interest included, by equal payments at the end of each 6 months for twelve years. Determine the semi-annual payment.

13. On each March 1, beginning in 1985 and ending in 1998 Bob A. Long's uncle, Al A. Long, deposits $50 in a special bank account for Bob. If money is worth 5%/a compounded annually, and Bob does not take out any money from his account, how much will be in this account at the time of the last deposit?

14. Find the value on January 1, 1986 at 4% compounded annually of twelve payments of $200 each, the first payment to be made on January 1, 1986, and the remaining payments at intervals of one year.

15. Moo Valot wants to buy a new house that costs $40 000. By selling his old house he is able to make a down payment of $15 000. He takes out a ten-year mortgage for the rest of the money at 12%/a compounded quarterly.

    (a) If the mortgage is to be repaid by equal quarterly payments what is the value of each instalment if the first payment is made three months from the date of the mortgage?

    (b) Calculate the interest that Mr. Valot pays over the ten years.

    (c) If quarterly mortgage payments should not equal more than 25% of one's quarterly salary, what is the minimum annual salary Moo should have to carry the payments?

16. (a) Find the amount an investor should pay now for a $1000— 7%—ten-year bond bearing quarterly coupons if the investor wishes to make 8%/a compounded quarterly on his investment.

    (b) If the bond in part (a) matures at a premium of 15% what is its price now?

    (c) How much should the investor pay for the bond in (a) if it matures at a discount of 20%?

17. How much money must be invested now at 10%/a compounded semi-annually to provide a payment of $100 at the end of each half year for a total of 24 payments? The first payment is to be made two years from now.

18. Sailing Sam buys a sailboat. Sam agrees to pay 24 equal monthly payments of $50 with the first payment being made four months after he receives the sailboat. What is the present value of these payments at 24%/a compounded monthly? If this present value equals the cost price of the sailboat, how many dollars in interest did Sam pay?

19. A $10 000—twenty-year bond matures at a premium of 5%. For the first five years it bears annual coupons at 5% and for the last fifteen years bears annual coupons at 10%. What should an investor pay now for this bond if he wishes to make 8%/a compounded annually?

20. Stu D. Hard borrows $800 to meet college expenses during his senior year. He promises to repay the loan with interest at 5%/a compounded semi-annually, in 10 equal semi-annual instalments. If the first payment is to be made three years after the date of the loan, find the size of the semi-annual payments.

21. Assuming an interest rate of 3%/a compounded semi-annually, find the values which the following two sets of payments will have on January 1, 1984.
    (a) 10 yearly payments of $500 each, the first payment to be made on July 1, 1987, the second on July 1, 1988, and so on.
    (b) 20 half-yearly payments of $250 each, the first payment to be made on January 1, 1985, the second on July 1, 1985, and so on.

22. Mye Zoor opens a bank account today by making a deposit of $1000. He undertakes to make 10 further deposits of $100 each at dates 2, 3, 4, $\cdots$, 11 years from now. The bank agrees to accumulate the account at an interest rate of 2%/a compounded annually. Find the amount in Mye's account four years after the date of the last deposit.

23. A loan of $10 000 bears interest at 8%/a payable semi-annually. A sinking fund is created to pay the principal in one instalment at the end of six years. Find the semi-annual expense of the debt if the sinking fund earns interest at 6%/a compounded semi-annually.

370

24. At the end of each year for twenty years, Rich Keed invested $1000 at 6%/a compounded yearly. At the end of each year from the twenty-first to the thirtieth, Rich withdrew x dollars. At the end of the thirtieth year the funds were depleted. If the money earned interest at the rate of 8%/a compounded annually from the twenty-first to the thirtieth year, what is the value of x?

25. If $S_k = \dfrac{(1 + i)^k - 1}{i}$, show that the sequence $S_1,\ S_2,\ S_3,\ \cdots,$ $S_n,\ \cdots$ satisfies the recursion formula $S_{n+1} = (1 + i)S_n + 1$. Interpret this result with a diagram showing times of payment. If $S_1 = 1$, calculate $S_2,\ S_3$ and S_4.

26. Show the amount of an annuity of $\$R$ per year for n years at a rate of interest i per annum compounded k times a year equals $\dfrac{R \cdot s_{\overline{kn}|\,t}}{s_{\overline{k}|\,t}}$ where $t = \dfrac{i}{k}$.

12/ Introduction to Mathematical Logic

Logic or, the science of correct reasoning, has been used by mathematicians for over 2500 years. Even so, the first treatment of logic adequate for use in modern mathematics was described in the famous *Principia Mathematica* of Whitehead and Russell in 1910.

The subject matter of this chapter is designed to illustrate how one might determine whether or not a given instance of mathematical reasoning is correct. The components of mathematical reasoning are mathematical statements. Because ordinary language contains many words with multiple and ambiguous meanings, the language of symbolic logic is used to make precise the meaning of a mathematical statement.

12.1 Statements

Man has continuously been beset by the problem of communicating his ideas to other men. His basic medium of communication of ideas is *language*. To convey our ideas we must assume that a *basic vocabulary* and a set of *undefined terms* are known.

Ideas are usually conveyed by means of sentences. Sentences may be classified as declarative, exclamatory, interrogative and imperative. In logic we restrict ourselves to *declarative sentences* that are meaningful and to which a *truth value*, *true* or *false*, can be assigned. For example,

Harry excels in mathematics

13 is greater than 12

$2 + 2 = 5$

are sentences that can be judged to be either true or false. The idea each sentence conveys is a *statement*. A true sentence describes a true statement and a false sentence a false statement.

We shall insist that only one of the truth values *true* or *false* may be assigned to any sentence that we consider. The necessity of some such restriction was already known to the Cretan, Epimenides, about 600 B.C. He asserted

"I am uttering a falsehood."

and then asked his audience to decide whether his statement was true or false.

If his statement is true, then Epimenides told a truth which says that *he is uttering a falsehood*. This is self contradictory.

If his statement is false, then he lied. Thus, *the statement he uttered is true*. This is also self contradictory.

The Epimenides statement can be neither true nor false. Such statements are called *paradoxes* and are henceforth excluded from our studies.

Is the equation

$$3x + 2 = 14$$

true or false? Clearly, we cannot say until we know the value of x. Thus, the sentence '$3x + 2 = 14$' does not convey a statement in the above sense. However, substituting 3, and 4 for x results in one false and one true statement. This equation, involving the *variable x*, has the *form* of a sentence and may be used to manufacture true and false statements. Such sentence forms are called *open sentences*. We shall use the latter term even though an open sentence is not a declarative sentence in that it does not convey a statement which is either true or false.

A new word or symbol is *defined* when that word is used solely to replace a collection of other words or symbols without in any way changing or modifying the meaning of those words. Thus, a definition is introduced in order to decrease the number of symbols used to communicate an idea. For example, we may use 'isosceles triangle' to replace the words 'a triangle with two equal sides'.

A good definition should have the following characteristics.

(1) A definition should be *restrictive*. The term being defined should be classified by naming the collection of objects to which the term belongs and then stating the additional characteristics that make it unique in the set. The set of objects should be the smallest possible and the number of additional characteristics should be a minimum. For example,

A square is a rhombus in which one angle is a right angle.

(2) A definition should employ only *previously accepted terms.* The terms used should belong to the given set of undefined terms or to the set of terms that have previously been defined. Even in mathematics there must be some undefined terms because it is impossible to define all terms without some starting place.

(3) A statement defining a term should be *reversible.* For example,

'An even number is an integer that is divisible by 2'

could be stated as

'An integer that is divisible by 2 is an even number'.

(4) A defined term should be *interchangeable* with the defining words. For example,

'An isosceles triangle contains two equal angles'

means precisely the same as

'A triangle with two equal sides contains two equal angles'.

Notice that in the preceding discussion we have used single quotes to denote words or symbols. For example,

'Helen' is a name whereas Helen is my friend.

Exercise 12.1

A 1. Criticize each of the following definitions.

(*a*) An equilateral triangle is a triangle with three equal sides and three equal angles.
(*b*) A parallelogram is a geometric figure with four sides, opposite sides parallel and opposite angles equal.
(*c*) A rectangle is a parallelogram.
(*d*) A triangle consists of three line segments.
(*e*) Perpendicularity is a property of two perpendicular lines.

2. Which of the following are usually undefined terms?

(*a*) point   (*c*) angle   (*e*) line
(*b*) circle   (*d*) right angle   (*f*) set

3. Which of the following represent statements?

  (a) Admiral Horatio Nelson won the battle of 1812.
  (b) Who won the basketball game?
  (c) A stitch in time saves nine.
  (d) Stop.
  (e) Thought travels faster than light.
  (f) One for me and one for you.
  (g) There'll always be an England.
  (h) $5 < 10$.

B 4. Give a definition for each of the following, if possible.

  (a) point   (c) sour   (e) equals
  (b) truth   (d) between   (f) rational number

5. Show that each of the following sentences is a paradox.

  (a) The barber shaves everyone who does not shave himself.
      (Hint: Who shaves the barber?)
  (b) X is the set of all sets that are not members of themselves.
      (Hint: Does X belong to X?)

6. Rewrite each of the following sentences using single quotes to indicate a reference to words or symbols. Give reasons.

  (a) Write John on the blackboard.
  (b) The 23 on your football jersey should be red.
  (c) Use 2, 7, and 9 to write 279.
  (d) $\triangle TOP$ and $\triangle POT$ name the same triangle.

12.2 Negation and Conjunction

We often encounter sentences that are formed from other simpler sentences. For example, from the sentence

$$\text{'}2 + 2 = 4\text{'}$$

we can form its *negation*

$$\text{'It is not true that } 2 + 2 = 4\text{'}.$$

The negation of a sentence can be obtained by preceding it with the words

$$\text{"It is not true that"}.$$

Often it is possible to negate the verb instead of using the prefix 'it is not true that'. For example, $2 + 2 \neq 4$. However, in such cases caution should be exercised since the resulting sentence may be ambiguous. For example,

'All triangles are isosceles'

becomes upon negation

'It is not true that all triangles are isosceles'.

Negating the verb gives the sentence

'All triangles are not isosceles'

which can have two meanings.

(1) 'There are some triangles that are not isosceles'

or (2) 'No triangle is isosceles'.

It is sentence (1) that is the negation of 'All triangles are isosceles'. Thus, negating the verb may be misleading in some cases.

If 'p' is the name of a sentence such as '$2 + 2 = 4$' we shall denote the negation of p by

'$\sim p$' which is read "not p".

The symbol '$\sim$' is called "curl" or "tilde". Thus, if

'p' = '$2 + 2 = 4$',   '$\sim p$' = '$2 + 2 \neq 4$'

'p' = 'New York is a village', '$\sim p$' = 'New York is not a village'.

The above examples illustrate that if p is true then $\sim p$ is false and if p is false then $\sim p$ is true. The following table summarizes the truth value relation between p and $\sim p$.

p	$\sim p$
T	F
F	T

FIGURE 12.1

Figure 12.1 is called a *truth table*. In the table T signifies the truth value *true* and F the truth value *false*.

Oral Exercise

1. Give the negation of each of the following.

   (a) It is raining.
   (b) New York is a large city.
   (c) Canada is not a large country
   (d) Betty made first class honours in mathematics.
   (e) $7 + 9 \neq 15$.
   (f) $-5 < -6$.

Two or more sentences can be joined by means of the connective *'and'*. For example, from the sentences

$$\text{'This card is an ace.'} \quad = P$$

$$\text{'This card is a heart.'} \quad = Q$$

we may form the *compound sentence*, 'P and Q' called a *conjunction*.

'This card is an ace and this card is a heart'.

This new compound sentence is formed from the original two simple sentences by means of the connective 'and'. In common usage, which we follow in this case, the conjunction is regarded as true only if *both* of the simple sentences are true. That is, P and Q is true only if the card is the Ace of Hearts.

The connective 'and' is symbolized by '$\wedge$' so that the sentence 'P and Q' can be written '$P \wedge Q$'. Similarly, if p and q are variables that denote sentences, then $p \wedge q$ denotes a compound (open) sentence which we read "p and q" or more formally "the conjunction of the sentences p and q". The truth table for *conjunction* is as follows.

p	q	$p \wedge q$
T	T	T
T	F	F
F	T	F
F	F	F

FIGURE 12.2

Notice that we need know only the truth values of the *components* p and q in order to determine the truth value of the compound sentence $p \wedge q$. It is not necessary to know the precise statements represented by p and q.

Example 1

Find the truth table for $p \land \sim q$.

Solution

The components of the compound sentence $p \land \sim q$ are p and $\sim q$.

p	q	$\sim q$	$p \land \sim q$
T	T	F	F
T	F	T	T
F	T	F	F
F	F	T	F

There is an important and far reaching analogy between logic and set theory that can be illustrated at this point. Notice that *conjunction* is a binary operation on sentences. That is, for any two sentences p and q we can form a sentence $p \land q$. Similarly from any two sets A and B we can form the intersection $A \cap B$, which is also a set. For example, if

$$A = \{1, 2, 3, 4, 5, 6\} \quad \text{and} \quad B = \{4, 5, 6, 7, 8, 9\}$$

$$A \cap B = \{4, 5, 6\}.$$

The accompanying Venn diagram illustrates the idea of intersection.

$A \cap B$ is the set of elements common to A and B.

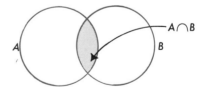

If $x \in A$ is true, and $x \in B$ is true, then $x \in A \cap B$ is true. Similarly, if $x \notin A$, $x \in B$ then $x \notin A \cap B$. Thus,

if $\quad p = `x \in A$'

and $\quad q = `x \in B$'

then $p \land q = `x \in A \cap B$'

The concept of *conjunction* in logic thus corresponds in the analogy to the *intersection* of sets.

12.2/Negation and Conjunction

Exercise 12.2

A 1. Given: 'P' = 'It is raining.'
'Q' = 'The sun is shining.'
'R' = 'The temperature is 30°C.'

read the following.

(a) $\sim P$	(d) $\sim P \wedge Q$	(g) $(P \wedge Q) \wedge R$
(b) $P \wedge Q$	(e) $\sim P \wedge \sim Q$	(h) $P \wedge (\sim Q \wedge R)$
(c) $P \wedge \sim Q$	(f) $P \wedge R$	(i) $(\sim P \wedge Q) \wedge R$

B 2. Represent 'x is an irrational number' by P
and 'x is a complex number' by Q
and translate each of the following symbolically.

(a) x is not a complex number
(b) x is not an irrational number
(c) x is an irrational and complex number
(d) x is a complex and not an irrational number

3. List the elements of the set that makes each of the following true.
$x \in I$.

(a) $(x < 5) \wedge (x > 0)$ (c) $(-x > 1) \wedge (x > 0)$
(b) $(x + 5 > 2) \wedge (x < 1)$ (d) $(x - 2 > -1) \wedge (3 - x < 1)$

4. Show that $\sim(\sim p)$ has the same truth table as p.

5. Show that $p \wedge q$ has the same truth table as $q \wedge p$.

6. Find the truth table for $\sim p \wedge \sim q$.

7. Find the truth table for $\sim(\sim p \wedge \sim q)$.

8. Show that a statement and its negation cannot both be true at the same time by showing that $p \wedge \sim p$ is always false. (Law of the Excluded Middle.)

9. Write the negation of each of the following in common language.

(a) Bill is ill today.
(b) Our high school has 730 students.
(c) Some people are afraid.
(d) No two people have the same fingerprints.
(e) All men are created equal.
(f) None of us is capable of jumping 2 m.
(g) Some boys are mischievous.
(h) Only clever students score more than 95 per cent.

C 10. Find the truth table for $(p \wedge q) \wedge r$. (There are eight cases to consider.)

11. Show that $(p \wedge q) \wedge r$ has the same truth table as $p \wedge (q \wedge r)$.

12.3 Disjunction

It can be shown that the two connectives '$\sim$' and '$\wedge$' are sufficient to produce all the compound sentences needed in mathematics. However, it is convenient to use other connectives that can be defined in terms of '$\sim$' and '$\wedge$'. The first of these connectives is 'or'. For example, consider the two sentences

(1) I will watch the hockey game on TV tonight.

(2) I will do my homework tonight.

These sentences can be joined by means of the connective 'or' to give the compound sentence

I will watch the hockey game on TV tonight or I will do my homework tonight.

Sentences joined by means of the connective 'or' yield sentence forms called *disjunctions*. In general a disjunction has the form

$$p \vee q \quad \text{(read ``}p \text{ or } q\text{'')}$$

where p, q are variables representing declarative sentences and '$\vee$' is a symbol for 'or'.

To find the conditions under which sentences such as $p \vee q$ are true we may consider the following cases.

(1) I watch the hockey game but do not do my homework.

(2) I do not watch the hockey game but I do my homework.

(3) I do neither.

(4) I do both.

Clearly in cases (1) and (2) we would say $p \vee q$ is true and in case (3) it is false. We must still consider the case (4).

'I watch the hockey game and I do my homework,' that is p and q are both true.

In everyday language, we sometimes consider $p \lor q$ to be false if both p and q are true. However, in mathematics it is more useful to consider $p \lor q$ to be true when both p and q are true. For example, the graph of

$$(x - y)(x + y) = 0$$

consists of the two lines $x - y = 0$ and $x + y = 0$. The solution set of $(x - y)(x + y) = 0$ consists of all those points on the line $x-y=0$ *or* on the line $x + y = 0$. The point $(0, 0)$ satisfies both equations and makes both components of the compound sentence

$$(x - y = 0) \lor (x + y = 0)$$

true. Since the point $(0, 0)$ is a point of the graph of $(x - y)(x + y) = 0$, we shall require that $(0, 0)$ makes $(x - y = 0) \lor (x + y = 0)$ true. When the connective 'or' is used in this mathematical sense, the disjunction is called the *inclusive* disjunction.

The truth table for the inclusive disjunction is given in Figure 12.3.

p	q	$p \lor q$
T	T	T
T	F	T
F	T	T
F	F	F

FIGURE 12.3

Note $p \lor q$ is false only if both p and q are false.

Example 1

Given two sets A and B. Let

$$p = \text{'}x \in A\text{'}$$

and $\quad q = \text{'}x \in B\text{'}$

For which x is $p \lor q$ true? Illustrate by means of a Venn diagram.

Solution

$x \in A \cup B$ if x belongs to either A or to B or to both A and B.

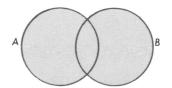

$$\therefore \quad p \lor q = \text{'}x \in A \cup B\text{'}$$

Example 1 further illustrates the analogy between logic and sets by showing how disjunction corresponds to the union of sets.

Example 2

Construct a truth table for the compound sentence

$$p \lor \sim q.$$

Solution

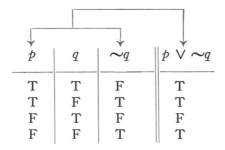

p	q	$\sim q$	$p \lor \sim q$
T	T	F	T
T	F	T	T
F	T	F	F
F	F	T	T

Example 3

Construct a table for the open sentence

$$\sim(\sim p).$$

Solution

p	$\sim p$	$\sim(\sim p)$
T	F	T
F	T	F

It follows from the truth table of Example 3 that whenever the sentence p is true so is the sentence $\sim(\sim p)$ and when p is false, $\sim(\sim p)$ is also false. Two such statements are said to be *logically equivalent*. The next example provides a more interesting example of logically equivalent statements.

Example 4

Construct the truth table for each of the compound sentences

$$(\sim p \land \sim q) \quad \text{and} \quad \sim(p \lor q).$$

Compare.

Solution

(1) p	(2) q	(3) $\sim p$	(4) $\sim q$	(5) $\sim p \wedge \sim q$	(6) $\sim (p \vee q)$
T	T	F	F	F	F
T	F	F	T	F	F
F	T	T	F	F	F
F	F	T	T	T	T

In this table we obtain the fifth column from columns three and four and the truth table for conjunction, page 377. The last column is obtained by negating the truth values of $p \vee q$, page 381.

Since $\sim p \wedge \sim q$ and $\sim (p \vee q)$ have the same truth table we may conclude that $\sim p \wedge \sim q$ is logically equivalent to $\sim (p \vee q)$. We symbolize this equivalence as follows.

$$\sim p \wedge \sim q \Leftrightarrow \sim (p \vee q)$$

This is a rather famous result in logic known as one of *De Morgan's Laws*. Augustus De Morgan, 1806-1871 was an English mathematician who analyzed logic mathematically. (He was a lively character and proposed the conundrum "I was x years of age in the year x^2" for the determination of his age.)

From the above equivalence it easily follows that

$$\sim (\sim p \wedge \sim q) \Leftrightarrow p \vee q.$$

This equivalence shows that the inclusive disjunction can be defined by means of the two connectives $\sim$ and $\wedge$.

The instances of logical equivalence discussed above involved open sentences in which the variables p and q denoted sentences. There is another type of equivalence that is very important in mathematics involving open sentences in which the variables denote numbers. For example, if

$$A_x = \text{'}x - 5 = 1\text{'}$$

$$\text{and} \quad B_x = \text{'}\frac{1}{x - 5} = 1\text{'}$$

and if the domain of x is all the real numbers except 5, then

$$A_x \Leftrightarrow B_x.$$

That is, A_x and B_x are logically equivalent in the sense that for every allowed value of x for which A_x is true, B_x is true, and for every allowed value of x for which A_x is false, B_x is false.

12.3/Disjunction

383

Exercise 12.3

A

1. Let A = 'I peeled the potatoes' and B = 'I carved the meat'. Interpret each of the following.

   (a) $A \wedge B$ (c) $\sim A \wedge \sim B$ (e) $A \wedge \sim B$
   (b) $\sim B$ (d) $A \vee B$ (f) $\sim A \vee \sim B$

B

2. Prove the following.

   (a) $(p \vee q) \Leftrightarrow (q \vee p)$ (b) $(p \wedge q) \Leftrightarrow (q \wedge p)$

3. Prove $\sim(p \wedge q) \Leftrightarrow (\sim p \vee \sim q)$ and hence show that the negation of a conjunction is equivalent to the disjunction of the negations of the component sentences.

4. Use the result of Question 3 to negate each of the following by means of a disjunction.

   (a) He put mustard and relish on his hot dog.
   (b) The triangle is isosceles and right-angled.
   (c) The opposite sides are equal and parallel.
   (d) The roots are real and equal.
   (e) $2 < x < 7$.

5. Prove $(p \vee q) \Leftrightarrow \sim(\sim p \wedge \sim q)$. Thus, verify that a disjunction is equivalent to the negation of the conjunction of the negations of the component sentences.

6. Use the result of Question 5 to negate each of the following.

   (a) The triangles are congruent or similar.
   (b) $x = 3$ or $x = 5$.
   (c) x is a rational or an irrational number.
   (d) $x \geq 5$.

7. Graph the solution set of each of the following. $x \in I$.

   (a) $(x > 2) \vee (x < 0)$ (c) $(x + 2 > -1) \vee (x - 1 > 3)$
   (b) $(2x + 3 = 9) \vee (x < 0)$ (d) $(3x - 2 = 7) \vee (x + 1 = 0)$

8. (a) Show that each of $(-2, 9)$, $(0, 7)$, $(2, 5)$, $(4, 3)$, $(6, 1)$ and $(8, -1)$ belong to $\{(x, y) \in R \times R \mid x + y - 7 = 0\}$.
   (b) Show that each of $(-3, -2)$, $(-1, 2)$, $(1, 6)$, $(3, 10)$, and $(5, 14)$ belong to $\{(x, y) \in R \times R \mid 2x - y + 4 = 0\}$.
   (c) Show that $(1, 6)$ belongs to both the sets in (a) and (b).
   (d) Express the condition $(x + y - 7)(2x - y + 4) = 0$ as an equivalent disjunction.

9. Express each of the following as equivalent disjunctions.
   (a) $(x - y - 3)(x + 4y + 2) = 0$.
   (b) $(3x + 4y - 12)(3x - 4y + 12) = 0$.
   (c) $x^2 - y^2 = 0$

C 10. Let $p \underline{\vee} q$ (which is read "p only or q only") denote the *exclusive disjunction* which is true only if one of p or q is true but not both.

   (a) Form a truth table for $p \underline{\vee} q$.
   (b) Show that $p \underline{\vee} q \Leftrightarrow [\sim(p \wedge q)] \wedge [\sim(\sim p \wedge \sim q)]$.

11. Show that $(x - 3)(x - 5) = 0$ may be expressed as an equivalent exclusive disjunction.

12. Express each of the following conditions as an equivalent exclusive disjunction.
   (a) $(x + 1)(x - 7) = 0$ (b) $x^2 - x - 12 = 0$

13. Show that $(p \vee q) \vee r \Leftrightarrow p \vee (q \vee r)$. Thus, show that disjunction is associative.

12.4 Conditionals and Implications

One of the most important types of compound sentences used in mathematics involves the use of 'If $---$ then $---$'. Sentences formed in this way are called *conditional sentences*. Such sentences are often disguised and it is difficult to recognize them. For example,

'All artists are clever.'

can be expressed as the conditional sentence

'If a person is an artist then he is clever.'

Conditional sentences have the form

If p then q

which is abbreviated to

$$p \Rightarrow q.$$

The truth table for a conditional sentence may be obtained by considering the sentence uttered by two small boys.

'If it rains today then we shall play indoors.'

The sentence has the form $(p \Rightarrow q)$. We shall decide the truth table of $p \Rightarrow q$ by considering whether the boys spoke the truth for the cases that follow.

Case 1

p true and q true. It rains and the boys play indoors. The boys have kept their promise since they made a true statement. Thus, the conditional is true.

Case 2

p is true and q is false. It rains and the boys play outdoors. The boys fail to keep their promise since they made a false statement. Thus, the conditional is false.

Case 3 and 4

p is false. It does not rain. The boys are not obligated to play indoors or outdoors. *No matter what they do the statement they made is not false.* But we agreed that any statement we entertained must be true or false. Thus, if we regard $p \Rightarrow q$ as a sentence, we must agree that the boys made a true statement. We shall agree that $p \Rightarrow q$ is true when p is false.

We summarize the above cases to form the truth table for the conditional $p \Rightarrow q$.

p	q	$p \Rightarrow q$
T	T	T
T	F	F
F	T	T
F	F	T

In the conditional, $p \Rightarrow q$, p is called the *hypothesis* and q is called the *conclusion*.

From the truth table we observe two things.

(1) When the hypothesis is false the conditional is always true.

(2) When the conclusion is true the conditional is always true.

A *true conditional*, $p \Rightarrow q$, is called an *implication* by logicians. Mathematicians are usually interested in proving implications. For this reason when the sentence $p \Rightarrow q$ occurs in the course of a mathematical argument it should be interpreted as an implication and can be read "p implies q".

12.4/Conditionals and Implications

Example 1

Construct a truth table to show that

$$p \Rightarrow q \text{ is logically equivalent to } \sim q \Rightarrow \sim p.$$

Solution

p	q	$\sim q$	$\sim p$	$\sim q \Rightarrow \sim p$	$p \Rightarrow q$
T	T	F	F	T	T
T	F	T	F	F	F
F	T	F	T	T	T
F	F	T	T	T	T

Since $\sim q \Rightarrow \sim p$ and $p \Rightarrow q$ have the same truth table, then

$$(\sim q \Rightarrow \sim p) \Leftrightarrow (p \Rightarrow q).$$

The result of Example 1 gives an extremely useful rule of logic.

$$(p \Rightarrow q) \Leftrightarrow (\sim q \Rightarrow \sim p)$$

The implication $\sim q \Rightarrow \sim p$ is called the *contrapositive* of the original implication $p \Rightarrow q$. Note that the contrapositive of the contrapositive, $\sim(\sim p) \Rightarrow \sim(\sim q)$ is just $p \Rightarrow q$, the original implication.

The rule of the contrapositive is frequently used in mathematics whenever the proof of the contrapositive is easier than the proof of the given implication.

Example 2

Use the contrapositive to prove

'If $a \in I$ and 2 divides a^2, then 2 divides a.'

$$(p \Rightarrow q)$$

Solution

Assume '2 does not divide a,' that is, assume $\sim q$.

$\therefore \quad a = 2m + 1, \qquad\qquad m \in I$
$\therefore \quad a^2 = 4m^2 + 4m + 1$
$\because \quad 4m^2 + 4m = 2(2m^2 + 2m)$
$\therefore \quad 4m^2 + 4m$ is even
$\therefore \quad 4m^2 + 4m + 1$ is odd $\qquad (\sim p)$
$\therefore \qquad\qquad \sim q \Rightarrow \sim p$
$\therefore \quad p \Rightarrow q$ by the rule of the contrapositive.

Example 3

Prove that $(p \Rightarrow q) \Leftrightarrow (\sim p \lor q)$.

Solution

p	q	$p \Rightarrow q$	$\sim p$	q	$\sim p \lor q$
T	T	T	F	T	T
T	F	F	F	F	F
F	T	T	T	T	T
F	F	T	T	F	T

Since $p \Rightarrow q$ and $\sim p \lor q$ have the same truth table, then

$$(p \Rightarrow q) \Leftrightarrow (\sim p \lor q).$$

Exercise 12.4

A

1. Let A = 'I work hard.'

   B = 'I pass.'

   C = 'I get promoted.'

   Translate each of the following.

   (a) $A \Rightarrow B$ (c) $B \Rightarrow C$ (e) $\sim A \Rightarrow \sim B$

   (b) $B \Rightarrow A$ (d) $C \Rightarrow A$ (f) $\sim B \Rightarrow \sim C$

2. State the hypothesis and conclusion for each of the following.

   (a) If $x + 3 = 9$, then $x = 6$.

   (b) If $x - 3 > 5$, then $x > 8$.

   (c) If a triangle has two sides equal then it is isosceles.

3. State the truth value of each of the following conditional statements.

   (a) If $2 + 3 = 5$, then $7 > -2$.

   (b) If $2 + 3 = 5$, then $8 < -2$.

   (c) If $2 + 3 = 9$, then $-1 > -3$.

   (d) If $2 + 3 = 9$, then $-1 < -3$.

4. State the contrapositive of each of the following implications.

   (a) If two triangles are congruent, then they are similar.

   (b) If a polygon is a square, then it is a rectangle.

   (c) If $x \neq 0$, then $x^2 > 0$.

     12.4/Conditionals and Implications

B 5. Prove that $(p \Rightarrow q) \Leftrightarrow \sim(p \land \sim q)$.

6. Interpret the equivalence in question 5 if

$$p = \text{'}A \text{ and } B \text{ are right angles'}$$

and $\qquad q = \text{'}A \text{ and } B \text{ are equal'}$.

7. Prove that $\sim(p \Rightarrow q) \Leftrightarrow (p \land \sim q)$.

8. Prove each of the following implications by proving its contrapositive.

   (a) If $PA = PB$, then P is on the right bisector of AB.
   (b) If a transversal meets two lines making the alternate angles equal, then the lines are parallel.

C 9. Find the negation of the conditional

   'If your name begins with B then you will be placed in 13A.'

10. Construct a truth table for $(p \Rightarrow q) \Rightarrow q$.

11. Construct a truth table for $(p \lor q) \land [\sim (p \land q)]$.

12.5 Two Methods of Proof

We have employed truth tables to determine the conditions under which a statement was true or false. We shall now show some methods of arriving at a conclusion from given data. An assertion that is given as true is called a *premise*.

Consider the following premises.

(1) If $x \in R$ then $x^2 \geq 0$.

(2) $\quad -\dfrac{\sqrt{3}}{2} \in R$.

If these premises are true, we may draw the *conclusion* that

$$\left(-\frac{\sqrt{3}}{2}\right)^2 \geq 0.$$

The above example illustrates the first rule of proof.
Given that *p implies q is true* and that *p is true*, then *q is true*.

> *Rule of Detachment* (Modus Ponens)
>
> $$(p \Rightarrow q) \wedge (p) \Rightarrow q$$
>
> $$p \Rightarrow q$$
> $$\underline{p}$$
> $$\therefore q$$

The Rule of Detachment is used frequently in mathematics as "reasoning from a general case to a particular instance".

The rule of Detachment may be proved using the truth table for implication.

	p	q	$p \Rightarrow q$
(1)	T	T	T
(2)	T	F	F
(3)	F	T	T
(4)	F	F	T

Since p and $p \Rightarrow q$ are both true only in row (1), it follows that q must be true.

A second rule of proof is the *Rule of Syllogism*. For example, consider the following two premises.

(1) If Joe is late then he will get a detention.

(2) If he gets a detention then he must stay in after school.

If the two premises are true we can conclude

(3) If Joe is late then he must stay in after school.

Symbolically we may write the following.

> *Rule of Syllogism*
>
> $$p \Rightarrow q$$
> $$\underline{q \Rightarrow r}$$
> $$\therefore p \Rightarrow r$$

The syllogism can be thought of as a transitive property of the conditional.

12.5/Two Methods of Proof

Exercise 12.5

B 1. Analyze each of the following arguments and show each is an instance of the Rule of Detachment.

(a) If Pat earns more than $10, then he will go to the dance. Pat earns $11. Hence he goes to the dance.

(b) If Mike was not in the math class at 14:00 when the fire-cracker went off, he could not possibly be the culprit. Mike was in the dentist's chair at 14:00. Therefore, Mike is not guilty.

2. What rule of proof is applied to the following argument?

If $\triangle ABC$ is isosceles, $\angle B = \angle C$

In $\triangle ABC$, $AB = AC$

$\therefore \quad \angle B = \angle C$

3. Identify the following syllogisms by using symbols such as P, $Q, \ldots$ to denote specific statements in the argument.

(a) Given: If there is a test tomorrow, then I shall study tonight.

If I study tonight, I will not attend basketball practice.

Conclusion: If there is a test tomorrow, then I will not attend basketball practice.

(b) Given: If I don't dress properly, then I will catch a cold. If I catch a cold, then I will have to go to bed.

Conclusion: If I don't dress properly, then I will have to go to bed.

4. Given the following premises prove C true.

(1) A (2) $A \Rightarrow B$ (3) $B \Rightarrow C$

5. Given (1) $p \Rightarrow q$, (2) $r \Rightarrow \sim q$ prove $p \Rightarrow \sim r$. (Hint: use the con-trapositive in (2).)

6. Establish the Rule of Syllogism by using a truth table. Show $[(p \Rightarrow q) \wedge (q \Rightarrow r)] \Rightarrow (p \Rightarrow r)$ is always true.

7. Given: Liars are untrustworthy.

Stout people are very jolly.

A man who speaks the truth is honest.

Prosperous merchants are all fat.

One can always trust a jolly person.

Prove: All prosperous merchants are honest. (From L. Carroll.)

8. Given: If prices are high, then wages are high.
   Prices are high or there are price controls.
   If there are price controls, then there is not inflation.
   There is inflation.

   Prove: Wages are high.

9. Draw valid conclusions in each of the following if possible.
   (a) If roses are red, then violets are blue.
   Roses are red.
   (b) If it snowed Friday, the schools were closed.
   Schools were closed Friday.
   (c) If I read this Chapter carefully, then logic is easy.
   I read this Chapter carefully.
   (d) If point A bisects segment XY, then XA and AY have the same length.
   XA and AY do not have the same length.

12.6 The Indirect Method of Proof

Indirect proof, known as proof by *reductio ad absurdum* by Euclid in 300 B.C., is frequently used in mathematics. In order to prove a theorem 'A', we assume that '$\sim A$' is true and attempt to show a contradiction results. If the contradiction occurs; '$\sim A$' must be false, that is 'A' is true. A contradiction is the negation of an axiom or a previously proved theorem. The simplest contradiction has the form '$B \wedge \sim B$' which is clearly false.

For example, to prove '$\sqrt{2}$ is irrational' (A)

we assume '$\sqrt{2}$ is rational' $(\sim A)$

$\therefore$ there are integers a, b with no common factors such that

$$\sqrt{2} = \frac{a}{b}, \qquad b \neq 0 \qquad\qquad (B)$$

$$\therefore \quad 2 = \frac{a^2}{b^2}$$

$$\therefore \quad a^2 = 2b^2$$

$$\therefore \quad a^2 \quad \text{is even}$$

$$\therefore \quad a \quad \text{is even}$$

$$\text{Let} \qquad a = 2c$$

$$\therefore \quad 4c^2 = 2b^2$$

$$\therefore \quad 2c^2 = b^2$$

$$\therefore \quad b^2 \text{ is even and } b \text{ is even.}$$

Since a and b are even, they have a factor in common. But, a and b have no factor in common. $\therefore \sim B$

Thus, by assuming $\sim A$ we arrive at $B \wedge \sim B$ which is a contradiction.

$$\therefore \quad \sim A \text{ is false,}$$

$$\therefore \quad A \text{ is true,}$$

$$\text{and} \quad \sqrt{2} \text{ is irrational.}$$

In many cases the statement to be proved is a conditional of the form $p \Rightarrow q$. Employing the indirect method of proof we commence with the assumption that $\sim(p \Rightarrow q)$ is true.

Since $(p \Rightarrow q) \Leftrightarrow (\sim p \vee q)$,
and, by De Morgan's law $\sim(p \vee q) \Leftrightarrow (\sim q \wedge \sim p)$.
$\therefore \quad \sim(p \Rightarrow q) \Leftrightarrow \sim(\sim p \vee q) \Leftrightarrow (p \wedge \sim q)$.

Thus, we may begin the indirect proof by assuming the truth of the statement $p \wedge \sim q$ and attempt to prove that this assumption leads to the truth of $p \wedge \sim p$ or $q \wedge \sim q$ or some other contradiction. Then we conclude that $\sim(p \Rightarrow q)$ is false, that is $p \Rightarrow q$ is true.

For example, to prove the theorem

'If alternate angles are equal, the lines are parallel' we assume the lines are not parallel.

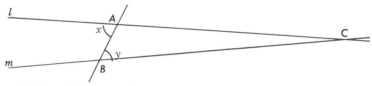

Let 'P' be '$\angle x = \angle y$'
and 'Q' be '$l \| m$'
$\qquad (P \Rightarrow Q)$ is $(\angle x = \angle y) \Rightarrow (l \| m)$

Assume $P \wedge \sim Q$, that is, P is true and $\sim Q$ is true.
$\therefore \quad (\angle x = \angle y)$ and (l is not parallel to m) are true.

Since l and m are not parallel they meet at a point, C, say as in the diagram.

But, we have a theorem which states that the exterior angle of a triangle equals the sum of the interior opposite angles.

$$\therefore \quad \angle x > \angle y$$
$$\therefore \quad {\sim}P \text{ is true}$$

Thus, P and ${\sim}P$ are both true, which is impossible.

$\therefore$ the assumption $P \wedge {\sim}Q$ is false

$$\therefore \quad {\sim}(P \Rightarrow Q) \text{ is false}$$
$$\therefore \quad P \Rightarrow Q \text{ is true}$$
and the theorem is proved.

We could have completed the theorem by using the contrapositive. We started with ${\sim}Q$ and concluded with ${\sim}P$.

$$\therefore \quad {\sim}Q \Rightarrow {\sim}P$$
$$\therefore \quad P \Rightarrow Q \qquad \text{(contrapositive)}$$

Exercise 12.6

B 1. Prove that $\sqrt{3}$ is irrational.

2. Prove: If two sides of a triangle are unequal, then the angles opposite these sides are unequal.

3. Prove that the product of a non-zero rational number and an irrational number is irrational.

4. If $x \neq y$ prove that $\dfrac{x}{y} \neq \dfrac{x+a}{y+a}$ for $a \neq 0$.

5. Prove that there is no largest prime number. (Hint: Form the product of all known primes and add one).

6. Prove that there is no greatest real number less than one.

12.7 Biconditional Statements

To every conditional statement there corresponds a *converse statement*. For example,

$p \Rightarrow q$ is a conditional statement
$q \Rightarrow p$ is the *converse*.

For example, $(x = 2) \Rightarrow (x^2 = 4)$

is a true conditional. The converse is

$$(x^2 = 4) \Rightarrow (x = 2).$$

This is false, since

$$(x^2 = 4) \Rightarrow (x = 2) \lor (x = -2).$$

Thus, the converse of a true conditional is not necessarily true.

The conjunction of a conditional and its converse is called a *biconditional* statement. Thus, the biconditional statement associated with p and q is

$$(p \Rightarrow q) \land (q \Rightarrow p).$$

We shall denote this biconditional statement by

$$p \Leftrightarrow q \quad \text{(read "} p \text{, if and only if } q \text{").}$$

Therefore,

$$(p \Leftrightarrow q) \Leftrightarrow [(p \Rightarrow q) \land (q \Rightarrow p)]$$

Example 1

Find the truth table for $p \Leftrightarrow q$.

Solution

p	q	$p \Rightarrow q$	$q \Rightarrow p$	$p \Leftrightarrow q$
T	T	T	T	T
T	F	F	T	F
F	T	T	F	F
F	F	T	T	T

Notice that $p \Leftrightarrow q$ is true only when p and q have the same truth value.

Two sentences p and q for which $p \Leftrightarrow q$ is true are logically equivalent.

Most mathematical manipulation involves expressing statements as simpler equivalent statements. For example,

$$(x + 3 = 5) \Leftrightarrow (x = 2)$$

and can be written

$$x + 3 = 5$$

$$\Leftrightarrow \quad x = 2$$

The equivalence indicates that the steps are reversible. In the solution of a problem, where each step is an equivalence the converse argument will hold. For example,

$$2x^2 - 5x + 3 = 0$$

$$\Leftrightarrow \quad (2x - 3)(x - 1) = 0$$

$$\Leftrightarrow \quad (2x - 3 = 0) \lor (x - 1 = 0)$$

$$\Leftrightarrow \quad (x = \tfrac{3}{2}) \lor (x = 1)$$

Since the steps are reversible we can conclude that the solution set is $\{\tfrac{3}{2}, 1\}$ without further checking.

The Power Rule for Equations (PRE) does not give an equivalent sentence and the argument is not reversible. For example,

$$x + \sqrt{x} = 20$$

$$\Leftrightarrow \quad \sqrt{x} = 20 - x$$

$$\Rightarrow \quad x = 400 - 40x + x^2$$

$$\Leftrightarrow \quad x^2 - 41x + 400 = 0$$

$$\Leftrightarrow \quad (x - 25)(x - 16) = 0$$

$$\Leftrightarrow \quad (x = 25) \lor (x = 16)$$

The second step is not reversible. (Why?) Thus, we must check before drawing conclusions. We find that 16 satisfies the original equation but 25 does not.

If a conditional has a conjunction in either the hypothesis or conclusion it is possible to form *Partial Converses*,
    For example,

$$(p \land q) \Rightarrow r$$

has the *complete converse* $r \Rightarrow (p \land q)$. By interchanging one of p or q with r in $(p \land q) \Rightarrow r$ we obtain a partial converse. Thus,

$$(p \wedge r) \Rightarrow q$$

and $$(q \wedge r) \Rightarrow p$$

are partial converses.

Faraday discovered electromagnetic induction by taking a known result and proving by physical experiment that a partial converse was true.

It was known that,

'If a current flows in a wire and the wire forms a closed circuit then a magnetic field is created around the wire.'

Faraday proved that,

'If a magnetic field is created around a wire and the wire forms a closed circuit, then a current flows in the wire.'

Recall that the contrapositive of an implication, $p \Rightarrow q$, is

$$\sim q \Rightarrow \sim p,$$

and $(p \Rightarrow q) \Leftrightarrow (\sim q \Rightarrow \sim p)$. Thus, if a conditional is true, its contrapositive is necessarily also true. Such is *not* the case for the converse of a conditional.

Exercise 12.7

A 1. For each of the following state (*i*) the converse; (*ii*) the contrapositive.

(*a*) If I lose, then I will not eat my shirt.
(*b*) If n is an even number, then $n + 1$ is odd.
(*c*) If he breathes, then he is alive.

B 2. Express each of the following as the conjunction of two conditionals.

(*a*) $3x - 6 = 0$ if and only if $x = 2$.
(*b*) Two circles have equal areas if and only if their radii are equal.
(*c*) A point P is equidistant from A and B if and only if P lies in the right bisector of AB.

3. If '*P*' = 'a current flows in a wire'

   '*Q*' = 'the wire forms a closed circuit'

   '*R*' = 'a magnetic field is created around the wire'

   state each of the following in symbols.

   (*a*) A statement known to Faraday before his experiment on page 383.
   (*b*) A partial converse shown by Faraday to be true.

4. Form three converses of the following.

   (*a*) 'If $x = 2$ and $y = 7$ then $x + y = 9$.'
   (*b*) 'If $x = 2$ and $y \geq 7$ then $x + y \geq 9$.'

5. Prove that the following biconditionals are true.

   (*a*) A number is even if and only if it is divisible by 2.
   (*b*) $2x + 3 = 17$ if and only if $x = 7$.

6. Prove the equivalences

$$(p \Rightarrow q) \Leftrightarrow (\sim p \lor q).$$

7. Prove $[(p \land q) \Rightarrow r] \Leftrightarrow [(p \land \sim r) \Rightarrow (\sim q)]$.

12.8 Necessary and Sufficient Conditions

The phrase "necessary and sufficient conditions" frequently occurs in mathematics. We shall find that conditional and biconditional sentences enable us to symbolize the meaning of necessary and sufficient conditions. For example, consider the following conditional statement.

'If two angles are right-angled then they are equal.'

Two angles being right-angled is *sufficient* for them to be equal but this condition is not necessary for equal angles since they may be equal but not right-angled.

Thus, the conditional statement

$$p \Rightarrow q$$

can be read "*p* is sufficient for *q*".

p is a *necessary* or indispensable condition of *q* if we are justified in stating

'If p is not true then q is not true.'

or $\qquad\qquad\qquad\qquad \sim p \Rightarrow \sim q$

which is the contrapositive of

$$q \Rightarrow p.$$

Thus, $\qquad\qquad\qquad\qquad q \Rightarrow p$

can be read "p is necessary for q".

The biconditional $p \Leftrightarrow q$ means

$$p \Rightarrow q \qquad \text{and} \qquad q \Rightarrow p.$$

Thus, $p \Leftrightarrow q$ can be read "p is sufficient for q and p is necessary for q" or "p is necessary and sufficient for q". It can also be read "q is necessary and sufficient for p", or "p, if and only if q".

If p is necessary and sufficient for q then p and q are logically equivalent.

Example 1

Is $3x + 2 = 17$ a necessary and sufficient condition for $x = 5$?

Solution

$$(3x + 2 = 17) \Rightarrow (x = 5) \text{ is true}$$
$$(x = 5) \Rightarrow (3x + 2 = 17) \text{ is true}$$
$$\therefore \quad (3x + 2 = 17) \text{ is necessary and sufficient for } x = 5.$$

Example 2

If $\quad$ 'P' = 'two angles are vertically opposite'

and $\quad$ 'Q' = 'the angles are equal'

which of the following is true?

(a) P is sufficient for Q $\qquad$ (b) P is necessary for Q.

Solution

(a) 'P is sufficient for Q' = '$P \Rightarrow Q$' and means that 'Two angles vertically opposite is a sufficient condition for equal angles', which is true.

(b) 'P is necessary for Q' = '$Q \Rightarrow P$' and means 'Two angles vertically opposite is a necessary condition for equal angles', which is false.

12.8/Necessary and Sufficient Conditions

We list the various ways of reading the symbol '$p \Rightarrow q$'.

> if p then q
> p implies q
> p is sufficient for q
> q is necessary for p
> p only if q

The symbol '$p \Leftrightarrow q$' may be read in one of the following ways.

> p is equivalent to q
> p if and only if q (p iff q)
> p is necessary and sufficient for q

Exercise 12.8

B   1.   Use one of the symbols $\Rightarrow$ or $\Leftrightarrow$ to rewrite the following.

    (a) A is sufficient for B.
    (b) P is necessary for Q.
    (c) X is necessary and sufficient for Y.
    (d)   If P then Q.
    (e) A if and only if B.
    (f) K only if L.

  2.   For each of the following determine which of $p \Rightarrow q$, $q \Rightarrow p$ and $p \Leftrightarrow q$ are true.

    (a) p is 'A number is exactly divisible by 3.'
         q is 'A number is exactly divisible by 9'.
    (b) p is '7 is a factor of 21'.
         q is '21 is a multiple of 7'.
    (c) p is 'A quadrilateral $ABCD$ has a pair of equal sides'.
         q is '$ABCD$ is a square'.
    (d) p is 'The diagonals of $ABCD$ bisect one another'.
         q is '$ABCD$ is a square'.
    (e) p is '$\tan \theta = 1$'.
         q is '$\theta = \dfrac{\pi}{4}$'
    (f) p is '$2x - 3 = 5$'.
         q is '$x = 4$'.

C   3.   Prove by means of a truth table that

$$\sim(p \Leftrightarrow q) \Leftrightarrow [(p \wedge \sim q) \vee (q \wedge \sim p)].$$

4. Negate the following biconditional statements.

(a) $3x - 5 = 13$ if and only if $x = 6$.

(b) A triangle is isosceles if and only if the angles opposite the equal sides are equal.

(c) The roots of $ax^2 + bx + c = 0$, $a \neq 0$ are equal if and only if $b^2 - 4ac = 0$.

12.9 Quantifiers and Counterexamples

Statements often involve words such as

> all
>
> some
>
> one

each of which indicates quantity and suggest 'how many'. Such words are called *quantifiers*.

Consider the following examples.

(1) All people like dogs.

(2) Some boys read avidly.

(3) There is one person with no hair.

Example (2) can be restated as

> *At least one* boy reads avidly.

Example (3) can be restated as

> *At least one* person has no hair.

We shall call the quantifier "all" the *universal quantifier*. We shall use the symbol $\forall_x$ to mean

> —for all x
>
> —for every x
>
> —for each x

For example,

$$\forall_{x \in R} [x(x + 1) = x^2 + x]$$

can be read "For all x belonging to R, $x(x + 1) = x^2 + x$." Recall that $x(x + 1) = x^2 + x$ is called an identity since its solution set is R.

The quantifier "some" is the *existential quantifier*. We shall use the symbol $\exists_x$ to mean

—for some x
—some x is such that
—there exists an x such that
—there is an x such that
—there is at least one x such that

For example,

$$\exists_{x \epsilon I} \, (x + 7 = 3)$$

can be read "There exists an x belonging to I such that $x + 7 = 3$."

Consider the statement

$$\forall_x \, (x^2 = 25).$$

We shall assume that the domain of the variable is R. We know that only 5 and -5 make the statement $x^2 = 25$ true.

$$\therefore \quad \forall_x \, (x^2 = 25) \quad \text{is false}$$

Thus, $\qquad\qquad \sim\!\forall_x \, (x^2 = 25) \quad \text{is true.}$

We can also say that

$$\forall_x \sim(x^2 = 25) \quad \text{is false}$$

Let P_x be an open sentence in the variable x. Consider the following chart.

Quantified sentence	is true	is false
$\forall_x P_x$	if for all x, P_x is true	if for at least one x, P_x is false
$\exists_x P_x$	if for at least one x, P_x is true	if for all x, P_x is false
$\forall_x \sim P_x$	if for all x, P_x is false	if for at least one x, P_x is true
$\exists_x \sim P_x$	if for at least one x, P_x is false	if for all x, P_x is true

From the above chart we observe the following.

12.9/Quantifiers and Counterexamples

$\forall_x P_x$ is true and $\exists_x \sim P_x$ is false under the same conditions. Also $\forall_x \sim P_x$ is false for the same conditions that $\exists_x P_x$ is true.

$$\therefore \quad \sim\forall_x P_x \Leftrightarrow \exists_x \sim P_x$$
Similarly, $\quad \sim\exists_x P_x \Leftrightarrow \forall_x \sim P_x$

Thus, to negate a quantified sentence we change the quantifier and negate the sentence that is quantified. For example, the negation of

'Some boys have long hair.'

is 'All boys do not have long hair.'

and the negation of

'All mathematicians are brilliant.'

is 'Some mathematicians are not brilliant.'

Quantified sentences occur with great frequency in mathematics although they are often not specifically formulated as such. For example,

(1) 'The medians of a triangle are concurrent' means 'For every triangle the medians are concurrent.'

(2) The identity $(x - 2)^2 \geq 0$, $x \in R$ can be expressed

$$\forall_{x \in R} (x^2 - 4x + 4 \geq 0).$$

(3) The statement that '$x^2 - x - 12 = 0$, $x \in R$ has a solution' can be expressed as

$$\exists_{x \in R}(x^2 - x - 12 = 0).$$

To demonstrate the falsity of a universally quantified sentence it is sufficient to establish the existence of one element from the domain of the variable that makes the open sentence false. For example, to show

$$\forall_{x \in R} \quad (x \text{ is rational})$$

is false, we need find only one element a belonging to R that makes the sentence 'x is rational' false. Such an element is called a *counterexample*. For example, $\sqrt{2}$ is such a counterexample.

Possibly the two most important processes in the advance of mathematics are:

(i) proving the truth of conjectured theorems

and (ii) inventing counterexamples to show that a conjectured theorem is false.

Sometimes the discovery of counterexamples requires great ingenuity. Though they may be temporarily disheartening to the researcher, a non-trivial counterexample frequently guides the mathematician to unusual and exciting discoveries in the end.

Exercise 12.9

A 1. Express each of the following as a quantified sentence.
  (a) Television programs are boring.
  (b) Rational numbers are real numbers.
  (c) The base angles of an isosceles triangle are equal.
  (d) $2x = 3$ where $x \in N$.
  (e) $x \leq 5$ where $x \in N$.

  2. Translate each of the following into a verbal sentence.
  (a) $\exists_{x \in R}(x^2 = 25)$ (c) $\sim\exists_{x \in I}(x^2 = 5)$
  (b) $\forall_{x \in I}(x^2 = 0)$ (d) $\sim\forall_{x \in R}\, x^2 > 0$

B 3. Find a counterexample to prove each of the following false.
  (a) All prime numbers are odd.
  (b) Every equiangular polygon is regular.
  (c) For every $n \in I$, $n^2 + n + 41$ is prime.

  4. Quantify each of the following open sentences to make it true.
  (a) $x^2 = 4$, $x \in R$.
  (b) The altitudes of a triangle are concurrent.
  (c) $(x - 2)(x + 2) = x^2 - 4$, $x \in R$.
  (d) $x^2 \leq 0$, $x \in R$.
  (e) $3x = 10$, $x \in I$.

  5. Negate each of the following.
  (a) All squares are similar.
  (b) Some triangles are equilateral.
  (c) $|x| \geq 0$ for all $x \in R$.

C 6. Translate each of the following and determine the truth value of the statement. The domain of the variables is R.

  (a) $\forall_x \forall_y (xy = yx)$ (b) $\exists_x \exists_y (x^2 = y^2 + 1)$

12.10 Tautologies and Contradictions

The notion of an *identity* in algebra or trigonometry should be a familiar one. If A_x and B_x are two expressions involving the variable x whose domain is some set of numbers then

$$A_x = B_x$$

is an identity, if it is true that

$$\forall_x (A_x = B_x).$$

There is an analogy to identities that involves expressions that contain variables with domain a set of sentences. For example,

$$p \Leftrightarrow \sim(\sim p)$$

is true for all sentences p.

$$\therefore \quad \forall_p [p \Leftrightarrow \sim(\sim p)] \text{ is true.}$$

Sentences such as these, that are true for all substitutions of its sentence variables are called *tautologies*.

The negation of a tautology is a sentence form that yields only false statements for all permissible substitutions of the variables. Such sentence forms are called contradictions. For example, $p \wedge \sim p$ is a contradiction.

Exercise 12.10

B 1. Prove the following tautologies.

(a) $p \vee \sim p$ (Rule of the excluded middle)
(b) $\sim(p \wedge \sim p)$ (Rule of contradiction)
(c) $[p \wedge (p \Rightarrow q)] \Rightarrow q$ (Rule of detachment)
(d) $[(p \Rightarrow q) \wedge (q \Rightarrow r)] \Rightarrow (p \Rightarrow r)$ (Rule of syllogism)
(e) $\sim(\sim p) \Leftrightarrow p$ (Rule of double negation)
(f) $(p \Rightarrow q) \Leftrightarrow (\sim q \Rightarrow \sim p)$ (Rule of contraposition)

Review Exercise 12.11

B 1. Which of the following are open sentences? Explain.

(a) Newton invented calculus.
(b) $x + 3 = 7$.
(c) She obtained the highest standing.
(d) $x^2 = -1$.

2. Criticize the following definitions.

    (*a*) A rectangle is a square quadrilateral.
    (*b*) A square is a rhombus with four right angles.
    (*c*) An irrational number is a number that is not rational.

3. Negate each of the following sentences.

    (*a*) The set of integers is a subset of the set of reals.
    (*b*) $5 + 2 > 9$ (*c*) $-6 \neq -5$

4. Express each of the following as a conjunction.

    (*a*) $-2 < x < 5$
    (*b*) The roots are real and equal.

5. Express each of the following as a disjunction.

    (*a*) An integer is odd or even.
    (*b*) The angles are equal or supplementary.

6. Let 'P' = 'I ate cake'
       'Q' = 'I ate ice cream'

    translate each of the following.

    (*a*) $P \lor Q$ (*c*) $P \land Q$ (*e*) $\sim(P \land Q)$
    (*b*) $P \lor \sim Q$ (*d*) $\sim P \land Q$ (*f*) $\sim(P \lor Q)$

7. Use a truth table to prove

$$\sim(p \land q) \Leftrightarrow (\sim p \lor \sim q).$$

8. If 'P' = 'I study'
     'Q' = 'I pass'
     'R' = 'I work hard'

    translate each of the following.

    (*a*) $P \Rightarrow Q$ (*c*) $\sim P \Rightarrow Q$ (*e*) $\sim P \Rightarrow \sim R$
    (*b*) $R \Rightarrow Q$ (*d*) $\sim Q \Rightarrow \sim P$ (*f*) $Q \Rightarrow \sim P$

9. Use a truth table to prove

$$(p \Rightarrow q) \Leftrightarrow (\sim p \lor q).$$

10. Prove that the following are always true.

    (*a*) $p \Rightarrow p$ (*b*) $p \Rightarrow (p \lor q)$ (*c*) $p \Rightarrow (q \Rightarrow p)$

11. State the contrapositive of each of the following.

  (a) If $x > 0$, then $\sqrt{x} \in R$.
  (b) If n is an even integer, then n^2 is even.
  (c) If $x = 3$ satisfies $x^3 - 27 = 0$, then $x - 3$ is a factor of $x^3 - 27$.

12. Use the symbols $\Rightarrow$ or $\Leftrightarrow$ to express each of the following.

  (a) p is necessary for q (d) q implies p
  (b) p is sufficient for q (e) p if and only if q
  (c) p only if q (f) p is necessary and sufficient for q

13. Prove the following and state which illustrates a commutative, associative, or distributive property.

  (a) $(p \wedge q) \Leftrightarrow (q \wedge p)$
  (b) $(p \vee q) \Leftrightarrow (q \vee p)$
  (c) $[(p \wedge q) \wedge r] \Leftrightarrow [p \wedge (q \wedge r)]$
  (d) $[(p \vee q) \vee r] \Leftrightarrow [p \vee (q \vee r)]$
  (e) $[p \wedge (q \vee r)] \Leftrightarrow [(p \wedge q) \vee (p \wedge r)]$
  (f) $[p \vee (q \wedge r)] \Leftrightarrow [(p \vee q) \wedge (p \vee r)]$

14. Prove $[\sim (p \wedge q)] \Leftrightarrow [p \Rightarrow (\sim q)]$.

Amount of 1
$$(1 + i)^n$$

n	½%	1%	1½%	2%	2½%	3%	3½%	n
1	1.005 00	1.010 00	1.015 00	1.020 00	1.025 00	1.030 00	1.035 00	1
2	1.010 03	1.020 10	1.030 23	1.040 40	1.050 63	1.060 90	1.071 23	2
3	1.015 08	1.030 30	1.045 68	1.061 21	1.076 89	1.092 73	1.108 72	3
4	1.020 15	1.040 60	1.061 36	1.082 43	1.103 81	1.125 51	1.147 52	4
5	1.025 25	1.051 01	1.077 28	1.104 08	1.131 41	1.159 27	1.187 69	5
6	1.030 38	1.061 52	1.093 44	1.126 16	1.159 69	1.194 05	1.229 26	6
7	1.035 53	1.072 14	1.109 85	1.148 69	1.188 69	1.229 87	1.272 28	7
8	1.040 71	1.082 86	1.126 49	1.171 66	1.218 40	1.266 77	1.316 81	8
9	1.045 91	1.093 69	1.143 39	1.195 09	1.248 86	1.304 77	1.362 90	9
10	1.051 14	1.104 62	1.160 54	1.218 99	1.280 08	1.343 92	1.410 60	10
11	1.056 40	1.115 67	1.177 95	1.243 37	1.312 09	1.384 23	1.459 97	11
12	1.061 68	1.126 83	1.195 62	1.268 24	1.344 89	1.425 76	1.511 07	12
13	1.066 99	1.138 09	1.213 55	1.293 61	1.378 51	1.468 53	1.563 96	13
14	1.072 32	1.149 47	1.231 76	1.319 48	1.412 97	1.512 59	1.618 69	14
15	1.077 68	1.160 97	1.250 23	1.345 87	1.448 30	1.557 97	1.675 35	15
16	1.083 07	1.172 58	1.268 99	1.372 79	1.484 51	1.604 71	1.733 99	16
17	1.088 49	1.184 30	1.288 02	1.400 24	1.521 62	1.652 85	1.794 68	17
18	1.093 93	1.196 15	1.307 34	1.428 25	1.559 66	1.702 43	1.857 49	18
19	1.099 40	1.208 11	1.326 95	1.456 81	1.598 65	1.753 51	1.922 50	19
20	1.104 90	1.220 19	1.346 86	1.485 95	1.638 62	1.806 11	1.989 79	20
21	1.110 42	1.232 39	1.367 06	1.515 67	1.679 58	1.860 29	2.059 43	21
22	1.115 97	1.244 72	1.387 56	1.545 98	1.721 57	1.916 10	2.131 51	22
23	1.121 55	1.257 16	1.408 38	1.576 90	1.764 61	1.973 59	2.206 11	23
24	1.127 16	1.269 73	1.429 50	1.608 44	1.808 73	2.032 79	2.283 33	24
25	1.132 80	1.282 43	1.450 95	1.640 61	1.853 94	2.093 78	2.363 24	25
26	1.138 46	1.295 26	1.472 71	1.673 42	1.900 29	2.156 59	2.445 96	26
27	1.144 15	1.308 21	1.494 80	1.706 89	1.947 80	2.221 29	2.531 57	27
28	1.149 87	1.321 29	1.517 22	1.741 02	1.996 50	2.287 93	2.620 17	28
29	1.155 62	1.334 50	1.539 98	1.775 84	2.046 41	2.356 57	2.711 88	29
30	1.161 40	1.347 85	1.563 08	1.811 36	2.097 57	2.427 26	2.806 79	30
31	1.167 21	1.361 33	1.586 53	1.847 59	2.150 01	2.500 08	2.905 03	31
32	1.173 04	1.374 94	1.610 32	1.884 54	2.203 76	2.575 08	3.006 71	32
33	1.178 91	1.388 69	1.634 48	1.922 23	2.258 85	2.652 34	3.111 94	33
34	1.184 80	1.402 58	1.659 00	1.960 68	2.315 32	2.731 91	3.220 86	34
35	1.190 73	1.416 60	1.683 88	1.999 89	2.373 21	2.813 86	3.333 59	35
36	1.196 68	1.430 77	1.709 14	2.039 89	2.432 54	2.898 28	3.450 27	36
37	1.202 66	1.445 08	1.734 78	2.080 69	2.493 35	2.985 23	3.571 03	37
38	1.208 68	1.459 53	1.760 80	2.122 30	2.555 68	3.074 78	3.696 01	38
39	1.214 72	1.474 12	1.787 21	2.164 74	2.619 57	3.167 03	3.825 37	39
40	1.220 79	1.488 86	1.814 02	2.208 04	2.685 06	3.262 04	3.959 26	40
41	1.226 90	1.503 75	1.841 23	2.252 20	2.752 19	3.359 90	4.097 83	41
42	1.233 03	1.518 79	1.868 85	2.297 24	2.821 00	3.460 70	4.241 26	42
43	1.239 20	1.533 98	1.896 88	2.343 19	2.891 52	3.564 52	4.389 70	43
44	1.245 39	1.549 32	1.925 33	2.390 05	2.963 81	3.671 45	4.543 34	44
45	1.251 62	1.564 81	1.954 24	2.437 85	3.037 90	3.781 60	4.702 36	45
46	1.257 88	1.580 46	1.983 53	2.486 61	3.113 85	3.895 04	4.866 94	46
47	1.264 17	1.596 26	2.013 28	2.536 34	3.191 70	4.011 90	5.037 28	47
48	1.270 49	1.612 23	2.043 48	2.587 07	3.271 49	4.132 25	5.213 59	48
49	1.276 84	1.628 35	2.074 13	2.638 81	3.353 28	4.256 22	5.396 06	49
50	1.283 23	1.644 63	2.105 24	2.691 59	3.437 11	4.383 91	5.584 93	50
n	½%	1%	1½%	2%	2½%	3%	3½%	n

Amount of 1
$$(1 + i)^n$$

n	4%	5%	6%	7%	8%	9%	10%	n
1	1.040 00	1.050 00	1.060 00	1.070 00	1.080 00	1.090 00	1.100 00	1
2	1.081 60	1.102 50	1.123 60	1.144 90	1.166 40	1.188 10	1.210 00	2
3	1.124 86	1.157 63	1.191 02	1.225 04	1.259 71	1.295 03	1.331 00	3
4	1.169 86	1.215 51	1.262 48	1.310 80	1.360 49	1.411 58	1.464 10	4
5	1.216 65	1.276 28	1.338 23	1.402 55	1.469 33	1.538 62	1.610 51	5
6	1.265 32	1.340 10	1.418 52	1.500 73	1.586 87	1.677 10	1.771 56	6
7	1.315 93	1.407 10	1.503 63	1.605 78	1.713 82	1.828 04	1.948 72	7
8	1.368 57	1.477 46	1.593 85	1.718 19	1.850 93	1.992 56	2.143 59	8
9	1.423 31	1.551 33	1.689 48	1.838 46	1.999 00	2.171 89	2.357 95	9
10	1.480 24	1.628 89	1.790 85	1.967 15	2.158 92	2.367 36	2.593 74	10
11	1.539 45	1.710 34	1.898 30	2.104 85	2.331 64	2.580 43	2.853 12	11
12	1.601 03	1.795 86	2.012 20	2.252 19	2.518 17	2.812 66	3.138 43	12
13	1.665 07	1.885 65	2.132 93	2.409 85	2.719 62	3.065 80	3.452 27	13
14	1.731 68	1.979 93	2.260 90	2.578 53	2.937 19	3.341 73	3.797 50	14
15	1.800 94	2.078 93	2.396 56	2.759 03	3.172 17	3.642 48	4.177 25	15
16	1.872 98	2.182 87	2.540 35	2.952 16	3.425 94	3.970 31	4.594 97	16
17	1.947 90	2.292 02	2.692 77	3.158 82	3.700 02	4.327 63	5.054 47	17
18	2.025 82	2.406 62	2.854 34	3.379 93	3.996 02	4.717 12	5.559 92	18
19	2.106 85	2.526 95	3.025 60	3.616 53	4.315 70	5.141 66	6.115 91	19
20	2.191 12	2.653 30	3.207 14	3.869 68	4.660 96	5.604 41	6.727 50	20
21	2.278 77	2.785 96	3.399 56	4.140 50	5.033 83	6.108 81	7.400 25	21
22	2.369 92	2.925 26	3.603 54	4.430 40	5.436 54	6.658 60	8.140 27	22
23	2.464 72	3.071 52	3.819 75	4.740 53	5.871 46	7.257 87	8.954 30	23
24	2.563 30	3.225 10	4.048 93	5.072 37	6.341 18	7.911 08	9.849 73	24
25	2.665 84	3.386 35	4.291 87	5.427 43	6.848 48	8.623 08	10.834 71	25
26	2.772 47	3.555 67	4.549 38	5.807 35	7.396 35	9.399 16	11.918 18	26
27	2.883 37	3.733 46	4.822 35	6.213 87	7.988 06	10.245 08	13.109 99	27
28	2.998 70	3.920 13	5.111 69	6.648 84	8.627 11	11.167 14	14.420 99	28
29	3.118 65	4.116 14	5.418 39	7.114 26	9.317 27	12.172 18	15.863 09	29
30	3.243 40	4.321 94	5.743 49	7.612 26	10.062 66	13.267 68	17.449 40	30
31	3.373 13	4.538 04	6.088 10	8.145 11	10.867 67	14.461 77	19.194 34	31
32	3.508 06	4.764 94	6.453 39	8.715 27	11.737 08	15.763 33	21.113 78	32
33	3.648 38	5.003 19	6.840 59	9.325 34	12.676 05	17.182 03	23.225 15	33
34	3.794 32	5.253 35	7.251 03	9.978 11	13.690 13	18.728 41	25.547 67	34
35	3.946 09	5.516 02	7.686 09	10.676 58	14.785 34	20.413 97	28.102 44	35
36	4.103 93	5.791 82	8.147 25	11.423 94	15.968 17	22.251 23	30.912 68	36
37	4.268 09	6.081 41	8.636 09	12.223 62	17.245 63	24.253 84	34.003 95	37
38	4.438 81	6.385 48	9.154 25	13.079 27	18.625 28	26.436 68	37.404 34	38
39	4.616 37	6.704 75	9.703 51	13.994 82	20.115 30	28.815 98	41.144 78	39
40	4.801 02	7.039 99	10.285 72	14.974 46	21.724 52	31.409 42	45.259 26	40
41	4.993 06	7.391 99	10.902 86	16.022 67	23.462 48	34.236 27	49.785 18	41
42	5.192 78	7.761 59	11.557 03	17.144 26	25.339 48	37.317 53	54.763 70	42
43	5.400 50	8.149 67	12.250 45	18.344 35	27.366 64	40.676 11	60.240 07	43
44	5.616 52	8.557 15	12.985 48	19.628 46	29.555 97	44.336 96	66.264 08	44
45	5.841 18	8.985 01	13.764 61	21.002 45	31.920 45	48.327 29	72.890 48	45
46	6.074 82	9.434 26	14.590 49	22.472 62	34.474 09	52.676 74	80.179 53	46
47	6.317 82	9.905 97	15.465 92	24.045 71	37.232 01	57.417 65	88.197 49	47
48	6.570 53	10.401 27	16.393 87	25.728 91	40.210 57	62.585 24	97.017 23	48
49	6.833 35	10.921 33	17.377 50	27.529 93	43.427 42	68.217 91	106.718 96	49
50	7.106 68	11.467 40	18.420 15	29.457 03	46.901 61	74.357 52	117.390 85	50
n	4%	5%	6%	7%	8%	9%	10%	n

Present Value of 1

$$\frac{1}{(1 + i)^n}$$

n	$\frac{1}{2}\%$	1%	$1\frac{1}{2}\%$	2%	$2\frac{1}{2}\%$	3%	$3\frac{1}{2}\%$	n
1	0.995 02	0.990 10	0.985 22	0.980 39	0.975 61	0.970 87	0.966 18	1
2	0.990 07	0.980 30	0.970 66	0.961 17	0.951 81	0.942 60	0.933 51	2
3	0.985 15	0.970 59	0.956 32	0.942 32	0.928 60	0.915 14	0.901 94	3
4	0.980 25	0.960 98	0.942 18	0.923 85	0.905 95	0.888 49	0.871 44	4
5	0.975 37	0.951 47	0.928 26	0.905 73	0.883 85	0.862 61	0.841 97	5
6	0.970 52	0.942 05	0.914 54	0.887 97	0.862 30	0.837 48	0.813 50	6
7	0.965 69	0.932 72	0.901 03	0.870 56	0.841 27	0.813 09	0.785 99	7
8	0.960 89	0.923 48	0.887 71	0.853 49	0.820 75	0.789 41	0.759 41	8
9	0.956 10	0.914 34	0.874 59	0.836 76	0.800 73	0.766 42	0.733 73	9
10	0.951 35	0.905 29	0.861 67	0.820 35	0.781 20	0.744 09	0.708 92	10
11	0.946 61	0.896 32	0.848 93	0.804 26	0.762 14	0.722 42	0.684 95	11
12	0.941 91	0.887 45	0.836 39	0.788 49	0.743 56	0.701 38	0.661 78	12
13	0.937 22	0.878 66	0.824 03	0.773 03	0.725 42	0.680 95	0.639 40	13
14	0.932 56	0.869 96	0.811 85	0.757 88	0.707 73	0.661 12	0.617 78	14
15	0.927 92	0.861 35	0.799 85	0.743 01	0.690 47	0.641 86	0.596 89	15
16	0.923 30	0.852 82	0.788 03	0.728 45	0.673 62	0.623 17	0.576 71	16
17	0.918 71	0.844 38	0.776 39	0.714 16	0.657 20	0.605 02	0.557 20	17
18	0.914 14	0.836 02	0.764 91	0.700 16	0.641 17	0.587 39	0.538 36	18
19	0.909 59	0.827 74	0.753 61	0.686 43	0.625 53	0.570 29	0.520 16	19
20	0.905 06	0.819 54	0.742 47	0.672 97	0.610 27	0.553 68	0.502 57	20
21	0.900 56	0.811 43	0.731 50	0.659 78	0.595 39	0.537 55	0.485 57	21
22	0.896 08	0.803 40	0.720 69	0.646 84	0.580 86	0.521 89	0.469 15	22
23	0.891 62	0.795 44	0.710 04	0.634 16	0.566 70	0.506 69	0.453 29	23
24	0.887 19	0.787 57	0.699 54	0.621 72	0.552 88	0.491 93	0.437 96	24
25	0.882 77	0.779 77	0.689 21	0.609 53	0.539 39	0.477 61	0.423 15	25
26	0.878 38	0.772 05	0.679 02	0.597 58	0.526 23	0.463 69	0.408 84	26
27	0.874 01	0.764 40	0.668 99	0.585 86	0.513 40	0.450 19	0.395 01	27
28	0.869 66	0.756 84	0.659 10	0.574 37	0.500 88	0.437 08	0.381 65	28
29	0.865 33	0.749 34	0.649 36	0.563 11	0.488 66	0.424 35	0.368 75	29
30	0.861 03	0.741 92	0.639 76	0.552 07	0.476 74	0.411 99	0.356 28	30
31	0.856 75	0.734 58	0.630 31	0.541 25	0.465 11	0.399 99	0.344 23	31
32	0.852 48	0.727 30	0.620 99	0.530 63	0.453 77	0.388 34	0.332 59	32
33	0.848 24	0.720 10	0.611 82	0.520 23	0.442 70	0.377 03	0.321 34	33
34	0.844 02	0.712 97	0.602 77	0.510 03	0.431 91	0.366 04	0.310 48	34
35	0.839 82	0.705 91	0.593 87	0.500 03	0.421 37	0.355 38	0.299 98	35
36	0.835 64	0.698 93	0.585 09	0.490 22	0.411 09	0.345 03	0.289 83	36
37	0.831 49	0.692 00	0.576 44	0.480 61	0.401 07	0.334 98	0.280 03	37
38	0.827 35	0.685 15	0.567 92	0.471 19	0.391 28	0.325 23	0.270 56	38
39	0.823 23	0.678 37	0.559 53	0.461 95	0.381 74	0.315 75	0.261 41	39
40	0.819 14	0.671 65	0.551 26	0.452 89	0.372 43	0.306 56	0.252 57	40
41	0.815 06	0.665 00	0.543 12	0.444 01	0.363 35	0.297 63	0.244 03	41
42	0.811 01	0.658 42	0.535 09	0.435 30	0.354 48	0.288 96	0.235 78	42
43	0.806 97	0.651 90	0.527 18	0.426 77	0.345 84	0.280 54	0.227 81	43
44	0.802 96	0.645 45	0.519 39	0.418 40	0.337 40	0.272 37	0.220 10	44
45	0.798 96	0.639 05	0.511 71	0.410 20	0.329 17	0.264 44	0.212 66	45
46	0.794 99	0.632 73	0.504 15	0.402 15	0.321 15	0.256 74	0.205 47	46
47	0.791 03	0.626 46	0.496 70	0.394 27	0.313 31	0.249 26	0.198 52	47
48	0.787 10	0.620 26	0.489 36	0.386 54	0.305 67	0.242 00	0.191 81	48
49	0.783 18	0.614 12	0.482 13	0.378 96	0.298 22	0.234 95	0.185 32	49
50	0.779 29	0.608 04	0.475 00	0.371 53	0.290 94	0.228 11	0.179 05	50
n	$\frac{1}{2}\%$	1%	$1\frac{1}{2}\%$	2%	$2\frac{1}{2}\%$	3%	$3\frac{1}{2}\%$	n

Present Value of 1

$$\frac{1}{(1+i)^n}$$

n	4%	5%	6%	7%	8%	9%	10%	n
1	0.961 54	0.952 38	0.943 40	0.934 58	0.925 93	0.917 43	0.909 09	1
2	0.924 56	0.907 03	0.890 00	0.873 44	0.857 34	0.841 68	0.826 45	2
3	0.889 00	0.863 84	0.839 62	0.816 30	0.793 83	0.772 18	0.751 31	3
4	0.854 80	0.822 70	0.792 09	0.762 90	0.735 03	0.708 43	0.683 01	4
5	0.821 93	0.783 53	0.747 26	0.712 99	0.680 58	0.649 93	0.620 92	5
6	0.790 31	0.746 22	0.704 96	0.666 34	0.630 17	0.596 27	0.564 47	6
7	0.759 92	0.710 68	0.665 06	0.622 75	0.583 49	0.547 03	0.513 16	7
8	0.730 69	0.676 84	0.627 41	0.582 01	0.540 27	0.501 87	0.466 51	8
9	0.702 59	0.644 61	0.591 90	0.543 93	0.500 25	0.460 43	0.424 10	9
10	0.675 56	0.613 91	0.558 39	0.508 35	0.463 19	0.422 41	0.385 54	10
11	0.649 58	0.584 68	0.526 79	0.475 09	0.428 88	0.387 53	0.350 49	11
12	0.624 60	0.556 84	0.496 97	0.444 01	0.397 11	0.355 53	0.318 63	12
13	0.600 57	0.530 32	0.468 84	0.414 96	0.367 70	0.326 18	0.289 66	13
14	0.577 48	0.505 07	0.442 30	0.387 82	0.340 46	0.299 25	0.263 33	14
15	0.555 26	0.481 02	0.417 27	0.362 45	0.315 24	0.274 54	0.239 39	15
16	0.533 91	0.458 11	0.393 65	0.338 73	0.291 89	0.251 87	0.217 63	16
17	0.513 37	0.436 30	0.371 36	0.316 57	0.270 27	0.231 07	0.197 84	17
18	0.493 63	0.415 52	0.350 34	0.295 86	0.250 25	0.211 99	0.179 86	18
19	0.474 64	0.395 73	0.330 51	0.276 51	0.231 71	0.194 49	0.163 51	19
20	0.456 39	0.376 89	0.311 80	0.258 42	0.214 55	0.178 43	0.148 64	20
21	0.438 83	0.358 94	0.294 16	0.241 51	0.198 66	0.163 70	0.135 13	21
22	0.421 96	0.341 85	0.277 51	0.225 71	0.183 94	0.150 18	0.122 85	22
23	0.405 73	0.325 57	0.261 80	0.210 95	0.170 32	0.137 78	0.111 68	23
24	0.390 12	0.310 07	0.246 98	0.197 15	0.157 70	0.126 40	0.101 53	24
25	0.375 12	0.295 30	0.233 00	0.184 25	0.146 02	0.115 97	0.092 30	25
26	0.360 69	0.281 24	0.219 81	0.172 20	0.135 20	0.106 39	0.083 90	26
27	0.346 82	0.267 85	0.207 37	0.160 93	0.125 19	0.097 61	0.076 28	27
28	0.333 48	0.255 09	0.195 63	0.150 40	0.115 91	0.089 55	0.069 34	28
29	0.320 65	0.242 95	0.184 56	0.140 56	0.107 33	0.082 15	0.063 04	29
30	0.308 32	0.231 38	0.174 11	0.131 37	0.099 38	0.075 37	0.057 31	30
31	0.296 46	0.220 36	0.164 26	0.122 77	0.092 02	0.069 15	0.052 10	31
32	0.285 06	0.209 87	0.154 96	0.114 74	0.085 20	0.063 44	0.047 36	32
33	0.274 09	0.199 87	0.146 19	0.107 23	0.078 89	0.058 20	0.043 06	33
34	0.263 55	0.190 35	0.137 91	0.100 22	0.073 05	0.053 39	0.039 14	34
35	0.253 42	0.181 29	0.130 11	0.093 66	0.067 63	0.048 99	0.035 58	35
36	0.243 67	0.172 66	0.122 74	0.087 54	0.062 62	0.044 94	0.032 35	36
37	0.234 30	0.164 44	0.115 79	0.081 81	0.057 99	0.041 23	0.029 41	37
38	0.225 29	0.156 61	0.109 24	0.076 46	0.053 69	0.037 83	0.026 73	38
39	0.216 62	0.149 15	0.103 06	0.071 46	0.049 71	0.034 70	0.024 30	39
40	0.208 29	0.142 05	0.097 22	0.066 78	0.046 03	0.031 84	0.022 09	40
41	0.200 28	0.135 28	0.091 72	0.062 41	0.042 62	0.029 21	0.020 09	41
42	0.192 57	0.128 84	0.086 53	0.058 33	0.039 46	0.026 80	0.018 26	42
43	0.185 17	0.122 70	0.081 63	0.054 51	0.036 54	0.024 58	0.016 60	43
44	0.178 05	0.116 86	0.077 01	0.050 95	0.033 83	0.022 55	0.015 09	44
45	0.171 20	0.111 30	0.072 65	0.047 61	0.031 33	0.020 69	0.013 72	45
46	0.164 61	0.106 00	0.068 54	0.044 50	0.029 01	0.018 98	0.012 47	46
47	0.158 28	0.100 95	0.064 66	0.041 59	0.026 86	0.017 42	0.011 34	47
48	0.152 19	0.096 14	0.061 00	0.038 87	0.024 87	0.015 98	0.010 31	48
49	0.146 34	0.091 56	0.057 55	0.036 32	0.023 02	0.014 66	0.009 37	49
50	0.140 71	0.087 20	0.054 29	0.033 94	0.021 32	0.013 45	0.008 52	50
n	4%	5%	6%	7%	8%	9%	10%	n

Amount of an Annuity

$$S_{\overline{n}|}\, i = \frac{(1 + i)^n - 1}{i}$$

n	½%	1%	1½%	2%	2½%	3%	3½%	n
1	1.000 00	1.000 00	1.000 00	1.000 00	1.000 00	1.000 00	1.000 00	1
2	2.005 00	2.010 00	2.015 00	2.020 00	2.025 00	2.030 00	2.035 00	2
3	3.015 03	3.030 10	3.045 23	3.060 40	3.075 63	3.090 90	3.106 23	3
4	4.030 10	4.060 40	4.090 90	4.121 61	4.152 52	4.183 63	4.214 94	4
5	5.050 25	5.101 01	5.152 27	5.204 04	5.256 33	5.309 14	5.362 47	5
6	6.075 50	6.152 02	6.229 55	6.308 12	6.387 74	6.468 41	6.550 15	6
7	7.105 88	7.213 54	7.322 99	7.434 28	7.547 43	7.662 46	7.779 48	7
8	8.141 41	8.285 67	8.432 84	8.582 97	8.736 12	8.892 37	9.051 69	8
9	9.182 12	9.368 53	9.559 33	9.754 63	9.954 52	10.159 11	10.368 50	9
10	10.228 03	10.462 21	10.702 72	10.949 72	11.203 38	11.463 88	11.731 39	10
11	11.279 17	11.566 83	11.863 26	12.168 72	12.483 47	12.807 80	13.141 99	11
12	12.335 56	12.682 50	13.041 21	13.412 09	13.795 55	14.192 03	14.601 96	12
13	13.397 24	13.809 33	14.236 83	14.680 33	15.140 44	15.617 79	16.113 03	13
14	14.464 23	14.947 42	15.450 38	15.973 94	16.518 95	17.086 32	17.676 98	14
15	15.536 55	16.096 90	16.682 14	17.293 42	17.931 93	18.598 91	19.295 68	15
16	16.614 23	17.257 86	17.932 37	18.639 29	19.380 22	20.156 88	20.971 03	16
17	17.697 30	18.430 44	19.201 36	20.012 07	20.864 73	21.761 59	22.705 02	17
18	18.785 79	19.614 75	20.489 38	21.412 31	22.386 35	23.414 44	24.499 69	18
19	19.879 72	20.810 90	21.796 72	22.840 56	23.946 01	25.116 87	26.357 18	19
20	20.979 12	22.019 00	23.123 67	24.297 37	25.544 66	26.870 37	28.279 68	20
21	22.084 01	23.239 19	24.470 52	25.783 32	27.183 27	28.676 49	30.269 47	21
22	23.194 43	24.471 59	25.837 58	27.298 98	28.862 86	30.536 78	32.328 90	22
23	24.310 40	25.716 30	27.225 14	28.844 96	30.584 43	32.452 88	34.460 41	23
24	25.431 96	26.973 46	28.633 52	30.421 86	32.349 04	34.426 47	36.666 53	24
25	26.559 12	28.243 20	30.063 02	32.030 30	34.157 76	36.459 26	38.949 86	25
26	27.691 91	29.525 63	31.513 97	33.670 91	36.011 71	38.553 04	41.313 10	26
27	28.830 37	30.820 89	32.986 68	35.344 32	37.912 00	40.709 63	43.759 06	27
28	29.974 52	32.129 10	34.481 48	37.051 21	39.859 80	42.930 92	46.290 63	28
29	31.124 39	33.450 39	35.998 70	38.792 23	41.856 30	45.218 85	48.910 80	29
30	32.280 02	34.784 89	37.538 68	40.568 08	43.902 70	47.575 46	51.622 68	30
31	33.441 42	36.132 74	39.101 76	42.379 44	46.000 27	50.002 68	54.429 47	31
32	34.608 62	37.494 08	40.688 29	44.227 03	48.150 28	52.502 76	57.334 50	32
33	35.781 67	38.869 01	42.298 61	46.111 57	50.354 03	55.077 84	60.341 21	33
34	36.960 58	40.257 70	43.933 09	48.033 80	52.612 89	57.730 18	63.453 15	34
35	38.145 38	41.660 28	45.592 09	49.994 48	54.928 21	60.462 08	66.674 01	35
36	39.336 11	43.076 88	47.275 97	51.994 37	57.301 41	63.275 94	70.007 60	36
37	40.532 79	44.507 65	48.985 11	54.034 25	59.733 95	66.174 22	73.457 87	37
38	41.735 45	45.952 72	50.719 89	56.114 94	62.227 30	69.159 45	77.028 89	38
39	42.944 13	47.412 25	52.480 68	58.237 24	64.782 98	72.234 23	80.724 91	39
40	44.158 85	48.886 37	54.267 89	60.401 98	67.402 55	75.401 26	84.550 28	40
41	45.379 64	50.375 24	56.081 91	62.610 02	70.087 62	78.663 30	88.509 54	41
42	46.606 54	51.878 99	57.923 14	64.862 22	72.839 81	82.023 20	92.607 37	42
43	47.839 57	53.397 78	59.791 99	67.159 47	75.660 80	85.483 89	96.848 63	43
44	49.078 77	54.931 76	61.688 87	69.502 66	78.552 32	89.048 41	101.238 31	44
45	50.324 16	56.481 07	63.614 20	71.892 71	81.516 13	92.719 86	105.781 62	45
46	51.575 79	58.045 89	65.568 41	74.330 56	84.554 03	96.501 46	110.484 03	46
47	52.833 66	59.626 34	67.551 94	76.817 18	87.667 89	100.396 50	115.350 97	47
48	54.097 83	61.222 61	69.565 22	79.353 52	90.859 58	104.408 40	120.388 26	48
49	55.368 32	62.834 83	71.608 70	81.940 59	94.131 07	108.540 65	125.601 85	49
50	56.645 16	64.463 18	73.682 83	84.579 40	97.484 35	112.796 87	130.997 91	50
n	½%	1%	1½%	2%	2½%	3%	3½%	n

Amount of an Annuity

$$s_{\overline{n}|\,i} = \frac{(1 + i)^n - 1}{i}$$

n	4%	5%	6%	7%	8%	9%	10%	n
1	1.000 00	1.000 00	1.000 00	1.000 00	1.000 00	1.000 00	1.000 00	1
2	2.040 00	2.050 00	2.060 00	2.070 00	2.080 00	2.090 00	2.100 00	2
3	3.121 60	3.152 50	3.183 60	3.214 90	3.246 40	3.278 10	3.310 00	3
4	4.246 46	4.310 13	4.374 62	4.439 94	4.506 11	4.573 13	4.641 00	4
5	5.416 32	5.525 63	5.637 09	5.750 74	5.866 60	5.984 71	6.105 10	5
6	6.632 98	6.801 91	6.975 32	7.153 29	7.335 93	7.523 33	7.715 61	6
7	7.898 29	8.142 01	8.393 84	8.654 02	8.922 80	9.200 43	9.487 17	7
8	9.214 23	9.549 11	9.897 47	10.259 80	10.636 63	11.028 47	11.435 89	8
9	10.582 80	11.026 56	11.491 32	11.977 99	12.487 56	13.021 04	13.579 48	9
10	12.006 11	12.577 89	13.180 79	13.816 45	14.486 56	15.192 93	15.937 42	10
11	13.486 35	14.206 79	14.971 64	15.783 60	16.645 49	17.560 29	18.531 17	11
12	15.025 81	15.917 13	16.869 94	17.888 45	18.977 13	20.140 72	21.384 28	12
13	16.626 84	17.712 98	18.882 14	20.140 64	21.495 30	22.953 38	24.522 71	13
14	18.291 91	19.598 63	21.015 07	22.550 49	24.214 92	26.019 19	27.974 98	14
15	20.023 59	21.578 56	23.275 97	25.129 02	27.152 11	29.360 92	31.772 48	15
16	21.824 53	23.657 49	25.672 53	27.888 05	30.324 28	33.003 30	35.949 73	16
17	23.697 51	25.840 37	28.212 88	30.840 22	33.750 23	36.973 70	40.544 70	17
18	25.645 41	28.132 38	30.905 65	33.999 03	37.450 24	41.301 34	45.599 17	18
19	27.671 23	30.539 00	33.759 99	37.378 96	41.446 26	46.018 46	51.159 09	19
20	29.778 08	33.065 95	36.785 59	40.995 49	45.761 96	51.160 12	57.275 00	20
21	31.969 20	35.719 25	39.992 73	44.865 18	50.422 92	56.764 53	64.002 50	21
22	34.247 97	38.505 21	43.392 29	49.005 74	55.456 76	62.873 34	71.402 75	22
23	36.617 89	41.430 48	46.995 83	53.436 14	60.893 30	69.531 94	79.543 02	23
24	39.082 60	44.502 00	50.815 58	58.176 67	66.764 76	76.789 81	88.497 33	24
25	41.645 91	47.727 10	54.864 51	63.249 04	73.105 94	84.700 90	98.347 06	25
26	44.311 74	51.113 45	59.156 38	68.676 47	79.954 42	93.323 98	109.181 77	26
27	47.084 21	54.669 13	63.705 77	74.483 82	87.350 77	102.723 13	121.099 94	27
28	49.967 58	58.402 58	68.528 11	80.697 69	95.338 83	112.968 22	134.209 94	28
29	52.966 29	62.322 71	73.639 80	87.346 53	103.965 94	124.135 36	148.630 93	29
30	56.084 94	66.438 85	79.058 19	94.460 79	113.283 21	136.307 54	164.494 02	30
31	59.328 34	70.760 79	84.801 68	102.073 04	123.345 87	149.575 22	181.943 42	31
32	62.701 47	75.298 83	90.889 78	110.218 15	134.213 54	164.036 99	201.137 77	32
33	66.209 53	80.063 77	97.343 16	118.933 43	145.950 62	179.800 32	222.251 54	33
34	69.857 91	85.066 97	104.183 75	128.258 76	158.626 67	196.982 34	245.476 70	34
35	73.652 22	90.320 31	111.434 78	138.236 88	172.316 80	215.710 75	271.024 37	35
36	77.598 31	95.836 32	119.120 87	148.913 46	187.102 15	236.124 72	299.126 81	36
37	81.702 25	101.628 14	127.268 12	160.337 40	203.070 32	258.375 95	330.039 49	37
38	85.970 34	107.709 55	135.904 21	172.561 02	220.315 95	282.629 78	364.043 43	38
39	90.409 15	114.095 02	145.058 46	185.640 29	238.941 22	309.066 46	401.447 78	39
40	95.025 52	120.799 77	154.761 97	199.635 11	259.056 52	337.882 45	442.592 56	40
41	99.826 54	127.839 76	165.047 68	214.609 57	280.781 04	369.291 87	487.851 81	41
42	104.819 60	135.231 75	175.950 54	230.632 24	304.243 52	403.528 13	537.636 99	42
43	110.012 38	142.993 37	187.507 58	247.776 50	329.583 01	440.845 66	592.400 69	43
44	115.412 88	151.143 01	199.758 03	266.120 85	356.949 65	481.521 77	652.640 76	44
45	121.029 39	159.700 16	212.743 51	285.749 31	386.505 62	525.858 73	718.904 84	45
46	126.870 57	168.685 16	226.508 12	306.751 76	418.426 07	574.186 02	791.795 32	46
47	132.945 39	178.119 42	241.098 61	329.224 39	452.900 15	626.862 76	871.974 85	47
48	139.263 21	188.025 39	256.564 53	353.270 09	490.132 16	684.280 41	960.172 34	48
49	145.833 73	198.426 66	272.958 40	378.999 00	530.342 74	746.865 65	1057.189 57	49
50	152.667 08	209.348 00	290.335 90	406.528 93	573.770 16	815.083 56	1163.908 53	50
n	4%	5%	6%	7%	8%	9%	10%	n

The Annuity that Will Amount to 1

$$\frac{1}{S\overline{n}|\, i}$$

n	½%	1%	1½%	2%	2½%	3%	3½%	n
1	1.000 00	1.000 00	1.000 00	1.000 00	1.000 00	1.000 00	1.000 00	1
2	0.498 75	0.497 51	0.496 28	0.495 05	0.493 83	0.492 61	0.491 40	2
3	0.331 67	0.330 02	0.328 38	0.326 75	0.325 14	0.323 53	0.321 93	3
4	0.248 13	0.246 28	0.244 44	0.242 62	0.240 82	0.239 03	0.237 25	4
5	0.198 01	0.196 04	0.194 09	0.192 16	0.190 25	0.188 35	0.186 48	5
6	0.164 60	0.162 55	0.160 53	0.158 53	0.156 55	0.154 60	0.152 67	6
7	0.140 73	0.138 63	0.136 56	0.134 51	0.132 50	0.130 51	0.128 54	7
8	0.122 83	0.120 69	0.118 58	0.116 51	0.114 47	0.112 46	0.110 48	8
9	0.108 91	0.106 74	0.104 61	0.102 52	0.100 46	0.098 43	0.096 45	9
10	0.097 77	0.095 58	0.093 43	0.091 33	0.089 26	0.087 23	0.085 24	10
11	0.088 66	0.086 45	0.084 29	0.082 18	0.080 11	0.078 08	0.076 09	11
12	0.081 07	0.078 85	0.076 68	0.074 56	0.072 49	0.070 46	0.068 48	12
13	0.074 64	0.072 41	0.070 24	0.068 12	0.066 05	0.064 03	0.062 06	13
14	0.069 14	0.066 90	0.064 72	0.062 60	0.060 54	0.058 53	0.056 57	14
15	0.064 36	0.062 12	0.059 94	0.057 83	0.055 77	0.053 77	0.051 83	15
16	0.060 19	0.057 94	0.055 77	0.053 65	0.051 60	0.049 61	0.047 68	16
17	0.056 51	0.054 26	0.052 08	0.049 97	0.047 93	0.045 95	0.044 04	17
18	0.053 23	0.050 98	0.048 81	0.046 70	0.044 67	0.042 71	0.040 82	18
19	0.050 30	0.048 05	0.045 88	0.043 78	0.041 76	0.039 81	0.037 94	19
20	0.047 67	0.045 42	0.043 25	0.041 16	0.039 15	0.037 22	0.035 36	20
21	0.045 28	0.043 03	0.040 87	0.038 78	0.036 79	0.034 87	0.033 04	21
22	0.043 11	0.040 86	0.038 70	0.036 63	0.034 65	0.032 75	0.030 93	22
23	0.041 13	0.038 89	0.036 73	0.034 67	0.032 70	0.030 81	0.029 02	23
24	0.039 32	0.037 07	0.034 92	0.032 87	0.030 91	0.029 05	0.027 27	24
25	0.037 65	0.035 41	0.033 26	0.031 22	0.029 28	0.027 43	0.025 67	25
26	0.036 11	0.033 87	0.031 73	0.029 70	0.027 77	0.025 94	0.024 21	26
27	0.034 69	0.032 45	0.030 32	0.028 29	0.026 38	0.024 56	0.022 85	27
28	0.033 36	0.031 11	0.029 00	0.026 99	0.025 09	0.023 29	0.021 60	28
29	0.032 13	0.029 90	0.027 78	0.025 78	0.023 89	0.022 11	0.020 45	29
30	0.030 98	0.028 75	0.026 64	0.024 65	0.022 78	0.021 02	0.019 37	30
31	0.029 99	0.027 68	0.025 57	0.023 60	0.021 74	0.020 00	0.018 37	31
32	0.028 88	0.026 66	0.024 58	0.022 61	0.020 77	0.019 05	0.017 44	32
33	0.027 95	0.025 73	0.023 64	0.021 69	0.019 86	0.018 16	0.016 57	33
34	0.027 06	0.024 84	0.022 76	0.020 82	0.019 01	0.017 32	0.015 76	34
35	0.026 22	0.024 00	0.021 93	0.020 00	0.018 21	0.016 54	0.015 00	35
36	0.025 42	0.023 21	0.021 15	0.019 23	0.017 45	0.015 80	0.014 28	36
37	0.024 67	0.022 47	0.020 41	0.018 51	0.016 74	0.015 11	0.013 61	37
38	0.023 96	0.021 76	0.019 72	0.017 82	0.016 07	0.014 46	0.012 98	38
39	0.023 29	0.021 09	0.019 05	0.017 17	0.015 44	0.013 84	0.012 39	39
40	0.022 65	0.020 46	0.018 43	0.016 56	0.014 84	0.013 26	0.011 83	40
41	0.022 04	0.019 85	0.017 83	0.015 97	0.014 27	0.012 71	0.011 30	41
42	0.021 46	0.019 28	0.017 26	0.015 42	0.013 73	0.012 19	0.010 80	42
43	0.020 90	0.018 73	0.016 72	0.014 89	0.013 22	0.011 70	0.010 33	43
44	0.020 38	0.018 20	0.016 21	0.014 39	0.012 73	0.011 23	0.009 88	44
45	0.019 87	0.017 71	0.015 72	0.013 91	0.012 27	0.010 79	0.009 45	45
46	0.019 39	0.017 23	0.015 25	0.013 45	0.011 83	0.010 36	0.009 05	46
47	0.018 93	0.016 77	0.014 80	0.013 02	0.011 41	0.009 96	0.008 67	47
48	0.018 49	0.016 33	0.014 38	0.012 60	0.011 01	0.009 58	0.008 31	48
49	0.018 06	0.015 91	0.013 96	0.012 20	0.010 62	0.009 21	0.007 96	49
50	0.017 65	0.015 51	0.013 57	0.011 82	0.010 26	0.008 87	0.007 63	50
n	½%	1%	1½%	2%	2½%	3%	3½%	n

The Annuity that Will Amount to 1

$$\frac{1}{s_{\overline{n}|}\,i}$$

n	4%	5%	6%	7%	8%	9%	10%	n
1	1.000 00	1.000 00	1.000 00	1.000 00	1.000 00	1.000 00	1.000 00	1
2	0.490 20	0.487 80	0.485 44	0.483 09	0.480 77	0.478 47	0.476 19	2
3	0.320 35	0.317 21	0.314 11	0.311 05	0.308 03	0.305 05	0.302 11	3
4	0.235 49	0.232 01	0.228 59	0.225 23	0.221 92	0.218 67	0.215 47	4
5	0.184 63	0.180 97	0.177 40	0.173 89	0.170 46	0.167 09	0.163 80	5
6	0.150 76	0.147 02	0.143 36	0.139 80	0.136 32	0.132 92	0.129 61	6
7	0.126 61	0.122 82	0.119 14	0.115 55	0.112 07	0.108 69	0.105 41	7
8	0.108 53	0.104 72	0.101 04	0.097 47	0.094 01	0.090 67	0.087 44	8
9	0.094 49	0.090 69	0.087 02	0.083 49	0.080 08	0.076 80	0.073 64	9
10	0.083 29	0.079 50	0.075 87	0.072 38	0.069 03	0.065 82	0.062 75	10
11	0.074 15	0.070 39	0.066 79	0.063 36	0.060 08	0.056 95	0.053 96	11
12	0.066 55	0.062 83	0.059 28	0.055 90	0.052 70	0.049 65	0.046 76	12
13	0.060 14	0.056 46	0.052 96	0.049 65	0.046 52	0.043 57	0.040 78	13
14	0.054 67	0.051 02	0.047 58	0.044 34	0.041 30	0.038 43	0.035 75	14
15	0.049 94	0.046 34	0.042 96	0.039 79	0.036 83	0.034 06	0.031 47	15
16	0.015 82	0.042 27	0.038 95	0.035 86	0.032 98	0.030 30	0.027 82	16
17	0.042 20	0.038 70	0.035 44	0.032 43	0.029 63	0.027 05	0.024 66	17
18	0.038 99	0.035 55	0.032 36	0.029 41	0.026 70	0.024 21	0.021 93	18
19	0.036 14	0.032 75	0.029 62	0.026 75	0.024 13	0.021 73	0.019 55	19
20	0.033 58	0.030 24	0.027 18	0.024 39	0.021 85	0.019 55	0.017 46	20
21	0.031 28	0.028 00	0.025 00	0.022 29	0.019 83	0.017 62	0.015 62	21
22	0.029 20	0.025 97	0.023 05	0.020 41	0.018 03	0.015 91	0.014 01	22
23	0.027 31	0.024 17	0.021 28	0.018 71	0.016 42	0.014 38	0.012 57	23
24	0.025 59	0.022 47	0.019 68	0.017 19	0.014 98	0.013 02	0.011 30	24
25	0.024 01	0.020 95	0.018 23	0.015 81	0.013 68	0.011 81	0.010 17	25
26	0.022 57	0.019 56	0.016 90	0.014 56	0.012 51	0.010 72	0.009 16	26
27	0.021 24	0.018 29	0.015 70	0.013 43	0.011 45	0.009 73	0.008 26	27
28	0.020 01	0.017 12	0.014 59	0.012 39	0.010 49	0.008 85	0.007 45	28
29	0.018 88	0.016 05	0.013 58	0.011 45	0.009 62	0.008 06	0.006 73	29
30	0.017 83	0.015 05	0.012 65	0.010 59	0.008 83	0.007 34	0.006 08	30
31	0.016 86	0.014 13	0.011 79	0.009 80	0.008 11	0.006 69	0.005 50	31
32	0.015 95	0.013 28	0.011 00	0.009 07	0.007 45	0.006 10	0.004 97	32
33	0.015 10	0.012 49	0.010 27	0.008 41	0.006 85	0.005 56	0.004 50	33
34	0.014 31	0.011 76	0.009 60	0.007 80	0.006 30	0.005 08	0.004 07	34
35	0.013 58	0.011 07	0.008 97	0.007 23	0.005 80	0.004 64	0.003 69	35
36	0.012 89	0.010 43	0.008 39	0.006 72	0.005 34	0.004 24	0.003 34	36
37	0.012 24	0.009 84	0.007 86	0.006 24	0.004 92	0.003 87	0.003 03	37
38	0.011 63	0.009 28	0.007 36	0.005 80	0.004 54	0.003 54	0.002 75	38
39	0.011 06	0.008 76	0.006 89	0.005 39	0.004 19	0.003 24	0.002 49	39
40	0.010 52	0.008 28	0.006 46	0.005 01	0.003 86	0.002 96	0.002 26	40
41	0.010 02	0.007 82	0.006 06	0.004 66	0.003 56	0.002 71	0.002 05	41
42	0.009 54	0.007 39	0.005 68	0.004 34	0.003 29	0.002 48	0.001 86	42
43	0.009 09	0.006 99	0.005 33	0.004 04	0.003 03	0.002 27	0.001 69	43
44	0.008 66	0.006 62	0.005 01	0.003 76	0.002 80	0.002 08	0.001 53	44
45	0.008 26	0.006 26	0.004 70	0.003 50	0.002 59	0.001 90	0.001 39	45
46	0.007 88	0.005 93	0.004 41	0.003 26	0.002 39	0.001 74	0.001 26	46
47	0.007 52	0.005 61	0.004 15	0.003 04	0.002 21	0.001 60	0.001 15	47
48	0.007 18	0.005 32	0.003 90	0.002 83	0.002 04	0.001 46	0.001 04	48
49	0.006 86	0.005 04	0.003 66	0.002 64	0.001 89	0.001 34	0.000 95	49
50	0.006 55	0.004 78	0.003 44	0.002 46	0.001 74	0.001 23	0.000 86	50
n	4%	5%	6%	7%	8%	9%	10%	n

Present Value of an Annuity

$$a_{\overline{n}|\,i} = \frac{1 - (1 + i)^{-n}}{i}$$

n	$\frac{1}{2}\%$	1%	$1\frac{1}{2}\%$	2%	$2\frac{1}{2}\%$	3%	$3\frac{1}{2}\%$	n
1	0.995 02	0.990 10	0.985 22	0.980 39	0.975 61	0.970 87	0.966 18	1
2	1.985 10	1.970 46	1.955 88	1.941 56	1.927 42	1.913 47	1.899 69	2
3	2.970 25	2.940 99	2.912 20	2.883 88	2.856 02	2.828 61	2.801 64	3
4	3.950 50	3.901 97	3.854 38	3.807 73	3.761 97	3.717 10	3.673 08	4
5	4.925 87	4.853 43	4.782 65	4.713 46	4.645 83	4.579 71	4.515 05	5
6	5.896 38	5.795 48	5.697 19	5.601 43	5.508 13	5.417 19	5.328 55	6
7	6.862 07	6.728 19	6.598 21	6.471 99	6.349 39	6.230 28	6.114 54	7
8	7.822 96	7.651 68	7.485 93	7.325 48	7.170 14	7.019 69	6.873 96	8
9	8.779 06	8.566 02	8.360 52	8.162 24	7.970 87	7.786 11	7.607 69	9
10	9.730 41	9.471 30	9.222 18	8.982 59	8.752 06	8.530 20	8.316 61	10
11	10.677 03	10.367 63	10.071 12	9.786 85	9.514 20	9.252 66	9.001 55	11
12	11.618 93	11.255 08	10.907 51	10.575 34	10.257 76	9.954 00	9.663 33	12
13	12.556 15	12.133 74	11.731 53	11.348 37	10.983 18	10.634 96	10.302 74	13
14	13.488 71	13.003 70	12.543 38	12.106 25	11.690 91	11.296 07	10.920 52	14
15	14.416 62	13.865 05	13.343 23	12.849 26	12.381 38	11.937 94	11.517 41	15
16	15.339 93	14.717 87	14.131 26	13.577 71	13.055 00	12.561 10	12.094 12	16
17	16.258 63	15.562 25	14.907 65	14.291 87	13.712 20	13.166 12	12.651 32	17
18	17.172 77	16.398 27	15.672 56	14.992 03	14.353 36	13.753 51	13.189 68	18
19	18.082 36	17.226 01	16.426 17	15.678 46	14.978 89	14.323 80	13.709 84	19
20	18.987 42	18.045 55	17.168 64	16.351 43	15.589 16	14.877 47	14.212 40	20
21	19.887 98	18.856 98	17.900 14	17.011 21	16.184 55	15.415 02	14.697 97	21
22	20.784 06	19.660 38	18.620 82	17.658 05	16.765 41	15.936 92	15.167 12	22
23	21.675 68	20.455 82	19.330 86	18.292 20	17.332 11	16.443 61	15.620 41	23
24	22.562 87	21.243 39	20.030 41	18.913 93	17.884 99	16.935 54	16.058 37	24
25	23.445 64	22.023 16	20.719 61	19.523 46	18.424 38	17.413 15	16.481 51	25
26	24.324 02	22.795 20	21.398 63	20.121 04	18.950 61	17.876 84	16.890 35	26
27	25.198 03	23.559 61	22.067 62	20.706 90	19.464 01	18.327 03	17.285 36	27
28	26.067 69	24.316 44	22.726 72	21.281 27	19.964 89	18.764 11	17.667 02	28
29	26.933 02	25.065 79	23.376 08	21.844 38	20.453 50	19.188 45	18.035 77	29
30	27.794 05	25.807 71	24.015 84	22.396 46	20.930 23	19.600 44	18.392 05	30
31	28.650 80	26.542 29	24.646 15	22.937 70	21.395 40	20.000 43	18.736 28	31
32	29.503 28	27.269 59	25.267 14	23.468 34	21.849 18	20.388 77	19.068 87	32
33	30.351 53	27.989 69	25.878 95	23.988 56	22.291 81	20.765 79	19.390 21	33
34	31.195 55	28.702 67	26.481 73	24.498 59	22.723 79	21.131 84	19.700 68	34
35	32.035 37	29.408 58	27.075 59	24.998 62	23.145 16	21.487 22	20.000 66	35
36	32.871 02	30.107 51	27.660 68	25.488 84	23.556 25	21.832 25	20.290 49	36
37	33.702 50	30.799 51	28.237 13	25.969 45	23.957 32	22.167 24	20.570 53	37
38	34.529 85	31.484 66	28.805 05	26.440 64	24.348 60	22.492 46	20.841 09	38
39	35.353 09	32.163 03	29.364 58	26.902 59	24.730 34	22.808 22	21.102 50	39
40	36.172 23	32.834 69	29.915 85	27.355 48	25.102 78	23.114 77	21.355 07	40
41	36.987 29	33.499 69	30.458 96	27.799 49	25.466 12	23.412 40	21.599 10	41
42	37.798 00	34.158 11	30.994 05	28.234 79	25.820 61	23.701 36	21.834 88	42
43	38.605 27	34.810 01	31.521 23	28.661 56	26.166 45	23.981 90	22.062 69	43
44	39.408 23	35.455 45	32.040 62	29.079 96	26.503 85	24.254 27	22.282 79	44
45	40.207 20	36.094 51	32.552 34	29.490 16	26.833 02	24.518 71	22.495 45	45
46	41.002 19	36.727 24	33.056 49	29.892 31	27.154 17	24.775 45	22.700 92	46
47	41.793 22	37.353 70	33.553 19	30.286 58	27.467 48	25.024 71	22.899 44	47
48	42.580 32	37.973 96	34.042 55	30.673 12	27.773 15	25.266 71	23.091 24	48
49	43.363 50	38.588 08	34.524 68	31.052 08	28.071 37	25.501 66	23.276 56	49
50	44.142 79	39.196 12	34.999 69	31.423 61	28.362 31	25.729 76	23.455 62	50
n	$\frac{1}{2}\%$	1%	$1\frac{1}{2}\%$	2%	$2\frac{1}{2}\%$	3%	$3\frac{1}{2}\%$	n

Present Value of an Annuity

$$a_{\overline{n}|\,i} = \frac{1 - (1 + i)^{-n}}{i}$$

n	4%	5%	6%	7%	8%	9%	10%	n
1	0.961 54	0.952 38	0.943 40	0.934 58	0.925 93	0.917 43	0.909 09	1
2	1.886 09	1.859 41	1.833 39	1.808 02	1.783 26	1.759 11	1.735 54	2
3	2.775 09	2.723 25	2.673 01	2.624 32	2.577 10	2.531 29	2.486 85	3
4	3.629 90	3.545 95	3.465 11	3.387 21	3.312 13	3.239 72	3.169 87	4
5	4.451 82	4.329 48	4.212 36	4.100 20	3.992 71	3.889 65	3.790 79	5
6	5.242 14	5.075 69	4.917 32	4.766 54	4.622 88	4.485 92	4.355 26	6
7	6.002 05	5.786 37	5.582 38	5.389 29	5.206 37	5.032 95	4.868 42	7
8	6.732 74	6.463 21	6.209 79	5.971 30	5.746 64	5.534 82	5.334 93	8
9	7.435 33	7.107 82	6.801 69	6.515 23	6.246 89	5.995 25	5.759 02	9
10	8.110 90	7.721 73	7.360 09	7.023 58	6.710 08	6.417 66	6.144 57	10
11	8.760 48	8.306 41	7.886 87	7.498 67	7.138 96	6.805 19	6.495 06	11
12	9.385 07	8.863 25	8.383 84	7.942 69	7.536 08	7.160 73	6.813 69	12
13	9.985 65	9.393 57	8.852 68	8.357 65	7.903 78	7.486 90	7.103 36	13
14	10.563 12	9.898 64	9.294 98	8.745 47	8.244 24	7.786 15	7.366 69	14
15	11.118 39	10.379 66	9.712 25	9.107 91	8.559 48	8.060 69	7.606 08	15
16	11.652 30	10.837 77	10.105 90	9.446 65	8.851 37	8.312 56	7.823 71	16
17	12.165 67	11.274 07	10.477 26	9.763 22	9.121 64	8.543 63	8.021 55	17
18	12.659 30	11.689 59	10.827 60	10.059 09	9.371 89	8.755 63	8.201 41	18
19	13.133 94	12.085 32	11.158 12	10.335 60	9.603 60	8.950 11	8.364 92	19
20	13.590 33	12.462 21	11.469 92	10.594 01	9.818 15	9.128 55	8.513 56	20
21	14.029 16	12.821 15	11.764 08	10.835 53	10.016 80	9.292 24	8.648 69	21
22	14.451 12	13.163 00	12.041 58	11.061 24	10.200 74	9.442 43	8.771 54	22
23	14.856 84	13.488 57	12.303 38	11.272 19	10.371 06	9.580 21	8.883 22	23
24	15.246 96	13.798 64	12.550 36	11.469 33	10.528 76	9.706 61	8.984 74	24
25	15.622 08	14.093 94	12.783 36	11.653 58	10.674 78	9.822 58	9.077 04	25
26	15.982 77	14.375 19	13.003 17	11.825 78	10.809 98	9.928 97	9.160 95	26
27	16.329 59	14.643 03	13.210 53	11.986 71	10.935 16	10.026 58	9.237 22	27
28	16.663 06	14.898 13	13.406 16	12.137 11	11.051 08	10.116 13	9.306 57	28
29	16.983 71	15.141 07	13.590 72	12.277 67	11.158 41	10.198 28	9.369 61	29
30	17.292 03	15.372 45	13.764 83	12.409 04	11.257 78	10.273 65	9.426 91	30
31	17.588 49	15.592 81	13.929 09	12.531 81	11.349 80	10.342 80	9.479 01	31
32	17.873 55	15.802 68	14.084 04	12.646 56	11.435 00	10.406 24	9.526 38	32
33	18.147 65	16.002 55	14.230 23	12.753 79	11.513 89	10.464 44	9.569 43	33
34	18.411 20	16.192 90	14.368 14	12.854 01	11.586 93	10.517 84	9.608 57	34
35	18.664 61	16.374 19	14.498 25	12.947 67	11.654 57	10.566 82	9.644 16	35
36	18.908 28	16.546 85	14.620 99	13.035 21	11.717 19	10.611 76	9.676 51	36
37	19.142 58	16.711 29	14.736 78	13.117 02	11.775 18	10.652 99	9.705 92	37
38	19.367 86	16.867 89	14.846 02	13.193 47	11.828 87	10.690 82	9.732 65	38
39	19.584 48	17.017 04	14.949 07	13.264 93	11.878 58	10.725 52	9.756 96	39
40	19.792 77	17.159 09	15.046 30	13.331 71	11.924 61	10.757 36	9.779 05	40
41	19.993 05	17.294 37	15.138 02	13.394 12	11.967 23	10.786 57	9.799 14	41
42	20.185 63	17.423 21	15.224 54	13.452 45	12.006 70	10.813 37	9.817 40	42
43	20.370 79	17.545 91	15.306 17	13.506 96	12.043 24	10.837 95	9.834 00	43
44	20.548 84	17.662 77	15.383 18	13.557 91	12.077 07	10.860 51	9.849 09	44
45	20.720 04	17.774 07	15.455 83	13.605 52	12.108 40	10.881 20	9.862 81	45
46	20.884 65	17.880 07	15.524 37	13.650 02	12.137 41	10.900 18	9.875 28	46
47	21.042 94	17.981 02	15.589 03	13.691 61	12.164 27	10.917 60	9.886 62	47
48	21.195 13	18.077 16	15.650 03	13.730 47	12.189 14	10.933 58	9.896 93	48
49	21.341 47	18.168 72	15.707 57	13.766 80	12.212 16	10.948 23	9.906 30	49
50	21.482 18	18.255 93	15.761 86	13.800 75	12.233 48	10.961 68	9.914 81	50
n	4%	5%	6%	7%	8%	9%	10%	n

The Annuity that 1 Will Buy

$$\frac{1}{a_{\overline{n}|\,i}} = (a_{\overline{n}|\,i})^{-1} = (s_{\overline{n}|\,i})^{-1} + i$$

n	$\frac{1}{2}\%$	1%	$1\frac{1}{2}\%$	2%	$2\frac{1}{2}\%$	3%	$3\frac{1}{2}\%$	n
1	1.005 00	1.010 00	1.015 00	1.020 00	1.025 00	1.030 00	1.035 00	1
2	0.503 75	0.507 51	0.511 28	0.515 05	0.518 83	0.522 61	0.526 40	2
3	0.336 67	0.340 02	0.343 38	0.346 75	0.350 14	0.353 53	0.356 93	3
4	0.253 13	0.256 28	0.259 44	0.262 62	0.265 82	0.269 03	0.272 25	4
5	0.203 01	0.206 04	0.209 09	0.212 16	0.215 25	0.218 35	0.221 48	5
6	0.169 60	0.172 55	0.175 53	0.178 53	0.181 55	0.184 60	0.187 67	6
7	0.145 73	0.148 63	0.151 56	0.154 51	0.157 50	0.160 51	0.163 54	7
8	0.127 83	0.130 69	0.133 58	0.136 51	0.139 47	0.142 46	0.145 48	8
9	0.113 91	0.116 74	0.119 61	0.122 52	0.125 46	0.128 43	0.131 45	9
10	0.102 77	0.105 58	0.108 43	0.111 33	0.114 26	0.117 23	0.120 24	10
11	0.093 66	0.096 45	0.099 29	0.102 18	0.105 10	0.108 08	0.111 09	11
12	0.086 07	0.088 85	0.091 68	0.094 56	0.097 49	0.100 46	0.103 48	12
13	0.079 64	0.082 41	0.085 24	0.088 12	0.091 05	0.094 03	0.097 06	13
14	0.074 14	0.076 90	0.079 72	0.082 60	0.085 54	0.088 53	0.091 57	14
15	0.069 36	0.072 12	0.074 94	0.077 83	0.080 77	0.083 77	0.086 83	15
16	0.065 19	0.067 94	0.070 77	0.073 65	0.076 60	0.079 61	0.082 68	16
17	0.061 51	0.064 26	0.067 08	0.069 97	0.072 93	0.075 95	0.079 04	17
18	0.058 23	0.060 98	0.063 81	0.066 70	0.069 67	0.072 71	0.075 82	18
19	0.055 36	0.058 05	0.060 88	0.063 78	0.066 76	0.069 81	0.072 94	19
20	0.052 67	0.055 42	0.058 25	0.061 16	0.064 15	0.067 22	0.070 36	20
21	0.050 28	0.053 03	0.055 87	0.058 78	0.061 79	0.064 87	0.068 04	21
22	0.048 11	0.050 86	0.053 70	0.056 63	0.059 65	0.062 75	0.065 93	22
23	0.046 13	0.048 89	0.051 73	0.054 67	0.057 70	0.060 81	0.064 02	23
24	0.044 32	0.047 07	0.049 92	0.052 87	0.055 91	0.059 05	0.062 27	24
25	0.042 65	0.045 41	0.048 26	0.051 22	0.054 28	0.057 43	0.060 67	25
26	0.041 11	0.043 87	0.046 73	0.049 70	0.052 77	0.055 94	0.059 21	26
27	0.039 69	0.042 45	0.045 32	0.048 29	0.051 38	0.054 56	0.057 85	27
28	0.038 36	0.041 12	0.044 00	0.046 99	0.050 09	0.053 29	0.056 60	28
29	0.037 13	0.039 90	0.042 78	0.045 78	0.048 89	0.052 11	0.055 45	29
30	0.035 98	0.038 75	0.041 64	0.044 65	0.047 78	0.051 02	0.054 37	30
31	0.034 90	0.037 68	0.040 57	0.043 60	0.046 74	0.050 00	0.053 37	31
32	0.033 89	0.036 67	0.039 58	0.042 61	0.045 77	0.049 05	0.052 44	32
33	0.032 95	0.035 73	0.038 64	0.041 69	0.044 86	0.048 16	0.051 57	33
34	0.032 06	0.034 84	0.037 76	0.040 82	0.044 01	0.047 32	0.050 76	34
35	0.031 22	0.034 00	0.036 93	0.040 00	0.043 21	0.046 54	0.050 00	35
36	0.030 42	0.033 21	0.036 15	0.039 23	0.042 45	0.045 80	0.049 28	36
37	0.029 67	0.032 47	0.035 41	0.038 51	0.041 74	0.045 11	0.048 61	37
38	0.028 96	0.031 76	0.034 72	0.037 82	0.041 07	0.044 46	0.047 98	38
39	0.028 29	0.031 09	0.034 05	0.037 17	0.040 44	0.043 84	0.047 39	39
40	0.027 65	0.030 46	0.033 43	0.036 56	0.039 84	0.043 26	0.046 83	40
41	0.027 04	0.029 85	0.032 83	0.035 97	0.039 27	0.042 71	0.046 30	41
42	0.026 46	0.029 28	0.032 26	0.035 42	0.038 73	0.042 19	0.045 80	42
43	0.025 90	0.028 73	0.031 72	0.034 89	0.038 22	0.041 70	0.045 33	43
44	0.025 38	0.028 20	0.031 21	0.034 39	0.037 73	0.041 23	0.044 88	44
45	0.024 87	0.027 71	0.030 72	0.033 91	0.037 27	0.040 79	0.044 45	45
46	0.024 39	0.027 23	0.030 25	0.033 45	0.036 83	0.040 36	0.044 05	46
47	0.023 93	0.026 77	0.029 80	0.033 02	0.036 41	0.039 96	0.043 67	47
48	0.023 49	0.026 33	0.029 38	0.032 60	0.036 01	0.039 58	0.043 31	48
49	0.023 06	0.025 91	0.028 96	0.032 20	0.035 62	0.039 21	0.042 96	49
50	0.022 65	0.025 51	0.028 57	0.031 82	0.035 26	0.038 87	0.042 63	50
n	$\frac{1}{2}\%$	1%	$1\frac{1}{2}\%$	2%	$2\frac{1}{2}\%$	3%	$3\frac{1}{2}\%$	n

The Annuity that 1 Will Buy

$$\frac{1}{a_{\overline{n}|\ i}} = (a_{\overline{n}|}\ i)^{-1} = (s_{\overline{n}|}\ i)^{-1} + i$$

n	4%	5%	6%	7%	8%	9%	10%	n
1	1.040 00	1.050 00	1.060 00	1.070 00	1.080 00	1.090 00	1.100 00	1
2	0.530 20	0.537 80	0.545 44	0.553 09	0.560 77	0.568 47	0.576 19	2
3	0.360 35	0.367 21	0.374 11	0.381 05	0.388 03	0.395 05	0.402 11	3
4	0.275 49	0.282 01	0.288 59	0.295 23	0.301 92	0.308 67	0.315 47	4
5	0.224 63	0.230 97	0.237 40	0.243 89	0.250 46	0.257 09	0.263 80	5
6	0.190 76	0.197 02	0.203 36	0.209 80	0.216 32	0.222 92	0.229 61	6
7	0.166 61	0.172 82	0.179 14	0.185 55	0.192 07	0.198 69	0.205 41	7
8	0.148 53	0.154 72	0.161 04	0.167 47	0.174 01	0.180 67	0.187 44	8
9	0.134 49	0.140 69	0.147 02	0.153 49	0.160 08	0.166 80	0.173 64	9
10	0.123 29	0.129 50	0.135 87	0.142 38	0.149 03	0.155 82	0.162 75	10
11	0.114 15	0.120 39	0.126 79	0.133 36	0.140 08	0.146 95	0.153 96	11
12	0.106 55	0.112 83	0.119 28	0.125 90	0.132 70	0.139 65	0.146 76	12
13	0.100 14	0.106 46	0.112 96	0.119 65	0.126 52	0.133 57	0.140 78	13
14	0.094 67	0.101 02	0.107 58	0.114 34	0.121 30	0.128 43	0.135 75	14
15	0.089 94	0.096 34	0.102 96	0.109 79	0.116 83	0.124 06	0.131 47	15
16	0.085 82	0.092 27	0.098 95	0.105 86	0.112 98	0.120 30	0.127 82	16
17	0.082 20	0.088 70	0.095 44	0.102 43	0.109 63	0.117 05	0.124 66	17
18	0.078 99	0.085 55	0.092 36	0.099 41	0.106 70	0.114 21	0.121 93	18
19	0.076 14	0.082 75	0.089 62	0.096 75	0.104 13	0.111 73	0.119 55	19
20	0.073 58	0.080 24	0.087 18	0.094 39	0.101 85	0.109 55	0.117 46	20
21	0.071 28	0.078 00	0.085 00	0.092 29	0.099 83	0.107 62	0.115 62	21
22	0.069 20	0.075 97	0.083 05	0.090 41	0.098 03	0.105 91	0.114 01	22
23	0.067 31	0.074 14	0.081 28	0.088 71	0.096 42	0.104 38	0.112 57	23
24	0.065 59	0.072 47	0.079 68	0.087 19	0.094 98	0.103 02	0.111 30	24
25	0.064 01	0.070 95	0.078 23	0.085 81	0.093 68	0.101 81	0.110 17	25
26	0.062 57	0.069 56	0.076 90	0.084 56	0.092 51	0.100 72	0.109 16	26
27	0.061 24	0.068 29	0.075 70	0.083 43	0.091 45	0.099 73	0.108 26	27
28	0.060 01	0.067 12	0.074 59	0.082 30	0.090 49	0.098 85	0.107 45	28
29	0.058 88	0.066 05	0.073 58	0.081 45	0.089 62	0.008 06	0.106 73	29
30	0.057 83	0.065 05	0.072 65	0.080 59	0.088 83	0.097 34	0.106 08	30
31	0.056 86	0.064 13	0.071 79	0.079 80	0.088 11	0.096 69	0.105 50	31
32	0.055 95	0.063 28	0.071 00	0.079 07	0.087 45	0.096 10	0.104 97	32
33	0.055 10	0.062 49	0.070 27	0.078 41	0.086 85	0.095 56	0.104 50	33
34	0.054 31	0.061 76	0.069 60	0.077 80	0.086 31	0.095 08	0.104 07	34
35	0.053 58	0.061 07	0.068 97	0.077 23	0.085 80	0.094 64	0.103 69	35
36	0.052 89	0.060 43	0.068 39	0.076 72	0.085 34	0.094 24	0.103 34	36
37	0.052 24	0.059 84	0.067 86	0.076 24	0.084 92	0.093 87	0.103 03	37
38	0.051 63	0.059 28	0.067 36	0.075 80	0.084 54	0.093 54	0.102 75	38
39	0.051 06	0.058 76	0.066 89	0.075 39	0.084 19	0.093 24	0.102 49	39
40	0.050 52	0.058 28	0.066 46	0.075 01	0.083 86	0.092 96	0.102 26	40
41	0.050 02	0.057 82	0.066 06	0.074 66	0.083 56	0.092 71	0.102 05	41
42	0.049 54	0.057 39	0.065 68	0.074 34	0.083 29	0.092 48	0.101 86	42
43	0.049 09	0.056 99	0.065 33	0.074 04	0.083 03	0.092 27	0.101 69	43
44	0.048 66	0.056 62	0.065 01	0.073 76	0.082 80	0.092 08	0.101 53	44
45	0.048 26	0.056 26	0.064 70	0.073 50	0.082 59	0.091 90	0.101 39	45
46	0.047 88	0.055 93	0.064 41	0.073 26	0.082 39	0.091 74	0.101 26	46
47	0.047 52	0.055 61	0.064 15	0.073 04	0.082 21	0.091 60	0.101 15	47
48	0.047 18	0.055 32	0.063 90	0.072 83	0.082 04	0.091 46	0.101 04	48
49	0.046 86	0.055 04	0.063 66	0.072 64	0.081 89	0.091 34	0.100 95	49
50	0.046 55	0.054 78	0.063 44	0.072 46	0.081 74	0.091 23	0.100 86	50
n	4%	5%	6%	7%	8%	9%	10%	n

Mortality Table, Canada, 1965–1967

Male   Female

Age	Number Living	Number Dying	Age	Number Living	Number Dying	Age	Number Living	Number Dying	Age	Number Living	Number Dying
0	100 000	2 525	55	84 119	1 065	0	100 000	2 008	55	90 568	587
1	97 475	156	56	83 054	1 152	1	97 992	130	56	89 981	635
2	97 319	102	57	81 902	1 245	2	97 862	86	57	89 346	689
3	97 217	88	58	80 657	1 346	3	97 776	68	58	88 657	748
4	97 129	74	59	79 311	1 450	4	97 708	61	59	87 909	808
5	97 055	65	60	77 861	1 558	5	97 647	53	60	87 101	875
6	96 990	58	61	76 303	1 667	6	97 594	46	61	86 226	946
7	96 932	53	62	74 636	1 777	7	97 548	38	62	85 280	1 027
8	96 879	47	63	72 859	1 885	8	97 510	34	63	84 253	1 113
9	96 832	45	64	70 974	1 990	9	97 476	31	64	83 140	1 199
10	96 787	44	65	68 984	2 092	10	97 445	29	65	81 941	1 294
11	96 743	44	66	66 892	2 193	11	97 416	28	66	80 647	1 396
12	96 699	50	67	64 699	2 295	12	97 388	30	67	79 251	1 509
13	96 649	59	68	62 404	2 387	13	97 358	32	68	77 742	1 627
14	96 590	74	69	60 017	2 469	14	97 326	35	69	76 115	1 742
15	96 516	90	70	57 548	2 547	15	97 291	41	70	74 373	1 865
16	96 426	107	71	55 001	2 625	16	97 250	44	71	72 508	2 004
17	96 319	121	72	52 376	2 711	17	97 206	48	72	70 504	2 167
18	96 198	135	73	49 665	2 793	18	97 158	51	73	68 337	2 341
19	96 063	148	74	46 872	2 868	19	97 107	51	74	65 996	2 515
20	95 915	162	75	44 004	2 926	20	97 056	52	75	63 481	2 694
21	95 753	171	76	41 078	2 971	21	97 004	53	76	60 787	2 877
22	95 582	177	77	38 107	2 995	22	96 951	54	77	57 910	3 064
23	95 405	176	78	35 112	2 996	23	96 897	56	78	54 846	3 241
24	95 229	169	79	32 116	2 971	24	96 841	56	79	51 605	3 397
25	95 060	161	80	29 145	2 920	25	96 785	57	80	48 208	3 528
26	94 899	154	81	26 225	2 841	26	96 728	59	81	44 680	3 632
27	94 745	148	82	23 384	2 736	27	96 669	62	82	41 048	3 707
28	94 597	146	83	20 648	2 605	28	96 607	64	83	37 341	3 737
29	94 451	144	84	18 043	2 450	29	96 543	69	84	33 604	3 717
30	94 307	145	85	15 593	2 277	30	96 474	74	85	29 887	3 645
31	94 162	147	86	13 316	2 086	31	96 400	79	86	26 242	3 523
32	94 015	151	87	11 230	1 886	32	96 321	85	87	22 719	3 354
33	93 864	158	88	9 344	1 680	33	96 236	92	88	19 365	3 136
34	93 706	166	89	7 664	1 472	34	96 144	98	89	16 229	2 876
35	93 540	175	90	6 192	1 269	35	96 046	106	90	13 353	2 583
36	93 365	189	91	4 923	1 075	36	95 940	115	91	10 770	2 272
37	93 176	204	92	3 848	894	37	95 825	125	92	8 498	1 950
38	92 972	222	93	2 954	730	38	95 700	136	93	6 548	1 633
39	92 750	242	94	2 224	583	39	95 564	148	94	4 915	1 329
40	92 508	266	95	1 641	456	40	95 416	162	95	3 586	1 049
41	92 242	291	96	1 185	349	41	95 254	177	96	2 537	801
42	91 951	320	97	836	260	42	95 077	194	97	1 736	592
43	91 631	352	98	576	190	43	94 883	213	98	1 144	420
44	91 279	386	99	386	134	44	94 670	233	99	724	286
45	90 893	422	100	252	92	45	94 437	255	100	438	185
46	90 471	464	101	160	62	46	94 182	280	101	253	115
47	90 007	513	102	98	40	47	93 902	306	102	138	67
48	89 494	567	103	58	25	48	93 596	333	103	71	37
49	88 927	628	104	33	15	49	93 263	362	104	34	19
50	88 299	691	105	18	8	50	92 901	394	105	15	9
51	87 608	761	106	10	5	51	92 507	428	106	6	4
52	86 847	834	107	5	3	52	92 079	464	107	2	1
53	86 013	909	108	2	1	53	91 615	503	108	1	1
54	85 104	985	109	1	1	54	91 112	544			

Squares and Square Roots

n	n^2	$\sqrt{n}$	n	n^2	$\sqrt{n}$	n	n^2	$\sqrt{n}$	n	n^2	$\sqrt{n}$
1	1	1.000	51	2601	7.141	101	10 201	10.050	151	22 801	12.288
2	4	1.414	52	2704	7.211	102	10 404	10.100	152	23 104	12.329
3	9	1.732	53	2809	7.280	103	10 609	10.149	153	23 409	12.369
4	16	2.000	54	2916	7.348	104	10 816	10.198	154	23 716	12.410
5	25	2.236	55	3025	7.416	105	11 025	10.247	155	24 025	12.450
6	36	2.449	56	3136	7.483	106	11 236	10.296	156	24 336	12.490
7	49	2.646	57	3249	7.550	107	11 449	10.344	157	24 649	12.530
8	64	2.828	58	3364	7.616	108	11 664	10.392	158	24 964	12.570
9	81	3.000	59	3481	7.681	109	11 881	10.440	159	25 281	12.610
10	100	3.162	60	3600	7.746	110	12 100	10.488	160	25 600	12.649
11	121	3.317	61	3721	7.810	111	12 321	10.536	161	25 921	12.689
12	144	3.464	62	3844	7.874	112	12 544	10.583	162	26 244	12.728
13	169	3.606	63	3969	7.937	113	12 769	10.630	163	26 569	12.767
14	196	3.742	64	4096	8.000	114	12 996	10.677	164	26 896	12.806
15	225	3.873	65	4225	8.062	115	13 225	10.724	165	27 225	12.845
16	256	4.000	66	4356	8.124	116	13 456	10.770	166	27 556	12.884
17	289	4.123	67	4489	8.185	117	13 689	10.817	167	27 889	12.923
18	324	4.243	68	4624	8.246	118	13 924	10.863	168	28 224	12.961
19	361	4.359	69	4761	8.307	119	14 161	10.909	169	28 561	13.000
20	400	4.472	70	4900	8.367	120	14 400	10.954	170	28 900	13.038
21	441	4.583	71	5041	8.426	121	14 641	11.000	171	29 241	13.077
22	484	4.690	72	5184	8.485	122	14 884	11.045	172	29 584	13.115
23	529	4.796	73	5329	8.544	123	15 129	11.091	173	29 929	13.153
24	576	4.899	74	5476	8.602	124	15 376	11.136	174	30 276	13.191
25	625	5.000	75	5625	8.660	125	15 625	11.180	175	30 625	13.229
26	676	5.099	76	5776	8.718	126	15 876	11.225	176	30 976	13.267
27	729	5.196	77	5929	8.775	127	16 129	11.269	177	31 329	13.304
28	784	5.292	78	6084	8.832	128	16 384	11.314	178	31 684	13.342
29	841	5.385	79	6241	8.888	129	16 641	11.358	179	32 041	13.379
30	900	5.477	80	6400	8.944	130	16 900	11.402	180	32 400	13.416
31	961	5.568	81	6561	9.000	131	17 161	11.446	181	32 761	13.454
32	1024	5.657	82	6724	9.055	132	17 424	11.489	182	33 124	13.491
33	1089	5.745	83	6889	9.110	133	17 689	11.533	183	33 489	13.528
34	1156	5.831	84	7056	9.165	134	17 956	11.576	184	33 856	13.565
35	1225	5.916	85	7225	9.220	135	18 225	11.619	185	34 225	13.601
36	1296	6.000	86	7396	9.274	136	18 496	11.662	186	34 596	13.638
37	1369	6.083	87	7569	9.327	137	18 769	11.705	187	34 969	13.675
38	1444	6.164	88	7744	9.381	138	19 044	11.747	188	35 344	13.711
39	1521	6.245	89	7921	9.434	139	19 321	11.790	189	35 721	13.748
40	1600	6.325	90	8100	9.487	140	19 600	11.832	190	36 100	13.784
41	1681	6.403	91	8281	9.539	141	19 881	11.874	191	36 481	13.820
42	1764	6.481	92	8464	9.592	142	20 164	11.916	192	36 864	13.856
43	1849	6.557	93	8649	9.644	143	20 449	11.958	193	37 249	13.892
44	1936	6.633	94	8836	9.695	144	20 736	12.000	194	37 636	13.928
45	2025	6.708	95	9025	9.747	145	21 025	12.042	195	38 025	13.964
46	2116	6.782	96	9216	9.798	146	21 316	12.083	196	38 416	14.000
47	2209	6.856	97	9409	9.849	147	21 609	12.124	197	38 809	14.036
48	2304	6.928	98	9604	9.899	148	21 904	12.166	198	39 204	14.071
49	2401	7.000	99	9801	9.950	149	22 201	12.207	199	39 601	14.107
50	2500	7.071	100	10 000	10.000	150	22 500	12.247	200	40 000	14.142

Table of Trigonometric Ratios

θ	sin θ	cos θ	tan θ	csc θ	sec θ	cot θ
0	0.0000	1.0000	0.0000		1.0000	
1	0.0175	0.9998	0.0175	57.299	1.0002	57.290
2	0.0349	0.9994	0.0349	28.654	1.0006	28.636
3	0.0523	0.9986	0.0524	19.107	1.0014	19.081
4	0.0698	0.9976	0.0699	14.336	1.0024	14.301
5	0.0872	0.9962	0.0875	11.474	1.0038	11.4301
6	0.1045	0.9945	0.1051	9.5668	1.0055	9.5144
7	0.1219	0.9925	0.1228	8.2055	1.0075	8.1443
8	0.1392	0.9903	0.1405	7.1853	1.0098	7.1154
9	0.1564	0.9877	0.1584	6.3925	1.0125	6.3138
10	0.1736	0.9848	0.1763	5.7588	1.0154	5.6713
11	0.1908	0.9816	0.1944	5.2408	1.0187	5.1446
12	0.2079	0.9781	0.2126	4.8097	1.0223	4.7046
13	0.2250	0.9744	0.2309	4.4454	1.0263	4.3315
14	0.2419	0.9703	0.2493	4.1336	1.0306	4.0108
15	0.2588	0.9659	0.2679	3.8637	1.0353	3.7321
16	0.2756	0.9613	0.2867	3.6280	1.0403	3.4874
17	0.2924	0.9563	0.3057	3.4203	1.0457	3.2709
18	0.3090	0.9511	0.3249	3.2361	1.0515	3.0777
19	0.3256	0.9455	0.3443	3.0716	1.0576	2.9042
20	0.3420	0.9397	0.3640	2.9238	1.0642	2.7475
21	0.3584	0.9336	0.3839	2.7904	1.0711	2.6051
22	0.3746	0.9272	0.4040	2.6695	1.0785	2.4751
23	0.3907	0.9205	0.4245	2.5593	1.0864	2.3559
24	0.4067	0.9135	0.4452	2.4586	1.0946	2.2460
25	0.4226	0.9063	0.4663	2.3662	1.1034	2.1445
26	0.4384	0.8988	0.4877	2.2812	1.1126	2.0503
27	0.4540	0.8910	0.5095	2.2027	1.1223	1.9626
28	0.4695	0.8829	0.5317	2.1301	1.1326	1.8807
29	0.4848	0.8746	0.5543	2.0627	1.1434	1.8041
30	0.5000	0.8660	0.5774	2.0000	1.1547	1.7321
31	0.5150	0.8572	0.6009	1.9416	1.1666	1.6643
32	0.5299	0.8480	0.6249	1.8871	1.1792	1.6003
33	0.5446	0.8387	0.6494	1.8361	1.1924	1.5399
34	0.5592	0.8290	0.6745	1.7883	1.2062	1.4826
35	0.5736	0.8192	0.7002	1.7434	1.2208	1.4281
36	0.5878	0.8090	0.7265	1.7013	1.2361	1.3764
37	0.6018	0.7986	0.7536	1.6616	1.2521	1.3270
38	0.6157	0.7880	0.7813	1.6243	1.2690	1.2799
39	0.6293	0.7771	0.8098	1.5890	1.2868	1.2349
40	0.6428	0.7660	0.8391	1.5557	1.3054	1.1918
41	0.6561	0.7547	0.8693	1.5243	1.3250	1.1504
42	0.6691	0.7431	0.9004	1.4945	1.3456	1.1106
43	0.6820	0.7314	0.9325	1.4663	1.3673	1.0724
44	0.6947	0.7193	0.9657	1.4396	1.3902	1.0355

Table of Trigonometric Ratios

θ	$\sin \theta$	$\cos \theta$	$\tan \theta$	$\csc \theta$	$\sec \theta$	$\cot \theta$
45	0.7071	0.7071	1.0000	1.4142	1.4142	1.0000
46	0.7193	0.6947	1.0355	1.3902	1.4396	0.9657
47	0.7314	0.6820	1.0724	1.3673	1.4663	0.9325
48	0.7431	0.6691	1.1106	1.3456	1.4945	0.9004
49	0.7547	0.6561	1.1504	1.3250	1.5243	0.8693
50	0.7660	0.6428	1.1918	1.3054	1.5557	0.8391
51	0.7771	0.6293	1.2349	1.2868	1.5890	0.8098
52	0.7880	0.6157	1.2799	1.2690	1.6243	0.7813
53	0.7986	0.6018	1.3270	1.2521	1.6616	0.7536
54	0.8090	0.5878	1.3764	1.2361	1.7013	0.7265
55	0.8192	0.5736	1.4281	1.2208	1.7434	0.7002
56	0.8290	0.5592	1.4826	1.2062	1.7883	0.6745
57	0.8387	0.5446	1.5399	1.1924	1.8361	0.6494
58	0.8480	0.5299	1.6003	1.1792	1.8871	0.6249
59	0.8572	0.5150	1.6643	1.1666	1.9416	0.6009
60	0.8660	0.5000	1.7321	1.1547	2.0000	0.5774
61	0.8746	0.4848	1.8041	1.1434	2.0627	0.5543
62	0.8829	0.4695	1.8807	1.1326	2.1301	0.5317
63	0.8910	0.4540	1.9626	1.1223	2.2027	0.5095
64	0.8988	0.4384	2.0503	1.1126	2.2812	0.4877
65	0.9063	0.4226	2.1445	1.1034	2.3662	0.4663
66	0.9135	0.4067	2.2460	1.0946	2.4586	0.4452
67	0.9205	0.3907	2.3559	1.0864	2.5593	0.4245
68	0.9272	0.3746	2.4751	1.0785	2.6695	0.4040
69	0.9336	0.3584	2.6051	1.0711	2.7904	0.3839
70	0.9397	0.3420	2.7475	1.0642	2.9238	0.3640
71	0.9455	0.3256	2.9042	1.0576	3.0716	0.3443
72	0.9511	0.3090	3.0777	1.0515	3.2361	0.3249
73	0.9563	0.2924	3.2709	1.0457	3.4203	0.3057
74	0.9613	0.2756	3.4874	1.0403	3.6280	0.2867
75	0.9659	0.2588	3.7321	1.0353	3.8637	0.2679
76	0.9703	0.2419	4.0108	1.0306	4.1336	0.2493
77	0.9744	0.2250	4.3315	1.0263	4.4454	0.2309
78	0.9781	0.2079	4.7046	1.0223	4.8097	0.2126
79	0.9816	0.1908	5.1446	1.0187	5.2408	0.1944
80	0.9848	0.1736	5.6713	1.0154	5.7588	0.1763
81	0.9877	0.1564	6.3138	1.0125	6.3925	0.1584
82	0.9903	0.1392	7.1154	1.0098	7.1853	0.1405
83	0.9925	0.1219	8.1443	1.0075	8.2055	0.1228
84	0.9945	0.1045	9.5144	1.0055	9.5668	0.1051
85	0.9962	0.0872	11.4301	1.0038	11.474	0.0875
86	0.9976	0.0698	14.301	1.0024	14.336	0.0699
87	0.9986	0.0523	19.081	1.0014	19.107	0.0524
88	0.9994	0.0349	28.636	1.0006	28.654	0.0349
89	0.9998	0.0175	57.290	1.0002	57.299	0.0175
90	1.0000	0.0000		1.0000		0.0000

	Degrees to Radians				Radians to Degrees				

Degrees	Radians	Degrees	Radians	Real Nos. or Radians	Degrees	Degrees and Minutes	Real Nos. or Radians	Degrees	Degrees and Minutes
1	0.0175	51	0.8901	0.01	0.5730	0° 34′	0.51	29.2209	29° 13′
2	0.0349	52	0.9076	0.02	1.1459	1° 09′	0.52	29.7938	29° 48′
3	0.0524	53	0.9250	0.03	1.7189	1° 43′	0.53	30.3668	30° 22′
4	0.0698	54	0.9425	0.04	2.2918	2° 18′	0.54	30.9397	30° 56′
5	0.0873	55	0.9599	0.05	2.8648	2° 52′	0.55	31.5127	31° 31′
6	0.1047	56	0.9774	0.06	3.4377	3° 26′	0.56	32.0857	32° 05′
7	0.1222	57	0.9948	0.07	4.0107	4° 01′	0.57	32.6586	32° 40′
8	0.1396	58	1.0123	0.08	4.5837	4° 35′	0.58	33.2316	33° 14′
9	0.1571	59	1.0297	0.09	5.1566	5° 09′	0.59	33.8045	33° 48′
10	0.1745	60	1.0472	0.10	5.7296	5° 44′	0.60	34.3775	34° 23′
11	0.1920	61	1.0647	0.11	6.3025	6° 18′	0.61	34.9505	34° 57′
12	0.2094	62	1.0821	0.12	6.8755	6° 53′	0.62	35.5234	35° 31′
13	0.2269	63	1.0996	0.13	7.4485	7° 27′	0.63	36.0964	36° 06′
14	0.2443	64	1.1170	0.14	8.0214	8° 01′	0.64	36.6693	36° 40′
15	0.2618	65	1.1345	0.15	8.5944	8° 36′	0.65	37.2423	37° 15′
16	0.2793	66	1.1519	0.16	9.1673	9° 10′	0.66	37.8152	37° 49′
17	0.2967	67	1.1694	0.17	9.7403	9° 44′	0.67	38.3882	38° 23′
18	0.3142	68	1.1868	0.18	10.3132	10° 19′	0.68	38.9612	38° 58′
19	0.3316	69	1.2043	0.19	10.8862	10° 53′	0.69	39.5341	39° 32′
20	0.3491	70	1.2217	0.20	11.4592	11° 28′	0.70	40.1071	40° 06′
21	0.3665	71	1.2392	0.21	12.0321	12° 02′	0.71	40.6800	40° 41′
22	0.3840	72	1.2566	0.22	12.6051	12° 36′	0.72	41.2530	41° 15′
23	0.4014	73	1.2741	0.23	13.1780	13° 11′	0.73	41.8260	41° 50′
24	0.4189	74	1.2915	0.24	13.7510	13° 45′	0.74	42.3989	42° 24′
25	0.4363	75	1.3090	0.25	14.3240	14° 19′	0.75	42.9719	42° 58′
26	0.4538	76	1.3264	0.26	14.8969	14° 54′	0.76	43.5448	43° 33′
27	0.4712	77	1.3439	0.27	15.4699	15° 28′	0.77	44.1178	44° 07′
28	0.4887	78	1.3614	0.28	16.0428	16° 03′	0.78	44.6907	44° 41′
29	0.5061	79	1.3788	0.29	16.6158	16° 37′	0.79	45.2637	45° 16′
30	0.5236	80	1.3963	0.30	17.1887	17° 11′	0.80	45.8367	45° 50′
31	0.5411	81	1.4137	0.31	17.7617	17° 46′	0.81	46.4096	46° 25′
32	0.5585	82	1.4312	0.32	18.3347	18° 20′	0.82	46.9826	46° 59′
33	0.5760	83	1.4486	0.33	18.9076	18° 54′	0.83	47.5555	47° 33′
34	0.5934	84	1.4661	0.34	19.4806	19° 29′	0.84	48.1285	48° 08′
35	0.6109	85	1.4835	0.35	20.0535	20° 03′	0.85	48.7015	48° 42′
36	0.6283	86	1.5010	0.36	20.6265	20° 38′	0.86	49.2744	49° 16′
37	0.6458	87	1.5184	0.37	21.1995	21° 12′	0.87	49.8474	49° 51′
38	0.6632	88	1.5359	0.38	21.7724	21° 46′	0.88	50.4203	50° 25′
39	0.6807	89	1.5533	0.39	22.3454	22° 21′	0.89	50.9933	51° 00′
40	0.6981	90	1.5708	0.40	22.9183	22° 55′	0.90	51.5662	51° 34′
41	0.7156	91	1.5882	0.41	23.4913	23° 29′	0.91	52.1392	52° 08′
42	0.7330	92	1.6057	0.42	24.0642	24° 04′	0.92	52.7122	52° 43′
43	0.7505	93	1.6232	0.43	24.6372	24° 38′	0.93	53.2851	53° 17′
44	0.7679	94	1.6406	0.44	25.2102	25° 13′	0.94	53.8581	53° 51′
45	0.7854	95	1.6581	0.45	25.7831	25° 47′	0.95	54.4310	54° 26′
46	0.8029	96	1.6755	0.46	26.3561	26° 21′	0.96	55.0040	55° 00′
47	0.8203	97	1.6930	0.47	26.9290	26° 56′	0.97	55.5770	55° 35′
48	0.8378	98	1.7104	0.48	27.5020	27° 30′	0.98	56.1499	56° 09′
49	0.8552	99	1.7279	0.49	28.0750	28° 05′	0.99	56.7229	56° 43′
50	0.8727	100	1.7453	0.50	28.6479	28° 39′	1.00	57.2958	57° 18′

Answers

10. (a) $\{(-1, -2), (0, 0), (1, 2),$
  $(2, 4), (3, 6)\}$

  (b) $\{(-1, -2), (0, 1), (1, 4),$
  $(2, 7), (3, 10)\}$

  (c) $\{(-1, 1), (0, 0), (1, 1), (2, 4),$
  $(3, 9)\}$

  (d) $\{(-1, 0), (0, 0), (1, 2), (2, 6),$
  $(3, 12)\}$

  (e) $\{(-1, -1), (0, 0), (1, 1),$
  $(2, 8), (3, 27)\}$

  (f) $\{(-1, 1), (0, 0), (1, 1),$
  $(2, 16), (3, 81)\}$

11. (a) $f : x \rightarrow x^2$ (d) $h : x \rightarrow |x|$
  (b) $f : x \rightarrow x + 2$ (e) $f : x \rightarrow 12 - 2x$
  (c) $g : x \rightarrow x^3$ (f) $h : x \rightarrow -x^2 - 2$

12. (e) For part (a), $D_M = \{1, 4, 5\}$,
    $R_M = \{0, 1, 2\}$
  For part (b), $D_M = \{1, 4\}$,
    $R_M = \{1, 2\}$
  For part (c), $D_M = \{x \mid x = 5 - y^2,$
    $y \in I\}\ R_M = I$
  For part (d), $D_M = \{x \in R \mid x \leqslant 5\}$,
    $R_M = R$

14. (a) $1 + 2x$ (c) $1 + \dfrac{1}{x}$

  (b) $1 + x + h$ (d) $1 + x^2$

15. All equal 2

16. The functions are (a), (c), (f).

Exercise 1.2, Page 13

6. (a) $(9, 5)$ (d) $(7, 4)$
  (b) $(-6, -\frac{5}{2})$ (e) $(-3, -1)$
  (c) $(0, \frac{1}{2})$ (f) $(-1, 0)$

7. $f^{-1} = \{(2, 0), (3, 1), (4, 2), (5, 3)\}$
  is a function.

8. (a) $f^{-1} = \{(x, y) \mid y = \frac{1}{4}(x + 5)\}$
    is a function
  (b) $g^{-1} = \{(x, y) \mid y = \pm\sqrt{x - 1}\}$
    is not a function
  (c) $h^{-1} : x \rightarrow \frac{1}{2}(-x + 4)$ is a
    function
  (d) $m^{-1} : x \rightarrow x^2 - 1$ is a function

9. (a) $f^{-1} = \{(x, y) \mid 3y = x - 1\}$
  (c) $f \cap f^{-1} = \{(-\frac{1}{2}, -\frac{1}{2})\}$

10. $g^{-1} : x \rightarrow \dfrac{x + 3}{2}$

11. (b) $g^{-1} = \{(x, y) \mid y^2 = 4x\}$
  (d) No, because the relation g^{-1}
    is not a function.

12. Both are functions.

15. (b) $f^{-1} = \{(x, y) \mid x = \sqrt{y}\}$
  (d) f is a one-to-one
    correspondence.

16. (a) $f^{-1}(x) = \dfrac{x - 7}{3}$ (b) 10

17. (a) identical
  (b) identical if $x \geqslant 0$, symmetrical
    about $y = x$ if $x \leqslant 0$.
  (c) identical

18. (c) g is a function; g^{-1} is not a
    function
  (d) $g \cap g^{-1} = \{(0, 0), (1, 1)\}$

19. (c) $g \cap g^{-1} = \{(0, 0), (-1, -1)\}$

Exercise 1.4, Page 21

7. (a) $y = 0$
  (b) $y = 1$
  (c) $y = 1$
  (d) $y = 1, x = 1, x = -1$;
    exclude $1, -1$
  (e) $y = 0, x = 1, x = -1$;
    exclude $1, -1$
  (f) $y = 3, x = 2, x = -2$;
    exclude $2, -2$

8. (b) f is undefined at $x = 1$

11. (b) -1.33 (approx.)

Exercise 1.5, Page 24

3. $x \geqslant 1, x \in R$

5. $y = x + \sqrt{x^2 - 5x}$
  $y = x - \sqrt{x^2 - 5x}$

Exercise 1.6, Page 27

10. (b) $f(xy) = f(x) + f(y)$

12. (a) 300   (c) 150×2^{10}
  (b) 1200   (d) 150×2^n

16. (a) 10 000, 16 487 (b) 13.86

17. (a) 2000, 7057, 8917, 9602, 9853

18. (a) 10, 6.95, 5.39, 3.80

19. (a) 0, 13, 39, 47, 50

20. (b) $K(1) = 44$ (c) 18, 7, 2

Exercise 1.7, Page 32

1. (a) $f \circ g = \{(-4, 5), (3, 1), (0, 1)\}$
   (b) $g \circ f = \{(-5, -3), (-2, -3),$
   $(-1, 2), (5, 2)\}$
   (c) $D_{f \circ g} = \{-4, 0, 3\}$
   (d) $D_{g \circ f} = \{-5, -2, -1, 5\}$

2. (a) $13 - 6x$ (e) $9 - 6x$
   (b) -5 (f) 21
   (c) 19 (g) -21
   (d) 13 (h) 9

3. (a) $f \circ g = 9x^2 - 6x + 3$
   $g \circ f = 3x^2 + 5$
   (b) $f \circ g = 47 - 120x + 72x^2$
   $g \circ f = 23 - 12x^2$

7. (a) $\dfrac{14 - 5x}{6}$ (c) $\dfrac{25x}{16}$
   (b) $\dfrac{35 - 10x}{12}$ (d) $\dfrac{7 + 4x}{9}$

8. (a) $\sin 3x$ (b) $2 \cos x$

9. $f \circ g = 3^{\log_3 x}$ $g \circ f = x$

13. (c) any two straight lines through origin

Review Exercise 1.8, Page 35

6. $g \circ f = \{(3, -2), (4, -3), (5, -5)\}$

7. (a) $y = \frac{1}{2}x$
   (b) $y = \sqrt{x}$ or $-\sqrt{x}$
   (c) $3y + 4x = 12$
   (d) $y^2 + xy = 1$

8. (a) $y = 2x^2 - 6$
   (b) $y = 6x + 3$
   (c) $y = 3 - x^2$
   (d) $y = x^2 + 2x - 2$
   (e) $y = x^2 - 2x - 4$
   (f) $y = -x^2 + 2x + 4$
   (g) $y = 2x^3 + x^2 - 6x - 3$
   (h) $y = 2x^2 + 6x - 3$
   (i) $y = \dfrac{x^2 - 3}{2x + 1}$

9. (a) $1, 5, -3$ (b) $0, \frac{1}{2}$

10. (a) $x = -3, 2$ (c) $x = \frac{5}{2}$
    (b) $x = 1, -1$ (d) $x = -3, 4$

11. (a) $\dfrac{1}{2}$ (d) $\dfrac{(a + 2)^2}{a + 3}$ (g) $\dfrac{(x + 2)^2}{x + 3}$
    (b) $-\dfrac{9}{2}$ (e) $\dfrac{(b - 1)^2}{b}$ (h) $\dfrac{(x - 1)^2}{x}$
    (c) 0 (f) $\dfrac{a^4}{a^2 + 1}$ (i) $\dfrac{x^4}{x^2 + 1}$

12. (a), (c), (e), (f)

18. (a) $f^{-1} : x \to \dfrac{x - 2}{5}$
    (c) $\{(-\frac{1}{2}, -\frac{1}{2})\}$
    (d) $f : x \to 5x + 2$

20. $g : x \to \dfrac{3x + 11}{4}$

21. yes

23. (a) $9x^2 + 6x + 3$
    (b) $3x^2 + 7$

24. (a) $f \circ g(x) = 3x^2 + 3x - 5$
    $g \circ f(x) = 9x^2 - 27x + 20$
    (b) $f \circ g(x) = x^4 - 5$
    $g \circ f(x) = x^4 - 10x^2 + 25$
    (c) $f \circ g(x) = -2x^2 - x^4$
    $g \circ f(x) = 2 - 2x^2 + x^4$

25. (a) $f^{-1} = \frac{1}{3}(x + 5)$
    (b) $f^{-1} = 5x + 3$
    (c) $f^{-1} = \pm\sqrt{x^2 + 5}, x \geq 0$
    (d) $f^{-1} = x^2 + 2, x \geq 0$
    (e) $f^{-1} = \frac{1}{4}x^2 - 3, x \geq 0$
    (f) $f^{-1} = \dfrac{2x - 1}{x}, x \neq 0$

26. $a = -d, b = 0$
    or $b = c = 0, a = d$

Exercise 2.1, Page 41

4. $\left(-\dfrac{1}{\sqrt{2}}, \dfrac{1}{\sqrt{2}}\right)$

7. $x = \dfrac{(4n + 1)}{4}\pi, n \in I$ 18. -2

5.

Point		A	B	C	D	E	F	G	H	A
Coordinates of point	(u, v)	$(1, 0)$	$\left(\frac{1}{\sqrt{2}}, \frac{1}{\sqrt{2}}\right)$	$(0, 1)$	$\left(-\frac{1}{\sqrt{2}}, \frac{1}{\sqrt{2}}\right)$	$(-1, 0)$	$\left(-\frac{1}{\sqrt{2}}, -\frac{1}{\sqrt{2}}\right)$	$(0, -1)$	$\left(\frac{1}{\sqrt{2}}, -\frac{1}{\sqrt{2}}\right)$	$(1, 0)$
Arc length from A	x	0	$\frac{\pi}{4}$	$\frac{\pi}{2}$	$\frac{3\pi}{4}$	π	$\frac{5\pi}{4}$	$\frac{3\pi}{2}$	$\frac{7\pi}{4}$	2π
1st Coord.	$\cos x$	1	$\frac{1}{\sqrt{2}}$	0	$-\frac{1}{\sqrt{2}}$	-1	$-\frac{1}{\sqrt{2}}$	0	$\frac{1}{\sqrt{2}}$	1
2nd Coord.	$\sin x$	0	$\frac{1}{\sqrt{2}}$	1	$\frac{1}{\sqrt{2}}$	0	$-\frac{1}{\sqrt{2}}$	-1	$-\frac{1}{\sqrt{2}}$	0

Exercise 2.2, Page 49

1.

x	0	$\dfrac{\pi}{6}$	$\dfrac{\pi}{4}$	$\dfrac{\pi}{3}$	$\dfrac{\pi}{2}$	$\dfrac{2\pi}{3}$	$\dfrac{3\pi}{4}$	$\dfrac{5\pi}{6}$	π
$\sin x$	0	$\dfrac{1}{2}$	$\dfrac{1}{\sqrt{2}}$	$\dfrac{\sqrt{3}}{2}$	1	$\dfrac{\sqrt{3}}{2}$	$\dfrac{1}{\sqrt{2}}$	$\dfrac{1}{2}$	0
$\cos x$	1	$\dfrac{\sqrt{3}}{2}$	$\dfrac{1}{\sqrt{2}}$	$\dfrac{1}{2}$	0	$-\dfrac{1}{2}$	$-\dfrac{1}{\sqrt{2}}$	$-\dfrac{\sqrt{3}}{2}$	-1
$\tan x$	0	$\dfrac{1}{\sqrt{3}}$	1	$\sqrt{3}$	und	$-\sqrt{3}$	-1	$-\dfrac{1}{\sqrt{3}}$	0
$\sec x$	1	$\dfrac{2}{\sqrt{3}}$	$\sqrt{2}$	2	und	-2	$-\sqrt{2}$	$-\dfrac{2}{\sqrt{3}}$	-1
$\csc x$	und	2	$\sqrt{2}$	$\dfrac{2}{\sqrt{3}}$	1	$\dfrac{2}{\sqrt{3}}$	$\sqrt{2}$	2	und
$\cot x$	und	$\sqrt{3}$	1	$\dfrac{1}{\sqrt{3}}$	0	$-\dfrac{1}{\sqrt{3}}$	-1	$-\sqrt{3}$	und

2.

x	$\dfrac{7\pi}{6}$	$\dfrac{5\pi}{4}$	$\dfrac{4\pi}{3}$	$\dfrac{3\pi}{2}$	$\dfrac{5\pi}{3}$	$\dfrac{7\pi}{4}$	$\dfrac{11\pi}{6}$	2π
$\sin x$	$-\dfrac{1}{2}$	$-\dfrac{1}{\sqrt{2}}$	$-\dfrac{\sqrt{3}}{2}$	-1	$-\dfrac{\sqrt{3}}{2}$	$-\dfrac{1}{\sqrt{2}}$	$-\dfrac{1}{2}$	0
$\cos x$	$-\dfrac{\sqrt{3}}{2}$	$-\dfrac{1}{\sqrt{2}}$	$-\dfrac{1}{2}$	0	$\dfrac{1}{2}$	$\dfrac{1}{\sqrt{2}}$	$\dfrac{\sqrt{3}}{2}$	1
$\tan x$	$\dfrac{1}{\sqrt{3}}$	1	$\sqrt{3}$	und	$-\sqrt{3}$	-1	$-\dfrac{1}{\sqrt{3}}$	0
$\sec x$	$-\dfrac{2}{\sqrt{3}}$	$-\sqrt{2}$	-2	und	2	$\sqrt{2}$	$\dfrac{2}{\sqrt{3}}$	1
$\csc x$	-2	$-\sqrt{2}$	$-\dfrac{2}{\sqrt{3}}$	-1	$-\dfrac{2}{\sqrt{3}}$	$-\sqrt{2}$	-2	und
$\cot x$	$\sqrt{3}$	1	$\dfrac{1}{\sqrt{3}}$	0	$-\dfrac{1}{\sqrt{3}}$	-1	$-\sqrt{3}$	und

3.

	Domain	Range
tan	$\dfrac{(2n-1)\pi}{2} < x < \dfrac{(2n+1)\pi}{2},\ n \in I$	$y \in R$
cot	$n\pi < x < (n+1)\pi,\ n \in I$	$y \in R$
csc	$n\pi < x < (n+1)\pi,\ n \in I$	$y \geq 1,\ y \leq -1$
sec	$\dfrac{(2n-3)\pi}{2} < x < \dfrac{(2n-1)\pi}{2},\ n \in I$	$y \geq 1,\ y \leq -1$

4. $\dfrac{(2n-1)\pi}{4},$
$-8 \leq n \leq 8$

$\sin x = -\dfrac{2\sqrt{2}}{3}$

$\tan x = -2\sqrt{2}$

7. (a) $\cos x = \frac{4}{5}$
$\tan x = \frac{3}{4}$
$\sec x = \frac{5}{4}$
$\csc x = \frac{5}{3}$
$\cot x = \frac{4}{3}$

(b) $\sin x = \frac{5}{13}$
$\tan x = -\frac{5}{12}$
$\sec x = -\frac{13}{12}$
$\csc x = \frac{13}{5}$
$\cot x = -\frac{12}{5}$

(c) $\cos x = -\frac{12}{13}$
$\tan x = \frac{5}{12}$
$\sec x = -\frac{13}{12}$
$\csc x = -\frac{13}{5}$
$\cot x = \frac{12}{5}$

(d) $\sec x = 3$
$\csc x = -\dfrac{3}{2\sqrt{2}}$
$\cot x = -\dfrac{1}{2\sqrt{2}}$

Answers/Chapter 2

10. *(a)* $\sin\left(x + \dfrac{\pi}{2}\right) = \cos x$

Shift the sin graph 90° horizontally.

(b) Reflect the tan graph through

$x = \dfrac{(4n + 1)}{4}\pi$

(c) Shift the csc graph 90° horizontally and then reflect csc graph through the *x* axis.

Exercise 2.3, Page 56

3. *(a)* 3, 2π *(c)* 1, $\dfrac{2\pi}{3}$ *(e)* 2, 4π

(b) 1, $\dfrac{2\pi}{3}$ *(d)* $\frac{1}{2}$, π *(f)* 4, 6π

4. *(a)* 2, 2π, $-\dfrac{\pi}{2}$ *(d)* $\frac{1}{2}$, $\dfrac{2\pi}{3}$, $\dfrac{\pi}{3}$

(b) 1, $\dfrac{2\pi}{3}$, $-\dfrac{\pi}{3}$ *(e)* 3, 4π, $\dfrac{2\pi}{3}$

(c) 1, π, $-\dfrac{\pi}{4}$ *(f)* 4, 6π, $-\dfrac{\pi}{2}$

5. *(a)* $y = 3 \sin\left(x - \dfrac{\pi}{6}\right)$

(b) $y = 5 \sin\left(2x - \dfrac{2\pi}{3}\right)$

(c) $y = 2 \sin\left(\dfrac{2}{3}x - \dfrac{\pi}{6}\right)$

(d) $y = 7 \sin (4x + \pi)$

11. *(a)* 2π, 2   *(c)* 4π, 2.1
    (b) 2π, 1.4   *(d)* π, 3.2

Exercise 2.4, Page 60

3. *(a)* $\dfrac{\pi}{3}$ *(d)* $\dfrac{\pi}{4}$ *(g)* $-\dfrac{\pi}{4}$

(b) π *(e)* 0   *(h)* $\dfrac{\pi}{6}$

(c) 0   *(f)* $\dfrac{\pi}{4}$ *(i)* $-\dfrac{\pi}{3}$

4. *(a)* 0   *(c)* -1 *(e)* 0

(b) $\dfrac{\sqrt{3}}{2}$ *(d)* $\dfrac{\pi}{6}$ *(f)* $\dfrac{\pi}{4}$

5. *(a)* $\dfrac{2\sqrt{2}}{3}$ *(b)* $\dfrac{12}{13}$

6. $x = \dfrac{5\pi}{12}$

10. *(b)* $\cos (\sin^{-1}x) = \sqrt{1 - x^2}$

428

Exercise 2.6, Page 67

5. *(a)* $a^2y^2 - b^2x^2 + a^2b^2 = 0$
    (b) $x^2 + y^2 = 25$

6. $x = r\theta - a \sin \theta$
    $y = r - a \cos \theta$

7. $x = r\theta - a \sin \theta$
    $y = r - a \cos \theta$

8. $x = r \cos \theta + r\theta \sin \theta$
    $y = r \sin \theta - r\theta \cos \theta$

10. $x = a \sin \theta$
    $y = a \tan \theta(1 + \sin \theta)$
    $x' = -a \sin \theta$
    $y' = a \tan \theta(1 - \sin \theta)$

Review Exercise 2.7, Page 70

2. *(a)* 0   *(d)* $-\dfrac{\sqrt{3}}{2}$ *(g)* 2

(b) $\frac{1}{2}$ *(e)* $-\dfrac{1}{\sqrt{2}}$ *(h)* $\dfrac{2}{\sqrt{3}}$

(c) 1   *(f)* $-\dfrac{1}{\sqrt{3}}$ *(i)* 1

4. *(a)* 2, 2π, 0   *(e)* 5, 2π, $-\dfrac{\pi}{3}$

(b) 1, π, 0   *(f)* 7, 6π, $-\dfrac{3\pi}{2}$

(c) 2, $\dfrac{2\pi}{3}$, 0   *(g)* 2, $\dfrac{\pi}{2}$, 0

(d) $\dfrac{1}{3}$, 4π, 0

6. *(a)* $\dfrac{12}{13}$, $\dfrac{5}{12}$ *(c)* $-\dfrac{2\sqrt{2}}{3}$, $2\sqrt{2}$

(b) $\dfrac{4}{5}$, $-\dfrac{4}{3}$ *(d)* $-\dfrac{\sqrt{21}}{5}$, $-\dfrac{2\sqrt{21}}{21}$

9. *(a)* $-\dfrac{\pi}{3}$ *(d)* $-\dfrac{\pi}{4}$ *(g)* 0

(b) $\dfrac{\pi}{3}$ *(e)* $\dfrac{5\pi}{6}$ *(h)* $\dfrac{\sqrt{3}}{2}$

(c) $\dfrac{\pi}{6}$ *(f)* $\dfrac{\pi}{6}$ *(i)* $\dfrac{3}{5}$

Exercise 3.1, Page 76

3. *(a)* $\sin x$ *(c)* $\sin x$
    (b) $-\cos x$ *(d)* $-\cos x$

4. $\dfrac{\sqrt{6} - \sqrt{2}}{4}$

5. $\dfrac{\sqrt{6} + \sqrt{2}}{4}$

6. $-\frac{1}{2}$

7. (a) $-\dfrac{\sqrt{3}}{2}$ (c) $-\dfrac{1}{2}$

(b) $-\dfrac{1}{\sqrt{2}}$ (d) $-\dfrac{1}{\sqrt{2}}$

9. (a) $-\dfrac{33}{65}$ (b) $\dfrac{63}{65}$ (c) $\dfrac{63}{65}$

10. $\cos(a+b) = \dfrac{24}{25}$, $\cos(a-b) - 0$

11. $-\dfrac{85}{13}$

Exercise 3.2, Page 79

3. $\dfrac{\sqrt{3}-1}{2\sqrt{2}}$

4. $\dfrac{\sqrt{3}}{2}$

5. (a) $\dfrac{1}{2}$ (b) $\dfrac{1}{\sqrt{2}}$ (c) $-\dfrac{1}{2}$ (d) $-\dfrac{1}{\sqrt{2}}$

7. (a) $\dfrac{56}{65}$ (b) $\dfrac{16}{65}$ (c) $-\dfrac{16}{65}$

8. -1, $\dfrac{7}{25}$

9. $\dfrac{85}{84}$

Exercise 3.3, Page 82

3. $\dfrac{\sqrt{3}-1}{1+\sqrt{3}}$

4. $\dfrac{\sqrt{3}+1}{\sqrt{3}-1}$

5. $\tan\dfrac{\pi}{2}$ is undefined

6. (a) $-\dfrac{1}{\sqrt{3}}$ (c) $\sqrt{3}$

(b) -1 (d) $\dfrac{1+\sqrt{3}}{1-\sqrt{3}}$

8. $x+y \neq n\pi,\ x \neq n\pi,$
$y \neq n\pi,\ n \in I$

9. $x-y \neq n\pi,\ x \neq n\pi,$
$y \neq n\pi,\ n \in I$

10. (a) $\dfrac{56}{33}$ (b) $\dfrac{16}{63}$ (c) $-\dfrac{16}{63}$

11. $\dfrac{103}{25}$

13. 1

Exercise 3.4, Page 85

4. (a) $\dfrac{24}{25}$ (b) $\dfrac{7}{25}$ (c) $\dfrac{24}{7}$

5. (a) $-\dfrac{120}{169}$ (b) $-\dfrac{119}{169}$ (c) $\dfrac{120}{119}$

7. (b) $\dfrac{1}{\sqrt{5}}$, $-\dfrac{2}{\sqrt{5}}$

8. (a) $-\dfrac{2\sqrt{2}}{3}$ (b) $\dfrac{7}{9}$ (c) $-\dfrac{4\sqrt{2}}{9}$

13. (a) $\dfrac{3}{\sqrt{13}}$ (b) $-\dfrac{2}{\sqrt{13}}$ (c) $-\dfrac{3}{2}$

14. $-\dfrac{3}{\sqrt{10}}$, $\dfrac{1}{\sqrt{10}}$

Exercise 3.5, Page 91

4. $\dfrac{7}{25}$, $\dfrac{7}{24}$, $\dfrac{25}{7}$, $\dfrac{25}{24}$, $\dfrac{24}{7}$

5. $\dfrac{5}{\sqrt{34}}$, $-\dfrac{3}{\sqrt{34}}$, $\dfrac{\sqrt{34}}{5}$, $-\dfrac{\sqrt{34}}{3}$, $-\dfrac{3}{5}$

6. $-\dfrac{2}{\sqrt{29}}$, $\dfrac{5}{2}$, $-\dfrac{\sqrt{29}}{5}$, $-\dfrac{\sqrt{29}}{2}$, $\dfrac{2}{5}$

7. $-\dfrac{1}{\sqrt{50}}$, $\dfrac{7}{\sqrt{50}}$, $-\dfrac{1}{7}$, $-\sqrt{50}$, -7

8. $\dfrac{1}{\sqrt{2}}$, $\dfrac{1}{\sqrt{2}}$, 1, $\sqrt{2}$, $\sqrt{2}$, 1

9. (a) $\dfrac{\sqrt{3}}{2}$, $\dfrac{1}{2}$, $\sqrt{3}$, $\dfrac{2}{\sqrt{3}}$, 2, $\dfrac{1}{\sqrt{3}}$

(b) $\dfrac{1}{2}$, $\dfrac{\sqrt{3}}{2}$, $\dfrac{1}{\sqrt{3}}$, 2, $\dfrac{2}{\sqrt{3}}$, $\sqrt{3}$

10. (a) $\dfrac{1+\sqrt{3}}{2\sqrt{2}}$ (c) $-\dfrac{(1+\sqrt{3})}{2\sqrt{2}}$

(b) $\dfrac{1-\sqrt{3}}{2\sqrt{2}}$ (d) $-\dfrac{(1+\sqrt{3})}{2\sqrt{2}}$

11. (a) $\dfrac{\sqrt{3}-1}{2\sqrt{2}}$ (c) $\dfrac{1-\sqrt{3}}{2\sqrt{2}}$

(b) $\dfrac{1+\sqrt{3}}{2\sqrt{2}}$ (d) $\dfrac{\sqrt{3}+1}{2\sqrt{2}}$

12. 18 cm   **15.** $225°$

13. $\dfrac{7}{5}$ rad   **18.** (b) $426\frac{2}{3}$

14. $\dfrac{\pi}{3}$ rad   (c) $101\frac{1}{4}$

Exercise 3.6, Page 95

1. (a) $77°$ (c) $11°$

(b) $18°$ (d) $27°$

3. $18°$, $72°$

4. $20°$, $15°$, $145°$

5. $-\dfrac{1}{3}$ or 3

6. $5x+y+13 = 0$ or $x-5y+13 = 0$

7. $37°$, $34°$, $109°$

8. $-7-5\sqrt{2}$, $-7+5\sqrt{2}$

Exercise 3.7, Page 101

3. (a) $-\sin 40°$ (d) $-\sec 28°$
  (b) $-\cos 17°$ (e) $-\csc 32°$
  (c) $-\tan 64°$ (f) $\cot 80°$

4. (a) $-\sin 75°$ (d) $-\sec 40°$
  (b) $-\cos 30°$ (e) $-\csc 10°$
  (c) $\tan 65°$ (f) $-\tan 30°$

5. (a) $-\sin 10°$ (f) $\cot 30°$
  (b) $\cos 15°$ (g) $\sin 20°$
  (c) $-\tan 20°$ (h) $\cot 5°$
  (d) $\csc 20°$ (i) $-\csc 20°$
  (e) $-\sec 20°$

6. for secant: $-\sec x,\ -\sec x,\ \sec x$
  for cosecant: $\csc x,\ -\csc x,\ -\csc x$
  for cotangent: $-\cot x,\ \cot x,\ -\cot x$

7. for secant: $\csc x,\ -\csc x,\ -\csc x,$
  $\csc x$
  for cosecant: $\sec x,\ \sec x,\ -\sec x,$
  $-\sec x$
  for cotangent: $\tan x,\ -\tan x,$
  $\tan x,\ -\tan x$

Exercise 3.8, Page 104

2. (a) $5 \sin (x + 0.927)$; amp $= 5$,
    phase shift $= -0.927$
  (b) $5 \sin (x - 0.927)$; amp $= 5$,
    phase shift $= 0.927$
  (c) $B\sqrt{2} \sin (x + 0.785)$;
    amp $= B\sqrt{2}$,
    phase shift $= -0.785$
  (d) $\sqrt{26} \sin (x + 1.37)$
    amp $= \sqrt{26}$,
    phase shift $= -1.37$

3. (a) $5 \cos (x - 0.927)$
  (b) $5 \cos (x - 2.22)$

4. (b) $\sqrt{5} \sin (2x - 0.463)$
    phase shift $= 0.2315$;
    amp $= \sqrt{5}$

Review Exercise 3.9, Page 105

2. (a) $\frac{63}{65}$ (c) $\frac{56}{65}$ (e) $-\frac{63}{16}$
  (b) $-\frac{33}{65}$ (d) $-\frac{16}{65}$ (f) $-\frac{33}{56}$

3. $\dfrac{\sqrt{3} - 1}{2\sqrt{2}}, \ \dfrac{\sqrt{3} + 1}{2\sqrt{2}}$

4. (a) $-\frac{475}{493}$ (b) $\frac{468}{493}$

6. (a) $\frac{33}{65}$ (b) $\frac{16}{65}$

7. (a) 0.052 (b) 0.999 (c) 0.358

8. $-\frac{140}{221}, \ \frac{220}{221}, \ \frac{140}{221}, \ -\frac{220}{221}$

9. (a) $\frac{24}{25}$ (b) $\frac{7}{25}$ (c) $\frac{24}{7}$

10. $\frac{119}{169}$; quadrant 4

11. $\frac{4}{3}$; quadrant 1

12. (a) $\dfrac{\sqrt{3}}{2}$ (b) $\dfrac{1}{2}$

13. (a) $37°$ (c) parallel
   (b) $90°$ (d) $79°$

14. $7x - y = 35, \ x + 7y = 5$

15. (a) $\dfrac{\sqrt{2}}{10}$ (b) $-\dfrac{7\sqrt{2}}{10}$ (c) $-\dfrac{1}{7}$

17. $-\sqrt{74} \cos (2x + 0.63)$
   or $\sqrt{74} \cos (2x + 3.76)$

18. $\sqrt{34} \sin (x - 1.03)$

Exercise 4.1, Page 112

7. (a) $A'(-4, 3)$ (c) $C'(-6, 0)$
  (b) $B'(-16, 8)$ (d) $D'(-7, 1)$

8. (a) $(3, 4)$ (c) $(1, 4)$
  (b) $(-9, -4)$ (d) $(-10, -2)$

9. (a) $(-3, -4)$ (c) $(-1, -4)$
  (b) $(9, 4)$ (d) $(10, 2)$

10. (a) $P_1' (4, 6), \ P_2'(-1, 9)$

11. (a) $P_1' (x_1 + h, \ y_1 + k)$
    $P_2' (x_2 + h, \ y_2 + k)$

12. $x - y + 2 = 0$

13. $4x + 11y + 86 = 0$

14. $3x + y - 17 = 0$

15. $3x - y - 16 = 0$

16. (a) $x^2 + y^2 - 4x - 8y - 5 = 0$
  (b) $(2, 4), \ 5$

17. (a) $y = -(x + 3)^2 + 2$
  (b) $(-3, 2), \ x = -3$

18. (b) Centre (h, k), radius $= r$

20. $\{(x, y) \mid x^2 + y^2 = 4\}$

21. $3x + 4y = 15$

23. $(x, y) \rightarrow (x + c + g - a - e,$
             $y + d + h - b - f)$

Exercise 4.2, Page 118

5. (a) $(-1, 0)$ (d) $(0, 2)$
  (b) $(-3, 0)$ (e) $(-1, 1)$
  (c) $(0, 1)$ (f) $(4, 3)$

430

6. (a) $(-2, 0)$ (c) $(-4, -3)$
   (b) $(0, 4)$ (d) $(-x, -y)$

7. (a) $\left(\dfrac{1}{2}, \dfrac{\sqrt{3}}{2}\right)$

   (b) $\left(\dfrac{-3\sqrt{3}}{2}, \dfrac{3}{2}\right)$

   (c) $\left(\dfrac{2 - 5\sqrt{3}}{2}, \dfrac{5 + 2\sqrt{3}}{2}\right)$

   (d) $\left(\dfrac{-1 - \sqrt{3}}{2}, \dfrac{1 - \sqrt{3}}{2}\right)$

   (e) $\left(\dfrac{1 + 2\sqrt{3}}{2}, \dfrac{\sqrt{3} - 2}{2}\right)$

   (f) $(0, 0)$

8. (a) $\left(\dfrac{1}{\sqrt{2}}, \dfrac{1}{\sqrt{2}}\right), \left(\dfrac{1}{\sqrt{2}}, \dfrac{7}{\sqrt{2}}\right)$

   (b) $\left(\dfrac{1}{2}, \dfrac{\sqrt{3}}{2}\right), \left(\dfrac{4 - 3\sqrt{3}}{2}, \dfrac{4\sqrt{3} + 3}{2}\right)$

   (c) $(0, 1), (-3, 4)$

   (d) $\left(\dfrac{\sqrt{3}}{2}, \dfrac{1}{2}\right), \left(\dfrac{4\sqrt{3} - 3}{2}, \dfrac{4 + 3\sqrt{3}}{2}\right)$

9. (a) $3\sqrt{2}$ (c) $3\sqrt{2}$
   (b) $3\sqrt{2}$ (d) $3\sqrt{2}$

10. (a) $30°$ (b) $225°$

11. $(-3, 4)$

12. (a) $-30°$

   (b) $x = \dfrac{\sqrt{3}u + v}{2}, y = \dfrac{-u + \sqrt{3}v}{2}$

13. (a) A rotation of $-\theta$
   (b) $x = u \cos \theta + v \sin \theta$
      $y = v \cos \theta - u \sin \theta$

14. $3y^2 - 4x^2 = 12$

15. $3x + y = 1$

16. No. A rotation is a rigid motion. Distance of $(3, 2)$ from $(0, 0)$ does not equal distance of $(-1, 4)$ from $(0, 0)$.

17. circle, centre $(2, 0)$, radius 3

19. Length is unchanged.

21. (a) $Q(-3, 2)$
   (b) $R(-2, -3)$
   (c) $P'(3, -2)$
   (e) $(x, y) \rightarrow$
      $[(x - a) \cos \theta - (y - b) \sin \theta,$
      $(x - a) \sin \theta + (y - b) \cos \theta]$

22. (a) Yes (b) Yes

23. $53°$

Exercise 4.3, Page 123

7. (a) $(3, -5), (-1, -2)$
   (c) $(-3, 5), (1, 2)$
   (d) $(5, 3), (2, -1)$

8. (a) $(x_1, -y_1), (x_2, -y_2)$
   (c) $(-x_1, y_1), (-x_2, y_2)$
   (d) $(y_1, x_1), (y_2, x_2)$

9. (a) $(0, 3)$ (d) $(2, 5)$
   (b) $(6, 3)$ (e) $(2, -9)$
   (c) $(2, -1)$ (f) $(-3, -2)$

10. (a) $y = -x^2 - 4$
   (b) $y = x^2 + 4$
   (c) $x = y^2 + 4$

11. (a) $y = -3(x - 2)^2 - 5$
   (b) $y = 3(x + 2)^2 + 5$
   (c) $x = 3(y - 2)^2 + 5$

12. (a) $(x, y) \rightarrow (x + 2, y)$
   (b) $(x, y) \rightarrow (x, y - 6)$
   (c) $(x, y) \rightarrow (-x, -y)$

Exercise 4.4, Page 129

4. (a) $A'(-3, -6), B'(-12, -18),$
      $C'(-21, -3)$
   (b) $AB = 5, A'B' = 15$
      $BC = \sqrt{34}, B'C' = 3\sqrt{34}$
      $AC = \sqrt{37}, A'C' = 3\sqrt{37}$

5. (a) $P'(8, 0), Q'(-4, 0),$
      $R'(0, -3), T'(0, 6)$
   (b) $PQ = 3, RT = 9$
      $P'Q' = 12, R'T' = 9$

6. (a) $P'(2, 0), Q'(-1, 0),$
      $R'(0, 9), T'(0, -18)$
   (b) $PQ = 3, RT = 9$
      $P'Q' = 3, R'T' = 27$

7. (a) $P'(4, 0), Q'(-2, 0),$
      $R'(0, -15), T'(0, 30)$
   (b) $PQ = 3, RT = 9$
      $P'Q' = 6, R'T' = 45$

8. (a) $x^2 + y^2 = 4$
   (b) $9x^2 + y^2 = 9$
   (c) $4x^2 + 9y^2 = 36$

12. (a) $A'(0, 0), B'(1, 0),$ (c) No
      $C'(7, 2), D'(8, 2)$

13. (a) $A'(0, 0), B'(1, 2),$ (b) No
      $C'(1, 4), D'(2, 6)$

15. $(x, y) \rightarrow (abx, aby)$

16. $(x, y) \rightarrow (-x, -y)$; symmetry about origin

17. The ratio of the two areas is $1 : a^2$.

18. $(x, y) \rightarrow (ax, by)$

19. $(x, y) \rightarrow (x, -y)$; symmetry about the x axis

20. The area is increased by a factor of b.

22. Increases from 4 to $4ab$ square units

23. $|x - ky| \leq 1$, $|y| \leq 2$. Area invariant

Exercise 4.5, Page 135

1. (a) $\begin{bmatrix} x + 2y \\ 3x + y \end{bmatrix}$ (e) $\begin{bmatrix} 17 \\ 2 \end{bmatrix}$

(b) $\begin{bmatrix} 3x - y \\ 4x \end{bmatrix}$ (f) $\begin{bmatrix} 4 \\ 5 \end{bmatrix}$

(c) $\begin{bmatrix} 2x \\ 2y \end{bmatrix}$ (g) $\begin{bmatrix} -14 \\ -8 \end{bmatrix}$

(d) $\begin{bmatrix} -2x + 8y \\ 6x - y \end{bmatrix}$ (h) $\begin{bmatrix} -4 \\ -16 \end{bmatrix}$

2. (a) Stretch in the x direction
$\begin{bmatrix} a & 0 \\ 0 & 1 \end{bmatrix}$

(b) Stretch in the y direction
$\begin{bmatrix} 1 & 0 \\ 0 & b \end{bmatrix}$

(c) Two-way stretch
$\begin{bmatrix} a & 0 \\ 0 & b \end{bmatrix}$

(d) Shear in the x direction
$\begin{bmatrix} 1 & k \\ 0 & 1 \end{bmatrix}$

(e) Shear in the y direction
$\begin{bmatrix} 1 & 0 \\ k & 1 \end{bmatrix}$

(f) Reflection through the y axis
$\begin{bmatrix} -1 & 0 \\ 0 & 1 \end{bmatrix}$

3. (a) $A'(1, 1), B'(1, -1),$
$C'(-1, -1), D'(-1, 1)$

(b) $A'(2, 2), B'(2, -2),$
$C'(-2, -2), D'(-2, 2)$

(c) $A'(-3, 2), B'(-1, 4),$
$C'(3, -2), D'(1, -4)$

4. (a) $P'(2x + 5y, x + 3y)$
(b) $P''(x, y)$

5. (a) $A'(2, -2), B'(-2, -2),$
$C'(-2, 2), D'(2, 2)$

(b) $A'(2, 2), B'(2, -2),$
$C'(-2, -2), D'(-2, 2)$

(c) $A'(-2, 2), B'(2, 2),$
$C'(2, -2), D'(-2, -2)$

6. (a) $\begin{bmatrix} \cos \theta & -\sin \theta \\ \sin \theta & \cos \theta \end{bmatrix}$

(b) $\begin{bmatrix} -1 & 0 \\ 0 & -1 \end{bmatrix}$ $\begin{bmatrix} 1 & 0 \\ 0 & 1 \end{bmatrix}$

8. (a) A rotation of $-\theta$ about the origin

(b) $\begin{bmatrix} \cos \theta & \sin \theta \\ -\sin \theta & \cos \theta \end{bmatrix}$

9. (b) Reflection in the y axis
(c) Reflection in the y axis
(d) $\begin{bmatrix} -1 & 0 \\ 0 & 1 \end{bmatrix}$

11. (a) $(1, 0) \rightarrow (-1, 0)$
$(0, 1) \rightarrow (0, -1)$

(b) $\begin{bmatrix} -1 & 0 \\ 0 & -1 \end{bmatrix}$

(c) $(x, y) \rightarrow (-x, -y)$

Exercise 4.6, Page 141

1. (a) $\begin{bmatrix} 2 & -3 \\ 4 & 1 \end{bmatrix}$ (c) $\begin{bmatrix} -4 & 7 \\ -3 & -5 \end{bmatrix}$

(b) $\begin{bmatrix} 1 & 0 \\ 3 & 5 \end{bmatrix}$ (d) $\begin{bmatrix} 1 & -4 \\ 1 & 0 \end{bmatrix}$

2. (a) $AB = \begin{bmatrix} 1 & 0 \\ 2 & -1 \end{bmatrix}$ (c) $AB = \begin{bmatrix} 7 & -7 \\ -9 & 15 \end{bmatrix}$

(b) $AB = \begin{bmatrix} 8 & 6 \\ 10 & 0 \end{bmatrix}$

3. (a) $BA = \begin{bmatrix} 1 & 0 \\ -2 & -1 \end{bmatrix}$ (c) $BA = \begin{bmatrix} -2 & -6 \\ 15 & 24 \end{bmatrix}$

(b) $BA = \begin{bmatrix} 5 & 15 \\ 5 & 3 \end{bmatrix}$

$AB \neq BA$

4. $\begin{bmatrix} 0 & -1 \\ -1 & 0 \end{bmatrix}$ **5.** $\begin{bmatrix} -1 & k \\ 0 & 1 \end{bmatrix}$ **6.** $\begin{bmatrix} k & 0 \\ 0 & -k \end{bmatrix}$

7. $\begin{bmatrix} \dfrac{a}{\sqrt{2}} & \dfrac{-b}{\sqrt{2}} \\ \dfrac{a}{\sqrt{2}} & \dfrac{b}{\sqrt{2}} \end{bmatrix}$

8. $\begin{bmatrix} 0 & -1 \\ 1 & 0 \end{bmatrix}$ **9.** $\begin{bmatrix} 0 & 1 \\ -1 & 0 \end{bmatrix}$

Quarter-turn

10. $AB - \begin{bmatrix} 0 & 1 \\ 1 & 0 \end{bmatrix}$ $BA - \begin{bmatrix} 0 & -1 \\ -1 & 0 \end{bmatrix}$

11. (a) $(x, y) \rightarrow (x + 4, -y + 5)$
(b) $(x, y) \rightarrow (x + 4, -y - 5)$

12. (a) $(x, y) \rightarrow (x + ay + h, y + k)$
(b) $(x, y) \rightarrow (x + ay + h + ak,$
$y + k)$

13. (a) $AB = \begin{bmatrix} au + bw & av + bt \\ cu + dw & cv + dt \end{bmatrix}$

(b) $BA = \begin{bmatrix} au + cv & bu + dv \\ aw + ct & bw + dt \end{bmatrix}$
$\therefore AB \neq BA$

14. $\begin{bmatrix} \cos(\theta_1 + \theta_2) & -\sin(\theta_1 + \theta_2) \\ \sin(\theta_1 + \theta_2) & \cos(\theta_1 + \theta_2) \end{bmatrix}$

15. (a) $\begin{bmatrix} 2x + y \\ 7x + 4y \end{bmatrix}$ (b) $\begin{bmatrix} 4 & -1 \\ -7 & 2 \end{bmatrix}$

16. (a) $\begin{bmatrix} 2 & -3 \\ -1 & 2 \end{bmatrix}$ (c) $\begin{bmatrix} \frac{1}{3} & 0 \\ 0 & \frac{1}{3} \end{bmatrix}$

(b) $\begin{bmatrix} 1 & -2 \\ 0 & 1 \end{bmatrix}$

17. (a) $\dfrac{1}{aw - ub} \begin{bmatrix} w & -b \\ -u & a \end{bmatrix}$ (b) $aw = ub$

Review Exercise 4.7, Page 143

5. Translations, rotations of 180° and 360°, dilatations.

6. (a) $(2, -7)$ (c) (a, b)
(b) $(-1, -5)$

7. (a) $(x, y + 1)$
(b) $(x - 1, y - 2)$
(c) $(x + 5, y - 5)$

8. (a) $(-3, -2)$ (c) $(-m, -s)$
(b) $(4, -5)$

9. $(-9, 8)$

Answers/Chapter 4

10. (a) $(4 - x, y)$ (c) $(2a - x, y)$
(b) $(x, -6 - y)$ (d) $(x, 2b - y)$

11. $x - 2y + 12 = 0$

12. (a) $(0, 2)$ (c) $(-3, 4)$
(b) $(3, 0)$ (d) $(6, -5)$

13. (a) $(-2, 0)$ (c) $(-4, -3)$
(b) $(0, 3)$ (d) $(5, 6)$

14. (a) $\left(\dfrac{1}{\sqrt{2}}, \dfrac{1}{\sqrt{2}} \right)$ (d) $(-\sqrt{2}, 0)$

(b) $\left(-\dfrac{1}{\sqrt{2}}, \dfrac{1}{\sqrt{2}} \right)$ (e) $\left(\dfrac{x - y}{\sqrt{2}}, \dfrac{x + y}{\sqrt{2}} \right)$

(c) $(0, \sqrt{2})$ (f) $(\sqrt{2}b, \sqrt{2}a)$

15. (a) $\left(\dfrac{1}{2}, \dfrac{\sqrt{3}}{2} \right)$

(b) $\left(-\dfrac{3\sqrt{3}}{2}, \dfrac{3}{2} \right)$

(c) $\left(\dfrac{\sqrt{3} - 1}{2}, -\dfrac{\sqrt{3} + 1}{2} \right)$

(d) $\left(\dfrac{-3 - 4\sqrt{3}}{2}, \dfrac{-3\sqrt{3} + 4}{2} \right)$

16. (a) $(-y, x)$ (b) $(-x, -y)$

(c) $\left(\dfrac{x - y}{\sqrt{2}}, \dfrac{x + y}{\sqrt{2}} \right)$

(d) $\left(\dfrac{\sqrt{3}x - y}{2}, \dfrac{x + \sqrt{3}y}{2} \right)$

(e) $(y, -x)$ (f) $\left(\dfrac{y - x}{\sqrt{2}}, \dfrac{-x - y}{\sqrt{2}} \right)$

17. (a) $u = \dfrac{1}{2}x - \dfrac{\sqrt{3}}{2}y,$
$v = \dfrac{\sqrt{3}}{2}x + \dfrac{1}{2}y$

(b) A rotation of $-\dfrac{\pi}{3}$ rad

(c) $x = \dfrac{1}{2}u + \dfrac{\sqrt{3}}{2}v, y = -\dfrac{\sqrt{3}}{2}u + \dfrac{1}{2}v$

18. $x = u \cos \theta + v \sin \theta$
$y = -u \sin \theta + v \cos \theta$

19. $CA \neq CB$ and a rotation is a rigid motion.

20. $x^2 + y^2 + 4x - 6y + 9 = 0$
$y = x^2 + 4x + 7$

21. $9x^2 + 4y^2 = 144$

22. (a) $A'(3, -4)$, $B'(-6, 8)$
    (b) $A'(12, -8)$, $B'(-24, 16)$
    (c) $A'(18, 6)$, $B'(-36, -12)$
    (d) $A'(-1, -2)$, $B'(2, 4)$

23. (a) one way stretch parallel to the y axis
    (b) dilatation of factor 4
    (c) two-way stretch
    (d) shear of factor 2 in the x direction.

25. (a) parallel to x axis
    (b) parallel to y axis

26. (a) 4, $\frac{1}{2}$
    (b) $\sqrt{20}$

27. (a) $\begin{bmatrix} x + 3y \\ 2x - y \end{bmatrix}$ (c) $\begin{bmatrix} mx + ty \\ sx + py \end{bmatrix}$

    (b) $\begin{bmatrix} 2x + y \\ -2y \end{bmatrix}$

28. (a) $\begin{bmatrix} \dfrac{1}{\sqrt{2}} & -\dfrac{1}{\sqrt{2}} \\ \dfrac{1}{\sqrt{2}} & \dfrac{1}{\sqrt{2}} \end{bmatrix}$ (d) $\begin{bmatrix} 1 & 0 \\ -4 & 1 \end{bmatrix}$

                           (e) $\begin{bmatrix} 6 & 0 \\ 0 & 6 \end{bmatrix}$

    (b) $\begin{bmatrix} 0 & 1 \\ -1 & 0 \end{bmatrix}$ (f) $\begin{bmatrix} 2 & 7 \\ -4 & 0 \end{bmatrix}$

    (c) $\begin{bmatrix} 0 & 1 \\ 1 & 0 \end{bmatrix}$ (g) $\begin{bmatrix} 1 & -3 \\ 8 & 1 \end{bmatrix}$

29. $a = -\frac{5}{4}$, $b = 10$

30. $P'(4, -8)$, $Q'(12, -4)$, $R'(-4, 8)$, $S'(-12, 4)$

32. (a) $\begin{bmatrix} -3 & 0 \\ 0 & -3 \end{bmatrix}$ (c) $\begin{bmatrix} 2 & 3 \\ 1 & 19 \end{bmatrix}$

    (b) $\begin{bmatrix} -2 & -1 \\ -1 & 0 \end{bmatrix}$

33. $\begin{bmatrix} 0 & -1 \\ -1 & 0 \end{bmatrix}$

34. $\begin{bmatrix} -5 & -2 \\ 3 & 1 \end{bmatrix}$

35. (a) $\begin{bmatrix} \frac{1}{2} & 0 \\ 0 & \frac{1}{2} \end{bmatrix}$ (c) $\begin{bmatrix} 1 & -2 \\ 0 & 1 \end{bmatrix}$

    (b) $\begin{bmatrix} -1 & 0 \\ 0 & -1 \end{bmatrix}$ (d) $\begin{bmatrix} 2 & -1 \\ -3 & 2 \end{bmatrix}$

37. $4\sqrt{5}$

434

Exercise 5.1, Page 150

1. (a) $x^2 + y^2 - 10x - 16y + 25 = 0$
   (b) $x^2 + y^2 - 10x + 24y = 0$
   (c) $x^2 + y^2 + 12x = 0$
   (d) $x^2 + y^2 + 6x + 6y + 2 = 0$

2. (a) $x^2 + y^2 \pm 20x + 16y + 64 = 0$
   (b) $x^2 + y^2 + 10x - 10y + 25 = 0$
   (c) $x^2 + y^2 + 6x - 8y = 0$
   (d) $x^2 + y^2 - 4x - 10y - 72 = 0$
   (e) $x^2 + y^2 - 8x + 4y = 0$
   (f) $x^2 + y^2 \pm 8x - 10y + 16 = 0$

3.

	Centre	Radius
(a)	(3, 5)	10
(b)	(−6, 8)	10
(c)	$(2\frac{1}{4}, 0)$	$\frac{9}{4}$
(d)	(−6, 4)	7
(e)	$(-\frac{1}{2}, 0)$	1

6. (a) $x^2 + y^2 - 6x + 8y + 16 = 0$
       or
       $x^2 + y^2 - 6x + 20y + 100 = 0$
   (b) $x^2 + y^2 \pm 14x \pm 14y + 49 = 0$
   (c) $x^2 + y^2 \pm 16x \pm 8y + 64 = 0$
   (d) $x^2 + y^2 - 6x = 0$ or
       $x^2 + y^2 - 2x - 8 = 0$

7. $x^2 + y^2 - 2x - 4 = 0$

8. $x^2 + y^2 + 6y - 32 = 0$

9. $x^2 + y^2 - 10x - 10y + 25 = 0$
   $x^2 + y^2 - 58x - 58y + 841 = 0$

10. $x^2 + y^2 - 6x - 28y + 99 = 0$

11. $x^2 + y^2 - 8y - 9 = 0$

12. $x^2 + y^2 - 14x - 4y - 5 = 0$

13. $x + 2y + 4 = 0$

15. $x^2 + y^2 - 4x + 6y - 12 = 0$

16. $x^2 + y^2 - 18x - 4y + 65 = 0$
    $x^2 + y^2 - 18x + 36y + 385 = 0$

17. (a) (1, 1), 2
    (b) perpendicular diameters

Exercise 5.2, Page 155

3. (a) $x^2 + y^2 + 6x + 9$
   (b) $x^2 + y^2$
   (c) $x^2 + y^2 - 4x + 104 - 20\sqrt{(x - 2)^2 + y^2}$
   (d) $x^2 + y^2 + 2x + 10 - 6\sqrt{(x + 1)^2 + y^2}$

4. (a) $4x^2 + y^2 = 100$
(b) $4x^2 + y^2 = 400$
(c) $16x^2 + y^2 = 400$
(d) $9x^2 + 16y^2 = 576$

5. (a) The x and y axes.
(b) (i) Major axis, y axis, 20.
Minor axis, x axis, 10.
(ii) Major axis, y axis, 40.
Minor axis, x axis, 20.
(iii) Major axis, y axis, 40.
Minor axis, x axis, 10.
(iv) Major axis, x axis, 16.
Minor axis, y axis, 12.

6. (a) $16x^2 + 25y^2 = 400$
(c) $16x^2 + 25y^2 = 400$
(d) The same.
(e) Major axis, x axis, 10.
Minor axis, y axis, 8.
(g) $5, -5$
(h) The same.

7. (a) $25x^2 + 16y^2 = 400$
(c) $25x^2 + 16y^2 = 400$
(d) The same.
(e) Major axis, y axis, 10.
Minor axis, x axis, 8.
(g) $5, -5$

8. (a) $x^2 + 4y^2 = 100$
$4x^2 + y^2 = 400$
(c) $k < 1$ (d) $k > 1$

9. (a) $A_1A_2 = 2a$

10. (a) $b^2x^2 + a^2y^2 = a^2b^2$
(b) $b^2x^2 + a^2y^2 = a^2b^2$

11. (a) $a^2x^2 + b^2y^2 = a^2b^2$
(b) $a^2x^2 + b^2y^2 = a^2b^2$

13. $(x, y) \to (x, 3y)$

15. $(x, y) \to (\frac{10}{3}x, 5y)$

19. $9x^2 + y^2 = 81$

Exercise 5.3, Page 161

3. (a) x axis
(b) x-intercepts 5, -5
y-intercepts 3, -3
(c) $\dfrac{x^2}{25} + \dfrac{y^2}{9} = 1$
(d) $c = 4$
(e) $(-4, 0), (4, 0)$

4. (a) y axis
(b) x-intercepts 5, -5
y-intercepts 13, -13

(c) $\dfrac{x^2}{25} + \dfrac{y^2}{169} = 1$
(d) $c = 12$
(e) $(0, 12), (0, -12)$

5.

	a	b	c
(a)	5	4	3
(b)	13	12	5
(c)	10	5	$5\sqrt{3}$
(d)	5	1	$2\sqrt{6}$
(e)	3	2	$\sqrt{5}$
(f)	8	$2\sqrt{7}$	6

6. (a) $4x^2 + 9y^2 = 36$
(b) $\dfrac{x^2}{289} + \dfrac{y^2}{64} = 1$
(c) $\dfrac{x^2}{169} + \dfrac{y^2}{144} = 1$

7. (a) $3\frac{4}{5}, 6\frac{1}{5}$

8. (a) $x^2 + y^2 - 6x - 8y - 39 = 0$
(b) $\dfrac{(x - 3)^2}{64} + \dfrac{(y - 2)^2}{16} = 1$
(c) $a = 8, b = 4$

9. (a) $\dfrac{(x - 2)^2}{36} + \dfrac{(y - 3)^2}{9} = 1$
(b) $\dfrac{(x + 2)^2}{64} + \dfrac{(y + 7)^2}{4} = 1$
(c) $\dfrac{(x + 4)^2}{9} + \dfrac{(y - 6)^2}{81} = 1$
(d) $\dfrac{(x - 3)^2}{16} + \dfrac{(y + 5)^2}{36} = 1$

10. $\dfrac{x^2}{64} + \dfrac{y^2}{48} = 1$

11. $9x^2 + 16y^2 = 324$

12. (c) $10\sqrt{2}, 10$

Exercise 5.4, Page 166

3. (a) $y = \frac{1}{8}x^2$
(c) Focus of original $= (2, 0)$
Focus of image $= (0, 2)$

5. (a) $x^2 = 4y$ (c) $x^2 = -4y$
(b) $y^2 = -4x$

6. (a) $x^2 = -10y$ (c) $y^2 = 10x$
(b) $y^2 = -10x$ (d) $x^2 = 10y$

7. (a) $y = -\frac{1}{16}x^2$
(b) $y^2 = 10x, \ y = -\frac{1}{10}x^2$
(c) $x^2 = 24y$

Answers/Chapter 5

8. (a) (3, 0) $x = -3$
   (b) (0, -2) $y = 2$
   (c) (0, $\frac{1}{6}$) $y = -\frac{1}{6}$
   (d) ($-\frac{7}{8}$, 0) $x = \frac{7}{8}$
   (e) ($\frac{3}{20}$, 0) $x = -\frac{3}{20}$
   (f) (0, $1\frac{5}{12}$) $y = -1\frac{5}{12}$

9. (a) $y^2 = 4x$ (c) $y^2 = \frac{4}{9}x$
   (b) $y^2 = 2x$

10. (a) $y = \dfrac{1}{k^2} \times x^2$

   (b) For $k > 1$, the image becomes wider as k increases.
   (c) As k increases, the focus moves farther from the vertex.
   (d) $0 < k < 1$, the image becomes narrower as k decreases.
   (e) As k decreases, the focus moves nearer the vertex.

11. (a) (7, 5)   (c) $y^2 = 16x$
   (b) $(y - 5)^2 = 16(x - 3)$

13. (a) $x^2 = -50y$ (b) 40 m

14. (a) $x^2 = 630\,y$ (c) 3.97 m
   (b) 17.5 m

15. 29 m

16. 2.5 cm

17. 18 m

18. (a) 16   (b) $\left|4a\right|$ (c) $\left|4a\right|$

20. $y^2 = 2ax$

22. $AB = 2$, $BP = 3$

Exercise 5.5, Page 174

2. (a) $D_A = \{x \in R \mid \left|x\right| \geqslant 2\}$
   Range is R.
   Asymptotes $x = y$, $x = -y$
   (b) $D_B = \{x \in R \mid \left|x\right| \geqslant 2\}$
   Range is R.
   Asymptotes $y = 4x$, $y = -4x$
   (c) Domain is R.
   $R_C = \{y \in R \mid \left|y\right| \geqslant 2\}$
   Asymptotes $x = \frac{3}{2}y$, $x = -\frac{3}{2}y$
   (d) Domain is R.
   $R = \{y \in R \mid \left|y\right| \geqslant 1\}$
   Asymptotes $x = y$, $x = -y$
   (e) Domain and Range are R.

3. (a) ellipse or circle
   (b) two straight lines parallel to y axis

   (c) hyperbola
   (d) If $k > 0$, the curve is an ellipse with major axis 2. The minor axis decreases as k increases causing the ellipse to flatten out.
   If $k < 0$, the curve is a hyperbola undergoing similar change.

4. (a) hyperbola, foci on the x axis; symmetric about both axis and origin
   (b) two intersecting straight lines
   (c) hyperbola, foci on the y axis
   (d) hyperbola, the distance of the vertices from the origin is large

5. (a) $144x^2 - 25y^2 = 3600$

6. (a) $16x^2 - 9y^2 = -144$

Exercise 5.6, Page 179

1. $y^2 = -8x$

2. (a) $9x^2 + 25y^2 = 225$
   (b) $9x^2 + 25y^2 = 225$
   (c) $(-4, 0)$, $(4, 0)$
   $x = \frac{25}{4}$, $-\frac{25}{4}$

3. (a) $5x^2 - 4y^2 = 180$
   (b) $5x^2 - 4y^2 = 180$
   (c) $(9, 0)$, $(-9, 0)$, $x = 4$, $x = -4$

4. $3x^2 + 4y^2 - 48x + 144 = 0$

5. $5x^2 - 4y^2 + 40x - 16y - 116 = 0$

6. $x = 3$, -6

7. (a) (3, 0)
   (b) (4, 0), (12, 0)
   (c) $(-12, 0)$, (2.4, 0); no

8. (a) $25x^2 + 16y^2 + 400y + 1600 = 0$
   (b) $y = -5$, -20
   (c) 15
   (d) (0, $-12\frac{1}{2}$)
   (e) 12

9. (a) $5x^2 + 9y^2 - 180x + 900 = 0$
   (b) $x = 6$, 30
   (c) $(x, y) \rightarrow (x - 18, y)$
   (d) $\dfrac{x^2}{144} + \dfrac{y^2}{80} = 1$
   (e) Ellipse

10. (a) $x^2(1 - e^2) + y^2 - 2fx + f^2 = 0$
   (c) Hyperbola
   (f) $y^2 = 2fx - f^2$: Parabola

(d)

	Intercepts	
e	$\dfrac{f}{1+e}$	$\dfrac{f}{1-e}$
$1\frac{1}{2}$	$\dfrac{2f}{5}$	$-2f$
$1\frac{1}{4}$	$\dfrac{4f}{9}$	$-4f$
$1\frac{1}{10}$	$\dfrac{10f}{21}$	$-10f$
$1\frac{1}{100}$	$\dfrac{100f}{201}$	$-100f$
$1\frac{1}{1000}$	$\dfrac{1000f}{2001}$	$-1000f$

Exercise 5.7, Page 187

4. (a) 4, 2
   (b) $(4, 0)$, $(-4, 0)$
   (c) $(2\sqrt{3}, 0)$, $(-2\sqrt{3}, 0)$
   (d) $\dfrac{\sqrt{3}}{2}$
   (e) $x = \dfrac{8\sqrt{3}}{3}$ or $x = -\dfrac{8\sqrt{3}}{3}$

5. (a) 4, 3; vertices $(4, 0)$, $(-4, 0)$;
   foci $(\sqrt{7}, 0)$, $(-\sqrt{7}, 0)$;
   $e = \dfrac{\sqrt{7}}{4}$; $x = \dfrac{16\sqrt{7}}{7}$, $x = -\dfrac{16\sqrt{7}}{7}$

   (b) 2, $\sqrt{3}$; vertices $(2, 0)$, $(-2, 0)$;
   foci $(1, 0)$, $(-1, 0)$; $e = \frac{1}{2}$;
   $x = 4$, $x = -4$

   (c) 2, 4; vertices $(0, 4)$, $(0, -4)$;
   foci $(0, 2\sqrt{3})$, $(0, -2\sqrt{3})$;
   $e = \dfrac{\sqrt{3}}{2}$; $y = \dfrac{8}{\sqrt{3}}$, $y = -\dfrac{8}{\sqrt{3}}$

   (d) 2, $\sqrt{3}$; vertices $(0, 2)$, $(0, -2)$;
   foci $(0, 1)$, $(0, -1)$;
   $e = \frac{1}{2}$; $y = 4$, $y = -4$

6. (a) 4, 6
   (b) $(4, 0)$, $(-4, 0)$
   (c) $(2\sqrt{13}, 0)$, $(-2\sqrt{13}, 0)$
   (d) $e = \dfrac{\sqrt{13}}{2}$
   (e) $x = \dfrac{8\sqrt{13}}{13}$, $x = -\dfrac{8\sqrt{13}}{13}$

7. (a) 4, 3; vertices $(4, 0)$, $(-4, 0)$;
   foci $(5, 0)$, $(-5, 0)$; $e = \frac{5}{4}$;
   $x = \frac{16}{5}$, $x = -\frac{16}{5}$

(b) 6, $3\sqrt{2}$; vertices $(6, 0)$, $(-6, 0)$;
   foci $(3\sqrt{6}, 0)$, $(-3\sqrt{6}, 0)$;
   $e = \dfrac{\sqrt{6}}{2}$; $x = 2\sqrt{6}$, $x = -2\sqrt{6}$

(c) 5,5; vertices $(0, 5)$, $(0, -5)$;
   foci $(0, 5\sqrt{2})$, $(0, -5\sqrt{2})$;
   $e = \sqrt{2}$; $y = \dfrac{5\sqrt{2}}{2}$, $y = -\dfrac{5\sqrt{2}}{2}$

(d) $3\sqrt{2}$, 6; vertices $(0, 3\sqrt{2})$,
   $(0, -3\sqrt{2})$;
   foci $(0, 3\sqrt{6})$, $(0, -3\sqrt{6})$;
   $e = \sqrt{3}$; $y = \sqrt{6}$, $y = -\sqrt{6}$

8. $e = \dfrac{\sqrt{3}}{2}$

9. (a) $x^2 + 4y^2 = 64$
   (b) $4x^2 + 3y^2 = 108$
   (c) $x^2 + 2y^2 = 50$
   (d) $3x^2 + 4y^2 = 192$
   (e) $9x^2 + 5y^2 = 180$

10. $3x^2 + 4y^2 = 12$

11. (a) $25x^2 - 9y^2 = 225$
    (b) $9x^2 - 16y^2 = 144$
    (c) $4x^2 - 5y^2 = 180$
    (d) $x^2 - y^2 = 25$
    (e) $7x^2 - 9y^2 = 252$
    (f) $7x^2 - 9y^2 = 144$
    (g) $5x^2 - 4y^2 = 80$
    (h) $x^2 - 9y^2 = 36$

12. (a) $5x^2 - 4y^2 = 180$
    (b) $16x^2 - 9y^2 = -144$
    (c) $3x^2 - y^2 = 48$
    (d) $9x^2 - 16y^2 = -144$

13. $x^2 - 3y^2 + 108 = 0$

14. $x^2 + 4y^2 = 12$

15. $\dfrac{\sqrt{2}}{2}$

17. 4 cm, 14.4 cm

18. (a) $x^2 + 4y^2 = 400$, $y \geqslant 0$
    (b) $5\sqrt{3}$ m

19. $x^2 + 5y^2 = 9$

20. $16x^2 + 7y^2 = 256$

21. $3x^2 + 5y^2 = 32$

22. (a) $3x^2 - 4y^2 = 48$
    (b) $7x^2 - 4y^2 = 108$

25. (a) $a = b$ (c) $(0, 0)$
    (b) $x^2 + y^2 = a^2$

Review Exercise 5.8, Page 192

1. $(5, -6)$, $\sqrt{59}$ $(0, \frac{7}{4})$, $\dfrac{\sqrt{41}}{4}$
   $(3, 4)$, 5

2. (a) $x^2 + y^2 + 4x - 6y - 3 = 0$
   (b) $x^2 + y^2 + 12x - 6y + 36 = 0$
   (c) $x^2 + y^2 + 6x - 10y - 7 = 0$
   (d) $x^2 + y^2 + 6x + 6y + 9 = 0$

3. (a) parabola   (e) parabola
   (b) circle   (f) ellipse
   (c) ellipse   (g) hyperbola
   (d) hyperbola   (h) point $(0, 0)$

4. (a) $(2, 0)$, $x = -2$
   (b) $(0, -5)$, $y = 5$
   (c) $(-\frac{4}{3}, 0)$, $x = \frac{4}{3}$

5. $x^2 = -20y$

6. $49x^2 + 9y^2 = 441$

7. (a) 4, 3, $\sqrt{7}$, $\dfrac{\sqrt{7}}{4}$

   (b) 3, 2, $\sqrt{5}$, $\dfrac{\sqrt{5}}{3}$

   (c) 8, 5, $\sqrt{89}$, $\dfrac{\sqrt{89}}{8}$

   (d) 2, 4, $2\sqrt{5}$, $\sqrt{5}$

   (e) 6, 4, $2\sqrt{5}$, $\dfrac{\sqrt{5}}{3}$

   (f) 2, 4, $2\sqrt{5}$, $\sqrt{5}$

8. (a) $49x^2 + 9y^2 = 441$
   (b) $25x^2 + 9y^2 = 225$
   (c) $64x^2 + 25y^2 = 1600$
   (d) $25x^2 + 9y^2 = 900$

9. (a) $81x^2 - 25y^2 = -2025$
   (b) $4x^2 - 49y^2 = -196$
   (c) $9x^2 - 4y^2 = -144$
   (d) $5x^2 - 4y^2 = -180$

10. $9x^2 - 16y^2 = 144$

11. $\dfrac{5\sqrt{17}}{2}$

12. (a) 2, $\sqrt{3}$
    (b) $(0, 1)$, $(0, -1)$
    (c) $(0, 2)$, $(0, -2)$
    (d) $\frac{1}{2}$
    (e) $y = 4$

13. $x^2 + 2y^2 = 64$

14. (a) $5x^2 + 9y^2 + 4x - 64 = 0$
    (b) $8x^2 - y^2 + 28x + 20 = 0$

15. 24 m

16. (a) $\sqrt{2059}$ m from centre,
    $e = \frac{1}{50}\sqrt{2059}$
    (b) $\dfrac{x^2}{2500} + \dfrac{y^2}{441} = 1$
    (c) $\dfrac{21\sqrt{3}}{2}$ m

17. 15 m or 45 m

18. $(10\sqrt{5} - 10)$ m

19. (a) $4x^2 + y^2 = 4$
    (b) $x^2 + 9y^2 = 9$
    (c) $x^2 + 16y^2 = 1$
    (d) $4x^2 + y^2 = 1$

20. (a) $y = 2x^2$ (b) $x^2 = -y$

21. (a) slope increases
    (b) slope decreases

23. (a) $9x^2 + y^2 = 1$
    (b) $3x^2 + 3y^2 - 2x = 0$
    (c) $9x^2 - 4y^2 = 36$
    (d) $y^2 = -36x$

24. (a) $(x, y) \rightarrow (2x, y)$
    (b) $(x, y) \rightarrow \left(x, \dfrac{y}{2}\right)$

25. (a) $25x^2 + 9y^2 = 225$
    (b) $x^2 + y^2 = 1$

26. (a) $9x^2 + 4y^2 = 900$
    (b) $x^2 + 4y^2 = 25$
    (c) $9x^2 + 16y^2 = 3600$
    (d) $16x^2 + 9y^2 = 3600$

28. (a) $(x, y) \rightarrow (4x, 6y)$
    (b) $(x, y) \rightarrow \left(\dfrac{3x}{4}, \dfrac{5y}{4}\right)$
    (c) $(x, y) \rightarrow (2x, y)$
    (d) $(x, y) \rightarrow (\frac{5}{6}x, \frac{1}{3}y)$

29. ellipse, hyperbola

30. $3x^2 + 4y^2 = 84$

31. $4x^2 = 9y$

33. $2x^2 - 2y^2 = 9$

34. $144x^2 - 25y^2 = -3600$

35. $16x^2 + 7y^2 = 112$

36. $4x^2 - y^2 = 144$

38. $\frac{1}{59}$

39. $\dfrac{x^2}{900} - \dfrac{y^2}{9100} = 1$

Exercise 6.1, Page 200

1. (a) (3, 4)
   (b) (4, −3), (−4, 3)
   (c) none

3. (a) (15, −25), (−6, −4)
   (b) (−2, −2), (−3, 1)
   (c) (1, 4), (−2, 7)
   (d) (3, $\frac{1}{3}$), ($\frac{1}{3}$, 3)

4. (a) (2, −4), (−1, −1)
   (b) (2, 3), (4, 1)
   (c) (1, −1), (−3, 5)
   (d) no real roots

5. (−5, −$\frac{20}{3}$)

6. $3x − y = 0$, $3x + y = 0$

7. no real roots

8. 1

9. 3, −3

Exercise 6.2, Page 203

1. $2x − 3y + 18 = 0$

2. $y = x − 5$

3. $x − y + 1 = 0$, $x − 5y + 25 = 0$

4. $2x + y − 6 = 0$, $2x − 3y + 2 = 0$

5. (a) $x − y + 3 = 0$
   (b) $x + 2y − 5 = 0$
   (c) $x + y + 2 = 0$
   (d) $3x + y − 9 = 0$

6. (a) (3, 0)
   (b) (12, 12), ($\frac{3}{4}$, −3)
   (c) $x − 2y + 12 = 0$,
       $4x + 2y + 3 = 0$
   (d) (−3, $\frac{9}{2}$)
   (e) 90°

7. (a) $x − y + 3 = 0$
   (b) $y^2 = 3x$
   (c) $P'(3, 3)$. Yes
   (d) $x − 2y + 3 = 0$
   (e) $x − 2y + 3 = 0$

8. (a) $x + y + 2 = 0$
   (b) $x^2 = 4y$
   (c) (−2, 1). Yes
   (d) $x + y + 1 = 0$
   (e) $x + y + 1 = 0$

9. (a) $x − 2y + 6 = 0$
   (b) $2x + y − 18 = 0$
   (c) 12
   (d) 3

Exercise 6.3, Page 206

1. $3x − 2y = 12$, $3x − 2y = −12$

2. $16x + 9y − 28 = 0$,
   $16x + 9y + 28 = 0$

3. $2x − 9y = 26$, $2x − 9y = −26$

4. $3x − y = 10$, $3x − y = −10$

5. $x + 8y − 30 = 0$, $x + 8y + 30 = 0$

6. No tangent is possible.

8. (a) $3x + 4y − 25 = 0$
   (b) $x^2 + 4y^2 = 25$
   (c) (3, 2)
   (d) $3x + 8y − 25 = 0$
   (e) $3x + 8y − 25 = 0$

9. $2x − 9y − 20 = 0$

10. $3x + y − 7 = 0$

Exercise 6.4, Page 212

Apply the principles of reflection as outlined in Section 6.4.

Exercise 6.5, Page 215

1. (a) (4, 0), (−4, 0)
   (b) (4, 3), (−4, 3), (4, −3), (−4, −3)
   (c) ϕ
   (d) (0, 5)

3. {(0, 5), (0, −5), (6, 3), (−6, −3)}

4. (a) (3, 1), (−3, −1), (3, −1), (−3, 1)
   (b) (6, 3), (−6, −3)

5. (a) $x − 2y = 0$, $x − 4y = 0$
   (b) $\left(\sqrt{2}, \dfrac{1}{\sqrt{2}} \right), \left(-\sqrt{2}, -\dfrac{1}{\sqrt{2}} \right),$
       $\left(\dfrac{4}{\sqrt{5}}, \dfrac{1}{\sqrt{5}} \right), \left(\dfrac{-4}{\sqrt{5}}, \dfrac{-1}{\sqrt{5}} \right)$

6. (2, −2), (−2, 2), $\left(\dfrac{8}{\sqrt{31}}, \dfrac{2}{\sqrt{31}} \right),$
   $\left(\dfrac{-8}{\sqrt{31}}, \dfrac{-2}{\sqrt{31}} \right)$

7. (0, 1), (0, −1)

8. (a) $\left(\dfrac{2}{\sqrt{5}}, \dfrac{\pm 2}{\sqrt{5}} \right), \left(\dfrac{-2}{\sqrt{5}}, \dfrac{\pm 2}{\sqrt{5}} \right)$
   (b) $\left(\dfrac{12}{\sqrt{7}}, \dfrac{\pm 12}{\sqrt{7}} \right), \left(\dfrac{-12}{\sqrt{7}}, \dfrac{\pm 12}{\sqrt{7}} \right)$

9. (−3, 0), (1.5, 2.25)

10. (4, 6), (5, 5)

1. circle and parabola;
   $\{(4, -3), (-4, -3)\}$
   line and circle;
   $\{(5, 0), (-4, -3)\}$
   line and parabola;
   $\{(-4, -3), (\frac{20}{9}, -\frac{25}{27})\}$

Exercise 6.7, Page 220

1. $y^2 = 20x$

3. $y^2 = 2x$

4. $xy = \dfrac{k}{4}$

6. $y^2 + 4a(x - a) = 0$

7. $y = 0$
   $x^2 + y^2 - \dfrac{y}{2} = 0$

8. $y^2 = 2ax - a^2$

10. $(x^2 + y^2)^2 = 16xy$
    lemniscate

Review Exercise 6.8, Page 221

1. (a) $(1, 2)$, $(2, 1)$
   (b) $(\frac{85}{21}, \frac{13}{21})$, $(5, 3)$
   (c) $(3 + 2\sqrt{2}, 2 + 2\sqrt{2})$,
       $(3 - 2\sqrt{2}, 2 - 2\sqrt{2})$
   (d) $(4, -1)$, $(3, 2)$

2. (a) no real roots   (b) $(-4, 2)$

3. $x - y + 1 = 0$, $(1, 2)$

4. $3x + 4y + 16 = 0$

5. no tangents possible

6. $x + y - 3 = 0$

7. $x + y - 2 = 0$, $x + y + 2 = 0$

8. $2x - y + 18 = 0$, $2x - y - 18 = 0$

9. $2x - 3y + 25 = 0$,
   $2x - 3y - 25 = 0$

10. $5x - y - 4 = 0$, $5x - y + 4 = 0$

11. tangent at $(3, -2)$

12. $x + 2y = 12$, $x + 2y = -12$

14. (a) $(5, 3)$, $(-5, -3)$, $(5, -3)$, $(-5, 3)$
    (b) $(4, 9)$, $(9, 4)$, $(-4, -9)$, $(-9, -4)$
    (c) $(2, 4)$, $(-2, 4)$
    (d) $(4, 1)$, $(-4, -1)$, $(-4, 1)$, $(4, -1)$

19. (a) $(2, 2)$, $(2, -2)$, $(-2, 2)$, $(-2, -2)$

20. $(-3 + 2\sqrt{2})x - 5y = -20 + 10\sqrt{2}$
    $(-3 - 2\sqrt{2})x - 5y = -20 - 10\sqrt{2}$

21. $x + 2y - 12 = 0$

Exercise 7.1, Page 226

2. (a) $4x^2 + 9y^2 - 56x + 72y + 304 = 0$
   (b) $(4, -4)$, $(10, -4)$, $(7, -4)$,
       $(7 + \sqrt{5}, -4)$, $(7 - \sqrt{5}, -4)$;
       $x = 7$, $y = -4$

3. (a) $9x^2 - 16y^2 + 90x - 96y = 63$
   (b) $(-9, -3)$, $(-1, -3)$,
       $(-5, -3)$, $(0, -3)$, $(-10, -3)$;
       $x = -5$, $y = -3$

4. (a) $x^2 - 4y = 0$; parabola
   (b) $x^2 + y^2 = 25$; circle
   (c) $2x^2 + y = 0$; parabola
   (d) $4x^2 + 9y^2 = 144$; ellipse
   (e) $x^2 - 4y^2 + 4 = 0$; hyperbola

6. (a) $4x^2 - 48x + y^2 - 6y + 149 = 0$
       $(6, 1)$, $(6, 5)$, $(6, 3 + \sqrt{3})$,
       $(6, 3 - \sqrt{3})$; $x = 6$, $y = 3$
   (b) $y^2 - 6y - 87 + 16x = 0$
       $(6, 3)$, $(2, 3)$; $y = 3$
   (c) $x^2 - 12x + 60 = 8y$
       $(6, 3)$, $(6, 5)$; $x = 6$
   (d) $9x^2 + 4y^2 - 108x - 24y + 324 = 0$
       $(6, 6)$, $(6, 0)$, $(6, 3 + \sqrt{5})$,
       $(6, 3 - \sqrt{5})$; $x = 6$, $y = 3$
   (e) $4x^2 - y^2 - 48x + 6y + 139 = 0$
       $(6, 5)$, $(6, 1)$, $(6, 3 + \sqrt{5})$,
       $(6, 3 - \sqrt{5})$; $x = 6$, $y = 3$
   (f) $x^2 + y^2 - 12x - 6y - 36 = 0$

7. (a) $xy - 4y + 3x = 24$
   (b) $(4, -3)$; $x = 4$, $y = -3$

8. (a) $4x^2 - y^2 + 48x + 4y + 140 = 0$

9. $y^2 - 2y - 8x - 23 = 0$

10. the axes; $xy - 3x + 2y - 6 = 0$

12. (a) $3h + 4k = 0$
    (b) $ah + bk = 0$

13. $(x, y) \rightarrow (x + \frac{1}{2}, y + \frac{1}{4})$

14. $(x, y) \rightarrow (x - 2, y)$

Exercise 7.2, Page 233

2. (a) $(x, y) \rightarrow (x - 1, y + 2)$
   (b) $(x, y) \rightarrow (x + 1, y + 2)$
   (c) $(x, y) \rightarrow (x + 2, y - 2)$
   (d) $(x, y) \rightarrow (x + 6, y - \frac{3}{4})$

3. (a) $(x, y) \to (x + 1, y - 5)$
(b) $(x, y) \to (x - 3, y + 1)$
(c) $(x, y) \to (x - 1, y + 2)$
(d) $(x, y) \to (x - 8, y - 6)$;
(e) $(x, y) \to (x + 2, y - 1)$
(f) $(x, y) \to (x - 3, y + 2)$

6. (a) $(x, y) \to (x + \frac{1}{4}, y - \frac{1}{2})$
(b) two intersecting lines
(d) $4, -1$

7. (a) hyperbola; centre $(-1, 1)$; vertices $(-1, 0)$, $(-1, 2)$
(b) ellipse; centre $(-3, 4)$; vertices $(0, 4)$, $(-6, 4)$

8. (a) $(-1, -6)$, $(-1, -5\frac{23}{24})$
(b) $(-7, -4)$, $(-6, -4)$

9. (a) $(-a, a)$, a, a
(b) $(2a, -a)$, $2a$, $\sqrt{2}a$
(c) $(-a, b)$, a, b (d) (a, a), 1, 1

10. (b) $g^2 + f^2 = c$, $g^2 + f^2 - c < 0$

11. There is no locus.

13. Two intersecting straight lines called asymptotes.

Exercise 7.3, Page 240

2. $x^2 + 3y^2 - 8\sqrt{3}x - 8y - 2\sqrt{3}xy = 0$
3. $5x^2 + 5y^2 + 6xy = 8$
4. $x^2 - \sqrt{3}xy + 6 = 0$
5. (a) $y^2 - x^2 = 2$
(b) $x^2 + 3y^2 = 18$
(c) $y^2 + 16x = 0$
7. $y = 0$
8. (a) $x^2 - y^2 = -3$
(b) $2x^2 + y^2 = 4$
(c) $3x^2 - 4y^2 = -6$
(d) $x^2 + y^2 = 3$
9. (a) $xy = \frac{1}{2}$
(b) $13x^2 + 13y^2 - 10xy = 2$
(c) $x^2 + 2xy + y^2 - 16\sqrt{2}y + 16\sqrt{2}x = 0$
(d) $x^2 + y^2 + 10xy = 12$
10. (a) $\sqrt{3}x + y = 0$
(b) $x^2 + y^2 = 4$
(c) $2x^2 - 2\sqrt{3}xy + 1 = 0$
(d) $5x^2 - 2\sqrt{3}xy + 3y^2 = 3$

Exercise 7.4, Page 248

1. $32°$

2. (a) hyperbola; $\frac{\pi}{4}$ rad
(b) hyperbola; $\frac{\pi}{8}$ rad
(c) hyperbola; $\frac{\pi}{6}$ rad
(d) parabola; $\frac{\pi}{4}$ rad
(e) hyperbola; $-\frac{\pi}{12}$ rad
(f) ellipse; $\frac{3\pi}{8}$ rad

3. (a) ellipse; $\frac{\pi}{4}$; $4x^2 + 9y^2 = 4$
(b) hyperbola; $\frac{\pi}{6}$; $x^2 - y^2 = 1$
(c) hyperbola; $\frac{\pi}{4}$; $x^2 - y^2 = 8$
(d) parabola; $\frac{\pi}{4}$; $y^2 = 2x$
(e) ellipse; $-\frac{\pi}{6}$; $x^2 + 3y^2 = 18$
(f) parabola; $-\frac{\pi}{6}$; $y^2 = 2x$

4. (b) two parallel straight lines
(d) $(x + y + 1)(x + y - 1) = 0$
6. (a) $\frac{\pi}{4}, \frac{3\pi}{4}$ (b) $\sqrt{\dfrac{c}{h + a}}$, $\sqrt{\dfrac{c}{h - a}}$
(c) (i) $a^2 > h^2$; (ii) $a^2 < h^2$; (iii) $a = h$

Exercise 7.5, Page 253

1. (a) $\frac{\pi}{4}$ (b) $-36°$ (c) $63°$ (d) $32°$
2. (a) hyperbola   (d) parabola
(b) ellipse   (e) ellipse
(c) hyperbola   (f) ellipse
3. (a) Centre $(\sqrt{2}, -5\sqrt{2})$
Vertices $(2 + \sqrt{2}, -2 - 5\sqrt{2})$, $(-2 + \sqrt{2}, 2 - 5\sqrt{2})$
Foci $(3\sqrt{2}, -7\sqrt{2})$, $(-\sqrt{2}, -3\sqrt{2})$
(b) Centre $\left(\dfrac{-2\sqrt{3} + 1}{2}, \dfrac{2 + \sqrt{3}}{2}\right)$
Vertices $\left(\dfrac{1}{2}, \dfrac{\sqrt{3}}{2}\right)$,
$\left(\dfrac{-4\sqrt{3} + 1}{2}, \dfrac{4 + \sqrt{3}}{2}\right)$
Foci $(2 - \sqrt{3}, 1)$, $(-1 - \sqrt{3}, \sqrt{3} + 1)$

(c) Centre $(-2, 2)$

Vertices

$$\left(\sqrt{\frac{11}{2}} - 2, -\sqrt{\frac{11}{2}} + 2\right),$$

$$\left(-\sqrt{\frac{11}{2}} - 2, \sqrt{\frac{11}{2}} + 2\right)$$

Foci $\left(\sqrt{\frac{22}{3}} - 2, -\sqrt{\frac{22}{3}} + 2\right),$

$$\left(-\sqrt{\frac{22}{3}} - 2, \sqrt{\frac{22}{3}} + 2\right)$$

(e) Centre $\left(\dfrac{1}{\sqrt{2}}, \dfrac{3}{\sqrt{2}}\right)$

Vertices

$$\left(\frac{3}{\sqrt{2}}, \frac{5}{\sqrt{2}}\right), \left(-\frac{1}{\sqrt{2}}, \frac{1}{\sqrt{2}}\right)$$

Foci $\left(\dfrac{\sqrt{3} + 1}{\sqrt{2}}, \dfrac{\sqrt{3} + 3}{\sqrt{2}}\right),$

$$\left(\frac{-\sqrt{3} + 1}{\sqrt{2}}, \frac{-\sqrt{3} + 3}{\sqrt{2}}\right)$$

(f) Centre $\left(-\dfrac{1}{3}, \dfrac{1}{3}\right)$

Vertices

$$\left(\frac{-1 + \sqrt{30}}{3}, \frac{1 + \sqrt{30}}{3}\right),$$

$$\left(\frac{-1 - \sqrt{30}}{3}, \frac{1 - \sqrt{30}}{3}\right)$$

Foci

$$\left(\frac{-1 + 2\sqrt{5}}{3}, \frac{1 + 2\sqrt{5}}{3}\right),$$

$$\left(\frac{-1 - 2\sqrt{5}}{3}, \frac{1 - 2\sqrt{5}}{3}\right)$$

4. (d) Vertex $\left(\dfrac{1}{8}, \dfrac{-\sqrt{3}}{8}\right)$

Focus $\left(\dfrac{5}{8}, \dfrac{-5\sqrt{3}}{8}\right)$

$y = -\sqrt{3}x$

5. $(-6, -10)$

6. (c) $\cos\theta = \frac{4}{5}$, $\sin\theta = \frac{3}{5}$
   (e) $2x^2 + y^2 = 4$

8. (a) $x^2 + y^2 - 2y - 2x - 2xy + 1 = 0$

   (b) Vertex $\left(0, \dfrac{1}{2\sqrt{2}}\right)$

442

1. (a) $x^2 - 6x = 2y - 13$
   (b) $x^2 + y^2 - 8x - 4y + 19 = 0$
   (c) $2x^2 - y^2 - 12x + 4y + 11 = 0$
   (d) $x^2 + 3y^2 - 2x - 18y + 19 = 0$
   (e) $4x^2 + 9y^2 - 24x - 36y + 36 = 0$
   (f) $y^2 - 4y - 4x + 12 = 0$

2. (a) $x^2 + y^2 + 20x - 2y + 85 = 0$
   (b) $(-10, 1)$, 4

3. (a) $144x^2 - 25y^2 - 864x - 100y + 4796 = 0$
   (b) $(3, -2)$, $(3, 10)$, $(3, -14)$, $(3, 11)$, $(3, -15)$; $x = 3$, $y = -2$

4. $16x^2 + 25y^2 - 64x + 200y + 64 = 0$

5. (a) $(x, y) \rightarrow (x - 1, y + 3)$
   (b) ellipse; centre $(1, -3)$; major axis 8, minor axis 4

6. (a) $(x, y) \rightarrow (x + 2, y - 1)$
   (b) parabola; vertex $(-2, 1)$; focus $(-1, 1)$ and directrix $x = -3$

7. (a) $(2, -2)$ (c) $(\frac{1}{2}, -2)$
   (b) $(3, -1)$ (d) $(-2, -3)$

8. (a) parabola   (d) ellipse
   (b) parabola   (e) hyperbola
   (c) circle   (f) hyperbola

9. (a) hyperbola   (c) parabola
   (b) ellipse   (d) hyperbola

10. (a) $x^2 - xy + y^2 = 2$
    (b) $y^2 - x^2 = -4$
    (c) $x^2 + y^2 - 2xy - 4\sqrt{2}x - 4\sqrt{2}y = 0$
    (d) $5x^2 - 26xy + 5y^2 + 2 = 0$

11. (a) $5x^2 + 7y^2 + 2\sqrt{3}xy = 24$
    (b) $17x^2 + 3y^2 - 14\sqrt{3}xy + 48 = 0$
    (c) $x^2 + 3y^2 + 2\sqrt{3}xy - 2y + 2\sqrt{3}x = 0$
    (d) $x^2 - 2\sqrt{3}xy - y^2 + 2 = 0$

12. (a) $\dfrac{\pi}{4}$ rad (b) $81°$ (c) $\dfrac{\pi}{8}$ rad (d) $60°$

13. (a) hyperbola   (c) ellipse
    (b) hyperbola   (d) parabola

14. $60°$

15. (a) ellipse   (c) ellipse
    (b) hyperbola   (d) parabola

16. (a) hyperbola   (d) parabola
    (b) ellipse   (e) ellipse
    (c) parabola   (f) parabola

17. (a) Centre $(-4, 2)$
Vertices $(2\sqrt{2} - 4, \ -2\sqrt{2} + 2)$,
$\qquad (-2\sqrt{2} - 4, 2\sqrt{2} + 2)$
Foci $(0, -2), (-8, 6)$
Semi-axes 4, 4.

(b) Centre $(-1, 1)$
Vertices $(1, -1), (-3, 3)$
Foci

$$\left(\frac{4}{\sqrt{6}} - 1, \ -\frac{4}{\sqrt{6}} + 1\right),$$

$$\left(-\frac{4}{\sqrt{6}} - 1, \ \frac{4}{\sqrt{6}} + 1\right)$$

Semi-axes $2\sqrt{2}, \ 2\sqrt{\dfrac{2}{3}}$

(e) Centre $\left(\dfrac{3}{\sqrt{2}}, \dfrac{1}{\sqrt{2}}\right)$,

Vertices

$$\left(\frac{5}{\sqrt{2}}, \frac{3}{\sqrt{2}}\right), \left(\frac{1}{\sqrt{2}}, \frac{-1}{\sqrt{2}}\right)$$

Foci

$$\left(\frac{\sqrt{3} + 3}{\sqrt{2}}, \frac{\sqrt{3} + 1}{\sqrt{2}}\right),$$

$$\left(\frac{-\sqrt{3} + 3}{\sqrt{2}} \ \frac{-\sqrt{3} + 1}{\sqrt{2}}\right)$$

Semi-axes 2, 1

Exercise 8.1, Page 261

6. 1320

7. 6840

8. (a) 720   (b) 240, 480

9. 676

10. 72

11. (a) 6840   (b) 8000

12. 720

13. 360

14. 120

15. 95 040

16. 14 400

17. 3 628 799

18. 17 576 000

19. 2

20. (a) 5040   (b) 5040

21. 86 400   **22.** 720

23. (a) 90 000   (c) 52 488
    (b) 1000   (d) 18 000

24. 3 999 960   **25.** 325

26. (a) 116   (b) 186   (c) 182

Exercise 8.2, Page 266

1. (a) 1320   (e) 504
    (b) 42   (f) 95 040
    (c) 9   (g) 10 100
    (d) 120   (h) 6720

2. (a) 95 040   (f) r
    (b) 210   (g) $n - r$
    (c) 190   (h) $(n - r + 1)(n - r)$
    (d) $n + 1$
    (e) $2n(2n - 1)$ (i) $\dfrac{1}{n - r + 1}$

3. (a) 7   (b) 8

4. 360

5. (a) 362 880   (c) 3024
    (b) 362 880

6. 151 200

7. 720

8. 87 091 200

9. (a) 2520 (b) 360 (c) 7560

10. 18

11. 720

12. (a) 10 080   (b) 30 240

13. 119

14. 4920

15. (a) 6   (b) 120

16. 600

18. 362 880

19. 720

20. (a) 5040   (b) 720

21. 720

23. 7

Exercise 8.3, Page 271

1. (a) 84   (c) 66
    (b) 84   (d) 190

2. (a) 10   (c) 10
    (b) 7   (d) 8

3. (a) 10 (b) 28 (c) 4845

4. 15   **5.** 28   **6.** 20

7. $\dfrac{n^2 - 3n}{2}$

8. 11 sides

9. 58 212

10. 220

11. 4950

12. 55

13. (a) 210 (b) 126 (c) 84

15. 383

16. 31

17. 47

18. 30

19. 66

20. $\dfrac{52!}{(13!)^4}$

21. $\dfrac{52!}{4!(13!)^4}$

Exercise 8.4, Page 277

4. (a) $a^4 + 8a^3b + 24a^2b^2 + 32ab^3$
$+ 16b^4$

(b) $x^5 - 5x^4y + 10x^3y^2 - 10x^2y^3$
$+ 5xy^4 - y^5$

(c) $27 - 162c + 324c^2 - 216c^3$

(d) $p^6 - 12p^5q + 60p^4q^2 - 160p^3q^3$
$+ 240p^2q^4 - 192pq^5 + 64q^6$

5. (a) $x^5 + 10x^3 + 40x + \dfrac{80}{x} + \dfrac{80}{x^3} + \dfrac{32}{x^5}$

(b) $1 - 4x^2 + 6x^4 - 4x^6 + x^8$

(c) $x^3 - 3x + \dfrac{3}{x} - \dfrac{1}{x^3}$

(d) $1 - 5x^3 + 10x^6 - 10x^9 + 5x^{12}$
$- x^{15}$

6. (a) $a^{50} + 50a^{49}x + 1225a^{48}x^2$

(b) $x^{100} - 100x^{99}y + 4950x^{98}y^2$

(c) $x^{80} - 40x^{78} + 780x^{76}$

(d) $\dfrac{a^{12}}{4096} + \dfrac{3a^{11}b^2}{128} + \dfrac{33a^{10}b^4}{32}$

Review Exercise 8.5, Page 278

1. (a) 360 (c) 1 (e) 8
(b) 15 (d) 362 880 (f) 924

2. 45

3. 16

4. 1440

5. 225

6. 12 144

7. (a) 8! or 40 320
(b) 8! × 3! or 241 920

8. (a) 10 (b) 10 (c) 20

9. $\dfrac{52!}{13!39!}$

10. $\dfrac{13!}{8!5!} \times \dfrac{13!}{9!4!} \times \dfrac{13!}{11!2!} \times \dfrac{13!}{11!2!}$

11. (a) 66 (b) 220

12. 10

13. 77

14. 3168

15. 70

16. 1 441 440

17. (a) 360 (c) 240
(b) 120 (d) 12

18. 14 400

19. 62

20. $n = 10$

21. (a) $1 - 5b + 10b^2 - 10b^3 + 5b^4 - b^5$

(b) $1 + 6x^2 + 15x^4 + 20x^6 + 15x^8$
$+ 6x^{10} + x^{12}$

(c) $16a^4 - 160a^3x + 600a^2x^2 -$
$1000ax^3 + 625x^4$

(d) $1 - 6x^3 + 15x^6 - 20x^9 + 15x^{12}$
$- 6x^{15} + x^{18}$

22. (a) $q^4 + 4q^3p + 6q^2p^2 + 4qp^3 + p^4$

(b) $q^4 = \frac{1}{81}, 4q^3p = \frac{8}{81}, 6q^2p^2 = \frac{24}{81},$
$4qp^3 = \frac{32}{81}, p^4 = \frac{16}{81}$

Exercise 9.1, Page 281

1. (a) $\{-2, -1, 0, 1, 2, 3, 4, 5\}$

(b) $\{-4, -3, -2, -1, 0\}$

(c) $\{2\}$

(d) ϕ

2. $\{1\}, \{2\}, \{3\}, \{1, 2\}, \{1, 3\},$
$\{2, 3\}, \{1, 2, 3\}, \phi$

3.

Set	Number of Subsets
ϕ	1
$\{a\}$	2
$\{a, b\}$	4
$\{a, b, c\}$	8
$\{a, b, c, d\}$	16

4. 2^n

5. (a) $\{2, 4, 6\}$

(b) $\{0, 1, 2, 3, 4, 5, 6\}$

6. (a) $\{2, 4, 6, 8\}$

(b) $\{1, 7, 8\}$

(c) ϕ

(d) A

444

1. (a) (1, 1), (1, 2), (1, 3), (1, 4),
      (1, 5), (1, 6)
      (2, 1), (2, 2), (2, 3), (2, 4),
      (2, 5), (2, 6)
      (3, 1), (3, 2), (3, 3), (3, 4),
      (3, 5), (3, 6)
      (4, 1), (4, 2), (4, 3), (4, 4),
      (4, 5), (4, 6)
      (5, 1), (5, 2), (5, 3), (5, 4),
      (5, 5), (5, 6)
      (6, 1), (6, 2), (6, 3), (6, 4),
      (6, 5), (6, 6)
   (b) (1, 1), (2, 1), (3, 1), (4, 1),
      (5, 1), (6, 1), (1, 2), (1, 3),
      (1, 4), (1, 5), (1, 6)
   (c) (1, 6), (2, 5), (3, 4), (4, 3),
      (5, 2), (6, 1)
   (d) (3, 6), (4, 5), (4, 6), (5, 4),
      (5, 5), (5, 6), (6, 3), (6, 4),
      (6, 5), (6, 6)

2. (a) (H, H, H)
   (b) (H, H, T), (H, T, H), (T, H, H)
   (c) (H, T, T), (T, H, T), (T, T, H)
   (d) (T, T, T)

3. (a) (H, 1), (II, 2), (H, 3), (H, 4),
      (H, 5), (H, 6), (T, 1), (T, 2),
      (T, 3), (T, 4), (T, 5), (T, 6)
   (b) (H, 1), (H, 3), (H, 5)
   (c) (T, 1), (T, 2)

4. (a) 13   (c) 1
   (b) 4

5. (a) equally likely   (d) face card
   (b) equally likely   more likely
   (c) heart more   (e) face card
       likely   more likely

6. (a) 5 red, 5 white
   (b) 6 red, 4 white; 7R, 3W;
       8R, 2W; 9R, 1W

7. (a) (1, 3), (2, 3), (3, 3), (3, 4),
      (3, 5), (3, 6), (4, 3), (5, 3),
      (6, 3), (3, 1), (3, 2)
   (b) (1, 1), (1, 2), (1, 4), (1, 5),
      (1, 6), (2, 1), (2, 2), (2, 4),
      (2, 5), (2, 6), (4, 1), (4, 2),
      (4, 4), (4, 5), (4, 6), (5, 1),
      (5, 2), (5, 4), (5, 5), (5, 6),
      (6, 1), (6, 2), (6, 4), (6, 5),
      (6, 6)
   (c) (1, 1), (2, 2), (3, 3), (4, 4),
      (5, 5), (6, 6)

   (d) (1, 2), (1, 3), (1, 4), (1, 5),
      (1, 6), (2, 1), (2, 3), (2, 4),
      (2, 5), (2, 6), (3, 1), (3, 2),
      (3, 4), (3, 5), (3, 6), (4, 1),
      (4, 2), (4, 3), (4, 5), (4, 6),
      (5, 1), (5, 2), (5, 3), (5, 4),
      (5, 6), (6, 1), (6, 2), (6, 3),
      (6, 4), (6, 5)

8. Represent cards by A_1, A_2, K_1,
   K_2, K_3. Proceed as in Question 7.

1. (a) $\frac{1}{36}$ (d) $\frac{1}{6}$
   (b) $\frac{1}{6}$ (e) $\frac{13}{18}$
   (c) $\frac{1}{12}$

2. (a) $\frac{1}{4}$ (c) $\frac{1}{2}$
   (b) $\frac{1}{4}$

3. (a) $\frac{1}{8}$ (d) $\frac{3}{8}$
   (b) $\frac{7}{8}$ (e) $\frac{1}{8}$
   (c) $\frac{3}{8}$

4. (a) $\frac{1}{4}$ (c) $\frac{1}{52}$
   (b) $\frac{1}{13}$ (d) $\frac{3}{13}$

5. (a) $\frac{2}{3}$ (b) $\frac{1}{3}$

6. $\frac{1}{3}$

8. (a) $\frac{4}{11}$ (b) $\frac{1}{11}$

9. (a) $\frac{1}{5}$ (c) $\frac{1}{2}$
   (b) $\frac{3}{10}$ (d) No chance

10. $\frac{3}{500}$

11. (a) $\frac{1}{2}$ (c) $\frac{1}{2}$
    (b) $\frac{1}{8}$ (d) $\frac{1}{4}$

12. $\frac{1}{66}$

13. $\frac{1}{120}$

14. (a) 2.5%   (b) 49.5%

5. (a) $\frac{1}{6}$ (f) $\frac{4}{9}$
   (b) $\frac{17}{18}$ (g) $\frac{5}{9}$
   (c) $\frac{11}{36}$ (h) $\frac{1}{9}$
   (d) $\frac{5}{12}$ (i) $\frac{4}{9}$
   (e) $\frac{4}{9}$

6. (a) $\frac{4}{9}$ (c) $\frac{2}{9}$
   (b) $\frac{7}{9}$ (d) 0

7. (a) $\frac{5}{39}$ (c) $\frac{1}{39}$
   (b) $\frac{1}{13}$ (d) $\frac{7}{39}$

8. $\frac{3}{5}$

Exercise 9.5, Page 294

4. (a) 0.28   (b) 0.42

5. 0.000 003

6. 0.027

7. $\frac{49}{120}$

8. 0.32

9. (a) 1 white in one container
9 white and 10 black in the other
(b) $\frac{1}{2} + \frac{1}{2} \times \frac{9}{19} \doteq 0.74$

10. (a) 0.9973   (c) 0.0082
    (b) 0.9918

Exercise 9.6, Page 297

1. $\frac{3}{20}$

3. (a) 0.04   (b) 24

4. (a) 96 198   (c) 0.033 54
    (b) 3226   (d) 0.966 46

5. (a) 97 158   (c) 0.015 01
    (b) 1458   (d) 0.984 99

6. (a) 0.714 74   (b) 0.842 23

7. (a) 0.841 67   (b) 0.912 86

10. (a) 50.997   (b) 32.509

Review Exercise 9.7, Page 299

1. (a) $\frac{5}{36}$ (c) $\frac{7}{36}$
    (b) $\frac{1}{18}$ (d) $\frac{5}{12}$

2. (a) $\frac{11}{36}$ (b) $\frac{3}{4}$ (c) $\frac{1}{6}$

3. (a) $\frac{1}{2}$ (b) $\frac{1}{2}$ (c) $\frac{2}{3}$

4. (a) $\frac{2}{9}$ (b) $\frac{2}{9}$
    (c) Yes. P(win) = P(lose)

5. (a) $\frac{1}{2}$ (c) $\frac{1}{3}$ (e) $\frac{4}{9}$
    (b) $\frac{2}{3}$ (d) $\frac{5}{6}$ (f) $\frac{31}{36}$

6. (a) $\frac{1}{6}$ (b) $\frac{1}{12}$ (c) $\frac{1}{11}$

7. (a) $\frac{1}{4}$ (b) $\frac{5}{22}$

8. $\frac{1}{128}$

9. (a) $\frac{1}{12}$ (b) $\frac{7}{12}$ (c) $\frac{5}{12}$

10. $\frac{1}{221}$

11. (a) $\frac{5}{72}$ (b) $\frac{35}{216}$

12. (a) $\frac{7}{45}$ (b) $\frac{1}{9}$ (c) $\frac{2}{9}$

13. $\frac{1}{3}$

14. $\frac{5}{18}$

15. (a) $\frac{1}{4}$ (b) $\frac{13}{16}$ (c) 1

16. (a) $\frac{1}{3}$ (b) $\frac{4}{9}$ (c) $\frac{2}{7}$

17. $\frac{1}{120}$

18. $\frac{1}{10}$

19. $\frac{49}{100}$

20. (a) 0.504   (c) 0.092
    (b) 0.398   (d) 0.006

21. (a) 0.5982   (b) 0.5043

Exercise 10.1, Page 305

1. (b) Median = 82
    (c) Upper quartile = 85
        Lower quartile = 78
    (d) Range = 18

2. (b) Median = 77.0
        Upper quartile = 80.5
        Lower quartile = 74.0

3. (b) Median = 167
        Upper quartile = 170
        Lower quartile = 165

Exercise 10.2, Page 308

2. (c) Median = 77.5 kg
        Upper quartile = 84.5 kg
        Lower quartile = 71.4 kg

3. (c) Median = 54
        Upper quartile = 71
        Lower quartile = 32

Exercise 10.3, Page 315

1. Mean = 75

2. (a) 5.3   (b) 5.3   (c) 6.2

4. \$69.12

5. (a) 5, 13 = 5 + 8
    (b) 5, 35 = 5 × 7

7. 68.9

8. 169.3 cm

9. 196.2

10. 11

11. (a) 175.3   (c) 175.7
     (b) 175.3

Exercise 10.4, Page 320

2. (a) 75   (c) 3.2
    (b) 76   (d) 3.8

3. Mean deviation = 7.6
    Standard deviation = 10.2

4.

	Machine A	Machine B
(a)	$\bar{X} = 1040$	$\bar{X} = 1020.4$
(b)	29.6	15.5

5. (a) 65   (c) 20.21
   (b) 68.33   (d) 24.7

6. (a) 7.12   (c) 7.12
   (b) 7.12

7. 1.63

10. (a) 75%   (b) 93.8%

11. (a) 2.9   (b) 1.16

12. (a) 65.2   (b) 10.8

Exercise 10.5, Page 325

3. $\frac{19}{27}$

4. 0.265

6. (a) $(\frac{3}{4} + \frac{1}{4})^5$ (b) $\frac{90}{1024}$
   (c) 90

7. $\frac{16}{81}, \frac{24}{81}$

8. (b) 0.349

Exercise 10.6, Page 330

1. (a) 0.2258   (d) 0.0606
   (b) 0.4821   (e) 0.7698
   (c) 0.4452   (f) 0.6853

2. (a) $4\frac{1}{2}$ (c) 2.3
   (b) 2.89   (d) 1.69

3. (a) 2   (c) 0.9105
   (b) $1\frac{1}{2}$ (d) 91.05%

4. 0.8186

5. 0.1728

6. (a) 84.13   (b) 27.42

7. (a) 1.5 deviations from the mean in the 93.32 percentile.
   (b) 0.5 deviations from the mean in the 30.85 percentile.

8. (a) 2.27%   (b) 454   (c) 1336

9. (a) 15.87% (b) 0.13% (c) 84%

10. (a) 6.68%   (c) 34 656
   (b) 6.68%   (d) 0:24

11. (a) 968   (b) 1540

12. Math, by 4.41 percentiles

Review Exercise 10.7, Page 332

1. (b) $\bar{X} = 0.55$
   (c) 0.86

2. (a) (i) 2   (ii) 2

4. (b) 1284   (e) 33.9
   (d) 1282

5. (b) 806   (e) 100.5
   (d) 816

7. (a) 42.3   (d) 6.17
   (b) 43   (e) 7.75

8. (a) 2.27% (b) 4761 (c) 81.86%

9. (b) 100   (c) 35.5

10. (a) 93.33   (b) 140

11. 7

Exercise 11.1, Page 339

4. (a) 1.425 76   (c) 2.292 02
   (b) 3.869 68   (d) 1.675 35

5. (a) $133.82   (d) $134.39
   (b) $1368.57   (e) $537.96
   (c) $938.07   (f) $1423.31

6. $15\frac{1}{2}$ years

7. $2508.05

8. $17\frac{1}{2}$ years

9. $269.16, $169.16

10. (a) 4.825 billion
   (b) 6.485 billion
   (c)

	1970	1980	1990	2000	2010	2020	2030	2040	2050	2060	2070
Rate of 1%	3.580	3.954	4.368	4.825	5.330	5.888	6.504	7.184	7.936	8.766	9.683
Rate of 2%	3.580	4.364	5.320	6.485	7.905	9.636	11.746	14.318	17.453	21.276	25.935

11. 1.7%

12. 5.997 billion, 19.990 billion

13. (b) $2 + \dfrac{(t-1)}{2t} + \dfrac{(t-1)(t-2)}{6t^2}$
$+ \cdots + \dfrac{1}{t^t}$

Exercise 11.2, Page 345

1. (a) 29.778 08   (c) 0.015 05
   (b) 16.096 90   (d) 0.076 68

2. (a) $5731.94   (c) $11 463.88
   (b) $30 516.22

3. $60 030.55

4. $3478.49, $578.49

5. 410.90

6. $292.00

7. $189.18

8. (a) $564.73

9. $442.15

10. $495.03

Exercise 11.3, Page 349

3. (a) 0.676 84   (c) 0.820 75
   (b) 0.553 68

4. (a) $84.75   (d) $441.01
   (b) $396.05   (e) $296.77
   (c) $820.35

5. $781.20

6. $310.70

7. 5.1%

8. $674.69

9. $33 229.69 Mike: $27 900.36
   Greg: $22 099.64

Exercise 11.4, Page 354

1. (a) 8.530 20   (c) 0.112 96
   (b) 18.424 38   (d) 0.166 61

2. (a) $7811.04   (d) $2431.64
   (b) $5405.21   (e) $1032.31
   (c) $7019.69

3. (a) $5808.53   (b) $461.78

4. $1349.33

5. $129.43, $8.57

6. $778.61

7. $85 637.40

8. (a) $36   (b) $4000

9. (a) $623.11   (b) $376.89

10. $871.80

11. $188.28

12. $644.64

Exercise 11.5, Page 360

1. $1081.60

3. (a) $237.40   (c) $38.75
   (b) $117.23

4. (a) $21.18   (b) $2.15

5. (a) $522.03   (b) $1176.24

6. $1097.90

7. (a) (i) $1527.75   (b) (i) $15 555.00
   (ii) $757.80   (ii) $15 312.00

8. $49.86

9. $2986.97

10. $1826.65

11. $21 051.32

12. $2672.47

13. $583.45

Exercise 11.6, Page 366

1. (a) $865.79   (c) $819.48
   (b) $912.11

2. $1827.08

3. $781.45

4. $826.26

5. $883.08

6. (a) $2.75\ a_{\overline{2n}|2\frac{1}{2}\%} + \dfrac{100}{(1.025)^{2n}}$

   (b) 12

7. $868.28

8. (b) $877.11

Review Exercise 11.7, Page 367

1. (a) $106.12   (d) $966.19
   (b) $651.56   (e) $317.43
   (c) $2427.26

2. (a) $67.68   (d) $371.78
   (b) $224.18   (e) $117.02
   (c) $208.29

3. 12

4. (a) $1200.61   (c) $6706.05
   (b) $8062.75   (d) $4307.69

5. (a) $938.51   (c) $27 355.48
   (b) $6527.50   (d) $212.43

6. (a) $667.03   (b) $1475.62

7. $733.59

8. $20.92

9. $271.80

10. $27.46

11. (a) $154.72

12. $738.13

13. $979.93

14. $1952.10

15. (a) $1081.50   (c) $17 304.00
    (b) $18 260.00

16. (a) $931.61   (c) $841.03
    (b) $999.54

17. $1191.98

18. $891.15, $308.85

19. $10 074.55

20. $103.42

21. (a) $3954.59   (b) $4228.73

22. $2531.04

23. $1104.60

24. $5482.16

3. (a) {1, 2, 3, 4}   (c) ϕ
   (b) {−2, −1, 0} (d) {3, 4, 5, ...}

5. T, F, F, F

6. F, F, F, T

7. T, T, T, F

9. (a) Bill is not ill today.
   (b) Our school does not have 730
       students.
   (c) No one is afraid.
   (d) Two people may have the
       same fingerprints.
   (e) Not all men are created
       equal.
   (f) At least one of us is capable
       of jumping 2 m.
   (g) No boys are mischievous.
   (h) Some students who are not
       clever score more than 95%.

10. T, F, F, F, F, F, F, F

Exercise 12.1, Page 375

4. (a) Point is undefined in
       mathematics.
   (b) Truth is undefined.
   (c) An object is sour if it has an
       acid or tart taste.
   (d) Between is undefined in
       mathematics.
   (e) Equals is a relation and
       $A = B$ if A and B are names
       for the same thing.
   (f) A rational number x is a
       member of the set Q where
       $$Q = \left\{ a, b \,\middle|\, \frac{a}{b} = x, a, b \in I, b \neq 0 \right\}.$$

6. (a) Write 'John' on the
       blackboard.
   (b) The '23' on your football
       jersey should be red.
   (c) Use '2', '7', or '9' to write
       '279'.
   (d) '$\triangle TOP$' and '$\triangle POT$' name
       the same triangle.

Exercise 12.2, Page 379

2. (a) $\sim Q$ (c) $P \wedge Q$
   (b) $\sim P$ (d) $Q \wedge \sim P$

Exercise 12.3, Page 384

4. (a) He did not put mustard on his
       hot dog or he did not put
       relish on his hot dog.
   (b) The triangle is not isosceles
       or the triangle is not
       right-angled.
   (c) The opposite sides are not
       equal or the opposite sides
       are not parallel.
   (d) The roots are not real or the
       roots are not equal.
   (e) $x \not> 2$ or $x \not< 7$.

6. (a) The triangles are not
       congruent and the triangles
       are not similar.
   (b) $x \neq 3$ and $x \neq 5$.
   (c) x is not a rational number and
       x is not an irrational number.
   (d) $x \not> 5$ and $x \neq 5$.

7. (a) −4 −3 −2 −1 0 1 2 3 4

   (b) −4 −3 −2 −1 0 1 2 3 4

   (c) −4 −3 −2 −1 0 1 2 3 4

   (d) −4 −3 −2 −1 0 1 2 3 4

8. (d)
$$\begin{matrix} (x + y - 7 = 0) \\ \vee \quad (2x - y + 4 = 0) \end{matrix}$$

9. (a)
$$\begin{matrix} (x - y - 3 = 0) \\ \vee \quad (x + 4y + 2 = 0) \end{matrix}$$
(b)
$$\begin{matrix} (3x + 4y - 12 = 0) \\ \vee \quad (3x - 4y + 12 = 0) \end{matrix}$$
(c) $(x - y = 0) \vee (x + y = 0)$

12. (a) $x + 1 = 0$ or $x - 7 = 0$
(b) $x - 4 = 0$ or $x + 3 = 0$

Exercise 12.4, Page 389

6. 'A and B are right angles implies that A and B are equal' is logically equivalent to 'It is not true that both A and B are right angles and $A \neq B$'.

9. 'Your name begins with B and you will not be placed in 13 A.'

Exercise 12.5, Page 391

2. Law of Detachment

3. (a) Argument is of the form
$$\frac{\begin{matrix} T \Rightarrow S \\ S \Rightarrow B \end{matrix}}{\therefore T \Rightarrow B}$$
(b) Argument is of the form
$$\frac{\begin{matrix} D \Rightarrow C \\ C \Rightarrow B \end{matrix}}{\therefore D \Rightarrow B}$$

4. $A \Rightarrow B$
$$\frac{A}{\therefore B}$$
$B \Rightarrow C$
$$\frac{B}{\therefore C}$$

8. $c \Rightarrow \sim i$
$\therefore i \Rightarrow \sim c$
$$\frac{i}{\therefore \sim c}$$
$p \vee c \Leftrightarrow \sim p \Rightarrow c$
$\sim p \Rightarrow c$
$\therefore \sim c \Rightarrow p$
$$\frac{\sim c}{\therefore \ p}$$
$p \Rightarrow w$
$$\frac{p}{\therefore w}$$

9. (a) $r \Rightarrow v$
$$\frac{r}{\therefore v}$$
Violets are blue.
(b) No valid conclusion possible.
(c) $r \Rightarrow l$
$$\frac{r}{\therefore l}$$
Logic is easy.
(d) $b \Rightarrow l$
$\therefore \sim l \Rightarrow \sim b$
$$\frac{\sim l}{\therefore \sim b}$$
Point A does not bisect segment XY.

Exercise 12.6, Page 394

In all six of these questions begin by symbolically representing each statement in the question. Then assume the negation of the implication to be proved. Use De Morgan's Law to transfer this to the form '$p \wedge \sim q$'. Use this to find a contradiction.

Exercise 12.7, Page 397

2. (a) $(3x - 6 = 0 \Rightarrow x = 2)$
$\wedge (x = 2 \Rightarrow 3x - 6 = 0)$
(b) (Two circles having equal area $\Rightarrow$ The radii are equal) $\wedge$ (Two circles having equal radii $\Rightarrow$ The areas are equal)
(c) (A point P equidistant from A and B $\Rightarrow$ P is on the right bisector of AB) $\wedge$ (A point P on the right bisector of AB $\Rightarrow$ P is equidistant from A and B)

3. (a) $(P \wedge Q) \Rightarrow R$
(b) $(R \wedge Q) \Rightarrow P$

4. (a) If $x + y = 9$ then $x = 2$ and $y = 7$
If $x + y = 9$ and $x = 2$ then $y = 7$
If $x + y = 9$ and $y = 7$ then $x = 2$
(b) If $x + y \geq 9$ then $x = 2$ and $y \geq 7$
If $x + y \geq 9$ and $x = 2$ then $y \geq 7$
If $x + y \geq 9$ and $y \geq 7$ then $x = 2$

1. (a) $A \Rightarrow B$ (d) $P \Rightarrow Q$
   (b) $Q \Rightarrow P$ (e) $A \Leftrightarrow B$
   (c) $X \Leftrightarrow Y$ (f) $K \Rightarrow L$

2. (a) $q \Rightarrow p$ is true
   (b) $p \Rightarrow q$, $q \Rightarrow p$, $p \Leftrightarrow q$
   (c) $q \Rightarrow p$
   (d) $q \Rightarrow p$
   (e) $q \Rightarrow p$
   (f) $p \Rightarrow q$, $q \Rightarrow p$, $q \Leftrightarrow p$

4. (a) $3x - 5 = 13$ and $x \neq 6$ or
   $x = 6$ and $3x - 5 \neq 13$.
   (b) Two angles of a triangle are
   equal and the triangle is not
   isosceles or two sides of a
   triangle are equal and the
   angles opposite the equal
   sides are not equal.
   (c) The roots of
   $ax^2 + bx + c = 0$, $a \neq 0$, are
   equal and $b^2 - 4ac \neq 0$, or
   $b^2 - 4ac = 0$ and the roots
   of $ax^2 + bx + c = 0$, $a \neq 0$,
   are not equal.

3. (a) the number 2
   (b) any rectangle
   (c) not true for $n = 41$

4. (a) $\exists_{x \in R}(x^2 = 4)$
   (b) For all triangles, the altitudes
   are concurrent
   (c) $\forall_{x \in R}[(x - 2)(x + 2) = x^2 - 4]$
   (d) $\exists_{x \in R}(x^2 \leq 0)$
   (e) $\forall_{x \in I}(3x \neq 10)$

5. (a) There exists at least one
   square which is not similar to
   all squares.
   (b) For all triangles, no triangles
   are equilateral.
   (c) $\exists_{x \in R}(|x| \not> 0)$

6. (a) For each y and each x,
   $xy = yx$. True.
   (b) For some y and some x,
   $x^2 = y^2 + 1$. True.

Employ a truth table in each of these
problems.

Answers/Chapter 12

1. (a) closed   (c) open
   (b) open   (d) open

2. (a) too restricted
   (b) too inclusive
   (c) converse is false

3. (a) The set of integers is not a
   subset of the set of reals.
   (b) $5 + 2 \not> 9$
   (c) $-6 = -5$

4. (a) $(x > -2) \wedge (x < 5)$
   (b) (The roots are real) $\wedge$ (The
   roots are equal)

5. (a) (An integer is odd) $\vee$ (An
   integer is even)
   (b) (The angles are equal) $\vee$ (The
   angles are supplementary)

6. (a) I ate cake or I ate ice cream.
   (b) I ate cake or I did not eat ice
   cream.
   (c) I ate cake and I ate ice cream.
   (d) I did not eat cake and I ate
   ice cream.
   (e) It is not true that I ate cake
   and I ate ice cream.
   (f) It is not true that I ate cake or
   I ate ice cream.

8. (a) If I study then I pass.
   (b) If I work hard then I pass.
   (c) If I do not study then I pass.
   (d) If I do not pass then I do not
   study.
   (e) If I do not study then I do not
   work hard.
   (f) If I pass then I do not study.

11. (a) If $\sqrt{x} \notin R$ then $x \not> 0$.
    (b) If n^2 is not even then n is not
    an even integer.
    (c) If $x - 3$ is not a factor of
    $x^3 - 27$, then $x = 3$ does not
    satisfy $x^3 - 27 = 0$.

12. (a) $q \Rightarrow p$ (d) $q \Rightarrow p$
    (b) $p \Rightarrow q$ (e) $p \Leftrightarrow q$
    (c) $p \Rightarrow q$ (f) $p \Leftrightarrow q$

13. (a) commutative
    (b) commutative
    (c) associative
    (d) associative
    (e) distributive
    (f) distributive

Index